ELECTRICAL ENGINEERING

Introduction

and

Concepts

MATRIX SERIES
IN CIRCUITS AND SYSTEMS

Andrew P. Sage, *Editor*

ELECTRICAL ENGINEERING

*Introduction
and
Concepts*

Samuel Seely
*Professor Emeritus
Department of Electrical Engineering
University of Rhode Island*

and

Alexander D. Poularikas
*Professor
Department of Electrical Engineering
University of Rhode Island*

MATRIX PUBLISHERS, INC.
Beaverton, Oregon

Στή μνήμη τοῦ Πατέρα μου
καί τῶν Γιαγιάδων μου
A.D.P.

© **Copyright, Matrix Publishers, Inc., 1982**

10 9 8 7 6 5 4 3 2 1

Library of Congress Cataloging in Publication Data

Seely, Samuel, 1909-
   Electrical engineering, concept and applications.

   Bibliography: p.
   Includes index.
   1. Electric engineering. I. Poularikas,
Alexander D., 1933-   II. Title.
TK146.S34   621.3   81-12367
ISBN 0-916460-31-2   AACR2

Production: Patricia Miller
Illustrations: Scientific Illustrators
Printing: Pantagraph Printing
Editor: Merl K. Miller

Matrix Publishers, Inc.
11000 SW 11th St., Suite E
Beaverton, Oregon 97005

Contents

Preface

The field of electrical engineering has expanded markedly over the last several decades. This growth has imposed on electrical engineering education the need for including studies in new fields. This has been accomplished in various ways since all curriculums are faced with constraints on the number of courses and the number of credit hours that are physically and educationally possible within a normal college program.

It has been our experience and general observation that changes have been accomplished by rearranging course content, by changing course requirements, and by substituting a sequence of courses, often at the expense of basic courses covering the principles upon which general understanding depends. Furthermore, these methods seem to have often caused communication gaps since they assume a level of student sophistication at a given time which may not have been attained in prior studies. All too frequently the student must tell the professor that the assumption that the student has previously studied certain material basic to his subsequent study is not valid. This lack of sequence might result from the lack of careful coordination among courses within a department. It might also result from the educational gaps that are inherent within departmental offerings.

This text provides an overview of most areas of modern electrical engineering. It is our hope that sufficient depth and understanding can be gained at this early level so that future in-depth studies will take a recognized and understandable place in the total learning experience of the student. We have imposed no educational requirements to understand this material, except the limited time and experience of the student in the first year of college mathematics and physics. The content has been chosen to emphasize fundamental ideas, to show how they appear in the many areas of electrical engineering, and to introduce the student to some of the varied and often specialized terminology that has developed within these separate areas. Our emphasis and content are more concerned with opening and extending horizons than with details and subtleties that will be included ultimately in the student's educational career. Without requiring a mathematical sophistication, we believe that the content will provide the student with a sophisticated level of understanding in the real world of electrical engineering.

Also, the background that the student will acquire is sufficient for an understanding and for a working knowledge of such areas as networks, devices, system theory, computers, discrete time systems and signals, electronics, field theory, communications, electromechanical transducers and energy conversion devices, and control engineering. This book is suited, therefore, to curriculums in which students are not required to take higher level courses in all of these areas.

In addition to its use in an introductory course for electrical engineering students, this book is suitable for students in allied fields who must acquire a working knowledge of these subjects and a more definitive treatment of them than can be found in introductory surveys of electrical engineering science. It is specifically suited for all students who, in their careers, will use the principles and terminology of diverse electrical engineering fields, including students of physics, biology, and chemistry.

With ever increasing pressure to include more and more areas in the undergraduate electrical engineering curriculum, such as computer engineering, bioengineering, optical engineering, it seems appropriate to structure the modern electrical engineering curriculum with broad, though quantitative, requirements at the basic level, and to allow the student to pursue in depth only those few areas of special interest. We offer some thoughts on "where do we go from here" in sections called Postludes, which appear at the end of each chapter.

The book divides itself naturally into a number of related segments, with later segments dealing with areas of specialization. Chapter 1 through Chapter 6 provide the basic background for continuous time systems analysis. Chapter 1 addresses the general problem of describing in mathematical terms physical components and important signal waveshapes that constitute the real world-mathematical world interface that engages the attention of the electrical engineer. Chapter 2 establishes systematic methods for writing the equations that describe interconnected systems of physical elements. Chapter 3 is devoted to the classical solution of the linear differential equations that arise in systems problems in terms of complementary solutions and particular integral solutions. Chapter 4 discusses the response of systems to sinusoidal time excitation functions and is, therefore, an introduction to ac circuit analysis. Chapter 5 is an introduction to the Laplace transform and its application in solving differential equations. Chapter 6 introduces the graphical portrayal of interconnected systems to highlight the signal path from the input to output through a network.

Chapter 7 contains applications of basic principles to electronic devices and circuits, with principal attention to the bipolar junction class of transistors (BJT) in both large signal and incremental signal modes. The field effect transistor FET is also studied.

Chapter 8 reviews the fundamentals of electrical measurements and considers some of the basic equipment in general use. Also included is a discussion of estimates of accuracy of measurements.

Chapter 9 is concerned with digital devices and systems as they relate to the digital computer and the minicomputer. Machine language programming for basic operations receives some attention.

Chapter 10 considers wave phenomena in space, with applications in diverse fields, including transmission, radiation, diffraction and modern optics.

Chapter 11 introduces the basic concepts of communications under continuous, sampled and digital modulation and demodulation methods.

Chapter 12 is concerned with electromechanics. Following a review of important aspects of electricity and magnetism, energy converters, both incremental transducers and dc and ac rotating machinery are studied. Operating and starting characteristics of the more common rotating machines are discussed.

Chapter 13 relates the work of many previous chapters to a consideration of feedback principles with applications to feedback control systems. A discussion of the methods of compensation provides an opportunity for the student to appreciate the problems of system design in meeting prescribed specifications.

Chapter 14 is devoted to discrete time considerations, both in modeling, and in analysis. The mathematical formulation leads naturally into numerical methods of analysis. It also permits the introduction of Z-transform methods to solve the difference equations that describe such systems. Concepts of digital filtering are emphasized in this study.

As an educational feature to help direct the efforts of the student, we have included with each chapter: a summary of the essential content, a set of review questions to highlight the material of principal importance, and a number of problems to strengthen understanding of the subject matter. As an added feature the authors have prepared a student work book.

The scope and content of the book are broad and cannot be completed in a single course. The book lends itself to a variety of courses, depending on the particular curriculum needs. The first six chapters can easily be covered in a first semester course. The remainder of the book can provide the substance for a variety of follow-up courses. If the emphasis is to be on digital systems, Chapters 7, 8, 9 and 14 could be considered together. If the emphasis is to be on control systems, Chapters 7, 8, 12, 13 and 14 could serve the needs. If the emphasis is to be on communication systems, Chapters 7, 8, 10, 11, and 14 could provide the desired background material. Other groupings are possible for background studies for any reasonable course objectives within an electrical engineering curriculum.

A difficulty that warrants special attention is that of mathematical notation. Unfortunately the same letter is used to denote different quantities in discussions of different areas of engineering. This stems, in part, from a desire to use notation that has become reasonably standard in the different areas. It also stems from a desire to limit the notation to the usual acceptable English and Greek letters. We can only call attention to this problem and we urge caution when interpreting symbols in the different chapters of the book.

The following corporations have kindly permitted us to publish their material: Texas Instruments, Inc.: Figures 9.12-3, 9.12-4 and Section 9.17; Education Development Center: Figures 10.1-4, 10.2-1b and 10.4-1a; Pergamon Press: Figures 10.4-4b and 10.4-2b; W. H. Freeman and Co.: Figure 10.6-2; Society of Photo-Optical Instrumentation Engineers: Figure 10.7-3; The Institute of Electrical and Electronic Engineers: Figures 10.7-7, 11.4-10, 11.6-8 and 11.6-9; Optical Society of America: Figures 11.6-6 and 11.6-7; McGraw Hill Book Co.: Figures 10.4-4c, 12.15-3, 12.22-1, 12.22-2 and 12.23-1.

The authors are grateful to Professor Andrew P. Sage for his valuable comments and criticisms.

Samuel Seely
Alexander D. Poularikas

Chapter One

Signals, Models and Modeling

1.1 INTRODUCTION

Our purpose in this text is to provide an introductory overview of the broad field of electrical engineering. Because electrical engineers must carry out studies and designs employing devices and components other than electrical, it is important that they understand and be able to employ a very broad range of components.

The specific technical areas within electrical engineering of concern to the engineer are normally designated by such terms as: Circuits and Systems, Electronics, Communications, Controls and Servomechanisms, Digital Systems, Energy Conversion, Materials. Each of these is a highly developed area of study which cannot be covered in depth in a single course. Therefore, it is our purpose to present the key ideas and fundamentals of these broad fields.

It is important that the student understand at the outset that much of this study will be devoted to analysis. The emphasis will be on understanding the behavior of a group of interconnected components with some designated source of excitation, often to determine whether this interconnected "system" will meet some established performance criterion. But to carry out such an analysis also requires an understanding of the inherent limitations and constraints on the entire analysis process. For example, an engineering device is a "real world" structure that consists of "hardware," components made of materials with properties and in shapes designed to meet certain requirements and objectives. In analysis, however, any "real world" system is represented mathematically, and the process of analysis proceeds as a mathematical problem. Immediately involved, therefore, is a "modeling" process in which hardware component behavior is described mathematically. The quality of the model employed in a study may not necessarily be high since the modeling process itself is often less than exact. We shall find that the models often used are idealized in order to permit easier mathematical analysis. The resulting analysis and conclusions must always be assessed in light of the type of idealizations that have been made. The most precise modeling is achieved in digital circuits because of the nature of the components that are used. As a consequence, the performance predicted with digital devices and that actually achieved agree very closely. In nondigital circuits, close agreement is not necessarily achieved or even achievable.

System models are generally of three nonmutually exclusive types: *physical*, *analytical* and *descriptive*. The traditional, and perhaps the most familiar type of model, is a physical representation of the system, such as a pilot plant. Physical models have an advantage in that experiments can be conducted on them, but they have a disadvantage in that they may be very costly, and might not easily lend themselves to change. Analytical models, such as those discussed in detail in this book, are mathematical expressions representing characteristics of a system. Descriptive models, which may bridge the entire scale of abstraction, may be simple word pictures of the process that makes up a system. The description covers the interactions among the variables, the attributes of the variables, and constraints which limit performance. Such models can sometimes be prepared in a relatively short time, may be relatively low in cost, and may require few special skills for development. Descriptive models can be applied to solve a wide variety of problems requiring decisions. Models of business systems can usually be expressed in descriptive terms.

The analytical model considered here provides a relationship between two types of variables which have several names. Often they are called *input* and *output* variables; sometimes they are referred to as *excitation* and *response* variables; or they may be denoted as *cause* and *external effect* variables. The interconnection of different components, which requires interconnection of the respective models of the components for analysis, would then constitute the system. A graphical description of a system in terms of a *block diagram*, as shown in Figure. 1.1-1, may be used. Each element of a system or subsystem may be represented in a similar block form.

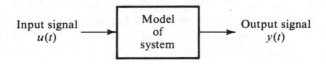

Figure 1.1-1. Block diagram representation of system

In analysis, the system input, whatever its form, is assumed known, and a model of the system is also assumed known. The problem to which we will give our major attention is to determine the response or behavior of the system at a designated output port or set of terminals. This might, in some cases, hide critical responses within the system itself, but these can be separately studied.

A second very important engineering problem for consideration is that of determining or developing a system that will provide a specified output for a designated input. This is the design process, often called the *synthesis* problem. A synthesis problem is inherently more difficult than an analysis problem, requiring selection of available components which have properties to insure satisfaction of prescribed input-output behavior. The question of ingenuity and experience in design becomes an essential ingredient in the synthesis process.

In another class of design, which will be discussed in connection with feedback control systems, a certain portion of the system may already have been established by others and the problem may be to effect an *add-on* subsystem which will provide a desired input-output behavior because the original system did not meet desired design or performance objectives.

Our study begins by considering certain aspects of input signals, certain aspects of the modeling process and the consequent models, and the behavior or response of specified interconnected arrays of elements or components to specified input signals.

SIGNALS

1.2 DEFINITION AND CHARACTERISTICS OF SIGNALS

Most signals characterize physical changes obtained from contacts with a physical environment. In most cases of interest, the system inputs and response, which we have termed input and output signals, are functions of the independent variable *time*. Interest in system behavior is ordinarily a concern with the performance of the system as a function of time. If provision is made to convert information presented to us from its original form such as temperature, light intensity, vibration, into an electrical quantity such as current or voltage, we call this quantity an electrical signal.

If the independent variable t is allowed to take on a continuum of values, the signal is said to be a *continuous-time* signal. We designate a continuous time signal by $u(t)$. We note that much of our world operates in continuous time. If the essential features of the signal are considered at isolated and often regular, instants of time, the signal is said to be a *discrete time* signal. A discrete time signal would be designated $u(t_k)$ or for uniform time intervals as $u(kT)$ where k is an integer and T is the basic time interval. Examples of discrete time problems are those based on census figures, which are taken at regular periods; and interest payments on bank accounts which are computed daily, monthly, quarterly, or semiannually. Examples of continuous time and discrete time signals are illustrated in Figure 1.2-1. Note that a discrete time function, given by $u(t_{-1})$, $u(t_0)$, $u(t_1)$,...is defined only at the instants..., t_{-1}, t_0, t_1,....

Another interpretation of a discrete time signal is that it consists of the sequence of numbers at the discrete times t_k.

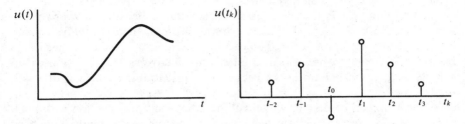

Figure 1.2-1.   (a) Continuous time signal   (b) Discrete time signal

A continuous time system is one whose essential signals are time continuous. Conversely, a discrete time system is one whose essential signals are all discrete time. A digital computer is probably the best known example of a discrete time system. Moreover, because of the nature of digital system operation, it can also be termed a discrete state system because only a finite number of different states are permissible.

A discrete signal is frequently generated by sampling a continuous time function. Such a sampler might be illustrated as shown in Figure 1.2-2. If the

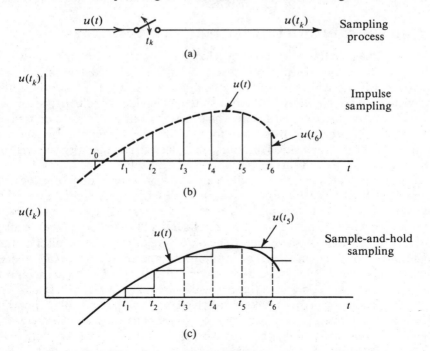

Figure 1.2-2. (a) The sampler   (b) Impulse sampling   (c) Sample-and-hold sampling

sampler is closed only for a very short time, it might be termed an *impulse sampler*. If the sampler is so designed that it samples the function at regular intervals and holds the signal from sample time to sample time, it is called a *sample-and-hold* circuit. Uniform impulse sampling and uniform sample-and-hold signals are illustrated, and both are important in engineering processes.

When the signal can be described explicitly in terms of mathematical functions it is called *deterministic*. However, the outputs of many physical processes are unpredictable, and, therefore, the signals derived from them are known as *random*. For this type of signal we cannot predict precisely its value at any given future instant in time.

A simple and most useful deterministic signal is the *sinusoidal* time function shown in Figure 1.2-3a

$$u(t) = V_m \sin (\omega t + \theta) \tag{1.2-1}$$

where V_m is a constant representing the peak value of the waveform, $\omega = 2\pi f$ is the *angular frequency* in rad/s, f is the *frequency* in Hz (cycles per second),

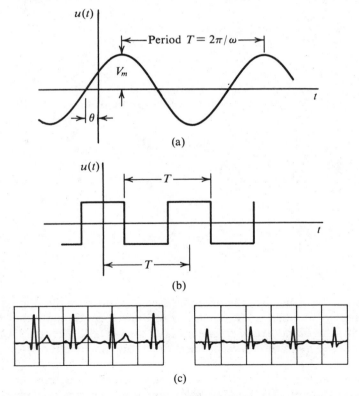

(a)

(b)

(c)

Figure 1.2-3. Periodic deterministic signals
(a) Sinusoid   (b) Square wave   (c) Electrocardiogram (two different leads)

and θ is the initial *phase angle* in radians with respect to the time origin. A distinct quality of the sinusoidal function is its regular repetitiveness. Its values at times $t + kT$ ($k = \ldots, -3, -2, -1, 0, 1, 2, \ldots$) are identical with the value for any t, where T is the *period* of the wave. Mathematically, a periodic wave is such that $u(t) = u(t + T)$. Functions which possess the repetitiveness characteristic are called *periodic*. Figure 1.2-3b shows a periodic function known as a recurring square wave. We shall meet this waveform when we study digital systems since it is usually the output of a pulsing clock, the heart of the digital computer.

An important mathematical consideration is that any *periodic* non-sinusoidal signal $u(t)$ can be represented by the sum of an infinite number of sinusoidal functions. Such a representation is known as a *Fourier series* expansion of the signal $u(t)$. Mathematically, the Fourier series expansion has the form

$$u(t) = A_o + \sum_{k=1}^{\infty} (A_k \cos k\omega_o t + B_k \sin k\omega_o t)$$

(a)   (1.2-2)

$$= A_o + \sum_{k=1}^{\infty} C_k \cos (k\omega_o t + \varphi_k)$$

where

$$A_o = \frac{1}{T} \int_{-T/2}^{T/2} u(t) dt = \text{d.c. term} = \text{average value of } u(t) \qquad \text{(b)}$$

$$A_k = \frac{2}{T} \int_{-T/2}^{T/2} u(t) \cos k\omega_o t \, dt = C_k \cos \varphi_k \qquad \text{(c)}$$

$$B_k = \frac{2}{T} \int_{-T/2}^{T/2} u(t) \sin k\omega_o t \, dt = -C_k \sin \varphi_k \qquad \text{(d)}$$

$$\omega_o = \frac{2\pi}{T} \qquad \text{(e)}$$

$$C_k = \sqrt{A_k^2 + B_k^2} \qquad \text{(f)}$$

$$\varphi_k = -\tan^{-1} (B_k / A_k) \qquad \text{(g)}$$

Although the frequencies which must be used to synthesize the original signal are infinite in number, they do not constitute a continuum; they are all multiples of the *fundamental frequency* $\omega_o / 2\pi = f_o = 1/T$. The set of C_k-s constitutes the *amplitude spectrum* for the periodic function and the φ_k-s the *phase spectrum*.

To show that the values for A_k and B_k are as specified, assume that a signal can be represented by the Fourier series Equation (1.2-2a). To determine the unknown constants A_o, A_k and B_k, first multiply Equation (1.2-2a) by dt and integrate over one full period. This gives

$$\int_{-T/2}^{T/2} u(t)\ dt = A_o \int_{-T/2}^{T/2} dt + \sum_{k=1}^{\infty} (A_k \int_{-T/2}^{T/2} \cos k\omega_o t\ dt + B_k \int_{-T/2}^{T/2} \sin k\omega_o t\ dt)$$

$$= TA_o + \sum_{k=1}^{\infty} (A_k \times 0 + B_k \times 0) = TA_o$$

or

$$A_o = \frac{1}{T} \int_{-T/2}^{T/2} u(t)\ dt$$

which is Equation (1.2-2b).

Next multiply Equation (1.2-2a) by $\cos k\omega_o t\ dt$ and integrate over one full period. This gives

$$\int_{-T/2}^{T/2} u(t)\ \cos k\omega_o t\ dt = A_o \int_{-T/2}^{T/2} \cos k\omega_o t\ dt + \sum_{k=1}^{\infty} A_k \int_{-T/2}^{T/2} \cos^2 k\omega_o t\ dt$$

$$+ B_k \int_{-T/2}^{T/2} \cos k\omega_o t \times \sin k\omega_o t\ dt$$

$$= A_o \times 0 + \sum_{k=1}^{\infty} (A_k \times \frac{T}{2} + B_k \times 0)$$

or

$$A_k = \frac{2}{T} \int_{-T/2}^{T/2} u(t)\ \cos k\omega_o t\ dt$$

which is Equation (1.2-2c). If Equation (1.2-2a) is multiplied by $\sin k\omega_o t\ dt$ and the resulting expression is integrated over a full period, we shall find the value for B_k given by Equation (1.2-2d).

Suppose that the first summation of Equation (1.2-2a) is written in the form

$$\sum_{k=1}^{\infty} A_k(\cos k\omega_o t + \frac{B_k}{A_k} \sin k\omega_o t) = \sum_{k=1}^{\infty} A_k(\cos k\omega_o t - \tan \varphi_k \sin k\omega_o t)$$

where we have written $B_k A_k = -\tan \varphi_k$. Now write this expression in the form

$$\sum_{k=1}^{\infty} \frac{A_k}{\cos \varphi_k}(\cos k\omega_o t \cos \varphi_k - \sin k\omega_o t \sin \varphi_k)$$

which is written

$$= \sum_{k=1}^{\infty} C_k \cos (k\omega_o t + \varphi_k)$$

where

$$C_k = \frac{A_k}{\cos \varphi_k} = \sqrt{A_k^2 + B_k^2} \, .$$

This is an equivalent representation of the Fourier series expansion. Although there are others, these are the easiest two to understand and the most appropriate for our purposes here.

EXAMPLE 1.2-1. Find the amplitude and phase spectra of the periodic wave shown in Figure 1.2-4.

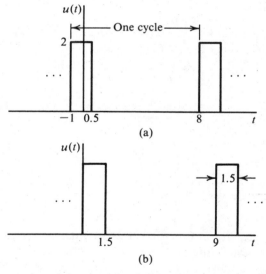

(a)

(b)

Figure 1.2-4.   A periodic function at two positions with respect to initial time

SOLUTION. Case (a): From the Fourier equations, Equations (1.2-2b, c, d, f, g), we obtain for the waveform in Figure 1.2-4a

$$A_o = \frac{1}{9} \left(\int_{-1}^{0.5} 2 \, dt + \int_{0.5}^{8} 0 \times dt \right) = \frac{3}{9} = \frac{1}{3}$$

$$A_k = \frac{2}{9} \left(\int_{-1}^{0.5} 2 \cos k \frac{2\pi}{9} t \, dt + \int_{0.5}^{8} 0 \times \cos k \frac{2\pi}{9} t \, dt \right)$$

$$= \frac{2}{\pi k} \left(\sin \frac{k\pi}{9} + \sin \frac{2\pi k}{9} \right)$$

$$B_k = \frac{2}{9} \left(\int_{-1}^{0.5} 2 \sin k \frac{2\pi}{9} t \, dt + \int_{0.5}^{8} 0 \times \sin k \frac{2\pi}{9} t \, dt \right)$$

$$= \frac{2}{\pi k} \left(-\cos \frac{k\pi}{9} + \cos \frac{2\pi k}{9} \right)$$

$$C_k = \sqrt{A_k^2 + B_k^2}$$

$$\varphi_k = -\tan^{-1}(B_k/A_k) \qquad \text{for } k = 1, 2, 3, \ldots$$

The amplitude and phase spectrums of this signal for the first eighteen harmonics are shown in Figure 1.2-5a.

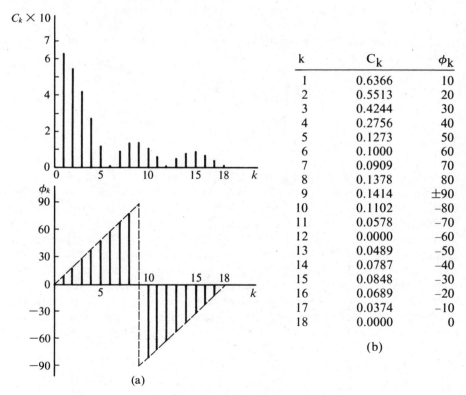

k	C_k	ϕ_k
1	0.6366	10
2	0.5513	20
3	0.4244	30
4	0.2756	40
5	0.1273	50
6	0.1000	60
7	0.0909	70
8	0.1378	80
9	0.1414	±90
10	0.1102	−80
11	0.0578	−70
12	0.0000	−60
13	0.0489	−50
14	0.0787	−40
15	0.0848	−30
16	0.0689	−20
17	0.0374	−10
18	0.0000	0

(b)

Figure 1.2-5. Amplitude and phase spectra for the signal shown in Figure 1.2-4a

Case (b): Using the same Fourier equation, we obtain for the waveform in Figure 1.2-4b

$$A_o = \frac{1}{3}, \qquad A_k = \frac{2}{\pi k} \sin \frac{\pi}{9} k, \qquad B_k = \frac{2}{\pi k}\left(1 - \cos \frac{\pi}{3} k\right)$$

$$C_k = \frac{2}{\pi k}\sqrt{2 - 2 \cos (\pi/9)k}, \qquad \varphi_k = -\tan^{-1}\left[\left(1 - \cos \frac{\pi}{9} k\right)/\sin \frac{\pi}{9} k\right]$$

for $k = 1, 2, 3, \ldots$

The reader should plot the spectra for this case and compare them with those plotted in Figure 1.2-5a.

◻ ◻ ◻

Nonperiodic and Transient Signals

Unlike periodic signals, a nonperiodic signal can be expressed in terms of a Fourier integral. In this representation the amplitude spectrum $|F(\omega)|$ appropriate to a function $f(t)$ is a continuous complex function of frequency and its relation to $f(t)$ is given by

$$F(\omega) = \int_{-\infty}^{\infty} f(t)e^{-j\omega t}\, dt \qquad\qquad \text{(a)} \quad (1.2\text{-}3)$$

$$f(t) = \frac{1}{2\pi}\int_{-\infty}^{\infty} F(\omega)e^{j\omega t}\, d\omega \qquad\qquad \text{(b)}$$

These equations are referred to as a Fourier transform pair, with $F(\omega)$ being the Fourier transform of $f(t)$, and $f(t)$ being the inverse Fourier transform of $F(\omega)$. The amplitude $|F(\omega)|$ and phase spectra arg $F(\omega)$ of such transient signals, in contrast to those of the periodic functions, are continuous functions of the frequency and no fundamental frequency is present. As we observed in Example 1.2-1, the distance between neighboring harmonics of a periodic signal is the fundamental frequency $1/T$. As the period increases, the fundamental frequency decreases and the spectral lines move closer to each other. In the limit when $T \to \infty$ only one signal pulse will remain (transient signal) and the spectral lines will be infinitesimally close together, thereby creating a continuous function of frequency and phase, as shown in Figure 1.2-6.

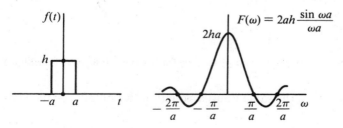

Figure 1.2-6. The pulse function and its Fourier transform

Another extremely important transient signal description involves the use of *singularity functions,* functions which have carefully defined shapes and discontinuities. Moreover, the singularity functions considered are mathematically related functions. We first consider the *unit impulse* function (or Dirac *delta* function) $u_o(t)$ or $\delta(t)$.

The impulse function $u_o(t)$ is defined to be zero everywhere except at $t=0$ where it has an infinite value. However, the area under this function is unity. A graphical representation of this signal at three arbitrary locations is shown in Figure 1.2-7a.

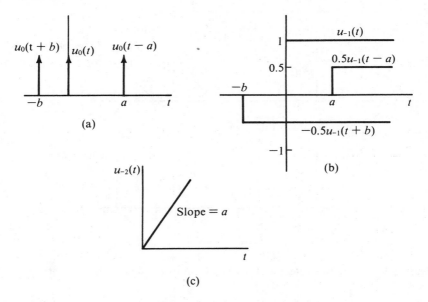

Figure 1.2-7.   Transient deterministic signals
(a) Impulse function, $u_o(t)$ (b) Step function, $u_{-1}(t)$ (c) Ramp function, $au_{-2}(t)$

A second transient function which will often be used in many of our examples and problems is the *unit step function $u_{-1}(t)$* which is shown in Figure 1.2-7b at three different positions. A third useful signal is shown in Figure 1.2-7c and is known as the *ramp function.*

$$au_{-2}(t) = \begin{cases} 0 & t<0 \\ at & t\geqslant 0 \end{cases} \qquad (1.2\text{-}3)$$

These signals are three out of a related group of *singularity* functions.

EXAMPLE 1.2-2. Construct the signal shown in Figure 1.2-8 using appropriately chosen singularity functions.

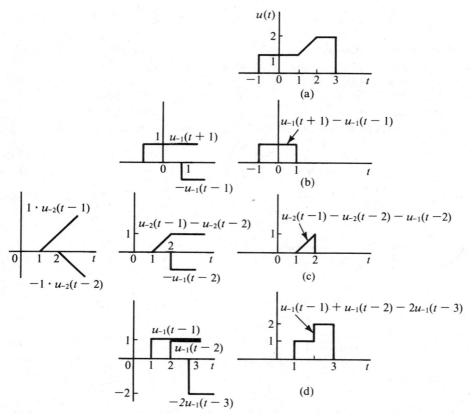

Figure 1.2-8. The construction of a signal from its fundamental singularity functions

SOLUTION. Figure 1.2-8 shows graphically the individual steps which must be followed in order to construct the desired signal. It should be pointed out that this particular sequence of steps is not unique. Adding the signals of Figure 1.2-8b, c, d, the signal in Figure 1.2-8a is easily found.

□ □ □

Random Signals

The deterministic signals we have discussed above can be repeated exactly, if identical conditions prevail during their recording. However, for many other signals (non-deterministic or probabilistic) this cannot be achieved. To study these probabilistic signals we must proceed in terms of statistical values from which, under special mathematical considerations, a deterministic relationship may be obtained. We shall not discuss such signals in this book. We advise the reader to become familiar in later studies with probabilistic signals since they are extremely important in all engineering and scientific fields.

General Comments on Signals

Signals of many types can be generated electrically, and the peak amplitudes can range over enormous values. For example, readily available, commercially produced electrical signal generators are possible for producing voltage signals from millivolts to kilovolts, and current sources from microamperes to amperes. Mechanical force sources are possible over very wide ranges from micronewton to meganewton. Mechanical velocity sources are limited, however, in amplitude and in recurrence period.

The signal sources with which we shall be concerned are of two general classes: one is called *across* sources; the other is called *through* sources. Correspondingly, the associated dynamic variables are across and through variables. In water flow, for example, pressure or head is an across variable and flow rate is a through variable. An across variable, whether it is water pressure, temperature, electric pressure (voltage), mechanical velocity, or rotational velocity, denotes the variable relative to some specified or implied reference or datum, such as the translational velocity of a body relative to the fixed earth. Conversely, the through variable denotes a flow or transfer quantity, whether it is water flow, heat flow, electric charge flow (current), mechanical force, or mechanical torque. In these cases, the direction of flow must be specified as well as the magnitude. One might distinguish through and across quantities by the type of instruments required and how they are connected in the system in making through and across measurements.

1.3 SIGNAL ACQUISITION AND STORAGE

It is important and necessary to consider carefully the way that data are collected and stored. The device which measures physical quantities and linearly or nonlinearly translates them to electrical signals is called a *transducer*. Basically, a transducer taps physical energy and translates it to an electrical signal such as voltage or current. Details of certain classes of electric and magnetic transducers are contained in Chapter 12. The choice of the particular type of transducer depends upon the type of energy, speed of phenomenon change, dimensions, economical considerations, accuracy, etc. The choice of storage media is dictated by the characteristics of the signal, economics, ease of access, and convenience for later processing. Typical recording media are strip-chart recorder, magnetic tape, digital magnetic tape recorder, and paper tape.

For a transducer to be useful, it must have accurate and reproducible input-output characteristics so that the expected results accurately describe the physical phenomenon. The performance is specified in terms of resolution, repeatability, hysteresis, and friction. Typical available transducers are those that measure displacement, velocity, acceleration, pressure, and temperature. For energy conversion type transducers, the physical phenomena used include electromagnetic, piezoelectric, magnetostrictive, thermoelectric or photoelectric. On the other hand, for a passive control type, the physical phenomena employed are resistance, inductance, capacitance, semiconductance, thermoresistance, Hall effect, radioactivity or photoresistance.

In the following paragraphs we shall discuss some transducers which are commonly used. We shall not examine all instrumentation used to collect signals. We do caution the reader that before a transducer is selected that its characteristics be carefully studied so that the final selection is the most appropriate one for the special need.

Displacement Transducers

RESISTIVE TRANSDUCER. The potentiometer is a commonly used resistive transducer. It is an electromechanical device made up of a resistive element and a movable slide as shown in Figure 1.3-1. The electrical output (voltage) is proportional to the displacement for uniformly wound elements.

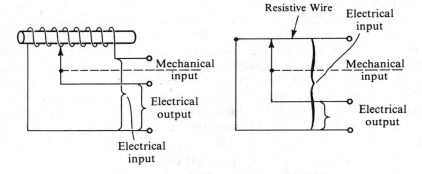

Figure 1.3-1. Two types of resistive potentiometers

The selection of such a device will be based on the following factors: (a) power rating, (b) electrical noise, (c) temperature coefficient (there is always an increase of resistance with temperature), (d) resistance range, and (e) environmental stability.

STRAIN GAUGE. Strain gauges, like potentiometers, are resistive devices. However, the resistance change of the strain gauges is the result of a mechanical deformation (or strain). The amount of stress (newton/m²) can be measured by using the relation

$$S = Ee = E\frac{\Delta L}{L} = E\left(\frac{1}{K}\frac{\Delta R}{R}\right)$$ (1.3-1)

where:

S = applied stress (newton/m²)

$e = \Delta L/L$ = measured strain

$$K = \text{gage factor } [(\Delta R/R)/(\Delta L/L)]$$

$$E = \text{Young's modulus (newton/m}^2)$$

$$R = \text{nominal gage resistance } (\Omega)$$

The factors K and R are given in the manufacturer's data sheets and the resistance change ΔR is found by using the balance technique in a Wheatstone bridge, as shown in Figure 1.3-2. However, most commercially available strain gauge bridges use an ac bridge power supply for better sensitivity.

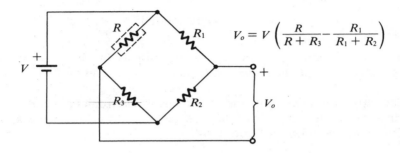

$$V_o = V \left(\frac{R}{R + R_3} - \frac{R_1}{R_1 + R_2} \right)$$

Figure 1.3-2.   Wheatstone bridge circuit for measuring resistance changes

For the selection of strain gages we must consider the filament wire material, the filament construction, the base material on which the gage is bonded, the method of bonding that has been used, and the lead wire connection.

INDUCTIVE TRANSDUCERS. This type of electromechanical transducer produces a voltage output proportional to the displacement of a movable core. A self-inductive type is shown in Figure 1.3-3a. Since the voltage is proportional to the inductance, a physical constant of the coil, and since the inductance varies with the volume of iron core close to it, any positional change of the iron core is reflected as a proportional voltage change.

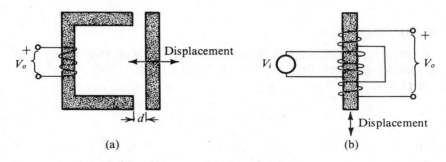

Figure 1.3-3.   Variable inductance transducers

The linear variable differential type shown in Figure 1.3-3b is a highly sensitive transducer. Such transducers are available with a sensitivity as high as 1 volt/0.0025 cm, linearity to 0.05% for small displacements, and they are rugged.

CAPACITIVE TRANSDUCERS. To obtain even higher sensitivity, it is most appropriate to use a capacitor transducer which can measure displacement down to 200 microns. The principle of operation is based on the familiar capacitance equation for a parallel-plate capacitor [see Equation (1.7-2)]

$$C = 8.85 \frac{\epsilon_r A}{d} \times 10^{-10} \text{ farad} \tag{1.3-2}$$

where $C =$ capacitance, $\epsilon_r =$ the relative permittivity (or dielectric constant), $A =$ effective area of the plates (cm²), and d the separation between plates (cm).

Capacitive transducers with the accompanying electronics detect the change of capacitance when any one of the three factors ϵ_r, A or d is changed. Three typical cases are shown in Figure 1.3-4.

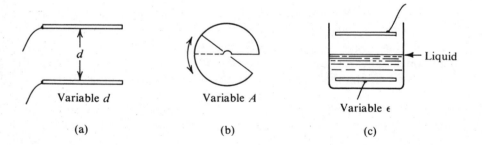

Figure 1.3-4.   Different types of capacitive transducers
(a) Variation of separation d (b) Variation of area A
(c) Variation of the dielectric constant

Velocity Transducers

A simple type of velocity transducer consists of an N turn coil which is moving across a magnetic field as shown in Figure 1.3-5a. From electrodynamic principles we have that

$$V_o = 2NBlv \quad \text{volt} \tag{1.3-3}$$

where $V_o =$ voltage, $B =$ magnetic field strength (weber/m²), $l =$ length of the side of the coil (m), $v =$ velocity of the coil (m/s). The constant 2 appears since two sides of the coil contribute to the total voltage.

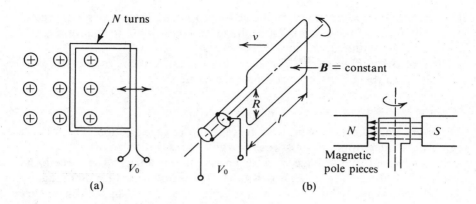

Figure 1.3-5.   Velocity transducers

A rotating type velocity transducer (called a tachometer generator) is shown in Figure 1.3-5b. The voltage is given by the equation

$$V_o = 2vBl \sin \omega t \qquad (1.3-4)$$

where $\omega = 2\pi f$ = radian rotational angular frequency, s^{-1}, v = velocity, and B is a constant magnetic field. From Equation (1.3-4) we observe that the peak voltage $2vBl$ is proportional to v.

Acceleration Transducers

Acceleration transducers are based on Newton's fundamental force equation

$$F = ma \qquad (1.3-5)$$

where F = force (newton, m = mass (kg), and a = acceleration (m/s²). The acceleration is commonly found indirectly by measuring the force produced by a known mass attached to the accelerating structure. A typical piezoelectric type accelerometer is shown in Figure 1.3-6 where the mass provides a pressure on

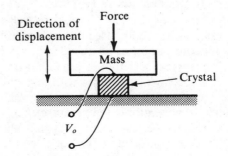

Figure 1.3-6.   A piezoelectric accelerometer

the crystal that is proportional to the acceleration and this creates a charge Q across the faces of the crystal. The voltage is proportional to the ratio Q/C, where C is the shunt capacitance of the crystal.

The sensitivity of accelerometers is ordinarily stated as the ratio of the output voltage to the gravity acceleration $g = 9.81$ m/s^2.

Pressure Transducers

Pressure transducers convert total force to a precise deflection. The force is the result of integration of pressure over a given area. Furthermore, the deflection is converted to a voltage by a displacement transducer. The three basic pressure transducers are (a) Bourdan tubes, (b) bellows, and (c) diaphragms.

A Bourdan type pressure transducer is composed of a C-shaped tube which tends to flatten out when it is under pressure. These are inexpensive instruments providing from one to five percent accuracy. However, the main difficulty is that the readings are not accurately repeatable (a hysteresis effect) with increasing and decreasing pressures.

Bellows transducers provide large displacements for a given pressure variation. When pressure is applied to the face of the bellows it causes it to contract and move an attached lever indicator. Such pressure transducers are smaller and are less susceptible to hysteresis than Bourdan instruments.

The most accurate pressure transducers are the diaphragm type which are available in a large range of sizes. They are also the most versatile available. When the diaphragm is exposed to pressure the displacement is measured. The most commonly used diaphragm transducers use strain gauges to monitor the deflection of the diaphragm. Well-known pressure transducers are the barometer and the altimeter in airplanes.

Temperature Transducers

The fundamental physical phenomena which are used for temperature transducers are heat transfer by conduction, convection and radiation. Because of these different types of heat transfer processes, care must be exercised in the selection of the transducer. Basically, the following parameters must be weighted: (a) temperature range, (b) type of material to be used, (c) accuracy, and (d) effects of the surrounding atmosphere.

The most common transducer in scientific work as well as in industry is the thermocouple. A thermocouple is composed of two dissimilar metals joined at one end. The heated junction produces its own dc voltage output without any external applied source. Typical sensitivities are 0.01 mv/C° to 0.06 mv/C°.

The resistance of many elements changes with variations in temperature. The application of this phenomenon in measuring temperature change is called resistance thermometry. In general, the temperature element is applied to one arm of a Wheatstone bridge. The temperature range is about 500° C and has an accuracy of ± 0.01° C. A solid-state electrical element, a *thermistor*, with high negative coefficient of resistivity is often used. Thermistors cover the range from $-40°$ to $300°$ C and have accuracies of $\pm 0.2°$ C. Commercially available thermistors are one percent devices.

Recording and Storage

In the past ten years a highly accurate storage medium for signals has been developed. This medium is the magnetic tape. This is convenient to use, it is accurate, and it has been standardized among manufacturers.

The magnetic tape recording system consists of three elements: (a) the electronic coding system (signal amplification, speed control, automatic gain control), (b) the magnetic head which records or senses this signal, and (c) the transport mechanism. All three elements must be carefully designed for the entire system to have good fidelity and a minimum of nonlinearity and noise. The adjustment of the gap between the recording head and tape, the use of a tape with a minimum number of surface irregularities, and the accurate control of tape transport all combine into accurate recording and reproduction of the signal.

Since amplitude recording has a number of limitations resulting in degradation of the signal, a frequency modulation technique is used to pre-condition the signal before it is recorded. In addition, other forms of modulation are possible, such as pulse-code modulation, phase modulation, and different forms of digital signal recording. In a later chapter we shall become familiar with these modulation techniques.

MODELING OF SYSTEM ELEMENTS

1.4 MODEL CHARACTERISTICS

Our study will be concerned only with *lumped* elements. A lumped element is one that can be isolated and treated as one that possesses the features of idealized elements. Actually in many cases the real elements are not lumped. It might appear quite unreasonable to consider that a long section of pipe or a long electrical transmission line could be considered as being lumped, yet in many cases this is a valid approximation. Also, clearly discernible springs exist, and if these are not too large, it seems reasonable that they would well satisfy any reasonable criterion of lumpiness. However, a solid rod also possesses compliance or spring qualities, and such a rod under loading does stretch. With the removal of the load, the rod will return to its original length, provided that it had not been stressed beyond its elastic limit. An easily stated criterion for lumpiness does not appear possible. However, one must be careful in any critical case that the assumption of lumpiness, if it is made, is indeed valid.

Often is is assumed that the elements are *linear*. This assumes that there is a linear relation between cause and effect, or between excitation and response. A casual inspection will not show linearity—both lumped or distributed elements can be linear. We shall find that systems analysis can often be carried out completely in closed mathematical form for systems composed of linear elements. This is rarely possible for nonlinear systems, and nonanalytic methods (graphical or numerical) must be employed in studying such systems. In an effort to deduce a closed-form solution, one often may assume linearity for a nonlinear system. Extreme care is necessary in such cases since the assumption of linearity may completely negate the important features of the system. The use of a digital computer in analysis often makes unnecessary such linearity approximations, since the computer can handle nonlinear systems with about the same ease as a linearized description.

Most elements that are considered linear are, in fact, nonlinear. However, there is usually a range over which their response-excitation characteristics are linear, to a reasonable engineering approximation. Where the approximation is not valid, the behavior of the real system will probably not agee with that predicted for the modeled system. Figure 1.4-1a helps clarify this discussion by showing graphically a response-excitation relationship. If the excitation were limtied to the small range *a-b* (this is often referred to as the *small-signal* or *incremental* operation), then the assumption of linearity of response over the associated range *a'-b'* is reasonably valid. If the excitation were to extend over the range 0-*b*, then of course, the assumption of a linear response would not be valid.

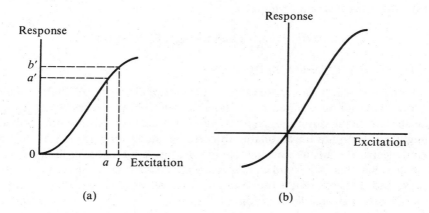

(a)   (b)

**Figure 1.4-1.   (a) A representative nonlinear response-excitation relationship
(b) A non-bilateral response-excitation characteristic**

It is not always the case that upon reversing the sense of the excitation the response-excitation relation will remain unchanged. Elements for which this is true are known as *bilateral* elements. However, there is a wide range of elements which are not bilateral. Figure 1.4-1b illustrates a nonbilateral characteristic. In the extreme case for which there is zero response for all excitations upon the reversal of the excitation, the element is said to be *unilateral*. Figure 1.4-2a shows a respresentative diode characteristic (this is typical of the semiconductor diode, and is also closely approximated by vacuum diodes).

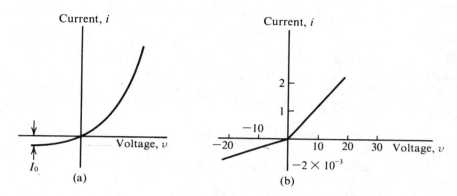

Figure 1.4-2. **(a) The response characteristic of a unilateral element (b) A piecewise linear approximation to the diode characteristic of part (a)**

1.5 MODEL APPROXIMATIONS

When attempting to carry out a study of a system that may include nonlinear nonbilateral elements, one is faced with providing a description of the elements. An exact description is not often possible and one must employ an approximate representation. The representation is usually chosen in a form that is most convenient to the method of analysis to be used. For example, if the analysis is to be done numerically or by a digital computer, a tabular numerical description with appropriately chosen intervals of the independent variable may suffice. Specifically, refer to Figure 1.4-2a which is now to represent the terminal characteristics of a silicon diode. A theoretical description of this diode characteristic is available which is based on semiconductor theory. The result is the semiconductor diode equation

$$I = I_o(e^{qV/KT} - 1) \tag{1.5-1}$$

where q, V, K, T are, respectively, electron charge, voltage, Boltzmann's constant, and absolute temperature.

The diode equation is not a particularly convenient expression to use in hand numerical calculations, although it is an analytical description of the device characteristics. In the case of numerical calculations, it might be more convenient to prepare a table giving the currents appropriate to selected values of the independent variable, which is voltage in this case. In other cases it might be found convenient to approximate the curve by a number of linear segments. A simple *piecewise linear* approximation for the diode characteristic will be of the form shown in Figure 1.4-2b. For the particular values which are shown on the figure, the characteristic is given by the expressions

$$i = 10^{-1} v \qquad\qquad\qquad v > 0$$
$$i = 10^{-4} v \qquad\qquad\qquad v < 0$$

Now consider a characteristic such as that shown in Figure 1.4-1a. This is a fairly general nonbilateral characteristic which is to represent the terminal characteristics of a device for which an exact theoretical description is not known. Almost any single-valued nonlinear curve of this type can be approximated by a polynomial of the form

$$i = a_o + a_1 v + a_2 v^2 + \ldots + a_n v^n \qquad\qquad (1.5\text{-}2)$$

We shall not consider the general techniques involved in fitting a polynomial to a given characteristic.

An alternate piecewise linear approximation to the nonlinear curve of Figure 1.5-1a is provided by the use of straight line segments, as shown in the figure. The choice of the number of linear segments to be used depends on the range of variation in the component terminal variables and the accuracy desired. It is cumbersome to write the equations for the straight line sections. For this reason, this type of representation is not particularly attractive in analytical studies. However, it is a very practical representation when an analog computer is used in the study of the system performance, since one can simulate such a piecewise linear curve by means of a diode function generator. In this case, the simulation almost exactly duplicates the piecewise linear approximation.

A form of approximation that we shall find very useful is the *stepwise constant* or *staircase* representation that is illustrated in Figure 1.5-1b. It is possible to extend the approximations to piecewise quadratic and piecewise higher order variations between sample points, although such approximations are seldom made.

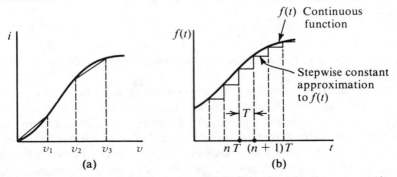

Figure 1.5-1.   (a) A general nonlinear curve, to define piecewise linear approximations
(b) A stepwise constant approximation, with uniform step size

These general ideas of function approximations will occur at a number of points in the text, and further discussion will be deferred until the need arises. Initially we shall consider lumped, linear and nonlinear, and bilateral elements, since such elements are particularly important in our studies.

ELECTRICAL ELEMENTS

1.6 INTRODUCTION

Electrical elements are described in terms of two dynamic variables, current (*through variable*) and voltage (*across variable*) or a simple functional form of these. Either can be chosen as the dependent or as the independent variable in any particular case.

In discussing these qualities we shall consider only the conduction current that exists in the connecting wires to the terminals of the electrical elements; it is implied that the current into and out of the element terminals is under survey. By restricting our discussion to the terminals, we avoid any need for considering the precise mechanism that may underlie the operation of the element. In this way, for example, we avoid the question of displacement current in the dielectric of a capacitor. We also avoid the fact that in a bipolar transistor both electrons and holes are involved in the conduction process and that in a gaseous conduction device electrons, positive ions, and negative ions are charge carriers involved in the current.

The voltage is the difference of electrical potential across the terminals of the element. For a specified voltage across the element, it is possible to specify the potential of each terminal relative to a reference datum. In electric circuits and apparatus, the reference datum is often the "ground" or "earth." This means, for example, that an element that has a 5 volt difference of potential between the terminals may have one terminal at 1000 volts (above ground potential) with the second terminal at 1005 volts. For most network problems the considerations do not concern themselves with any datum or reference level. The situation is somewhat different with mechanical systems in linear translation since inertial forces are related to the acceleration of the mass elements with respect to the earth as a fixed frame of reference.

1.7 THE CAPACITOR

The capacitor is the idealized circuit element in which energy may be stored in electric form. In its most elementary form the capacitor consists of two closely spaced metallic plates which are separated by a single or by multiple layers of nonconducting (insulating) dielectric material (air, glass, paper, oxide). The schematic representation of the capacitor is shown to the right of the broken line in Figure 1.7-1a.

Suppose that an initially uncharged capacitor is connected to a battery, as shown in Figure 1.7-1a. There will be a flow of electrons from the capacitor terminal that is connected to the positive terminal of the battery through the

battery to the capacitor terminal that is connected to the negative terminal of
the battery. The loss of electrons from one plate causes it to become positively
charged, whereas the plate that receives the excess electrons will be negatively
charged. The amount of charge transfer will be such that the capacitor will be
charged to the voltage of the battery to which it has been connected. Observe
that in the charging process no electrons have passed through the dielectric
material between the plates of the capacitor. Because of the changing potential
across the plates, or more precisely, because of the *changing* electric field
across the dielectric material, there is set up through the dielectric what is
called a *displacement* current. Thus one speaks of a *conduction* current in a
conductor and a displacement current in an insulator. For the situation illustrated in Figure 1.7-1a, the displacement current at every instant is equal to the
conduction current, which thus insures continuity of current through the
circuit.

The terminal properties of the capacitor are described graphically by a
charge-voltage relationship of the form shown in Figure 1.7-1b. In the case
where a linear q, v relationship exists, the charge is proportional to the voltage.
The proportionality constant is called the capacitance C and such a situation is
shown in Figure 1.7-1c. Thus by definition

$$C = \frac{q}{v} \quad \text{coulomb/volt} \, (= \text{farad}) \tag{1.7-1}$$

For the linear capacitor, C is a geometric factor which can be determined using
equations deduced from the theory of electricity. For a simple parallel plate
capacitor, C is given by the expression (see Equation 1.3-2)

$$C = \frac{\epsilon A}{d} \quad \text{farad} \tag{1.7-2}$$

where ϵ is the *permittivity* of the dielectric material, A is the area of the plate,

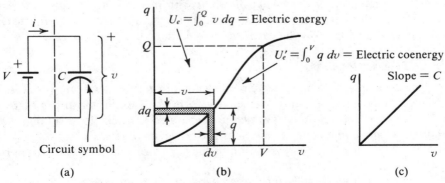

Figure 1.7-1.   (a) A capacitor across a battery
(b) Nonlinear charge-voltage relationship of a capacitor
(c) Linear charge-voltage relationship

and d is the separation of the plates. In general $\epsilon = \epsilon_r \epsilon_o$ where $\epsilon_o = 8.854 \times 10^{-12} \doteq 1/(36\pi \times 10^9)$ farad/meter, the free space permittivity, and ϵ_r is the *relative* permittivity (dielectric constant). In the case when the q,v relationship is nonlinear, the simple concept of capacitance is no longer valid, although one might deduce an analytic expression that describes the nonlinear q,v relationship given graphically in Figure 1.7-1b.

Another feature of Figure 1.71b is the area above and below the curve. These are known, respectively, as the energy stored in the capacitor and the corresponding coenergy. As shown in the figure, these functions are

$$\text{Coenergy } U'_e = \int_0^V q \, dv \qquad \text{(a)} \quad (1.7\text{-}3)$$

$$\text{Energy } U_e = \int_0^Q v \, dq \qquad \text{(b)}$$

This distinction is not essential to our present studies, but it becomes important when nonlinear circuit analysis is considered. Note in particular that when the q,v curve is linear the coenergy and the energy functions have equal values since the area above is equal to that below the curve.

For a linear relation between q and v (C constant) we may substitute Equation (1.7-1) into Equation (1.7-3b) to find that the total electric energy stored in the capacitor is

$$U_e = \frac{1}{C}\frac{Q^2}{2} = \frac{1}{2}CV^2 \qquad (1.7\text{-}4)$$

where Q and V are the final charge and voltage across the plates.

The important through-across variable relationships for the capacitor are readily obtained. The current is the time rate of change of charge; that is,

$$i = \frac{dq}{dt} = \frac{d(Cv)}{dt} \qquad \frac{\text{coulomb}}{\text{second}} = \text{ampere} \qquad (1.7\text{-}5)$$

In the linear case, C constant, this equation becomes

$$i = C\frac{dv}{dt} \qquad (1.7\text{-}6)$$

where v is the independent variable. Correspondingly, we may write

$$v = \frac{q}{C} = \frac{1}{C}\int_{-\infty}^t i \, dt \qquad (1.7\text{-}7)$$

when i is the independent variable. Both of these linear relations are of basic importance in electric circuit theory, and we shall employ them in our subsequent studies.

The integral of Equation (1.7-7) can also be written in the form

$$v = \frac{1}{C}\int_{-\infty}^{0} i\, dt + \frac{1}{C}\int_{0}^{t} i\, dt = v(o) + \frac{1}{C}\int_{0}^{t} i\, dt \qquad (1.7\text{-}8)$$

where $v(o)$ is known as the *initial voltage*. For currents that start at a finite time and with $v(o)=0$, Equation (1.7-8) takes the form

$$v = \frac{1}{C}\int_{0}^{t} i\, dt \qquad (1.7\text{-}9)$$

The range of practical physical capacitors extends from several picofarads ($= 10^{-12}$ farad) to perhaps 1000 microfarads ($= 10^{-3}$ farad). The physical size is determined by the material and thickness of the dielectric, the total capacitance, and the maximum allowable voltage across the dielectric without rupture. Whatever the material or design, a 1 farad capacitor would ordinarily be very bulky and would not be a practical circuit element, although it is used extensively in our later studies, which are usually on a normalized scale.

EXAMPLE 1.7-1. Find the current through a capacitor if the voltage generator across it produces the voltage functions shown in Figure 1.7-2a.

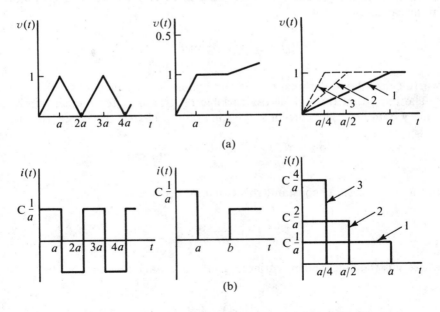

Figure 1.7-2. The voltage across and the current through a capacitor

SOLUTION. Since the current through the capacitor is the derivative of the voltage we easily find the corresponding currents as shown in Figure 1.7-2b.

Observe that the current form of the last drawing approximates the impulse function $u_o(t)$ in the limit of a step input function and that the area under the $i(t)$ curve will always remain equal to one.

□ □ □

EXAMPLE 1.7-2. Find the charge transfer in an axon.

SOLUTION. One of the three types of neurons in humans is called the *sensory neuron*. These neurons receive stimuli from sensory organs such as eyes, skin, and ears, and convey messages about heat, light, sound, etc., into the nervous system and into the brain for processing. Each neuron consists of a cell body to which are attached input ends called *dendrites* and a long tail called an *axon* through which the signal is propagating. The largest axons in the human nervous system have a diameter of only 20-30 μm. The giant squid, however, has an axon having a diameter of about 500 μm. The axon membrane is on the order of 50 to 100 Å thick (1 Å $= 10^{-8}$ cm) and has a capacitance of 10^{-9} farad/meter. The core of the axon is filled with sodium ($+$), potassium ($+$), chlorine ($-$), and other negative ions ($-$).

At equilibrium, the potential inside the axon rests at -70 mV (millivolt) and when stimulated this rises to $+30$ mV. Hence

$$\Delta Q = C\Delta v = 10^{-9} \times 100 \times 10^{-3} = 10^{-10} \qquad \text{coulomb/meter}$$

Since an ion has a charge of 1.6×10^{-19} coulomb, the number of sodium ions ($+$) which enter during the excitation is 6.25×10^{8}.

□ □ □

EXAMPLE 1.7-3. A current source across a capacitor is supplying current of the form $i(t) = I_o \sin \omega t$. Find the voltage across the capacitor.

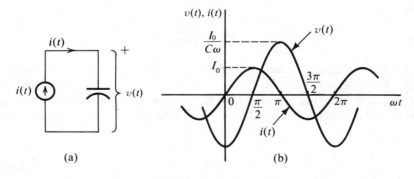

(a)   (b)

Figure 1.7-3.   Current-voltage waveforms for a sinusoidal excitation
(a) Circuit representation   (b) Waveform responses

SOLUTION. By applying Equation (1.7-9) we obtain

$$v(t) = \frac{1}{C}\int I_o \sin \omega t \, dt = -\frac{I_o}{C\omega}\int d(\cos \omega t) = -\frac{I_o}{C\omega}\cos \omega t$$

$$= \frac{I_o}{C\omega} \sin \left(\omega t - \frac{\pi}{2} \right)$$

(1.7-10)

which indicates that the voltage *lags* the current, or conversely that the current *leads* the voltage by 90 degrees. Their graphs are shown in Figure 1.7-3b. This phase-shift phenomenon is characteristic of specific electrical and mechanical elements. A detailed study of the phenomenon is given in Chapter 4.

□ □ □

1.8 THE INDUCTOR

As a rough parallel to the capacitor in which the energy storage associated with fixed charges is in the electric field, energy can also be stored in the magnetic field produced by moving charges or current. A detailed discussion of this matter requires consideration of the work of Oersted, Ampère, and Biot-Savart (see Chapter 12). We summarize the situation by noting that a wire carrying a current produces a magnetic field. The direction of the magnetic field is given by the pointing of our fingers on the right hand when our thumb points in the direction of the current as shown in Figure 1.8-1b. The magnetic flux that is produced will link the wire (see Figure 1.8-1a for the simple solenoid). The important parameters for describing the inductor are *flux linkages* and current i.

The terminal properties of the inductor are described graphically by a flux linkage-current ψ,i relationship which, in general, will be of the general form shown in Figure 1.8-1c. For the case when a linear ψ,i relationship exists, the flux linkages are proportional to the current. The proportionality constant is called the inductance L and this situation is shown in Figure 1.8-1d. That is,

$$L = \frac{\psi}{i} \qquad \text{henry} = \frac{\text{weber}}{\text{ampere}}$$

(1.8-1)

and is a geometric factor that can be deduced from basic considerations in the theory of magnetism.

To describe the inductor as a circuit element, we require a relation between the current i and the voltage v. This is given through Faraday's law which we write as

$$v = \frac{d\psi}{dt} = L\frac{di}{dt}$$

(1.8-2)

This is one of the fundamental circuit relations for the linear inductor. The corresponding relation when v is the independent variable is

$$i = \frac{\psi}{L} = \frac{1}{L}\int_{-\infty}^{t} v \, dt \qquad \left[\text{or } i = i(o) + \frac{1}{L}\int_{0}^{t} v \, dt \right] \qquad (1.8\text{-}3)$$

where $i(o)$ is the *initial current* at $t = 0$.

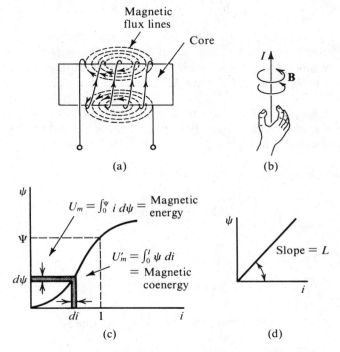

(a)   (b)

(c)   (d)

Figure 1.8-1.   To illustrate flux linkages in a simple solenoid and flux linkage-current relationship of an inductor

The graphical representation for the inductor as a circuit element is given in Figure 1.8-2.

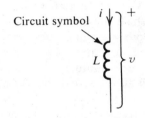

Figure 1.8-2.   Network representation of the inductor

The practical range of physical inductors extends from microhenry for coils of a few turns of wire in air to coils of several hundred henry with special magnetic cores.

To find the energy stored in the inductor we substitute Equation (1.8-1) into the equation for the magnetic energy U_m and obtain the following formula

$$U_m = \frac{1}{2}LI^2 = \frac{\psi^2}{2L} \quad \text{joule} \tag{1.8-4}$$

where I is the final value of the current through the inductor.

The interchange of v and i, and L and C in Equations (1.8-2) and (1.7-6) takes us from one relation to the other. This is known as *duality*, with v and i and L and C being called dual quantities.

EXAMPLE 1.8-1. A constant current, $i(o) = 1$ ampere exists in a coil, $L = 10^{-1}$ henry, and at $t = 0$ a voltage, $v(t) = t$, is applied across it. Find the total current and the energy stored in the inductor at time $t = 0.5$ seconds.

SOLUTION. Using Equation (1.8-3) we have

$$i(t)\bigg|_{t=0.5} = \frac{1}{10^{-1}}\int_{-\infty}^{0} v(t')dt' + \frac{1}{10^{-1}}\int_{0}^{t} v(t')dt' = i(o) + \frac{1}{10^{-1}}\int_{0}^{t} t'\,dt'$$

$$= 1 + \frac{1}{10^{-1}}\frac{t^2}{2}\bigg|_{t=0.5} = 2.25 \text{ ampere.}$$

The energy is found using Equation (1.8-4)

$$U_m = \frac{1}{2}LI^2 = \frac{1}{2}10^{-1}(2.25)^2 = 0.253 \text{ joule}$$

□   □   □

1.9   MUTUAL INDUCTANCE – TRANSFORMERS

When more than a single inductor is present in a given region, mutual inter-action of the magnetic fields of the inductors will exist. To examine this matter, refer to Figure 1.9-1 which illustrates two coils which interact magnetically. As drawn, the two coils are shown on a common core. This is just a schematic representation since in many cases no clearly discernible core exists (two coils in air would be an example). The advantage of indicating the presence of the core is that it aids in visualizing the mutual flux that links both coils.

We call specific attention to the intimate relation of the distribution of the windings on the core in Figure 1.9-1a and the dots on Figure 1.9-1b. The meaning of the dots is the following: when progressing along the winding from the dotted terminal, each winding encircles the core in the same sense. This means that if currents enter the dotted terminals, the component fluxes in the core will be in the same direction, and will add. An alternative, though equivalent, description follows by considering a variable source of voltage to be applied to one set of terminals, with an oscilloscope connected to the second set of terminals. The dotted terminals rise and fall together in voltage, or equivalently, the dotted terminals have the same instantaneous polarity.

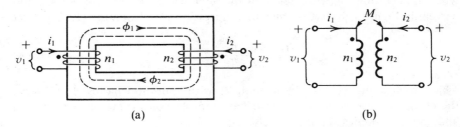

(a)   (b)

Figure 1.9-1.   Two coupled coils   (a) Schematic   (b) Network representation

The algebraic sign to be assiged to the mutual flux, and so to the mutual inductance, is intimately associated with the assumed current directions. Consider the case of *unity* coupled coils, which means that all of the flux φ_1 produced by the current in coil 1 links coil 2, and correspondingly, all of the flux φ_2 produced by current i_2 in coil 2 links coil 1. For the coupled inductors illustrated in Figure 1.9-1a we write, by Faraday's law,

$$v_1 = n_1\frac{d}{dt}(\varphi_{11} + \varphi_{12}) = \frac{d}{dt}[n_1(\varphi_{11} + \varphi_{12})] = \frac{d\psi_1}{dt}$$
$$v_2 = n_2\frac{d}{dt}(\varphi_{22} + \varphi_{21}) = \frac{d}{dt}[n_2(\varphi_{22} + \varphi_{21})] = \frac{d\psi_2}{dt} \tag{1.9-1}$$

where φ_{ij} denotes the flux coupling coil i that arises from a current in coil j.

If we take the ratio of these two equations with $\varphi_{11} + \varphi_{12} = \varphi_{22} + \varphi_{21}$ for unity coupling, we have that

$$\frac{v_1}{n_1} = \frac{v_2}{n_2}$$

which we write

$$v_1 = \frac{n_1}{n_2}v_2 = nv_2 \tag{1.9-2}$$

where n is the turns ratio n_1/n_2. This shows that for unity coupled coils the voltage per turn is the same for the two windings, and that with different number of turns, the voltage v_2 can be greater or less than v_1.

Another feature of the unity-coupled transformer can be deduced from considerations of the power to the coils (power $p = vi$). For zero power losses in the transformer, the total power to the system, by the principle of conservation of energy, is

$$v_1 i_1 + v_2 i_2 = 0 \qquad (1.9\text{-}3)$$

where due account has been taken of the reference conditions for voltage and current in Figure 1.9-1b. Combine this expression with Equation (1.9-2) to get

$$-\frac{i_2}{i_1} = \frac{v_1}{v_2} = \frac{n_1}{n_2} = n \qquad (1.9\text{-}4)$$

which relates the current in winding 2 with that in winding 1. Observe therefore that the electrical transformer imposes constraints on the through and across variables simultaneously.

In the manner of Equation (1.8-1), we write the following expressions

$$L_1 = \frac{\psi_1}{i_1} = \frac{n_1 \varphi_{11}}{i_1} \qquad\qquad L_2 = \frac{\psi_2}{i_2} = \frac{n_2 \varphi_{22}}{i_2}$$

$$M = \frac{n_1 \varphi_{12}}{i_2} = \frac{n_2 \varphi_{21}}{i_2} \qquad (1.9\text{-}5)$$

where M is known as the *mutual inductance*. It can be shown that

$$M = \sqrt{L_1 L_2} \qquad \text{henry} \qquad (1.9\text{-}6)$$

More detailed calculations for the case of non-unity coupling shows that M is related to L_1 and L_2 by the expression

$$M = k\sqrt{L_1 L_2} \qquad \text{henry} \qquad (1.9\text{-}7)$$

where k, the coefficient of coupling, may vary from zero to one. Actually it is very difficult to achieve unity coupling, but this can be approximated closely in tightly wound coils on high permeability cores. By Equations (1.9-5) we write Equation (1.9-1) in the form

$$v_1 = L_1 \frac{di_1}{dt} + M \frac{di_2}{dt} \qquad \text{(a)} \quad (1.9\text{-}8)$$

$$v_2 = M \frac{di_1}{dt} + L_2 \frac{di_2}{dt} \qquad \text{(b)}$$

For practical air-core transformers, the coupling is considerably less than unity; it is nearly unity in specially built iron-core transformers. Often the resistance of the wires of the transformer must be considered. It might also be necessary in some cases to take into account the power dissipation that occurs in the transformer core, if it is iron. Consequently, our simple coupled coil model will be adequate in some cases, but not in others.

1.10   THE RESISTOR

The inductor and capacitor store energy but the resistor dissipates energy. For a linear dissipative element the v,i characteristic is a straight line and the factor of proportionality is

$$R = \frac{v}{i} \quad \text{ohm } (\Omega) \tag{1.10-1}$$

or

$$i = \frac{1}{R}v = Gv$$

where $R = resistance$ (ohm) and $G = 1/R = conductance$ (mho). The network representation of the resistor is shown in Figure 1.10-1.

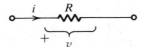

Figure 1.10-1.   Network representation of the resistor

The instantaneous power to the resistor is

$$p = vi = \frac{v^2}{R} = Gv^2 = Ri^2 \quad \text{watt} \tag{1.10-2}$$

and the total energy dissipated during the time T is

$$W = \int_0^T p\,dt = \int_0^T vi\,dt \quad \text{watt-sec} \triangleq \text{joule} \tag{1.10-3}$$

1.11   SOURCES

The sources supply the energy to be stored, transferred and dissipated in the electrical systems. They are of two kinds: (a) the *voltage source*, and (b) the *current source*. These sources are called *ideal* if their values do not change with load when connected to any electrical circuit. An ideal current source with its *v-i* characteristic is shown in Figure 1.11-1a and Figure 1.11-1b. In words, Figure

1.11-1b says that a current source will deliver a given current that is independent of the load, that is, the current is independent of the values of the circuit
elements connected to its terminals. Figure 1.11-1c shows the approximate
equivalent circuit of a non-ideal (a physical) current source.

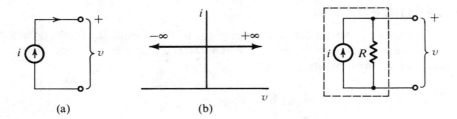

(a)   (b)

**Figure 1.11-1. (a) Ideal current source   (b) v-i characteristic
(c) Physical current source**

An ideal voltage source with its v-i characteristic is shown in Figure 1.11-2a,
1.11-2b and 1.11-2c. Figure 1.11-2c shows that the terminal voltage remains
constant, independent of the external load, that is, independent of the circuit
elements connected to the terminals. Figure 1.11-2d shows the approximate
equivalent circuit of a real (physical) voltage source.

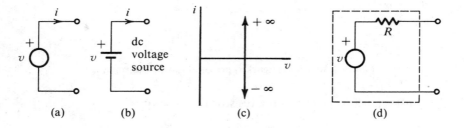

(a)   (b)   (c)   (d)

**Figure 1.11-2. (a) Ideal voltage source   (b) dc ideal voltage source
(c) v,i characteristic of ideal voltage source   (d) Physical voltage source**

The v-i characteristic curve of an ideal current source given in Figure 1.11-1b
indicates that the internal resistance of the source is

$$R = \frac{v}{i} = \frac{\infty}{\text{finite}} = \infty \qquad (1.11\text{-}1)$$

This means that when a current source in a circuit does not supply current, it is
an open circuit. Similarly, the ideal voltage source has an internal resistance
equal to

$$R = \frac{v}{i} = \frac{\text{finite}}{\infty} = 0 \qquad\qquad (1.11\text{-}2)$$

This means that when a voltage source in a circuit does not supply voltage, it can be considered to be a short circuit. However, for physical sources it is often necessary to take account of the internal resistances. Both considerations are very important, and they are used throughout the study of circuit theory.

Particular attention is called to the arrows associated with currents and + signs associated with voltages, and these are used without regard for whether the actual current direction or voltage vary or are constants with time. These designations express *reference conditions*, and these are essential in our studies.

The significance of the reference conditions stems from the fact that measurable electrical quantities are *physical entities*. Their algebraic representations (i, v) are *algebraic quantities*. Physical entities change their direction or polarity while their algebraic representations change their sense (algebraic sign). Refer to Figure 1.11-1 for the current source, but this discussion is not confined to sources alone. According to our system of notation, the reference direction is indicated by the arrow. The direction of the through variable when the symbol that represents it is positive is called the *reference direction*. If the algebraic sign is reversed, this implies a reversal of the reference direction. Thus in our subsequent work, we can arbitrarily assign reference directions to currents with the understanding that if the algebraic sign, upon completing a calculation, should be negative, then it merely means that the current is opposite to our assumed reference direction.

Now consider the symbol for voltage. Voltage exists between two points, one of which is the reference point. Such across variables exist between pairs of points or nodes, as shown by the brace in Figure 1.7-1a. Since the − sign is implied if the + sign is given, we shall not include the − sign with the brace. The polarity of an across variable when the symbol that represents it is positive is called the *reference polarity* and a reversal of the algebraic sign amounts to a reversal of the reference polarity.

The general term *reference condition* is used to imply either a reference direction or a reference polarity. Thus in general terms, the reference conditions of a physical entity correspond to the positive sense of the algebraic quantity that represents it. The implied positive sign in the defining relations for the capacitor, Equations (1.7-6) and (1.7-9); in the defining relations for the inductor, Equations (1.8-2) and (1.8-3); as well as for all other elements, reflects the reference conditions shown. It is important to note that for electrical sources the + sign is used to denote both the reference polarity and the algebraic sense. This distinction is important, but no confusion should result from this double use of the + sign.

MECHANICAL ELEMENTS

1.12   THE IDEAL MASS ELEMENT

Newton's second law of motion

$$f = M\frac{dv}{dt} = M\frac{d^2x}{dt^2} = Ma \qquad \text{newton}$$

relates the force with the acceleration. The unit of mass M is kg, the velocity is m/s, and the acceleration a is m/s². The motional variable v enters in a relative form, such as the difference of the absolute values observed at the terminals, and it is the *across* variable. The force acts through an element and it is the *through* variable.

Representations of considerable interest are the two equivalent schematic diagrams given in Figure 1.12-1. The analytic relations between the force and

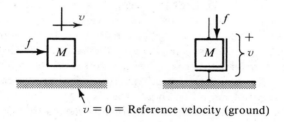

$v = 0 =$ Reference velocity (ground)

Figure 1.12-1.   Schematic representations of the mass element

the motional variables, depending on which is selected as the independent variable, are the pair of relations

$$f = M\frac{dv}{dt}$$

$$v = \frac{1}{M}\int_{-\infty}^{t} f\, dt \qquad \left[\text{or } v = v(o) + \frac{1}{M}\int_{0}^{t} f\, dt \right] \tag{1.12-1}$$

where $v(o)$ is the initial velocity and M is assumed constant. For varying M we must write $v = d(Mv)/dt$. We call attention to the exact equivalence in form that exists between this set of equations and Equations (1.7-6) and (1.7-7) for the capacitor. This establishes the *analogy* between the mass M in the mechanical system and the capacitor C in the electrical system. We shall have many occasions to exploit this analogy at later points in the text.

The power is the prime rate of flow of energy. If a constant force f acts on a mechanical system and changes its position by dx without any friction present in the same direction in which the force acts, it does dW work on the system, that is,

$$dW = f dx \qquad (1.12\text{-}2)$$

Hence the power is

$$p = \frac{dW}{dt} = f \frac{dx}{dt} = fv \qquad \text{watt} \qquad (1.12\text{-}3)$$

where v is the velocity of the point to which the force was applied. Upon integrating Equation (1.12-3) we obtain the energy of the system from an initial time zero to some time t

$$W = \int_0^t fv \, dt \qquad (1.12\text{-}4)$$

1.13   THE SPRING

A spring element is one which stores energy in the displacement due to the elastic deformation that results from the application of a force. For a linear force-displacement relation, the analytic expression is written

$$f = Kx \qquad \text{newton} \qquad (1.13\text{-}1)$$

where K is the spring constant (newton/m). Over this linear region, the spring satisfies Hooke's law. Physical springs satisfy this relationship for forces below the elastic limit of the material. Deviations from this linear relation may occur for a number of reasons, including temperature effects, rotation of the spring ends, hysteresis.

The schematic representation of the spring element is given in Figure 1.13-1.

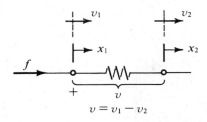

Figure 1.13-1.   Schematic representation of the spring

The analytic relations between the through and the across variables are the pair of equations

$$f = K(x_1 - x_2) = K \int_{-\infty}^{t} (v_1 - v_2)dt = K \int_{-\infty}^{t} v \, dt = f(o) + K \int_{0}^{t} v dt \quad \text{(a)} \quad (1.13\text{-}2)$$

$$v = \frac{1}{K} \frac{df}{dt} \qquad\qquad\qquad\qquad\qquad\qquad\qquad\qquad\qquad \text{(b)}$$

The first of these expressions shows that if $x_1 > x_2$ there is a compressive force and f is positive for the specified reference conditions. If $x_1 < x_2$ there is a negative or extensive force. Note the analogy between the spring and the inductor, both in the through-across relations and in the schematic representation.

Upon introducing Equation (1.13-2b) into Equation (1.12-4), we find that the energy is given by

$$W = \int f \frac{1}{K} \frac{df}{dt} dt = \frac{1}{K} \int f \, df = \frac{1}{K} \frac{f^2}{2} \qquad (1.13\text{-}3)$$

1.14 THE DAMPER

There are three important types of mechanical friction: *static*, *Coulomb*, and *viscous*. Static friction is directly concerned with motion and manifests itself through the greater force required to initiate motion between two surfaces in contact rather than to maintain the motion. Coulomb friction acts in a direction to oppose motion. The Coulomb friction force between rolling or sliding surfaces is dependent on the normal force, but is substantially independent of velocity. We shall limit ourselves here to viscous friction which, for a linear dependence of velocity on force, is

$$f = Dv \qquad \text{or} \qquad v = \frac{f}{D} \qquad (1.14\text{-}1)$$

where D is the damping constant (newton-second/m). A mechanical damper and its schematic representation are shown in Figure 1.14-1. The reader should observe the similarity of Equation (1.14-1) with that for a resistor.

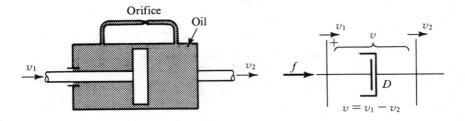

Figure 1.14-1. Physical and diagrammatic representations of a dash pot

The power associated with a damper is [see Equation (1.12-3)]

$$P = Dv^2 \qquad (1.14\text{-}2)$$

1.15   RIGID LINKAGE (MECHANICAL TRANSFORMER)

A rigid linkage is a device for transforming force and velocity variables.

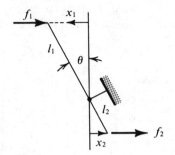

Figure 1.15-1.   A simple rigid linkage mechanism

Consider the simple rigid linkage shown in Figure 1.15-1. From that figure we see that

$$\sin \theta = \frac{x_1}{l_1} = \frac{x_2}{l_2}$$

We define the quantity n

$$n = \frac{l_1}{l_2} \qquad (1.15\text{-}1)$$

It follows that

$$x_1 = nx_2 \qquad \text{(a)} \quad (1.15\text{-}2)$$

so that

$$\frac{dx_1}{dt} = v_1 = n\frac{dx_2}{dt} = nv_2 \qquad \text{or} \qquad v_1 = nv_2 \qquad \text{(b)}$$

If there are no losses in the linkage, then the power input to the linkage must equal the power output from the linkage. This requires, for the reference conditions shown, that

$$f_1 v_1 = f_2 v_2 \qquad (1.15\text{-}3)$$

from which it follows that

$$\frac{f_1}{f_2} = \frac{v_2}{v_1} = \frac{1}{n} \qquad (1.15\text{-}4)$$

The linkage can be given schematic representation, as shown in Figure 1.15-2. This representation has been borrowed from electrical symbolism (see Section 1-9). The dots that appear in Figure 1.15-2 are included to specify points which are to be marked with + signs to specify the positive reference for velocity. Also, the arrows specify the positive reference directions for force.

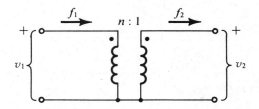

**Figure 1.15-2. Schematic representation of a rigid linkage
(a translational transformer)**

1.16 INDEPENDENT MECHANICAL SOURCES

In the foregoing discussion of M, K, D, which refer to passive elements, it has been assumed that sources or drivers exist which produce forces or velocities. It is convenient to define sources as force or velocity drivers, although velocity sources are less common than force drivers. These sources are represented schematically in Figure 1.16-1 and are assumed to maintain their terminal polarities independently of the magnitudes of the power at the terminals; that is, they are regarded as independent sources. This is an idealiza-

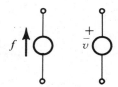

Figure 1.16-1. Schematic representation of force and velocity drivers

tion, of course, since any practical source would ordinarily be unable to maintain such an independence. In the more practical case, a driver can often be represented by an ideal source with associated lumped elements to account approximately for the terminal properties. This condition was discussed in connection with electrical drivers in Section 1.11.

1.17 MECHANICAL ELEMENTS – ROTATIONAL

A set of rotational mechanical elements and rotational variables exist which bear a one-to-one correspondence to the translational mechanical elements and the translational variables which have been discussed in the foregoing sections. In the rotational system, *torque* is the through variable and *angular velocity* is the motional or across variable. The corresponding fundamental quantities are:

J = polar moment of inertia,   corresponds to M in translation

K = rotational spring constant,   corresponds to K in translation

D = rotational damping,   corresponds to D in translation

$\mathcal{T}$ = torque,   corresponds to f in translation

$\omega = d\theta/dt$, angular velocity,   corresponds to $v = dx/dt$ in translation

The Inertial Element

In this rotational set, J is the rotational parameter and is the assumed proportionality factor between torque and angular acceleration,

$$\mathcal{T} = \frac{d(J\omega)}{dt} \quad \text{newton-meter} \qquad \text{(a)} \quad (1.17\text{-}1)$$

or for the systems with constant J

$$\mathcal{T} = J\frac{d\omega}{dt} = J\frac{d^2\theta}{dt^2} \qquad \text{(b)}$$

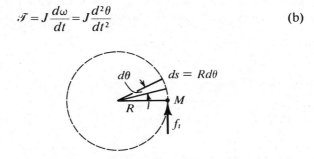

Figure 1.17-1. Rotational motion of a point mass M

To show that Equation (1.17-1) is true, consider the system shown in Figure 1.17-1. Newton's second principle specifies that

$$f_t = \text{tangential force} = Ma_t \qquad (1.17\text{-}2)$$

It is observed from the figure that $ds = R\,d\theta$ so that

$$\frac{ds}{dt} = v_t = R\frac{d\theta}{dt} = R\omega$$

or

$$v_t = R\omega \qquad (1.17\text{-}3)$$

Upon differentiating this expression once with respect to time, then

$$\frac{dv_t}{dt} = a_t = R\frac{d\omega}{dt} \qquad (1.17\text{-}4)$$

Substitute Equation (1.17-4) into Equation (1.17-2) and multiply the resulting expression by R. This gives

$$\mathcal{T} = Rf_t = MR^2\frac{d\omega}{dt} = J\frac{d\omega}{dt} \qquad (1.17\text{-}5)$$

In general the moment of inertia J of a rotational body depends on the square of a characteristic distance of the body called the *radius of gyration k*, with

$$J = Mk^2 \qquad \text{kg-m}^2 \qquad (1.17\text{-}6)$$

For a simple point mass rotating about an axis at a distance R from the center of mass, as in the situation discussed above, $k = R$, and as found above,

$$J = MR^2 \qquad (1.17\text{-}7)$$

For a simple disk of radius r rotating about its center, $k = r/\sqrt{2}$, and

$$J = \frac{1}{2}Mr^2 \qquad (1.17\text{-}8)$$

In general the moment of inertia is given by

$$J = \int r^2 \, dm \qquad (1.17\text{-}9)$$

where the integral is taken over the body and the rotation occurs only about one axis.

EXAMPLE 1.17-1. Find the moment of inertia and the radius of gyration of a homogeneous disk about its axis, as shown in Figure 1.17-2.

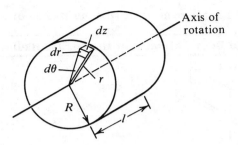

Figure 1.17-2.   Moment of inertia of a homogeneous solid disk

SOLUTION. Use Equation (1.17-9), where ϱ is the density of the material in kg/m³,

$$J = \iiint r^2 \, dm = \iiint_V r^2 \varrho \, dV = \varrho \int_0^l dz \int_0^{2\pi} d\theta \int_0^R r^2 r \, dr = \varrho l \frac{2\pi R^4}{4}$$

$$= \frac{M}{V} l 2\pi R^4 = \frac{M}{\pi R^2 l} l \frac{2\pi R^4}{4} = \frac{M}{2} R^2$$

By Equation (1.17-6) we find that

$$k = \sqrt{\frac{J}{M}} = \sqrt{\frac{MR^2}{2M}} = \frac{R}{\sqrt{2}}$$

□   □   □

Table 1.17-1 gives the moment of inertia and the radius of gyration for some common shapes.

The essential features of the rotational system are shown schematically in Figure 1.17-3. The pair of equations that apply for this element are

$$\mathscr{T} = J \frac{d\omega}{dt}$$

$$\omega = \frac{1}{J} \int_{-\infty}^{t} \mathscr{T} \, dt = \omega(o) + \frac{1}{J} \int_0^t \mathscr{T} \, dt$$
(1.17-10)

Since power is the product of force and velocity [see Equation (1.12-3)], the torque $\mathscr{T}$ delivers a power P to a system equal to

$$p = fv = f \frac{ds}{dt} = fR \frac{d\theta}{dt} = \mathscr{T}\omega \qquad \text{newton-meter/second} \qquad (1.17\text{-}11)$$

Table 1.17-1. Moment of Inertia and Radius of Gyration

Homogeneous Rigid Body	Moment of Inertia, J	Radius of Gyration, k
Slender rod	$\dfrac{1}{12}Ml^2$	$\dfrac{l}{\sqrt{12}}$
Solid disk	$\dfrac{1}{2}MR^2$	$\dfrac{R}{\sqrt{2}}$
Sphere	$\dfrac{3}{5}MR^2$	$\sqrt{\dfrac{3}{5}}\,R$
Annular disk	$\dfrac{1}{2}M(R_1^2 + R_2^2)$	$\sqrt{\dfrac{R_1^2 + R_2^2}{2}}$
Flat plate	$\dfrac{1}{12}M(a^2 + b^2)$	$\sqrt{\dfrac{a^2 + b^2}{12}}$

The work done on the system from initial time 0 to some later time t is

$$W = \int_0^t \mathcal{T}\omega \, dt \tag{1.17-12}$$

Upon combining Equations (1.17-10) and (1.17-12) we find

$$W = \int J \frac{d\omega}{dt}\,\omega \, dt = \frac{1}{2}J\,\omega^2 \tag{1.17-13}$$

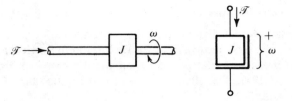

Figure 1.17-3.   Schematic representation of rotational inertia

The Rotational Spring Element

A rotational spring is one which will twist under the action of a torque. It is depicted in schematic form in Figure 1.17-4, and for constant K is described by the pair of equations

$$\mathcal{T} = K\theta = \mathcal{T}(o) + K\int_0^t \omega\, dt \qquad\qquad \omega = \frac{1}{K}\frac{d\mathcal{T}}{dt} \qquad\qquad (1.17\text{-}14)$$

where $\mathcal{T}(o)$ is the torque at $t = 0$. This relationship assumes a linear spring. The

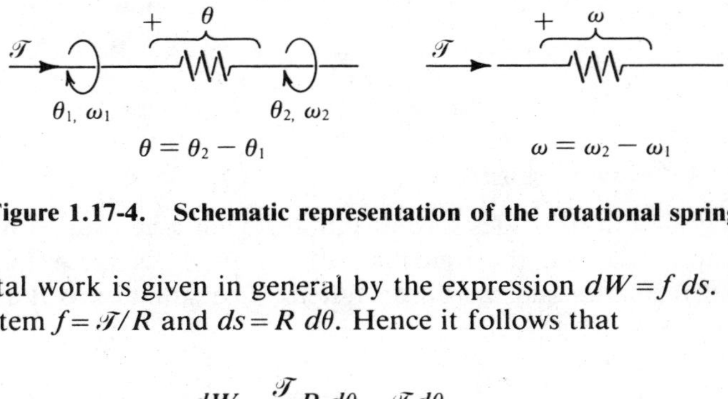

Figure 1.17-4.   Schematic representation of the rotational spring

incremental work is given in general by the expression $dW = f\, ds$. For a rotational system $f = \mathcal{T}/R$ and $ds = R\, d\theta$. Hence it follows that

$$dW = \frac{\mathcal{T}}{R}R\, d\theta = \mathcal{T}\, d\theta \qquad\qquad (1.17\text{-}15)$$

Divide this equation by dt to obtain the power

$$p = \frac{dW}{dt} = \mathcal{T}\frac{d\theta}{dt} = \mathcal{T}\omega \qquad\qquad (1.17\text{-}16)$$

which is equal to the torque times the angular velocity [see also Equation (1.17-11)].

From Equation (1.17-15) we find that the energy stored in a deformed spring is

$$W = \int_0^\theta \mathcal{T}\, d\theta = \int_0^\theta K\theta\, d\theta = \frac{K}{2}\theta^2 = \frac{1}{2K}\mathcal{T}^2 \qquad\qquad (1.17\text{-}17)$$

Rotational Viscous Damper

The rotational damper differs from the translational damper principally in the character of the motion. Much of the discussion in Section 1.14 applies, in essence, in the present case also. The schematic diagrams for this element are given in Figure 1.17-5. The element is described by the pair of relations, for linear viscous damping,

$$\mathcal{T} = D\omega \qquad\qquad \omega = \frac{\mathcal{T}}{D} \qquad\qquad (1.17\text{-}18)$$

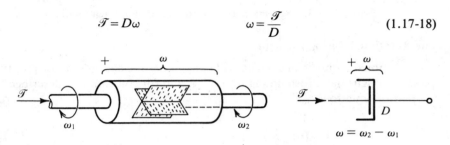

Figure 1.17-5. Schematic representation of the rotational viscous damper

From Equations (1.17-18) and (1.17-11) we obtain the power relation for the damper

$$P = D\omega^2 = \mathcal{T}^2/D \qquad\qquad (1.17\text{-}19)$$

Gear Train (Rotational Transformer)

A simple gear train provides torque and angle variable transformations in much the same way that the rigid linkage bar provides force and velocity variable transformations in the linear system. The situation is illustrated in

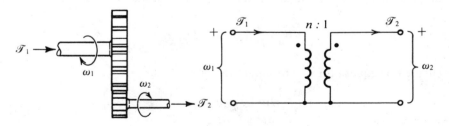

Figure 1.17-6. Simple gear train and its schematic representation

Figure 1.17-6. If there are n_1 teeth on gear 1 and n_2 teeth on gear 2, then the gear train requires that

$$\frac{\omega_1}{n_2} = \frac{\omega_2}{n_1} \qquad\qquad \text{(a)} \quad (1.17\text{-}20)$$

or

$$\frac{\omega_1}{\omega_2} = \frac{n_2}{n_1} = n, \text{ gear ratio} \qquad\qquad \text{(b)}$$

Further, if the gear train is lossless, then the total power input to one gear must equal the total power output from the second gear. This requires, for the specified reference conditions, that

$$P = \omega_1 \mathscr{T}_1 = \omega_2 \mathscr{T}_2$$

from which it follows that

$$\frac{\mathscr{T}_1}{\mathscr{T}_2} = \frac{\omega_2}{\omega_1} = \frac{1}{n} \qquad\qquad (1.17\text{-}21)$$

The parallel to the electrical transformer and to the linear mechanical transformer (the bar linkage) is obvious.

Rotational Drivers

Rotational drivers exist which produce torques or which produce angular velocities. Here, as for the translational system, not all drivers maintain constant torque or constant rotational velocity independent of load. Certain devices exist which do meet the idealized conditions. For example, a synchronous motor will maintain constant angular speed for all values of torque. The schematic representation of rotational drivers is given in Figure 1.17-7.

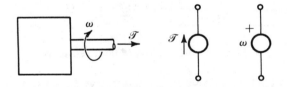

Figure 1.17-7.   Rotational driver and schematic representations

FLUID ELEMENTS

1.18   LIQUID SYSTEMS – RESISTANCE

In our study of liquid systems, we shall assume that liquid tanks have a free liquid surface, the pipes are considered to be full of liquid, and that steady flow persists.

Two different types of flow are important: *laminar* and *turbulent* flow. Since nonlinearities are associated with turbulent flow, we shall deal only with laminar flows.

For laminar flow in general, the flow in circular tubes or pipes is found from the Pouisuille-Hagen law

$$h = h_1 - h_2 = \frac{128\eta L}{\pi D^4} Q \qquad \text{meters} \qquad (1.18\text{-}1)$$

where

h = head, m

η = absolute viscosity, newton-second/meter^2

L = length of tube or pipe, m

D = inside diameter of pipe, m

Q = liquid flow rate, m^3/s

There is a direct analogy between the laminar flow law and Ohm's law for electric circuit resistance because the flow Q is directly proportional to the head h. The laminar resistance is found from

$$R = \frac{dh}{dQ} = \frac{128\eta L}{\pi D^4} \qquad \text{s/m}^2 \qquad (1.18\text{-}2)$$

However, laminar flow is not often encountered in industrial practice. The schematic representation of fluid resistance is given in Figure 1.18-1, with R constant for laminar flow.

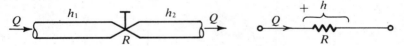

Figure 1.18-1.   Fluid (liquid) resistance

1.19   LIQUID CAPACITANCE, INDUCTANCE, AND SOURCES

The concept of liquid capacitance is a simple one to understand; it is simply a measure of the capacity of a tank to store a liquid. Refer to Figure 1.19-1 which illustrates the situation. Conservation of mass requires that the change in volume of the liquid being stored in a tank is specified by the fluid flow rate into the tank. Thus

$$Q = \frac{dV}{dt} = A\frac{dh}{dt} = \frac{dV}{dh}\frac{dh}{dt} \qquad \text{m}^3\text{/s} \qquad (1.19\text{-}1)$$

where V denotes the volume, and A the sectional area of the tank. In analogy with Equation (1.7-1) for electrical capacitance, we define C in terms of flow and time rate of change of head. Thus

$$C = \frac{dV}{dh} \quad \text{m}^2 \tag{1.19-2}$$

The liquid capacitance of a tank is equal to the cross-sectional area of the tank taken at the liquid surface. If the tank has a constant cross-sectional area, the liquid capacitance is a constant for any head. In the more general case, the liquid capacitance will not be constant.

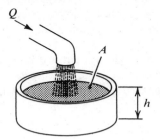

Figure 1.19-1. Fluid (liquid) capacitance

To examine the inertance of the flow in a pipe, which can be denoted as the fluid inductance, consider a pipe of length l containing a fluid. The force necessary to accelerate the mass (ϱAl) in a pipe is given by

$$F = A(h_2 - h_1) = \varrho Al \frac{dv}{dt}$$

But the flow rate $Q = Av$, so that

$$h_2 - h_1 = \frac{\varrho l}{A} \frac{dQ}{dt} = L \frac{dQ}{dt} \tag{1.19-3}$$

where the quantity $L = \varrho l / A$ is the fluid inductance.

A fluid source must comprise two parts: a reservoir (sump) of the liquid and a pump for causing the liquid to flow under some sort of pressure. A large variety of fluid pumps are available. We refer specifically to gear pumps and centrifugal pumps. The design and operation of the gear pumps is such that the liquid is provided at a relatively constant flow rate against a wide range of heads. Essentially, therefore, such a pump is a constant flow device, and is analogous to the current source in electricity. The centrifugal pump is one for which the pressure head remains substantially constant over wide ranges of flow, and is analogous to the voltage source. In essence, both through-type and across-type fluid sources are available.

1.20   GAS SYSTEMS

Gas systems that consist of pressure vessels or chambers and various connecting pipes, valves, etc., may be analyzed by using the basic laws for the flow of compressible gases. However, for systems in which the pressure differentials are less than about 5 percent of the static pressure, the compressibility is not usually important, and the systems may be treated as liquid systems. Ventilating and other air-transport systems where changes of air density are small may be treated as incompressible flow systems. Generally, though, the pressure differentials are substantial, and compressible flow considerations are necessary.

The system elements for a gas system are illustrated in Figure 1.20-1. To describe the features of these elements, the flow laws for both laminar and turbulent conditions must be used. For turbulent flow through pipes, orifices and

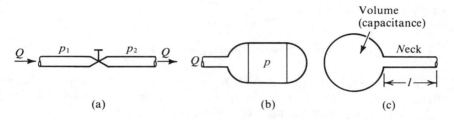

Figure 1.20-1.   Fluid (gas) resistance, capacitance, and inertance

valves, the steady-flow energy equation (the first law of thermodynamics) for adiabatic flow of ideal gases is

$$w = KAY\sqrt{2g(p_1 - p_2)/\varrho} \qquad \text{kg/s} \qquad (1.20\text{-}1)$$

where

$w = $ gas flow rate, kg/s

$A = $ area of restriction

$Y = $ rational expansion factor $= \varrho\sqrt{V\dfrac{\gamma}{\gamma - 1}}$

$\gamma = $ specific heat ratio for gases

$\varrho = $ gas density, kg/m³

$K = $ a flow coefficient

$p = $ pressure, kg/m²

The turbulent gas flow resistance is defined as

$$R = \frac{dp}{dw} \quad \text{s/m}^2 \tag{1.20-2}$$

It is not possible to calculate R easily from Equation (1.20-2) because the expansion factor Y depends on the pressure. In this case it is easier to determine resistance from a plot of pressure against flow for any particular device. For laminar gas flow through tubes and pipes, Equation (1.18-2) can be used.

To discuss the capacitance of a pressure vessel, we first write a flow law for the pressure vessel of Figure 1.20-1b. For constant volume

$$w = \frac{dM}{dt} = \frac{d(\varrho V)}{dt} = \frac{V d\varrho}{dt} \quad \text{kg/s} \tag{1.20-3}$$

The gas capacitance is defined as the ratio of change of weight of gas in the vessel to the change in pressure,

$$C = V \frac{d\varrho}{dp} \quad \text{m-s}^2 \tag{1.20-4}$$

By combining this expression with Equation (1.20-3) we have that

$$w = V \frac{d\varrho}{dp} \frac{dp}{dt} = C \frac{dp}{dt} \quad \text{kg/s} \tag{1.20-5}$$

The capacitance expression in Equation (1.20-4) must be calculated from thermodynamic relations because the gas expands from a region of high pressure into the vessel at lower pressure, or perhaps expands from the vessel into a region of lower pressure. It is desirable to assume a polytropic expansion process, since the expansion will probably follow a path between an isothermal and an adiabatic process. Thus it is assumed that

$$\frac{p}{\varrho^n} = \text{constant} = A \tag{1.20-6}$$

where the polytropic exponent n will lie between $n = 1.0$ for isothermal expansion and 1.41, the ratio of specific heats, for adiabatic expansion. From this expression, by differentiation, it follows that

$$\frac{dp}{p} = n \frac{d\varrho}{\varrho} \tag{1.20-7}$$

Combine this result with Equation (1.20-4) for $n = 1$ to get

$$C = \frac{V\varrho}{p} \tag{1.20-8}$$

Now use the equation of state for the ideal gas

$$pV = NRT \qquad (1.20\text{-}9)$$

where N = number of moles of the gas, R is the universal gas constant = 8316.6 joule/kg-mole-°K, and T is the temperature in deg. K. This gas law, when combined with Equation (1.20-8) gives

$$C = \frac{MV}{NRT} \qquad \text{m-s}^2 \qquad (1.20\text{-}10)$$

Numerous tests show that the exponent n ranges from 1.0 to 1.2 for uninsulated metal vessels at standard pressure and temperature. Hence for constant volume and temperature, the gas capacitance of a vessel is constant. It is analogous to electric capacitance.

As in the case of liquid systems, gas will sustain and transmit acoustic vibrations; acoustic pipes and acoustic resonators are well known. Such gas phenomena are possible, as with liquids, because gas possesses both inertia and elasticity. Refer to Figure 1.20-1c and focus on the mass of fluid that is contained in the neck. If the linear dimensions of the neck are small compared with the wavelength of the vibration, it has been found that the inertance is given by

$$\text{Inertance} = \varrho l \qquad (1.20\text{-}11)$$

THERMAL ELEMENTS

1.21 THERMAL SYSTEMS

Thermal systems are those that involve the transfer of heat from one point to another. There is no thermal element that is analogous to inductance, since such an element would permit actions that would be contrary to the second law of thermodynamics. There are three different heat transfer processes: *conduction*, *convection*, and *radiation*.

For the conduction of heat through a specific conductor, the heat flow is described by the Fourier law. This law relates the heat flow to the gradient of the temperature (see Figure 1.21-1a)

$$Q = KA \frac{T_1 - T_2}{L} \qquad \text{joule/second} \qquad (1.21\text{-}1)$$

where:

Q = heat flow, joule/second

K = thermal conductivity, joule/meter-second-degree

A = area normal to heat flow, m²

L = length of conductor, m

T = temperature, degree K

The direction of the heat flow is from the region of high temperature to the region of low temperature. The form of this law is identical with Ohm's law, Equation (1.10-1), which relates the current in a resistor and the difference of potential across its terminals. The thermal resistance (conduction) is, therefore,

$$R = \frac{dT}{dQ} = \frac{L}{KA} \qquad \text{degree-second/joule} \qquad (1.21\text{-}2)$$

The form of this equation is the same as Equation (1.10-1) for electrical resistance, the difference lying in the presence of thermal conductivity in one case and electrical conductivity in the other. It is true, in fact, that pure metals that are good thermal conductors are also good electrical conductors.

A fluid or gas is involved in convection heat transfer. Convection is the process by which heat transfers across a heated surface into (or from) the fluid (see Figure 1.21-1b). For convection heat transfer, by the Newton law of cooling,

$$Q = hA(T_1 - T_2) \qquad \text{joule/second} \qquad (1.21\text{-}3)$$

where h is the convection coefficient (joule/meter²-second-degree). It is expected that h will depend on the fluid and upon the state of the fluid flow, but in a given situation, h is nearly constant. We define a thermal resistance for convection

$$R = \frac{dT}{dQ} = \frac{1}{hA} \qquad \text{degree-second/joule} \qquad (1.21\text{-}4)$$

Since this resistance factor is related to the flow of heat to a fluid boundary layer, no factor of length appears.

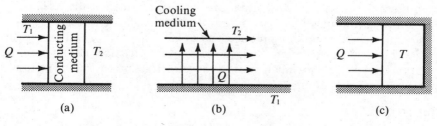

Figure 1.21-1. Thermal processes (a) Conduction
(b) Convection (c) Storage

Radiant heat transfer is a thermal process that is quite different from conduction and convection, both of which are molecular processes. Thermal
energy in radiant heat transfer flows from a region of high temperature to one
of lower temperature by an electromagnetic radiation process. The heat flow,
away from a surface under radiant conditions, is given by the Stefan-
Boltzmann law. Since the heat resistance is a nonlinear quantity we shall not
elaborate on this type of thermal process.

To discuss thermal capacitance, refer to Figure 1.21-1c. By adding heat to a
system, its internal energy is increased, according to the relation

$$Q = C\frac{dT}{dt} \quad \text{joule/second} \tag{1.21-5}$$

This expresses the heat added (or lost) with the consequent increase (or
decrease) of temperature. The thermal capacitance C (joule/degree) is written

$$C = Wc_p \tag{1.21-6}$$

where

    W = weight of the block, kg

    c_p = specific heat at constant pressure, joule/degree-kilogram

Thermal capacitance, which relates the heat added to the change in temperature, is precisely analogous to electrical capacitance which relates the charge
added to the change in voltage.

We have already noted that thermal systems do not always act as isolated
thermal resistors or capacitors. Fire brick is a material with a high resistance to
the flow of heat, but because of its appreciable thermal specific heat it
possesses a substantial thermal capacitance. Moreover, because these properties are distributed throughout the material, the foregoing considerations do
not apply exactly. Materials with distributed characteristics can be approximated by considering the material to be made up of slabs, each of which can be
described by both resistance and capacitance, and considering a series collection of such quantities. There are many physical problems of importance in
which thermal resistance and thermal capacitance are sufficiently isolated to
allow some calculations of significance to be made.

Thermal sources ordinarily produce heat at a constant rate, and depend on
the rate at which the excitation (fuel, electrical power, friction, etc.) is applied.
Hence thermal sources are analogous to the electrical current source or to the
constant flow liquid pump.

1.22 POSTLUDE

The discussion in Section 1.1 emphasizes that only a very restricted class of
system elements would receive much of our attention in our following studies.

These are the lumped linear, bilateral elements, and nonlinear elements that lend themselves to linearization. With these, the subsequent interconnected circuits are described by linear differential equations for which closed form solutions are possible using the standard techniques of differential equations. These approximations eliminate from consideration far more devices than are included, yet this restricted class is a very important one. This means that additional modeling might have to be pursued later on.

Actually, additional modeling is done in this book when electronic devices, electromechanical transducers, and rotating machinery are discussed. With in-depth studies in other fields, modeling becomes a critical issue, since the quality of the studies are generally no better than the quality of the model that is used. The problems are made more difficult by nonlinearities and inherent time delays that might exist in the actual device or process. Modeling the human eye is an example that includes an inherent time delay factor. Yet the bioengineer has developed an acceptable model for the eye and its motion.

It is a tribute to workers in varied fields that they can develop mathematical models of complicated devices or systems which allow reasonably good descriptions of the behavior of these devices or systems. But above all, remember that the model is the means for translating the physical world into the mathematical world, and vice versa. To the engineer, analysis involves translating the physical world into the mathematical world and then operating mathematically on his equations. The reverse process is also very important, and in synthesis or design, he must translate his mathematical studies into the world of hardware.

SUMMARY

- The analytic model of a system is characterized by input-output variables or, equivalently, by excitation-response variables.

- The two broad areas of signals are separated into deterministic and random signals, and each of these two areas is subdivided in continuous and discrete signals.

- A sinusoidal time function is characterized by its peak value V_m, angular frequency ω in radians/second, and phase angle $\theta°$: $v(t) = V_m \sin(\omega t + \theta)$ with respect to a designated reference time zero.

- Each periodic or nonperiodic signal is characterized by its amplitude and phase spectrum.

- Signal sources are of two general classes: one is called across source, the other is called through source.

- Signals are indicated or recorded electrically with the help of special devices called transducers. These include: displacement transducers (resistive type, strain gage, inductive, capacitive); velocity transducers; acceleration transducers; temperature transducers.

- Electrical elements are described in terms of two dynamic variables, current (through variable) and voltage (across variable).
- The capacitor is one of the three basic electrical elements. Its capacitance is defined as the ratio of the charge stored in it to the voltage across it. The capacitance of a parallel plate capacitor is given by

$$C = \frac{\epsilon A}{d} \quad \text{farad}$$

where $\epsilon = \epsilon_o \epsilon_r$ is the permittivity of the dielectric material ($\epsilon_o = 8.85 \times 10^{-12}$ farad/m = permittivity of free space), A is the area, and d is the separation of the plates. The electrical energy stored in the electric field in a capacitor is given by

$$U_e = \frac{1}{C} \frac{Q^2}{2} = \frac{1}{2} C V^2 \quad \text{joule}$$

- The inductor, a rough parallel to the capacitor, stores energy in the magnetic flux linkage field which is produced by the current in the coils. The proportionality constant of the ratio ψ/i is called inductance L,

$$L = \frac{\psi}{i} \quad \text{henry}$$

The energy stored in the magnetic field is given by

$$U_m = \frac{1}{2} L I^2 = \frac{1}{2} \frac{\psi^2}{L} \quad \text{joule}$$

- When two inductors are in proximity and there exists flux linkage between them an additional inductance is present known as mutual inductance.

$$M = k \sqrt{L_1 L_2} \quad \text{henry}$$

where k is the coefficient of coupling.
- The resistance of a resistor is defined by the relation

$$R = \frac{v}{i} \quad \text{ohm}$$

The dissipated power is given by

$$P = R i^2 \quad \text{watt}$$

- The ideal voltage source supplies a constant voltage and the ideal current source supplies a constant current independently of the electrical loads attached to them.
- The velocity in mechanical elements is an across variable and the force is a through variable.
- The mathematical relationships between cause and effect for all systems considered are given in Table S1.1.

REVIEW QUESTIONS

1. What are the two variables associated with a modeled system?
2. What do we call the process when we develop a system to produce a specified output for a designated input?
3. Name different types of signals.
4. Define the term "angular frequency." What type of signals have an associated angular frequency?
5. Name three natural periodic signals.
6. What is the difference between the unit impulse signal and the unit step signal?
7. What are the differences between the amplitude and phase spectra for periodic and transient signals?
8. Specify some across and through sources.
9. Name two displacement transducers.
10. Draw the response-excitation curves for the following systems: linear, bilateral, nonlinear, and nonbilateral.
11. What is the difference between a displacement and a conduction current?
12. Define the proportionality constant C of an electrical capacitor. What are the units of C? What is the total energy stored in the electric field of a capacitor charged by a voltage source of V volts? What is the relation between the current through the capacitor and the voltage across it?
13. Does the current lag or lead the voltage in a capacitor with sinusoidal excitation?
14. State the relations between the current through and the voltage across an inductor.
15. What is the use of an electrical transformer?
16. Define resistance and conductance.
17. What is the difference between an ideal and a real current or voltage source?
18. State the relation between force, mass and velocity.
19. What are the three important mechanical friction forces?
20. Is any mechanical system analogous to an electrical transformer?
21. State the relation between torque and angular acceleration.
22. Does a fluid resistance exist?

Table S1.1. Linear System Elements

System Element		Graphical Representation	Independent Variable	
			Through	**Across**
Electrical				
Capacitor	C		$v = \dfrac{1}{C}\displaystyle\int_0^t i\,dt + v(o)$	$i = C\dfrac{dv}{dt}$
Inductor	L		$v = L\dfrac{di}{dt}$	$i = \dfrac{1}{L}\displaystyle\int_0^t v\,dt + i(o)$
Resistor	R		$v = Ri$	$i = \dfrac{v}{R}$
Mechanical (translational)				
Mass	M		$v = \dfrac{1}{M}\displaystyle\int_0^t f\,dt + v(o)$	$f = M\dfrac{dv}{dt}$
Spring	K		$v = \dfrac{1}{K}\dfrac{df}{dt}$	$f = K\displaystyle\int_0^t v\,dt + f(o)$
Damper	D		$v = \dfrac{f}{D}$	$f = Dv$
Mechanical (rotational)				
Inertia	J		$\omega = \dfrac{1}{J}\displaystyle\int_0^t \mathcal{T}\,dt + \omega(o)$	$\mathcal{T} = J\dfrac{d\omega}{dt}$
Spring	K		$\omega = \dfrac{1}{K}\dfrac{d\mathcal{T}}{dt}$	$\mathcal{T} = K\displaystyle\int_0^t \omega\,dt + T(o)$
Damper	D		$\omega = \dfrac{\mathcal{T}}{D}$	$\mathcal{T} = D\omega$

Transformer	Transducer	Sources

Table S1.1.   Linear System Elements

System Element	Graphical Representation	Independent Variable	
		Through	Across
Fluid (liquid)			
Capacitance C		$h = \dfrac{1}{C}\displaystyle\int_0^t Q\,dt + h(o)$	$Q = C\dfrac{dh}{dt}$
Inertance L		$h = L\dfrac{dQ}{dt}$	$Q = \dfrac{1}{L}\displaystyle\int_0^t h\,dt + Q(o)$
Resistance R		$h = RQ$	$Q = \dfrac{h}{R}$
Fluid (gas)			
Capacitance C		$p = \dfrac{1}{C}\displaystyle\int_0^t w\,dt + p(o)$	$w = C\dfrac{dp}{dt}$
Inertance L		$p = L\dfrac{dw}{dt}$	$w = \dfrac{1}{L}\displaystyle\int_0^t p\,dt + w(o)$
Resistance R		$p = Rw$	$w = \dfrac{p}{R}$
Thermal			
Capacitance C		$T = \dfrac{1}{C}\displaystyle\int_0^t q\,dt + T(o)$	$q = C\dfrac{dT}{dt}$
Resistance R		$T = qR$	$q = \dfrac{T}{R}$

REFERENCES

1. Lindsay, J. F., and S. Katz, *Dynamics of Physical Circuits and Systems*, Matrix Publishers, Inc., Portland, OR, 1978.
   Written for the beginning engineering and engineering technology students. Presents system modeling and system dynamics in simple terms.

2. Shearer, J. L., A. T. Murphy and H. H. Richardson, *Introduction to System Dynamics*, Addison-Wesley Publishing Co., Reading, MA, 1967.
   Provides a unified and detailed engineering treatment of mechanical, electrical, and thermal dynamic systems.

3. Seely, S., *An Introduction to Engineering Systems*, Pergamon Press, Inc., Elmsford, NY, 1972.
   A junior-senior level text that provides sufficient background for a broad range of systems analysis methods. Includes both classical and matrix formulations.

PROBLEMS

1.1-1. Identify three different systems associated with the human body and name the inputs, outputs, and the parts which constitute the systems.

1.2-1. Sketch the signals $u(t) = 2 \cos(10t + 30°)$, $u(t) = 0.5 \sin(10t - 30°)$, and identify their amplitude, period, phase angle, and frequency.

1.2-2. A periodic signal has a Fourier series representation of the form

$$u(t) = 1 + \frac{8}{\pi^2} \sum_{k=1}^{\infty} \frac{1}{(2k-1)^2} \cos\left[(2k-1)\pi t - (2k-1)\frac{\pi}{4} \right]$$

Identify the signal by adding the dc term and four cosine terms.

1.2-3. Sketch the resulting signal:

(a) $2u_{-1}(t-2) \sin 10t$
(b) $u_{-1}(t-2) - u_{-1}(t-3)$
(c) $2u_{-1}(t+2) + 0.5u_{-1}(t+1) - 1.5u_{-1}(t-1)$.

1.2-4. Plot the following functions:

(a) $\sin t$
(b) $\sin(t - 20°)$
(c) $\sin(t + 10°)$
(d) $\cos(t + 25°)$

1.2-5. Find the amplitude and phase spectra for the periodic waves shown in Figure P1.2-5. Plot the values of the spectra versus frequency (not versus k). Plot the sum of the constant and the first three harmonics for each case. Compare the amplitude and phase spectra of the functions shown in Figures P1.2-5b and P1.2-5d and draw a conclusion as $T \to \infty$.

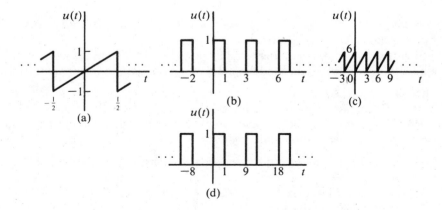

Figure P1.2-5

1.2-6. Using basic elementary signals, construct the signals shown in Figure P1.2-6.

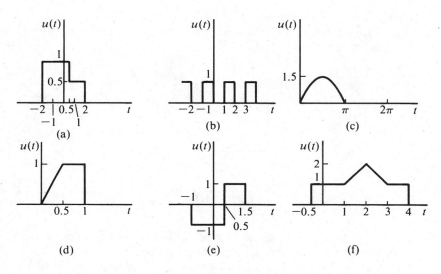

Figure P1.2-6

1.3-1. Find the capacitance of a parallel plate capacitor filled with distilled water ($\epsilon_r = 80$) having an area of 3 cm² and plate separation of 7.5 mm.

1.3-2. A rectangular coil of 1000 turns, length $l = 1.2$ m, width 0.5 m, is rotating at 800 rpm in the earth's magnetic field. Find the maximum induced voltage.

1.7-1. A source produces the current waveforms shown in Figure P1.7-1 in a capacitor. Sketch the voltage waveforms across the capacitor.

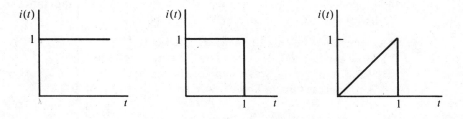

Figure P1.7-1

1.7-2. A voltage source $v(t) = V_o \cos \omega t$ is applied across a capacitor. Find the current waveform. Sketch both the voltage and current waveforms. Which one of the two waveforms leads?

1.7-3. The voltage-charge characteristic of a capacitor is given graphically in Figure P1.7-3.

  (a) Determine the capacitance of the capacitor.
  (b) How much energy is stored in the electric field of the capacitor, if it is charged to 10^3 volt?

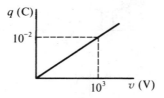

Figure P1.7-3

1.7-4. A capacitor is made up of 34 sheets of aluminum foil separated by a 0.007 cm dielectric film having a relative permittivity of 3.8. Alternate sheets of foil are connected together to form two intermeshed electrically insulated stacks. The area per sheet is 5 cm². Determine the capacitance of this capacitor.

1.8-1. Voltage sources across an inductor have the waveforms shown in Figure P1.7-1. Sketch the waveforms of the current through the inductor.

1.8-2. A current $i(t) = I_o \sin \omega t$ exists in an inductor. Find the associated voltage waveform and sketch both of them. Which one of the two waveforms lags?

1.8-3. The field structure of a 15 horsepower dc motor has an inductance of 2.2 henry and carries a current of 6.4 ampere.

  (a) Determine the flux linkages of this field.
  (b) How much energy is stored in the magnetic field?
  (c) What must be the waveshape of the applied voltage if the current is to increase linearly with time from 0 to 6.4 A in 0.2 s?

1.8-4. The ψ-i characteristic of an inductor is given in Figure P1.8-4. If the steady state current is $i = 1.5 \sin \omega t$, determine graphically the waveform for ψ. From this determine the approximate waveform of the applied voltage.

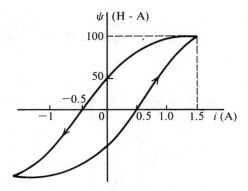

Figure P1.8-4

1.8-5. Repeat Problem 1.8-4 when the ψ-i characteristic curve is approximately that shown in Figure P1.8-5.

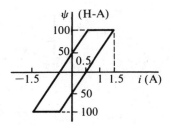

Figure P1.8-5

1.9-1. Two windings are closely wound on a toroid that has a mean radius R of 20 cm with a coil radius of 2 cm. There are $N = 1000$ turns per layer.

 (a) Calculate the inductance of each winding when the core is of non-magnetic material.
 (b) If the relative permeability of the core is $\mu_r = 1,400$, what is the inductance?
 (c) Find the mutual inductance between the two windings under the conditions in (b).
 (d) What is the total inductance of the toroidal coil if the windings are connected series aiding? series opposing?
      (Hint: $L = \mu_o \mu_r N^2 A / 2\pi R$ henry, A = cross section of the coil, $\mu_o = 4\pi 10^{-7}$ henry, μ_r = relative permeability.)

1.9-2. The network of coupled coils is shown in Figure P1.9-2. Write the appropriate equations for this circuit in the form given in Equation (1.9-8).

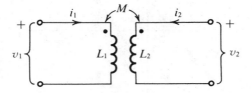

Figure P1.9-2

1.9-3. If i_1 and i_2 are those given in Figure P1.9-3, find v_1 and v_2 for the coupled network given in Figure P1.9-2. The following additional data are given: $L_1 = 2$ H, $L_2 = 0.5$ H, $M = 0.4$ H.

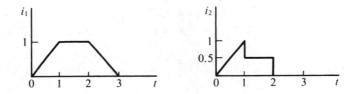

Figure P1.9-3

1.10-1. The approximate piecewise linear characteristic of a diode is shown in Figure P1.10-1. Write expressions (or an expression) for the terminal characteristics of this device.

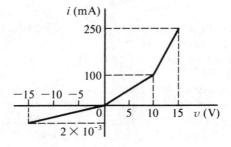

Figure P1.10-1

1.10-2. What is the resistance of an electric heater which draws 1100 watt from a 110 volt line? If during peak hours the utility reduces the line voltage by 5%, what is the power absorbed by the heater? What is the percentage drop in power?

1.10-3. A voltage of the form shown in Figure P1.10-3 is applied across a 10 ohm resistor. Find the total amount of energy that has been dissipated by the end of the 9th second.

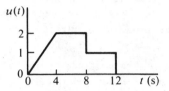

Figure P1.10-3

1.12-1. A force $f(t) = t$ N is applied at $t = 0$ to a mass of 15 kg. Find the power at $t = 4$ s later. How much energy was dissipated by the system during these 4 seconds?

1.13-1. The velocities of the edges of a spring are given in Figure P1.13-1. Determine whether the force is compressive or extensive at $t = 1.5$ s.

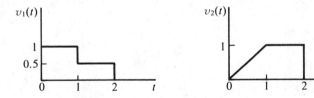

Figure P1.13-1

1.14-1. The damping factor of a linear bilateral damper is $D = 20$ N-s/m. A sinusoidal velocity with a peak amplitude of 20 m/s and with a period of 1 s is applied. Calculate the average energy dissipated during one complete period of the applied velocity wave.

1.17-1. Find the moment of inertia and the radius of gyration for each of the rigid bodies shown in Table 1.17-1.

1.17-2. A force of 12 N is applied at the rim of a disk of radius 0.75 m and mass of 15 kg. Find the power to the system at $t = 4$ s assuming that the force was applied at $t = 0$.

1.18-1. Water flow through a triangular weir is given by the equation $Q = C_v\sqrt{2gh^5}$, where C_v is the velocity constant. Find an expression for the effective resistance of the weir.

1.19-1. Calculate the capacitance as a function of head of a spherical liquid storage tank of radius a.

1.20-1. Calculate the gas capacitance of a 100-liter pressure vessel containing air at 150° C.

1.21-1. One side of a steel plate is maintained at 350° C, the other side at 175° C. The important data are: thickness 0.5 cm, area $A = 100$ cm², thermal conductivity $= 10^5$ joule/meter-degree-hour.
(a) Calculate the thermal resistance for conduction.
(b) Calculate the heat flow through A.

1.21-2. Determine the thermal capacitance of the following:
(a) A 100 liter tank of water. $c_p = 4182$ joule/kg-degree.
(b) A block of copper 5 cm on each side. $c_p = 385$ joule/kg-degree; specific gravity $= 8.9$.
(c) 1 kg of fire brick. $c_p = 190$ joule/kg-degree.

Chapter Two

Writing Equations for Interconnected Systems

Chapter 1 was concerned with the process of modeling elements that comprise many of the systems that we shall examine in our subsequent studies. For linear one-port elements, it was found that a simple terminal relationship exists between the through and the across variables that analytically describe each element. This chapter will be concerned with certain features of the interconnection into systems of a number of such simple elements.

2.1 INTERCONNECTED SYSTEMS

We shall consider mechanical, electrical, and other systems. Four separate aspects of such systems can be studied: (a) the terminal properties of the elements in the systems (these were discussed at some length in Chapter 1), (b) the geometrical or topological constraints that are imposed by the interconnection, (c) a description of the dynamics of the system, and (d) the response of the system when specified excitations are applied at one or more points in the system. This chapter will be devoted to (c). Later chapters will be concerned with (b) as it relates to (c), and with (d).

In writing the equilibrium or dynamical equations of an interconnected system, which include a mathematical description of the system elements and the constraints imposed by their interconnection, several rather different though fundamentally equivalent forms, may be used. The system may be described in terms of one or a set of integrodifferential equations; the description may be given graphically by means of a signal flow graph, a block diagram, or an analog computer diagram. Other representations also exist, but they all lead in the final analysis to the same dynamical description of the system. We shall not discuss all available methods for interconnected system description, but we shall devote considerable attention to the two methods mentioned above, namely, a Kirchhoff description that leads to integrodifferential equation formulations, and the use of the signal flow graph and block diagram in analysis.

We shall find that a characteristic feature of a Kirchhoff formulation of the dynamic equations of an interconnected system is that, for linear systems, the description appears in terms of sets of linear integrodifferential equations that relate the input and the output variables.

2.2 OPERATIONAL NOTATION

It is convenient to introduce the symbol p to denote the *time derivative operator* d/dt. An equivalent notation that is often used is the so-called dot notation, with one dot over a variable to denote the first time derivative, two dots to denote the second time derivative, etc. With these notations we would write

$$u = \frac{dv}{dt} \triangleq pv = \dot{v} \tag{2.2-1}$$

where the symbol $\triangleq$ means equal, by definition. From purely formal considerations, it follows that

$$v = \int u \, dt$$

By comparison with Equation (2.2-1), we see that this expression can be written

$$v = \frac{u}{p} \tag{2.2-2}$$

In summary, by definition, we write the functional pair involving p

$$\text{differentiation} \quad p = \frac{d}{dt}; p^2 = \frac{d^2}{dt^2} \quad \text{etc.} \qquad \text{(a)} \quad (2.2\text{-}3)$$

$$\text{integration} \quad \frac{1}{p} = \int dt \qquad \text{(b)}$$

Using these definitions, we write the description for all electrical elements that are contained in Table 2.2-1 (depending on whether i or v is the dependent variable). Table 2.2-2 represents the operational notation for linear and rotational mechanical elements.

Table 2.2-1. Properties of Electrical Elements

Element	Independent Variable	
	Voltage	**Current**
Capacitor	$i = Cpv = y(p)v$	$v = \dfrac{1}{Cp}i = z(p)i$
Resistor	$i = \dfrac{v}{R} = y(p)v$	$v = Ri = z(p)i$
Inductor	$i = \dfrac{1}{Lp}v = y(p)v$	$v = Lpi = z(p)i$

It is general practice, especially in the literature of electrical engineering, to introduce the symbol $z(p)$ to describe the functional v,i relationship, and $y(p)$ to describe the functional i,v relationship. In particular, the one-port or two-terminal element illustrated in Figure 2.2-1 is specified in general by the relation

$$v = z(p)\, i \tag{2.2-4}$$

and by

$$i = y(p)\, v \tag{2.2-5}$$

Clearly, of course, for a given element

$$y(p) = \frac{1}{z(p)} \tag{2.2-6}$$

The operator $z(p)$ is called an *impedance* operator, and $y(p)$ is called an *admittance* operator.

We shall extend the meanings of the functions $z(p)$ and $y(p)$ when we consider more complicated arrays of elements. In fact, the general forms for $z(p)$ and $y(p)$ play very important roles in the study of interconnected systems, both for analysis, with which we shall be largely interested, and in the general study of system synthesis.

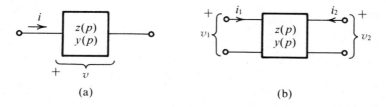

(a)   (b)

Figure 2.2-1.   Block representation of   (a) a one-port   (b) a two-port device

2.3 THROUGH-ACROSS DYNAMICAL LAWS, KIRCHHOFF CURRENT AND VOLTAGE LAWS

Two dynamical laws exist which provide the basis for writing the input-output system equations. One of these is expressed in terms of the through variables, the second is expressed in terms of the across variables. The first of these, when applied to systems of interconnected electrical elements, is the *Kirchhoff current law*, KCL. When applied to systems of interconnected mechanical elements, this is essentially D'Alembert's principle. The second relationship is the *Kirchhoff voltage law*, KVL.

The KCL is basically a statement of conservation of charge. It states that at any point in the circuit, usually a point chosen at the junction of several branches, the rate at which charge reaches the junction or node must equal the rate at which it leaves the node. More often the KCL is written, "the sum of the currents toward a node must be equal to the sum of the currents away from the node," or equivalently, "the algebraic sum of the currents toward a node must be zero." Symbolically, this law is written

$$\sum_{node} i_b = 0 \qquad\qquad (2.3\text{-}1)$$

where i_b denotes the branch currents. A graphical representation is shown in Figure 2-3-1.

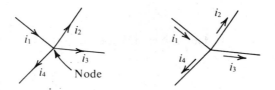

Figure 2.3-1.   Kirchhoff's current law representation

Table 2.2-2. Properties of Mechanical Elements

Element (translational)	Independent Variable	
	Velocity	**Force**
Spring	$f = \dfrac{K}{p} v = y(p)v$	$v = \dfrac{p}{K} f = z(p)f$
Mass	$f = Mpv = y(p)v$	$v = \dfrac{1}{Mp} f = z(p)f$
Damper	$f = Dv = y(p)v$	$v = \dfrac{1}{D} f = z(p)f$
Element (rotational)		
Spring	$\mathcal{T} = \dfrac{K}{p}\omega = y(p)\omega$	$\omega = \dfrac{p}{K}\mathcal{T} = z(p)\mathcal{T}$
Inertia	$\mathcal{T} = Jp\omega = y(p)\omega$	$\omega = \dfrac{1}{pJ}\mathcal{T} = z(p)\mathcal{T}$
Damper	$\mathcal{T} = D\omega = y(p)\omega$	$\omega = \dfrac{1}{D}\mathcal{T} = z(p)\mathcal{T}$

EXAMPLE 2.3-1. If the currents $i_1 = 10$, $i_2 = 3$, and $i_4 = 2$ are given for the node shown in Figure 2.3-1, find the current i_3.

SOLUTION. Applying Equation (2.3-1) with due account of the reference directions to get

$$\sum_{\text{node}} i_b = 0 = i_1 + i_2 + i_3 + i_4 = 10 - 3 - i_3 - 2$$

from which

$$i_3 = +5$$

which indicates that i_3 was assigned the correct direction, and its direction is away from the node. In this particular example we assigned the currents toward the node as positive.

□ □ □

EXAMPLE 2.3-2. Find the currents i_1 and i_2 in the circuit shown in Figure 2.3-2.

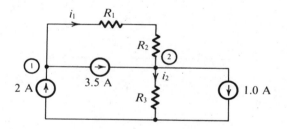

Figure 2.3-2.   Kirchhoff current law problem

SOLUTION. At node No. 1 the KCL gives

$$2 - 3.5 - i_1 = 0 \qquad \text{or} \qquad i_1 = -1.5 \text{ A}$$

At node No. 2, the KCL gives

$$-1.5 + 3.5 - 1.0 - i_2 = 0 \qquad \text{or} \qquad i_2 = 1.0 \text{ A}$$

The negative sign of i_1 indicates that the current direction is opposite to the reference direction chosen, and the current i_1 is into node No. 1.

□ □ □

The KVL is essentially a statement of conservation of energy when applied to a closed loop in the circuit. This law recognizes that the voltage across an element is the work done in carrying unit charge from the point of one potential at one terminal of the element to the second point of the element. This law states that "the algebraic sum of the voltages around any closed loop of a network must be zero," or alternatively, "the sum of the voltage rises must equal the sum of the voltage drops in traversing a closed path around a network." Symbolically, this law is written

$$\sum_{\text{loop}} v_b = 0 \qquad (2.3\text{-}2)$$

The significance of this is illustrated in the following example:

EXAMPLE 2.3-3. Refer to the circuit shown in Figure 2.3-3 which is made up of resistors connected in series. Apply the KVL to find v_{R_3} given that $v_s = 15$ V, $v_{R_1} = 5$ V, and $v_{R_2} = 2$ V.

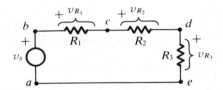

Figure 2.3-3. Illustration of Kirchhoff voltage law

SOLUTION. Apply Equation (2.3-2) to obtain

$$\sum_{\text{loop}} v_b = v_s + v_{R_1} + v_{R_2} + v_{R_3} + v_{ea} = 15 - 5 - 2 - v_{R_3} + 0 = 0$$

from which

$$v_{R_3} = 8 \text{ V}$$

□   □   □

EXAMPLE 2.3-4. Find the indicated voltages in the circuit shown in Figure 2.3-4.

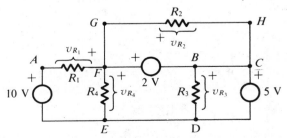

Figure 2.3-4. A Kirchhoff law problem

SOLUTION. Apply the KVL around the closed loop *FCDEF*. This yields

$$-2 - 5 + v_{R_4} = 0 \qquad \text{or} \qquad v_{R_4} = +7 \text{ V}$$

The KVL around loop *AFEA* yields

$$10 + v_{R_1} - 7 = 0 \qquad \text{or} \qquad v_{R_1} = -3 \text{ V}$$

Since points C and B are at the same potntial (i.e., no resistor exists between them), the voltage across R_3 is

$$v_{R_3} = 5 \text{ V}$$

Similarly across resistor R_2

$$v_{R_2} = 2 \text{ V}$$

To check the results, apply KVL around the loop *AFGHCBDEA*. The result is

$$10 - 3 - 2 - 5 = 0$$

This shows the validity of the KVL. The reader should observe that when a voltage is found to be opposite to the assumed reference polarity direction a negative sign will appear. This negatively signed voltage will be used in finding another unknown voltage.

□   □   □

Refer again to Figure 2.3-3 which shows three resistors in series connected to a voltage source. Since only one loop is present, the same current passes through each of them. By Ohm's law, the voltage drop across each is $R_i i$. An application of the KVL to this loop yields

$$v_s = iR_1 + iR_2 + iR_3 = i(R_1 + R_2 + R_3) = iZ(p)$$

where

$$Z(p) = R_1 + R_2 + R_3 \tag{2.3-3}$$

is the input impedance of the resistors in series (see Figure 2.3-5). As a logical extension of this result, the input impedance of n resistors in series is

$$Z(p) = R_1 + R_2 + \ldots + R_n \tag{2.3-4}$$

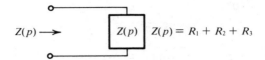

Figure 2.3-5.   The driving point or input impedance of three resistors in series

It is observed that for pure resistive networks, the input impedance, and as a consequence, the input admittance, are independent of the operator p.

Consider now the case of three resistors in parallel, as shown in Figure 2.3-6a. Since all the branches start from the same point, they all will have the same potential (voltage) with respect to ground. An application of the KCL at node A yields

$$i = i_1 + i_2 + i_3 \qquad (2.3\text{-}5)$$

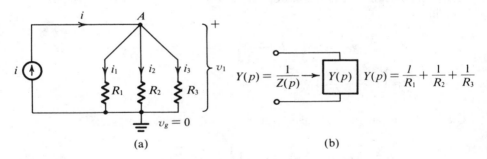

Figure 2.3-6.   The impedance of resistors in parallel

Now apply Ohm's law to this equation to write, since $v_g = 0$,

$$i = \frac{v_1}{R_1} + \frac{v_1}{R_2} + \frac{v_1}{R_3} = v_1 \left(\frac{1}{R_1} + \frac{1}{R_2} + \frac{1}{R_3} \right) \qquad (2.3\text{-}6)$$

This equation indicates that the equivalent admittance for resistors in parallel is

$$Y(p) = \frac{1}{R_1} + \frac{1}{R_2} + \frac{1}{R_3} \qquad (2.3\text{-}7)$$

For the general case of n resistors in parallel, the input admittance is

$$Y(p) = \frac{1}{R_1} + \frac{1}{R_2} + \ldots + \frac{1}{R_n} \qquad (2.3\text{-}8)$$

and the input impedance for the n resistors in parallel is

$$Z(p) = \frac{1}{Y(p)} = \frac{1}{\dfrac{1}{R_1} + \dfrac{1}{R_2} + \ldots + \dfrac{1}{R_n}} \qquad (2.3\text{-}9)$$

Refer now to Figure 2.3-7a which shows two capacitors in series. Figures 2.3-7b and 2.3-7c show equivalent representations of the circuit. It is apparent

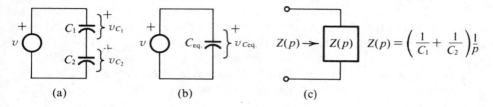

(a)   (b)   (c)

Figure 2.3-7. The impedance of capacitors in series

that the same current exists in both capacitors. Apply the KVL to the loop to obtain

$$v = v_{C_1} + v_{C_2} = \frac{1}{C_1} \int i \, dt + \frac{1}{C_2} \int i \, dt = \frac{1}{C_1 p} i + \frac{1}{C_2 p} i \qquad (2.3\text{-}10)$$

$$= \left(\frac{1}{C_1} + \frac{1}{C_2} \right) \frac{1}{p} \times i = Z(p) i$$

Clearly the input impedance operator for two capacitors in series is

$$Z(p) = \left(\frac{1}{C_1} + \frac{1}{C_2} \right) \frac{1}{p} = \frac{1}{C_{eq}} \frac{1}{p} \qquad (2.3\text{-}11)$$

with the equivalent capacitor of the two capacitors in series

$$\frac{1}{C_{eq}} = \frac{1}{C_1} + \frac{1}{C_2}$$

which is, equivalently,

$$C_{eq} = \frac{C_1 C_2}{C_1 + C_2} \qquad (2.3\text{-}12)$$

For n capacitors in series the input impedance operator is

$$Z(p) = \frac{1}{C_1 p} + \frac{1}{C_2 p} + \ldots + \frac{1}{C_n p} = \sum_{i=1}^{n} \frac{1}{C_i p} \qquad (2.3\text{-}13)$$

which is equal to the sum of the impedance operators of each capacitor. It is easily shown [see Problem (2.3-7)] that the input admittance operator of n capacitors in parallel is

$$Y(p) = \frac{1}{Z(p)} = C_1 p + C_2 p + \ldots + C_n p = \sum_{i=1}^{n} C_i p \qquad (2.3\text{-}14)$$

which is equal to the sum of the admittance operators of each capacitor.

The same procedure can be followed to show that the input impedance operator of n inductors in series is equal to the sum of the impedance operators of the n inductors,

$$Z(p) = L_1 p + L_2 p + \ldots + L_n p = \sum_{i=1}^{n} L_i p \qquad (2.3\text{-}15)$$

The input admittance operator of n inductors in parallel is equal to the sum of their admittance operators

$$Y(p) = \frac{1}{Z(p)} = \frac{1}{L_1 p} + \frac{1}{L_2 p} + \ldots + \frac{1}{L_n p} = \sum_{i=1}^{n} \frac{1}{L_i p} \qquad (2.3\text{-}16)$$

The foregoing has discussed the impedance and admittance of each type of element and of their series and parallel combinations. We now wish to expand our considerations to circuits involving mixed configurations of elements that include series and parallel combinations. Figure 2.3-8a shows a typical circuit.

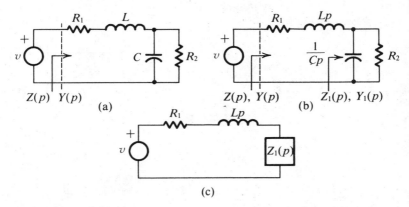

Figure 2.3-8. A circuit with series and parallel elements

The first step is to redraw the circuit into one which displays the impedance operators appropriate to the circuit elements, as shown in Figure 2.3-8b. Then proceed in a manner that uses the results just discussed above. By inspection, the input admittance operator $Y_1(p)$ is

$$Y_1(p) = Cp + \frac{1}{R_2}$$

Therefore it follows that

$$Z_1(p) = \frac{1}{Y_1(p)} = \frac{R_2}{R_2Cp + 1}$$

Since $Z_1(p)$ is in series with R_1 and Lp, the input impedace operator $Z(p)$ is

$$Z(p) = R_1 + Lp + \frac{R_2}{R_2Cp + 1}$$

Correspondingly, the input admittance operator is

$$Y(p) = \frac{1}{Z(p)} = \frac{1}{R_1 + Lp + \dfrac{R_2}{R_2Cp + 1}} = \frac{R_2Cp + 1}{LR_2Cp^2 + (R_1R_2C + L)p + R_1 + R_2}$$

To illustrate the procedure, we consider a number of examples of increasing complexity. Nodal type problems will first be considered, and then loop type problems will be studied.

Node Equations

EXAMPLE 2.3-5. Find the dynamical equations and the input impedance of the system shown in Figure 2.3-9a.

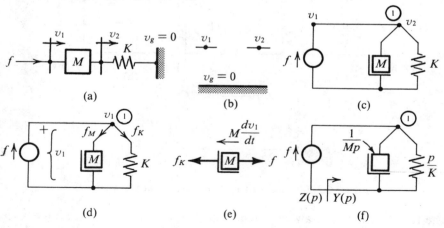

Figure 2.3-9.   A linear mechanical system whose elements have common velocities

SOLUTION. It is observed that v_1 and v_2 are equal with v_1 (or v_2) being the velocity of both the mass and the spring. It is also observed that owing to the action (reaction force) of the spring, the force f is divided into two parts, one for the mass and the other for the spring. Note specifically that even though the system appears to be connected in series, it is actually a parallel combination of elements, as shown in Figures 2.3-9c and 2.3-9d.

For mechanical circuits there exists a point law known as D'Alembert's principle which parallels the KCL and which is usually written

$$\sum_{\text{forces}} f_i - M_i \frac{dv_i}{dt} = 0 \qquad i = \text{node number} \tag{2.3-17}$$

The term $M(dv/dt)$ is often referred to as the *kinetic reaction*. This principle requires essentially that each node be isolated in the analysis and that the $M(dv/dt)$ force be distinguished from the other forces. This yields a "free body" diagram for each portion of the system. This is a technique that is used extensively in texts on dynamics. The appropriate free body diagram is shown in Figure 2.3-9e. Using the equivalent network representation for mechanical circuits, it is more convenient to write the mechanical dynamical equation by including f_M with other forces and considering Equation (2.3-17) as a point law.

From an examination of Figure 2.3-9d we write the dynamical equation by an application of the point law at node 1 (note that the algebraic sum of the forces is considered)

$$\text{Node 1:} \qquad -f + f_M + f_K = 0 \tag{2.3-18}$$

The known through-across relationships for mechanical elements are used (see Table S1.1) in Equation (2.3-18). This yields the form

$$-f + M \frac{dv_1}{dt} + K \int v_1 \, dt = 0$$

In operational notation this expression is rearranged to read

$$f = \left(Mp + \frac{K}{p} \right) v_1 \tag{2.3-19}$$

The input admittance operator of the system is

$$Y(p) = \frac{f}{v_1} = Mp + \frac{K}{p} \tag{2.3-20}$$

Note that if we introduce the impedance of each element, as shown in Figure 2.3-9f, then Equation (2.3-20) can be written by inspection. The impedance operator $Z(p)$ is the reciprocal of the input admittance operator $Y(p)$.

□ □ □

EXAMPLE 2.3-6. Find the dynamical equations for the system shown in Figure 2.3-10.

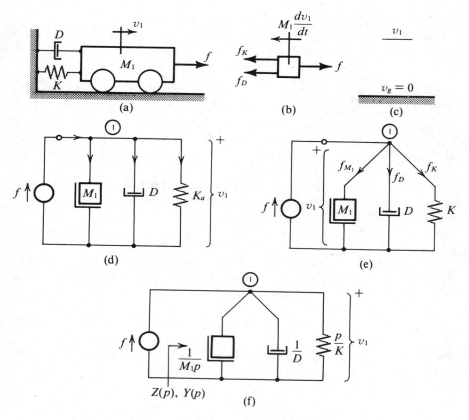

Figure 2.3-10.   A simple physical system under study

SOLUTION. The fact that a force driver is used strongly suggests that we choose the through variables as the independent ones. Thus, D'Alembert's principle given in Equation (2.3-17) is appropriate to the present problem.

To create the equivalent circuit model of Figures 2.3-10d and 2.3-10e we proceed as follows:

1. First identify the different velocities in the system (in this example v_1 and v_g = ground reference) and represent these as nodes, Figure 2.3-10c.

2. Next insert each of the elements M, K, D between the appropriate nodes. The mass M_1 is connected to the ground node.

3. Finally, incorporate the source from ground to the node (velocity) with which the source is associated (in this example, node 1).

From an examination of Figure 2.3-10e write the following equilibrium equation by an application of the point law at node 1

$$\text{Node 1:} \qquad -f + f_{M_1} + f_D + f_K = 0 \qquad (2.3\text{-}21)$$

Employing the known through-across relationships for the various elements as given in Table S1.1, this equation takes the form

$$\text{Node 1:} \qquad -f + M_1 \frac{dv_1}{dt} + Dv_1 + K \int v_1 \, dt = 0 \qquad (2.3\text{-}22)$$

This is the integrodifferential equation that completely describes the dynamics of the system. In terms of the operational notation $p = d/dt$ this equation becomes

$$M_1 pv_1 + Dv_1 + \frac{K}{p} v_1 - f = 0 \qquad (2.3\text{-}23)$$

or

$$\left(M_1 p + D + \frac{K}{p} \right) v_1 = f$$

The input admittance operator is

$$Y(p) = M_1 p + D + \frac{K}{p} \qquad (2.3\text{-}24)$$

If the impedance operator (the reciprocal of the admittance operator) of each element is designated, as in Figure 2.3-10f, then the input admittance operator can be written as the sum of the admittance operators by inspection.

□ □ □

EXAMPLE 2.3-7. Draw an equivalent mechanical network and find the equilibrium equations for the system shown in Figure 2.3-11a.

SOLUTION. We follow the same procedure that was outlined in the previous example. This requires identifying the two nodes associated with v_1 and v_2 plus the ground node or datum, $v_g = 0$. Connect the elements between the appropriate node pairs. This yields Figures 2.3-11c and 2.3-11d. The system equations at the two nodes are obtained by inspection of Figure 2.3-11d

$$\text{Node 1:} \qquad -f + f_{M_1} + f_K + f_D = 0 \qquad \text{(a)} \quad (2.3\text{-}25)$$

Node 2: $\qquad -f_K - f_D + f_{M_2} = 0 \qquad$ (b)

These two equations are now written in the form

Node 1: $\qquad M_1\dfrac{dv_1}{dt} + K\displaystyle\int (v_1 - v_2)\,dt + D(v_1 - v_2) - f = 0 \qquad$ (a) (2.3-26)

Node 2: $\qquad -K\displaystyle\int (v_1 - v_2)\,dt - D(v_1 - v_2) + M_2\dfrac{dv_2}{dt} = 0 \qquad$ (b)

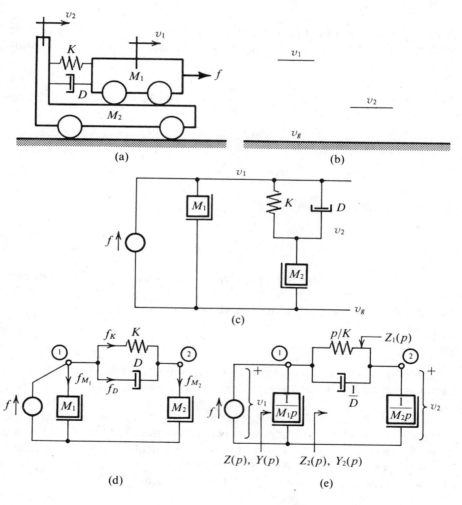

Figure 2.3-11. A complex physical system under study

Suppose that Equation (2.3-26b) is written in the form

$$\text{Node 2:} \quad K\int (v_2 - v_1)\, dt + D(v_2 - v_1) + M_2\frac{dv_2}{dt} = 0$$

This expression shows that relative to a particular node, the developed forces are away from the node. Equations (2.3-26) can be written to reflect Figure 2.3-11c as follows ($v_g = 0$, but it is shown explicitly)

$$\text{Node 1:} \quad -f + M_1\frac{d(v_1 - v_g)}{dt} + K\int (v_1 - v_2)\, dt + D(v_1 - v_2) = 0 \quad \text{(a)} \quad (2.3\text{-}27)$$

$$\text{Node 2:} \quad K\int (v_2 - v_1)\, dt + D(v_2 - v_1) + M_2\frac{d(v_2 - v_g)}{dt} = 0 \quad \text{(b)}$$

In operator form these equations are:

$$\text{Node 1:} \quad M_1 p v_1 + \frac{K}{p}(v_1 - v_2) + D(v_1 - v_2) - f = 0 \quad \text{(a)} \quad (2.3\text{-}28)$$

$$\text{Node 2:} \quad \frac{K}{p}(v_2 - v_1) + D(v_2 - v_1) + M_2 p v_2 = 0 \quad \text{(b)}$$

Some additional concepts can be drawn from these equations. This is possible after rearranging this set of equations in the following manner:

$$\left(\frac{K}{p} + D + M_1 p\right) v_1 - \left(\frac{K}{p} + D\right) v_2 = f \quad \text{(a)} \quad (2.3\text{-}29)$$

$$-\left(\frac{K}{p} + D\right) v_1 + \left(\frac{K}{p} + D + M_2 p\right) v_2 = 0 \quad \text{(b)}$$

These equations are written in the following functional form

$$y_{11}(p)v_1 + y_{12}(p)v_2 = f \quad \text{(a)} \quad (2.3\text{-}30)$$

$$y_{21}(p)v_1 + y_{22}(p)v_2 = 0 \quad \text{(b)}$$

The operators $y(p)$ that appear in these equations are easily established by comparing Equations (2.3-29) and (2.3-30). These have the following significance:

y_{11} = sum of all admittance operators connected to node 1

y_{22} = sum of all admittance operators connected to node 2

$y_{12} = y_{21}$ = negative sum of all admittance operators common to nodes 1 and 2

f = algebraic sum of all force drivers connected to node 1

The advantage of this generalized formulation is that the equation set Equation (2.3-30) is characteristic of all 2-node pair circuits, and it is only necessary to identify the y-s, which is done by inspection of the circuit.

By determinantal methods it follows that (see Appendix III)

$$v_1 = \frac{\begin{vmatrix} f & y_{12}(p) \\ 0 & y_{22}(p) \end{vmatrix}}{\begin{vmatrix} y_{11}(p) & y_{12}(p) \\ y_{21}(p) & y_{22}(p) \end{vmatrix}} = \frac{fy_{22}}{y_{11}y_{22} - y_{12}y_{21}} = \frac{f}{y_{11} - \dfrac{y_{12}y_{21}}{y_{22}}}$$

The input or driving point admittance operator $Y(p)$ is seen to be

$$Y(p) = \frac{f}{v_1} = y_{11} - \frac{y_{12}y_{21}}{y_{22}}$$

Inserting the known forms for the $y(p)$-s from Equation (2.3-29), the result is found to be

$$Y(p) = M_1 p + \frac{M_2 p(Dp + K)}{M_2 p^2 + Dp + K}$$

This procedure is a general one that involves the network equations. Another approach for finding the input admittance stems from the circuit diagram in terms of the impedances of the elements. Refer to Figure 2.3-11e, and observe that

$$Y_1(p) = D + \frac{K}{p}$$

Hence the corresponding impedance operator is

$$Z_1(p) = \frac{1}{Y_1(p)} = \frac{1}{D + \dfrac{K}{p}} = \frac{p}{Dp + K}$$

The impedance operator $Z_1(p)$ is in series with the impedance operator of the mass M_2. Thus

$$Z_2(p) = Z_1(p) + \frac{1}{M_2 p} = \frac{p}{Dp + K} + \frac{1}{M_2 p}$$

The corresponding admittance operator is

$$Y_2(p) = \frac{1}{Z_2(p)} = \frac{1}{\dfrac{p}{Dp+K} + \dfrac{1}{M_2p}} = \frac{M_2p(Dp+K)}{M_2p^2 + Dp + K}$$

The total input admittance operator is then

$$Y(p) = M_1p + Y_2(p) = M_1p + \frac{M_2p(Dp+K)}{M_2p^2 + Dp + K}$$

The corresponding input impedance operator is $Z(p) = 1/Y(p)$.

□ □ □

EXAMPLE 2.3-8. Find the system equations for the electrical system shown in Figure 2.3-12a.

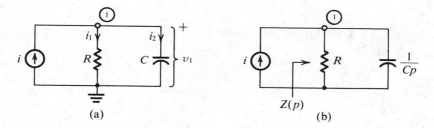

Figure 2.3-12. Electrical system

SOLUTION. Apply the KCL at node 1 to obtain

$$\text{Node 1:} \qquad -i + i_1 + i_2 = 0 \qquad\qquad (2.3\text{-}31)$$

With the help of Table S1.1 this equation becomes

$$\text{Node 1:} \qquad \frac{(v_1 - v_g)}{R} + C\frac{d(v_1 - v_g)}{dt} = i \qquad\qquad \text{(a)} \quad (2.3\text{-}32)$$

which, in operational notation is

$$\text{Node 1:} \qquad \frac{v_1}{R} + Cp\, v_1 = i \qquad\qquad \text{(b)}$$

or

$$\left(\frac{1}{R} + Cp\right) v_1 = Y(p)v_1 = i \qquad\qquad \text{(c)}$$

The input admittance operator is

$$Y(p) = \frac{1}{R} + Cp$$

The circuit showing the impedance operators of the elements is given in Figure 2.3-12b. By inspection it follows that, as found above,

$$Y(p) = \frac{1}{R} + Cp \qquad \qquad \text{(a)} \quad (2.3\text{-}33)$$

and

$$Z(p) = \frac{1}{Y(p)} = \frac{1}{\dfrac{1}{R} + Cp} = \frac{R}{1 + RCp} \qquad \qquad \text{(b)}$$

□ □ □

EXAMPLE 2.3-9. Find the system admittance operator for the circuit shown in Figure 2.3-13.

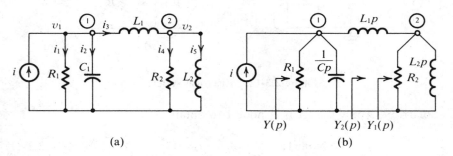

(a)   (b)

Figure 2.3-13. A complex electrical system

SOLUTION. The solution is effected by following the same general procedure as given above. This involves writing the nodal equations, which is done by an application of the KCL. There follows:

$$\text{Node 1:} \qquad -i + i_1 + i_2 + i_3 = 0$$
$$\text{Node 2:} \qquad -i_3 + i_4 + i_5 = 0$$

or

$$\text{Node 1:} \qquad \frac{v_1}{R_1} + C_1 \frac{dv_1}{dt} + \frac{1}{L_1} \int (v_1 - v_2)\, dt = i$$

$$\text{Node 2:} \qquad -\frac{1}{L_1} \int (v_1 - v_2)\, dt + \frac{v_2}{R_2} + \frac{1}{L_2} \int v_2\, dt = 0$$

We shall write the equilibrium equations, assuming that all the currents leave each node, except the source current. Also it is assumed that the voltage across the source is higher than any other node voltage. Obvious reversals simply carry a minus sign. To reflect these conditions, we rewrite the equations

Node 1: $\quad -i + \dfrac{(v_1 - v_g)}{R_1} + C_1 \dfrac{d(v_1 - v_g)}{dt} + \dfrac{1}{L_1} \displaystyle\int (v_1 - v_2)\, dt = 0$

Node 2: $\quad \dfrac{1}{L_1} \displaystyle\int (v_2 - v_1)\, dt + \dfrac{(v_2 - v_g)}{R_2} + \dfrac{1}{L_2} \displaystyle\int (v_2 - v_g)\, dt = 0$

These equations are written in operational form

$$\left(\frac{1}{R_1} + \frac{1}{L_1 p} + C_1 p \right) v_1 - \frac{1}{L_1 p} v_2 = i$$

$$-\frac{1}{L_1 p} v_1 + \left(\frac{1}{R_2} + \frac{1}{L_1 p} + \frac{1}{L_2 p} \right) v_2 = 0$$

(2.3-33)

which are seen in the general network form

$$y_{11}(p) v_1 + y_{12}(p) v_2 = i$$

$$y_{21}(p) v_1 + y_{22}(p) v_2 = 0$$

in the manner of Equation (2.3-30). These equations can be solved for v_1 from which $Z(p) = v_1/i$ can be found.

If only the system operator is required, we can proceed by inspection of Figure 2.3-13b. The following steps can be taken

$$Y_1(p) = \frac{1}{R_2} + \frac{1}{L_2 p}$$

It follows therefore that

$$Z_1(p) = \frac{1}{Y_1(p)} = \frac{L_2 R_2 p}{R_2 + L_2 p}$$

The input impedance operator $Z_2(p)$ is then

$$Z_2(p) = L_1 p + Z_1(p)$$

It therefore follows that

$$Y_2(p) = \frac{1}{L_1 p + Z_1(p)}$$

Finally the input admittance operator is

$$Y(p) = \frac{1}{R_1} + C_1 p + Y_2(p)$$

which is

$$Y(p) = \frac{1}{R_1} + C_1 p + \cfrac{1}{L_1 p + \cfrac{L_2 R_2 p}{R_2 + L_2 p}}$$

□   □   □

EXAMPLE 2.3-10. Find the equilibrium equations for the rotational mechanical system shown in Figure 2.3-14.

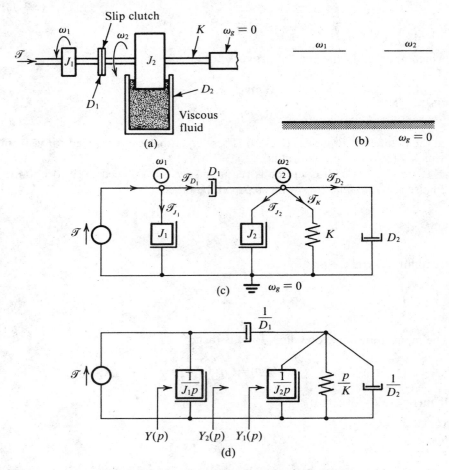

Figure 2.3-14.   A rotational mechanical system

SOLUTION. For this case we use D'Alembert's principle for rotational systems. This is a translation of Equation (2.3-17) for rotational systems. This states: For any system, the algebraic sum of externally applied torques resisting rotation about any axis is zero. Hence for each node, with due account of sign $\sum_{node} \mathcal{T}_b = 0$, or basically

$$\mathcal{T} + \mathcal{T}_I + \mathcal{T}_D + \mathcal{T}_K = 0 \qquad (2.3\text{-}34)$$

where

$$\mathcal{T} = \text{external applied torque}$$

$$\mathcal{T}_I = \text{inertial torque} = J\frac{d\omega}{dt}$$

$$\mathcal{T}_D = \text{damping torque} = D\omega$$

$$\mathcal{T}_K = \text{spring torque} = K\int \omega\, dt$$

To determine the circuit diagram of the rotational mechanical system shown, proceed in a manner that parallels that for mechanical systems in translational motion. This involves:

1. The two angular velocities, ω_1 and ω_2, are identified and two nodes are assigned (see Figure 2.3-14b).
2. Element J_1 is located from ω_1 to the reference node; element D_1 is located between ω_1 and ω_2; elements J_2, D_2, and K are located between node ω_2 and reference node (see Figure 2.3-14c).
3. The source $\mathcal{T}$ is then inserted.

With the help of Figure 2.3-14c and Equation (2.3-34), we obtain

Node 1: $\qquad \mathcal{T} + \mathcal{T}_{I_1} + \mathcal{T}_{D_1} = -\mathcal{T} + J_1\frac{d\omega_1}{dt} + D_1(\omega_1 - \omega_2) = 0 \qquad$ (a) $\quad$ (2.3-35)

Node 2: $\qquad \mathcal{T}_{D_1} + \mathcal{T}_{I_2} + \mathcal{T}_K + \mathcal{T}_{D_2} =$

$$-D_1(\omega_1 - \omega_2) + J_2\frac{d\omega_2}{dt} + K\int \omega_2 dt + D_2\omega_2 = 0 \qquad \text{(b)}$$

or equivalently

Node 1: $\qquad\qquad -\mathcal{T} + J_1\frac{d(\omega_1 - \omega_g)}{dt} + D_1(\omega_1 - \omega_2) = 0 \qquad$ (c)

Node 2: $\qquad D_1(\omega_2 - \omega_1) + J_2\frac{d(\omega_2 - \omega_g)}{dt}$

$$+ K\int (\omega_2 - \omega_g)dt + D_2(\omega_2 - \omega_g) = 0 \qquad \text{(d)}$$

where $\omega_g = 0$ was introduced for completeness. Equations (2.3-35) in operational form are

$$(J_1 p + D_1)\omega_1 - D_1\omega_2 = \mathcal{T} \qquad \text{(a)} \quad \text{(2.3-36)}$$

$$-D_1\omega_1 + \left(D_1 + D_2 + J_2 p + \frac{K}{p}\right)\omega_2 = 0 \qquad \text{(b)}$$

In generalized form, these equations can be written

$$y_{11}(p)\omega_1 + y_{12}(p)\omega_2 = \mathcal{T}$$

$$y_{21}(p)\omega_1 + y_{22}(p)\omega_2 = 0$$

These network equations can be used to calculate the input admittance in the manner of Example 2.3-7.

The input impedance operator can be found by direct inspection of Figure 2.3-14d, according to the following steps:

$$Y_1(p) = J_2 p + \frac{K}{p} + D_2$$

so that

$$Z_1(p) = \frac{1}{Y_1(p)} = \frac{1}{J_2 p + \dfrac{K}{p} + D_2} = \frac{p}{J_2 p^2 + K + D_2 p}$$

With this we find that the impedance operator $Z_2(p)$ is

$$Z_2(p) = \frac{1}{D_1} + Z_1(p)$$

From this

$$Y_2(p) = \frac{1}{Z_2(p)} = \frac{1}{\dfrac{1}{D_1} + Z_1(p)} = \frac{D_1}{1 + D_1 Z_1(p)}$$

The input or driving point admittance operator is then

$$Y(p) = J_1 p + Y_2(p) = J_1 p + \frac{D_1}{1 + \dfrac{D_1 p}{J_2 p^2 + K + D_2 p}}$$

$$= J_1 p + \frac{D_1(J_2 p^2 + D_2 p + K)}{J_2 p^2 + (D_1 + D_2)p + K}$$

□ □ □

EXAMPLE 2.3-11. Write the system equations and draw a network model for the fluid system shown in Figure 2.3-15a.

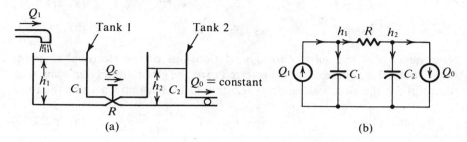

<table>
<tr><td>(a)</td><td>(b)</td></tr>
</table>

Figure 2.3-15.   A simple fluid system

SOLUTION. We write directly (see Table S1.1)

$$-Q_1 + C_1 p h_1 + \frac{h_1 - h_2}{R} = 0 \qquad \text{(a)} \quad (2.3\text{-}37)$$

$$- \left(\frac{h_1 - h_2}{R} \right) + C_2 p h_2 + Q_o = 0 \qquad \text{(b)}$$

The electric circuit analog representation of the system is shown in Figure 2.3-15b.

□ □ □

We now consider several loop type problems.

Loop Equations

EXAMPLE 2.3-12. Find the loop equations for the circuit shown in Figure 2.3-16 if the voltage variables are used as the independent ones.

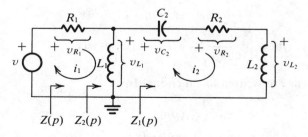

Figure 2.3-16.   The electric circuit under study

SOLUTION. To proceed, we employ the KVL law as the basis for our study. We use the closed loops shown to denote the paths that we shall employ when we write the KVL expressions. We have:

Loop 1: $\qquad -v + v_{R_1} + v_{L_1} = 0$ $\qquad$ (a)   (2.3-38)

Loop 2: $\qquad v_{C_2} + v_{R_2} + v_{L_2} - v_{L_1} = 0$ $\qquad$ (b)

Next we employ the across-through relationships of the electrical elements from Table S1.1. These are often referred to as the generalized Ohm's law relationships for the electrical elements. Equations (2.3-38) now assume the form

Loop 1: $\qquad -v + R_1 i_1 + L_1 \dfrac{d(i_1 - i_2)}{dt} = 0$ $\qquad$ (a)   (2.3-39)

Loop 2: $\qquad \dfrac{1}{C_2} \displaystyle\int i_2\, dt + R_2 i_2 + L_2 \dfrac{di_2}{dt} - L_1 \dfrac{d(i_1 - i_2)}{dt} = 0$ $\qquad$ (b)

which describe the dynamics of this electrical system. In operational notation we write this set of equations in the form

Loop 1: $\qquad -v + R_1 i_1 + L_1 p(i_1 - i_2) = 0$ $\qquad$ (a)   (2.3-40)

Loop 2: $\qquad \dfrac{1}{C_2 p} i_2 + R_2 i_2 + L_2 p i_2 - L_1 p(i_1 - i_2) = 0$ $\qquad$ (b)

This is a set of branch equations since each term explicitly specifies the voltage across an element of the circuit. We call attention to the fact that the current variables i_1 and i_2 as here selected can be interpreted to be quantities associated with the separate loops. Since they are assumed to circulate in the loops, then the current through the branch common to loops 1 and 2 will be $i_1 - i_2$. Note carefully, however, that while the concept of the loop current is a convenient topological scheme for writing equations, these do not necessarily have physical reality since they cannot always be associated directly with the actual conduction of charged carriers, as discussed in Chapter 1.

Now rearrange Equations (2.3-40) and write them in the form

$(R_1 + L_1 p) i_1 - L_1 p i_2 = v$ $\qquad$ (a)   (2.3-41)

$-L_1 p i_1 + \left[\dfrac{1}{C_2 p} + R_2 + (L_1 + L_2) p \right] i_2 = 0$ $\qquad$ (b)

These equations are written in functional form

$z_{11}(p) i_1 + z_{12}(p) i_2 = v$ $\qquad$ (a)   (2.3-42)

$z_{21}(p) i_1 + z_{22}(p) i_2 = 0$ $\qquad$ (b)

where the operators z_{ij} are easily identified, if Equation (2.3-42) is compared with Equation (2.3-41). It is observed that the various z-factors in these equations have the following meanings:

z_{11} = sum of all impedance operators on the contour of loop 1

z_{22} = sum of all impedance operators on the contour of loop 2

$z_{12} = z_{21}$ = negative of the sum of all impedance operators common to loops 1 and 2

v = algebraic sum of voltage sources in loop 1

This equation set is characteristic of all two loop networks. It is only necessary to identify the z-s and the v-s by inspection of the network in any application.

◻ ◻ ◻

EXAMPLE 2.3-13. The system shown in Figure 2.3-17a is a simplified model of the lungs. R represents the fluid resistance (air viscosity) in the bronchi; K represents the fluid spring due to the compressibility of air and the elasticity of the chest and lung tissue; p_c is the pressure within the chest cavity and is assumed identical with the pressure within the alveoli; p_a is the ambient air pressure measured at the buccal cavity, and w is the flow of air. Write the controlling dynamic equation for this system, and draw the network model.

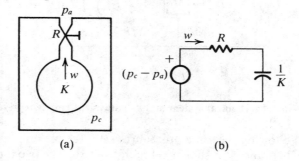

(a)   (b)

Figure 2.3-17. Simplified lung system and its equivalent circuit representation

SOLUTION. This is a simple system that is described by the equation

$$p_c - p_a = Rw + K\int w\,dt \qquad (2.3\text{-}43)$$

which has the following operational form

$$p_c - p_a = Rw + \frac{K}{p}w = \left(R + \frac{K}{p}\right)w \qquad (2.3\text{-}44)$$

◻ ◻ ◻

EXAMPLE 2.3-14. The system illustrated in Figure 2.3-18a is driven by a synchronous motor, hence the input is a known velocity function. Assume that the frictional forces are proportional to velocity. Write the system equations.

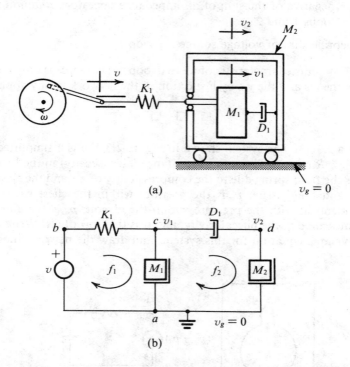

(a)

(b)

Figure 2.3-18. Mechanical system and its equivalent circuit representation

SOLUTION. Following the same procedures as in the previous examples, the network is easily found. It is shown in Figure 2.3-18b. The two loop equations are

$$v - v_{bc} - v_{ca} = 0 \qquad \text{(a)} \qquad (2.3\text{-}45)$$

$$v_{cd} + v_{da} + v_{ac} = 0 \qquad \text{(b)}$$

Using Table 2.2-2, the equivalent representation in operational form is

$$v - \frac{p}{K}f_1 - \frac{1}{M_1 p}f_1 + \frac{1}{M_1 p}f_2 = 0 \qquad \text{(a)} \qquad (2.3\text{-}46)$$

$$\frac{1}{D_1}f_2 + \frac{1}{M_2 p}f_2 + \frac{1}{M_1 p}f_2 - \frac{1}{M_1 p}f_1 = 0 \qquad \text{(b)}$$

or

$$\left(\frac{p}{K}+\frac{1}{M_1 p}\right)f_1 - \frac{1}{M_1 p}f_2 = v \qquad \text{(a)} \quad \text{(2.3-47)}$$

$$-\frac{1}{M_1 p}f_1 + \left(\frac{1}{D_1}+\frac{1}{M_2 p}+\frac{1}{M_1 p}\right)f_2 = 0 \qquad \text{(b)}$$

which we can write in the general form

$$z_{11}(p)f_1 + z_{12}(p)f_2 = v \qquad \text{(a)} \quad \text{(2.3-48)}$$

$$z_{21}(p)f_1 + z_{22}(p)f_2 = 0 \qquad \text{(b)}$$

where the z-s are defined in the equation set, Equation (2.3-47).

□ □ □

2.4* NODE EQUATION FOR MORE COMPLICATED SYSTEMS

We consider for study the mechanical system of Figure 2.4-1a and examine Figure 2.4-1b which is Figure 2.4-1a redrawn in network form and appropriately marked for our present needs. The fact that a force driver is used strongly suggests that we choose the through variables as the independent ones. Thus

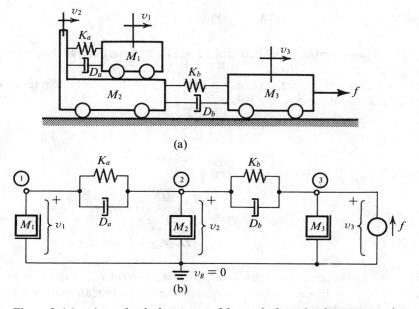

(a)

(b)

Figure 2.4-1. A mechanical system and its equivalent circuit representation

the dynamical law that is appropriate to the present problem is that given in Equation (2.3-17).

From an examination of Figure 2.4-1b the following set of equilibrium equations can be written. This involves an application of the point law at the three nodes:

Node 1: $\qquad\qquad f_{M_1} + f_{K_a} + f_{D_a} = 0$ $\qquad$ (a) $\quad$ (2.4-1)

Node 2: $\quad -f_{K_a} - f_{D_a} + f_{M_2} + f_{K_b} + f_{D_b} = 0$ $\qquad$ (b)

Node 3: $\qquad\qquad -f_{K_b} - f_{D_b} + f_{M_3} - f = 0$ $\qquad$ (c)

The known through-across relationships for the various elements are employed (see Table S1.1). This set of equations is now written as follows, with care in establishing the variables and in applying the reference conditions:

Node 1: $\qquad\qquad M_1\dfrac{dv_1}{dt} + K_a\displaystyle\int (v_1 - v_2)dt + D_a(v_1 - v_2) = 0 \quad$ (2.4-2)

Node 2: $\quad -K_a\displaystyle\int (v_1 - v_2)dt - D_a(v_1 - v_2) + M_2\dfrac{dv_2}{dt}$

$$+ K_b\int (v_2 - v_3)dt + D_b(v_2 - v_3) = 0$$

Node 3: $\qquad\quad -K_b\displaystyle\int (v_2 - v_3)dt - D_b(v_2 - v_3) + M_3\dfrac{dv_3}{dt} - f = 0$

This set of integrodifferential equations completely describes the dynamics of the system.

In the manner already discussed, we write this set of equations in terms of the operational variable p. We now have

Node 1: $\qquad\qquad M_1 p v_1 + \dfrac{K_a}{p}(v_1 - v_2) + D_a(v_1 - v_2) = 0 \quad$ (2.4-3)

Node 2: $\quad -\dfrac{K_a}{p}(v_1 - v_2) - D_a(v_1 - v_2) + M_2 p v_2$

$$+ \frac{K_b}{p}(v_2 - v_3) + D_b(v_2 - v_3) = 0$$

Node 3: $\qquad\quad -\dfrac{K_b}{p}(v_2 - v_3) - D_b(v_2 - v_3) + M_3 p v_3 - f = 0$

This set of equations is the *branch* set, since each term is written in a form which explicitly indicates the through-across relationship on an element by element (or branch by branch) basis.

As in the previous examples, it proves to be convenient to rearrange this set of equations in terms of the dependent variables

$$\left(\frac{K_a}{p} + D_a + M_1 p\right) v_1 - \left(\frac{K_a}{p} + D_a\right) v_2 = 0 \quad (2.4\text{-}4)$$

$$-\left(\frac{K_a}{p} + D_a\right) v_1 + \left[\frac{(K_a + K_b)}{p} + (D_a + D_b) + M_2 p\right] v_2$$

$$-\left(\frac{K_b}{p} + D_b\right) v_3 = 0$$

$$-\left(\frac{K_b}{p} + D_b\right) v_2 + \left(\frac{K_b}{p} + D_b + M_3 p\right) v_3 = f$$

These equations can be written in the following functional form

$$y_{11}(p)v_1 + y_{12}(p)v_2 + y_{13}(p)v_3 = 0 \quad (2.4\text{-}5)$$

$$y_{21}(p)v_1 + y_{22}(p)v_2 + y_{23}(p)v_3 = 0$$

$$y_{31}(p)v_1 + y_{32}(p)v_2 + y_{33}(p)v_3 = f$$

where the various operational factors $y(p)$ are seen to be

$$y_{11}(p) = \frac{K_a}{p} + D_a + M_1 p \quad (2.4\text{-}6)$$

$$y_{12}(p) = y_{21}(p) = -\left(\frac{K_a}{p} + D_a\right)$$

$$y_{22}(p) = \frac{K_a + K_b}{p} + (D_a + D_b) + M_2 p$$

$$y_{23}(p) = y_{32}(p) = -\left(\frac{K_b}{p} + D_b\right)$$

$$y_{33}(p) = \frac{K_b}{p} + D_b + M_3 p$$

$$y_{13}(p) = y_{31}(p) = 0$$

As in previous nodal examples, it is observed that the operators $Y(p)$ have the following significance:

y_{11} = sum of all admittance operators connected to node 1

y_{22} = sum of all admittance operators connected to node 2

y_{33} = sum of all admittance operators connected to node 3

$y_{12} = y_{21}$ = negative of sum of all admittance operators common to nodes 1 and 2

$y_{13} = y_{31}$ = negative of sum of admittance operators common to nodes 1 and 3

$y_{23} = y_{32}$ = negative of sum of all admittance operators common to nodes 2 and 3

f = algebraic sum of all force drivers to node 3

It is often convenient to express this set of equations in matrix form, as follows.

$$
\begin{bmatrix}
y_{11} & y_{12} & 0 \\
y_{21} & y_{22} & y_{23} \\
0 & y_{32} & y_{33}
\end{bmatrix}
\begin{bmatrix}
v_1 \\
v_2 \\
v_3
\end{bmatrix}
=
\begin{bmatrix}
0 \\
0 \\
f
\end{bmatrix}
\tag{2.4-7}
$$

In more compact form, this equation set may be written

$$[Y][V] = [F] \tag{2.4-8}$$

where each matrix is defined in Equation (2.4-7), with the matrix elements of the Y-matrix being specified in Equation (2.4-6). Observe that this is a generalization of Equation (2.2-5) that now expresses the entire network.

2.5*   LOOP EQUATIONS

We shall proceed by considering a specific example for detailed study. Now, however, we shall choose an electrical network. Refer to the circuit of Figure 2.5-1. In this example, a voltage driver is applied to the circuit; hence we shall choose the voltage variables as the independent ones. To proceed, we employ the KVL law as the basis for our study. We use the closed loops shown to denote the paths that we shall employ when we write the KVL expressions. We have

Loop 1: $\qquad\qquad\qquad v_{L_1} + v_{C_a} + v_{R_a} = 0 \qquad\qquad$ (2.5-1)

Loop 2: $\qquad -v_{R_a} - v_{C_a} + v_{L_2} + v_{C_b} + v_{R_b} = 0$

Loop 3: $\qquad\qquad -v_{R_b} - v_{C_b} + v_{L_3} - v = 0$

Now employ the across-through relationships of the electrical elements from Table S1.1. Equations (2.5-1) now assume the form

Loop 1: $\qquad\qquad L_1 \dfrac{di_1}{dt} + \dfrac{1}{C_a}\displaystyle\int (i_1 - i_2)dt + R_a(i_1 - i_2) = 0$ (2.5-2)

Loop 2: $\quad -R_a(i_1 - i_2) - \dfrac{1}{C_a}\displaystyle\int (i_1 - i_2)dt + L_2 \dfrac{di_2}{dt}$

$$\qquad\qquad\qquad + \frac{1}{C_b}\int (i_2 - i_3)dt + R_b(i_2 - i_3) = 0$$

Loop 3: $\qquad\qquad -R_b(i_2 - i_3) - \dfrac{1}{C_b}\displaystyle\int (i_2 - i_3)dt + L_3 \dfrac{di_3}{dt} - v = 0$

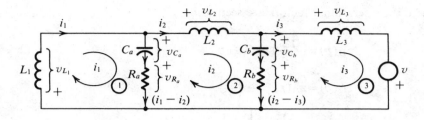

Figure 2.5-1. The electric circuit under study

This set of integrodifferential equations describes the dynamics of this electrical system.

We write this set of equations in operational form

Loop 1: $\qquad\qquad\qquad\qquad L_1 p i_1 + \dfrac{1}{C_a p}(i_1 - i_2) + R_a(i_1 - i_2) = 0 \quad (2.5\text{-}3)$

Loop 2: $\quad -R_a(i_1 - i_2) - \dfrac{1}{C_a p}(i_1 - i_2) + L_2 p i_2$

$$+ \frac{1}{C_b p}(i_2 - i_3) + R_b(i_2 - i_3) = 0$$

Loop 3: $\qquad\qquad -R_b(i_2 - i_3) - \dfrac{1}{C_b p}(i_2 - i_3) + L_3 p i_3 - v = 0$

As before, we rearrange Equations (2.5-3) by separating the various terms on the basis of the dependent variables. Thus

$$\left(\frac{1}{C_a p} + R_a + L_1 p\right) i_1 - \left(\frac{1}{C_a p} + R_a\right) i_2 = 0 \quad (2.5\text{-}4)$$

$$-\left(\frac{1}{C_a p} + R_a\right) i_1 + \left[\left(\frac{1}{C_a} + \frac{1}{C_b}\right)\frac{1}{p} + (R_a + R_b) + L_2 p\right] i_2$$

$$-\left(\frac{1}{C_b p} + R_b\right) i_3 = 0$$

$$-\left(\frac{1}{C_b p} + R_b\right) i_2 + \left(\frac{1}{C_b p} + R_b + L_3 p\right) i_3 = v$$

These equations are written in functional form

$$z_{11}(p)i_1 + z_{12}(p)i_2 + z_{13}(p)i_3 = 0 \qquad\qquad (2.5\text{-}5)$$

$$z_{21}(p)i_1 + z_{22}(p)i_2 + z_{23}(p)i_3 = 0$$

$$z_{31}(p)i_1 + z_{32}(p)i_2 + z_{33}(p)i_3 = v$$

where the operational factors are seen to be

$$z_{11}(p) = \frac{1}{C_a p} + R_a + L_1 p \qquad (2.5\text{-}6)$$

$$z_{12}(p) = z_{21}(p) = - \left(\frac{1}{C_a p} + R_a \right)$$

$$z_{22}(p) = \left(\frac{1}{C_a} + \frac{1}{C_b} \right) \frac{1}{p} + (R_a + R_b) + L_2 p$$

$$z_{23}(p) = z_{32}(p) = - \left(\frac{1}{C_b p} + R_b \right)$$

$$z_{33}(p) = \frac{1}{C_b p} + R_b + L_3 p$$

$$z_{13} = z_{31} = 0$$

Observe that the various z-factors in these equations have the following meanings:

z_{11} = sum of all impedance operators on the contour of loop 1

z_{22} = sum of all impedance operators on the contour of loop 2

z_{33} = sum of all impedance operators on the contour of loop 3

$z_{12} = z_{21}$ = negative of the sum of all impedance operators common to loops 1 and 2

$z_{23} = z_{32}$ = negative of the sum of all impedance operators common to loops 2 and 3

$z_{13} = z_{31}$ = negative of the sum of all impedance operators common to loops 1 and 3.

v = algebraic sum of all voltage sources in loop 3

This set of equations can be expressed conveniently in matrix form

$$\begin{bmatrix} z_{11}(p) & z_{12}(p) & 0 \\ z_{21}(p) & z_{22}(p) & z_{23}(p) \\ 0 & z_{32}(p) & z_{33}(p) \end{bmatrix} \begin{bmatrix} i_1 \\ i_2 \\ i_3 \end{bmatrix} = \begin{bmatrix} 0 \\ 0 \\ v \end{bmatrix}$$

where the matrix elements are defined in Equations (2.5-5) and (2.5-6). In general matrix notation, this may be written

$$[Z][I] = [V] \qquad (2.5\text{-}8)$$

This has the general form of Ohm's law, but applies to the entire system.

2.6 SOURCE TRANSFORMATIONS

The discussion in Section 2.4 was limited to node pair circuits with current drivers, and that in Section 2.5 was limited to loop circuits with voltage drivers. A reasonable question is whether these are essential limitations on these analyses. Such constraints are required for the formalism adopted, but this does not mean that circuits with both current and voltage drivers cannot be analyzed. It simply means that additional considerations are necessary.

Observe the node pair circuit that is voltage driven, as shown in Figure 2.6-1. Notice that this can be viewed as a 3-node circuit, with node voltage $v_1 = v$. In this particular case, the circuit can also be analyzed as a 3-loop circuit. However, since we wish to consider the circuit from a nodal point of view, we must employ both the KVL and the KCL to obtain the necessary controlling equations. The equations are

$$\text{(KVL):} \qquad v - i_1 R_1 - v_2 = 0 \qquad \text{(a)} \quad (2.6\text{-}1)$$

$$\text{node 2 (KCL):} \qquad -\frac{v_2 - v}{R_1} - \frac{v_2}{R_2} - \frac{v_2}{Lp} - Cp(v_2 - v_3) = 0 \qquad \text{(b)}$$

$$\text{node 3 (KCL):} \qquad -Cp(v_3 - v_2) - \frac{v_3}{R_3} = 0 \qquad \text{(c)}$$

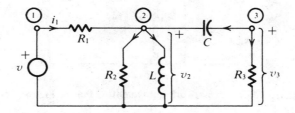

Figure 2.6-1. A mixed nodal circuit with voltage driver

We shall proceed by effecting a simple source transformation which replaces the portion of the network to the left of node 2. This involves the voltage source v and a series resistor R_1 which is replaced by an equivalent current source v/R_1 and a shunting R_1. That is, we shall show that the two source combinations shown in Figure 2.6-2 are equivalent relative to the output terminals. To show the equivalence, write the KVL controlling equation for Figure 2.6-2a. It is the simple relation

$$v_o = v - i_o R \qquad\qquad ((2.6\text{-}2)$$

Now divide each term by R and rearrange the resulting expression to the form

$$\frac{v}{R} - \frac{v_o}{R} = i_o \qquad\qquad (2.6\text{-}3)$$

Observe that this equation applies precisely to the network of Figure 2.6-2b which contains the current source driver v/R shunted by the resistor R.

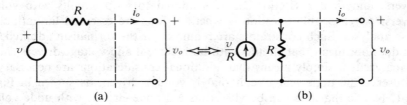

Figure 2.6-2.   Equivalent sources: (a) Voltage source   (b) Current source

With the application of a current source transformation to the network to the left of node 2, Figure 2.6-1 attains the form shown in Figure 2.6-3. The network is now in a form suitable for analysis by the node-pair methods discussed in Section 2.4.

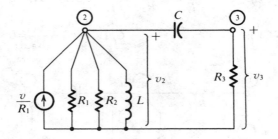

Figure 2.6-3.   A network equivalent to that in Figure 4.6-1

EXAMPLE 2.6-1. Transform the electrical circuit shown in Figure 2.6-4a into a form suitable for analysis by the node-pair method.

SOLUTION. First we transform the v_{o1} source to obtain Figure 2.6-4b. Next we transform source v_{o2} with the result shown in Figure 2.6-4c. Now deform the diagram for a clearer representation of the two nodes. The resulting two equilibrium equations are obtained from Figure 2.6-4d and are:

$$-\frac{v_{o1}}{R_1}+\frac{v_1}{R_1}+\frac{v_1-v_2}{R_2}-i_1=0 \qquad \text{(a)} \quad (2.6\text{-}4)$$

$$\frac{v_2-v_1}{R_2}+i_1+\frac{v_2}{R_3}+\frac{v_2}{R_4}+\frac{v_{o2}}{R_4}=0 \qquad \text{(b)}$$

The two unknown node voltages v_1 and v_2 can be found by solving this pair of equations.

☐ ☐ ☐

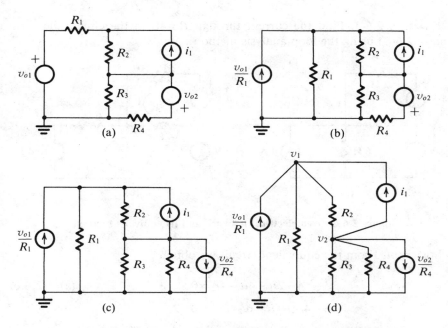

Figure 2.6-4.   An electrical network and its equivalent forms

EXAMPLE 2.6-2. Find an equivalent circuit of Figure 2.6-5a so that the loop-analysis method can be used.

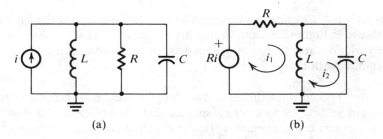

Figure 2.6-5.   An electrical network and its equivalent form

SOLUTION. From the equivalent circuit in Figure 2.6-5b, by transforming the current source, the two unknowns i_1 and i_2 can be found from the solution of the set of equations

$$Ri - Ri_1 - Lpi_1 + Lpi_2 = 0 \qquad \text{(a)} \quad (2.6\text{-}5)$$

$$-Lpi_2 + Lpi_1 - \frac{1}{Cp}i_2 = 0 \qquad \text{(b)}$$

□   □   □

EXAMPLE 2.6-3. Find the current through $R = 4\Omega$ in the circuit shown in Figure 2.6-6a using the loop-analysis method.

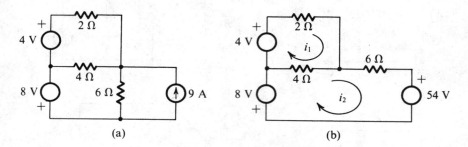

(a)   (b)

Figure 2.6-6.   An electrical network and its equivalent circuit

SOLUTION. From the equivalent circuit we obtain

$$4 - 2i_1 - 4i_1 + 4i_2 = 0 \qquad\qquad \text{(a)} \quad (2.6\text{-}6)$$

$$-8 - 4i_2 + 4i_1 - 6i_2 - 54 = 0 \qquad\qquad \text{(b)}$$

The simultaneous solution of this pair of equations yields $i_1 = -52/11$, and $i_2 = -89/11$, and therefore the current in $R = 4\Omega$ is 37/11 A from right to left.

◻   ◻   ◻

EXAMPLE 2.6-4. Consider a simple mechanical carriage having the equivalent model shown in Figure 2.6-7a to be moving over a highway which has a known surface variation $x(t)$ [hence $v_1(t)$] relative to a smooth earth. Deduce the equilibrium equations.

SOLUTION. The network model is drawn in Figure 2.6-7b according to the discussion in Section 2.4 assuming a smooth earth as a reference level with the surface variations being given as $v_1(t)$. Observe that this might be viewed as a two loop circuit, provided that the parallel circuits of K and D are replaced by an equivalent $Z(p)$, where

$$Z(p) = \frac{1}{Y(p)} = \frac{1}{D + \dfrac{K}{p}} = \frac{p}{Dp + K} \qquad (2.6\text{-}7)$$

If we employ a source transformation procedure, we have the equivalent form shown in Figure 2.6-7c, where $Z(p)$ is also that of Equation (2.6-7). From this figure we can write, as discussed in Section 2.4,

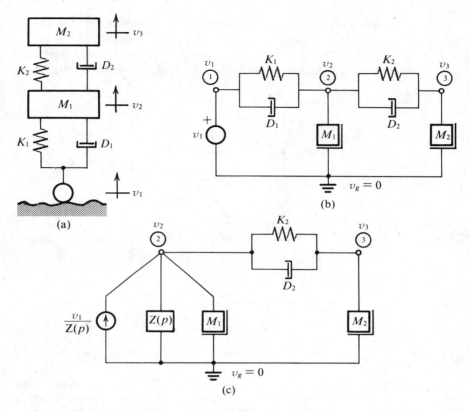

Figure 2.6-7.   A mechanical system and two equivalent network models

Node 2:

$$\left(\frac{D_1 p + K_1}{p} + M_1 p + \frac{K_2}{p} + D_2\right) v_2 - \left(\frac{K_2}{p} + D_2\right) v_3 = \frac{D_1 p + K_1}{p} v_1$$

$$\text{(2.6-8)}$$

Node 3:

$$-\left(\frac{K_2}{p} + D_2\right) v_2 + M_2 p v_3 = 0$$

2.7   THÈVENIN AND NORTON THEOREMS

The node-pair and loop methods of analysis provide equations which permit us to find the current or the voltage at every point in the circuit. Often interest might be limited to the current or voltage at a single point in the circuit. The Thèvenin and Norton theorems provide procedures for evaluating the voltage across or the current through some element of the circuit which may be excited by a number of different sources at various points in the circuit without setting up the network equations for the entire system. Actually, because of the essential intermediate steps, the total computational effort is not often materially reduced when using these theorems. However, the theorems do provide important steps for studying general network properties.

Refer to Figure 2.7-1 which represents a complex interconnected system of loops and node pairs. Assume that voltage sources may exist in any or all

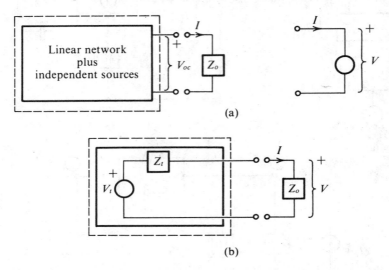

(a)

(b)

Figure 2.7-1.   (a) One port active network   (b) Thèvenin representation

loops, and current sources may exist across any or all node pairs. We confine our attention to the current in a single branch, such as impedance Z_o which forms part of one of the loops. The Thèvenin theorem states that relative to a specified pair of terminals in a linear network with independent sources, the entire active network contained within the broken lines can be replaced by a simple equivalent linear source consisting of a voltage driver and a series internal impedance. The voltage driver in the Thèvenin equivalent representation V_t is equal to the voltage across the open-circuited terminals with all sources active, but with the branch impedance Z_o removed, as shown. The impedance Z_t is found by reducing all voltage sources to zero, but retaining internal impedances; opening all current sources (open circuits); and measuring the impedance looking into the network at the output terminals. Therefore the components are

$$V_t = V_{oc} \qquad\qquad Z_t = \frac{V_t}{I_{sc}} = \frac{V_{oc}}{I_{sc}} \qquad\qquad (2.7\text{-}1)$$

where the subscripts *oc* denote open circuit and *sc* denote short circuit. We shall not give a proof of this theorem, but its validity will be demonstrated by examples.

EXAMPLE 2.7-1. Find the Thèvenin equivalent network for the circuit shown in Figure 2.7-2a.

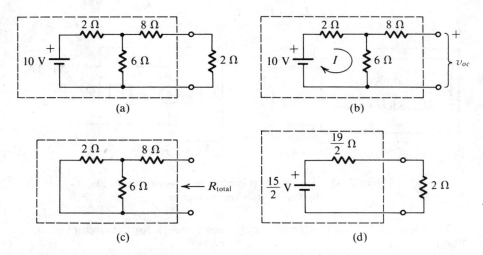

Figure 2.7-2.   Thèvenin equivalent network development

SOLUTION. Refer to Figure 2.7-2b for finding v_{oc}. The voltage v_{oc} is equal to $6 \times I$ since there is no current through the 8 ohm resistor. Hence $v_{oc} = [10/(2+6)] \times 6 = 60/8 = 15/2$ volt. To find the equivalent resistance we set the voltage source to zero as shown in Figure 2.7-2c. Since the 2-ohm and 6-ohm resistors are in parallel we obtain

$$R_{total} = \frac{2 \times 6}{2+6} + 8 = \frac{19}{2}$$

The final equivalent network is shown in Figure 2.7-2d.

◻ ◻ ◻

The Norton theorem is the dual of the Thèvenin theorem. It specifies that: relative to the terminals of Z_o of a linear network with independent sources, as shown in Figure 2.7-3a, the active circuit can be replaced by the equivalent configuration shown in Figure 2.7-3b consisting of a current source I_n shunted by a passive impedance Z_n. The current I_n is found by measuring the current in the output terminals when they are shorted, I_{sc}. The impedance Z_n is found the same way as in Thèvenin's theorem. This network representation follows by considering the rearranged Thèvenin expression

$$I = \frac{V_t}{Z_t} - \frac{V}{Z_t} = I_n - Y_n V \qquad (2.7\text{-}2)$$

where

$$I_n = \frac{V_t}{Z_t}; \qquad Y_n = \frac{1}{Z_t} = \frac{1}{Z_n}.$$

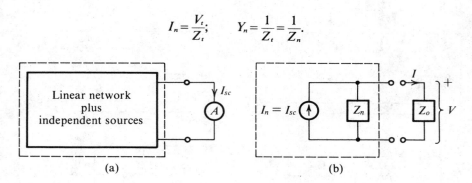

Figure 2.7-3. (a) One port relative to a specified output
(b) The Norton representation

EXAMPLE 2.7-2. Find the Norton equivalent network for the circuit shown in Figure 2.7-4a.

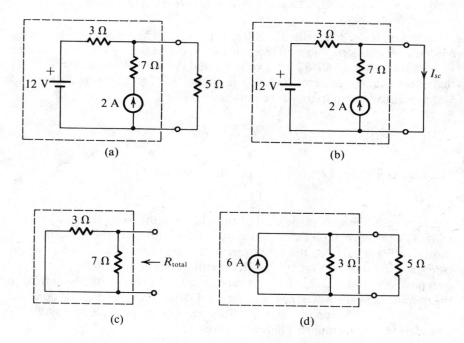

Figure 2.7-4. Norton equivalent network development

SOLUTION. Using simple circuit principles as discussed in Section 2.3, I_{sc} is found to be 6 A. Since the 7-ohm resistor is not connected to the circuit, $R_{total} = 3$ ohm (see Figure 2.7-4c). The final network is shown in Figure 2.7-4d. The reader will notice that the current through the 5 ohm resistor is $\frac{3}{4}$ A.

□   □   □

A certain similarity exists between the source transformation in Section 2.6 and the results of the Thèvenin and Norton transformations. Actually they are quite different, since in the source transformation we are operating only with simple sources, whereas with the Thèvenin and Norton theorems a simple equivalent network replaces an entire network plus sources, relative to a specified pair of terminals.

2.8 SUPERPOSITION

An important property of a linear system, exhibited by the procedures developed in writing loop and node-pair equations, is that the current in any branch (or the voltage between two points) of a network driven by two sources at different points of the network is the sum of the currents in that branch (or of the voltages between the two points) produced by each source acting independently. To evaluate the current due to voltage source 1, the second source is reduced to zero, then the procedure is reversed. In any circuit element the total current is the sum of the two contributing sources. This property is known as superposition. We shall see in our future work many obvious examples of the principle of superposition.

EXAMPLE 2.8-1. Find the current in the resistor $R = 5$ ohm for the circuit shown in Figure 2.8-1a.

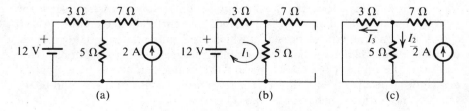

(a)   (b)   (c)

Figure 2.8-1. Illustration of the superposition theorem

SOLUTION. To apply the theorem, we have substituted the initial circuit with two equivalent ones. From Figure 2.8-1b we obtain $I_1 = 12/(3 + 5) = 12/8 = 3/2$ A. From Figure 2.8-1c we obtain $I_2 = (3 \times 2)/(3 + 5) = 6/8 = 3/4$ A and $I_3 = (5 \times 2)/(3 + 5) = 10/8 = 5/4$ A. Hence the total current through the 5 ohm resistor $I = I_1 + I_2 = 3/2 + 3/4 = 9/4$ A. This same problem was used to illustrate the Norton theorem, Example 2.7-2.

☐ ☐ ☐

2.9 DUALITY AND ANALOGS

We call attention to a unique feature of the general examples in Section 2.4 and 2.5. A comparison of Equations (2.4-1) and (2.5-1) shows a rather striking similarity between them. Also, the equilibrium equations Equations (2.4-5) and (2.4-6) for the nodal example are precisely of the same form as Equations (2.5-5) and (2.5-6) on a term by term basis. Two descriptions are involved here since both topology and field of activity (mechanial and electrical, respectively) play a role. Two networks within the same field of activity which lead to exactly similar sets of equilibrium equations but with the descriptive variables interchanged are known as *duals* of each other, and the comparable elements on an element-by-element basis are dually related. Thus if a nodal electrical circuit had been used as the sample in Section 2.4 instead of the mechanical network, then the nodal electrical circuit would be the dual of the loop circuit in Section 2.5, and we would find that the dually related elements are $C \sim L$; $L \sim C$; $R \sim G$; $G \sim R$. Since, in the present case Section 2.4 addresses a mechanical network, but we could draw an electrical network that would be described by a set of equations that exactly parallels Equations (2.4-5) and (2.4-6), such an electrical network is the *analog* of the mechanical network. Thus in our discussion we have a combined *dual-analog* situation.

This indicates that it is possible in principle, given a particular problem in a given discipline that is analyzed on a node-pair (loop) basis, to draw a network which yields an identical set of equations on a loop (node-pair) basis. Such networks are dually related. The discussion also shows that a given network in one discipline can be represented by an analog network in another discipline. Basically what this shows is that the equilibrium behavior of a network, no matter what its field of activity, is described by a differential equation. Also it shows that one can choose networks which are dually related, analog related, or dual-analog related, which have similar mathematical descriptions. If, in addition, the numerical coefficients are the same so that the mathematical descriptions become identical, then the response behavior of one would be the same as the response behavior of the other.

2.10 POSTLUDE

This chapter is essentially the beginning of the study of circuits and systems theory, and has introduced the methods for writing equations that describe interconnected systems. Subsequent chapters will extend this work, and together with the next three chapters, will provide a working background in the essentials of systems subject to continuous time and certain switched time inputs.

Your mathematical sophistication and, more importantly, your understanding of how to use mathematics as a tool for the understanding of systems, will develop markedly as you progress in this study.

SUMMARY

- The v,i relationship allows the definitions: $z(p) =$ impedance operator $= v/i$; $y(p) =$ admittance operator $= i/v$.

- Kirchhoff's current law, KCL, at a node is defined as follows:

$$\sum_{\text{node}} i_b = 0$$

- Kirchhoff's voltage law, KVL, around a loop is defined as follows:

$$\sum_{\text{loop}} v_b = 0$$

- D'Alembert's principle is defined as follows:

$$\sum_{\text{forces}} f_i - M_i \frac{dv_i}{dt} = 0$$

- When the equilibrium equations of two-node systems are arranged in the form

$$y_{11}(p)v_1 + y_{12}(p)v_2 = f_1 \qquad\qquad y_{11}(p)v_1 + y_{12}(p)v_2 = i_1$$
$$y_{21}(p)v_1 + y_{22}(p)v_2 = f_2 \qquad\qquad y_{21}(p)v_1 + y_{22}(p)v_2 = i_2$$

$$\text{mechanical network} \qquad\qquad \text{electrical network}$$

the operators $y_{ij}(p)$ have the following meaning:

$y_{11} =$ sum of all admittance operators connected to node 1

$y_{22} =$ sum of all admittance operators connected to node 2

$y_{12} = y_{21} =$ negative sum of all admittance operators common to nodes 1 and 2

$f_1 =$ algebraic sum of all force drivers to node 1

$f_2 =$ algebraic sum of all force drivers to node 2

$i_1 =$ algebraic sum of all currents to node 1

$i_2 =$ algebraic sum of all currents to node 2

- When the equilibrium equations of two-loop systems are arranged in the form

$$z_{11}(p)f_1 + z_{12}(p)f_2 = v_1 \qquad z_{11}(p)i_1 + z_{12}(p)i_2 = v_1$$
$$z_{21}(p)f_1 + z_{22}(p)f_2 = v_2 \qquad z_{21}(p)i_1 + z_{22}(p)i_2 = v_2$$

    mechanical network   electrical network

    the operators $z_{ij}(p)$ have the following meaning:

    z_{11} = sum of all impedance operators on the contour of loop 1

    z_{22} = sum of all impedance operators on the contour of loop 2

    $z_{12} = z_{21}$ = negative of the sum of all impedance operators common to loops 1 and 2

    v_1 = algebraic sum of voltage sources (or velocity sources) in loop 1

    v_2 = algebraic sum of voltage sources (or velocity sources) in loop 2

- The source transformations are shown in the figure.

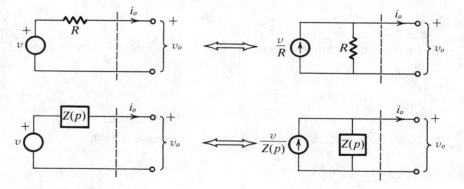

- The Thèvenin theorem replaces a complicated linear network plus voltage and current sources relative to a single pair of terminals anywhere in the network by a simple equivalent circuit comprising an equivalent voltage source and an equivalent internal impedance.

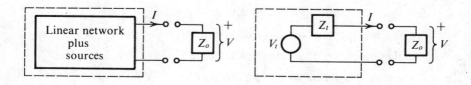

- The Norton theorem replaces a complicated linear network plus voltage and current sources relative to a single pair of terminals anywhere in the network by a simple equivalent circuit comprising an equivalent current source and an equivalent shunting admittance.

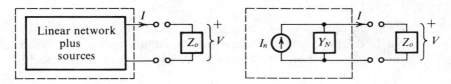

- Superposition in a linear system denotes that the effect of a number of independent sources anywhere in the circuit is the sum of the effects of each source acting independently.

REVIEW QUESTIONS

1. What are the operational notations for the operators $\frac{d}{dt}$ and $\int dt$?
2. What do we call the operators $z(p) = v/i$ and $y(p) = i/v$?
3. Define Kirchhoff's current and voltage laws.
4. Define D'Alembert's principle for mechanical systems.
5. Explain in physical terms what we mean by the relation $\sum_{node} i_b = 0$.
6. State the voltage and current-source transformations.
7. What elements can the following admittance and impedance operators contain: $y_{ii}(p)$, $y_{ij}(p)$, $z_{ii}(p)$, $z_{jk}(p)$?
8. State the Thèvenin and Norton theorems.
9. Discuss the superposition principle.

REFERENCES

1. Lindsay, J. F., and Katz, *Dynamics of Physical Circuits and Systems*, Matrix Publishers, Inc., Portland, OR, 1978.

    Written for the beginning engineering and engineering technology students. Presents system modeling and system dynamics in the simplest manner.

2. Reza, F. M., and S. Seely, *Modern Network Analysis*, McGraw Hill Book Co., New York, NY, 1959.

    An intermediate level text on network theory, with methods of solution.

3. Seely, S., *An Introduction to Engineering Systems*, Pergamon Press, Inc., Elmsford, NY, 1972.

    An intermediate level text that contains sufficient background to understand systems analysis. Includes both classical and matrix methods of formulation and solution.

PROBLEMS

2.2-1. Prepare a table giving the operational notation description for the fluid
element..

2.3-1. Verify Equations (2.3-14), (2.3-15), (2.3-16).

2.3-2. Using the operational notation and Tables 2.2-1 and 2.2-2, find the input or driving point impedance and admittance operational functions
for the circuits shown in Figure P2.3-2. Express the results explicitly as
$Z(p)$ or $Y(p)$.

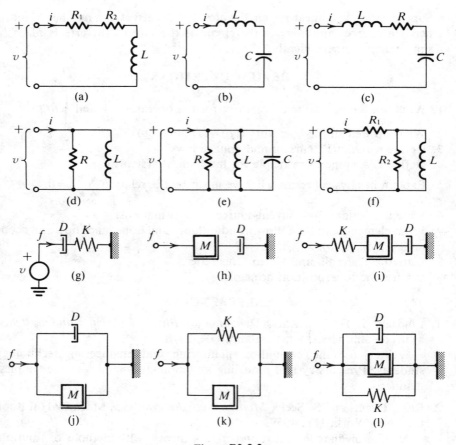

Figure P2.3-2

2.3-3. Develop the equilibrium equations for the systems shown in Figure
P2.3-3.

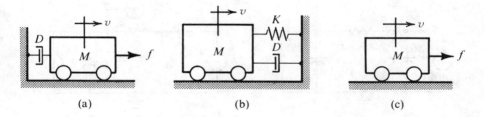

Figure P2.3-3

2.3-4. Find the admittance functions $Y(p)$ for the systems shown in Figure P2.3-4.

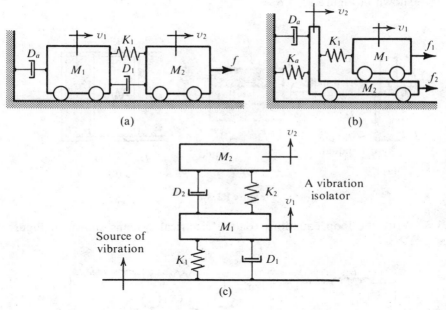

Figure P2.3-4

2.3-5. Find the driving point admittance functions $Y(p)$ for the electrical systems shown in Figure P2.3-5.

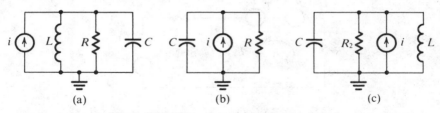

Figure P2.3-5 (continued on following page)

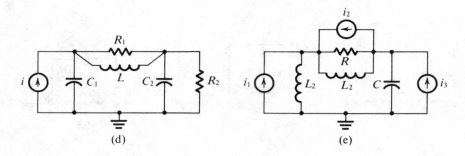

Figure P2.3-5

2.3-6. Find the equilibrium equations for the rotational mechanical systems shown in Figure P2.3-6.

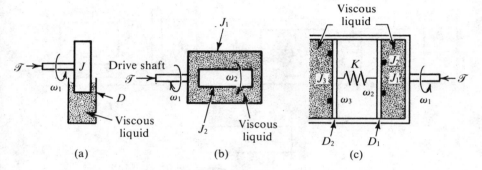

Figure P2.3-6

2.3-7. Write the loop equations for the electrical systems shown in Figure P2.3-7.

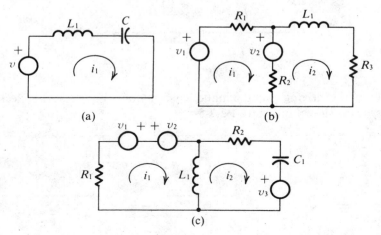

Figure P2.3-7

2.5-1. Write the equilibrium equations on a loop basis for each of the given circuits shown in Figure P2.5-1.

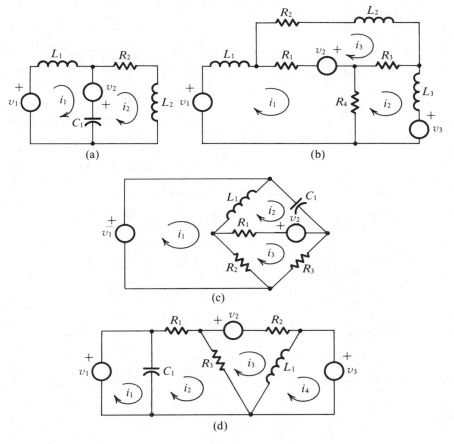

(a)

(b)

(c)

(d)

Figure P2.5-1

2.6-1. After the appropriate voltage to current source transformations, find the currents using the node-pair method.

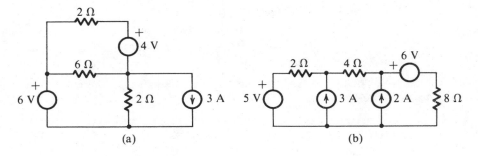

(a)

(b)

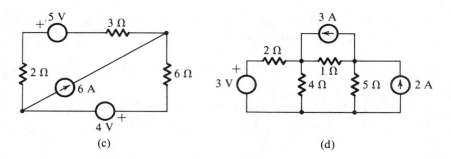

(c)

(d)

Figure P2.6-1

2.6-2. After the appropriate current to voltage source transformations applied to the circuits shown in Figure P2.6-1, find the currents through each resistor using the loop equilibrium equations.

2.7-1. Find the Thèvenin equivalent circuit at terminals AA' for the networks shown in Figure P2.7-1.

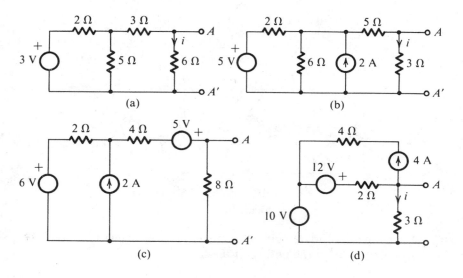

(a)   (b)

(c)   (d)

Figure P2.7-1

2.7-2. Find the current i in Figures P2.7-1a, P2.7-1b, and P2.7-1d using Thèvenin's equivalent circuit theorem.

2.7-3. Using Norton's theorem, find the currents indicated in the circuits of Figure P2.7-3.

2.7-4. Use the Thèvenin theorem to find the voltage across the 6 ohm resistor in Figure P2.6-1a.

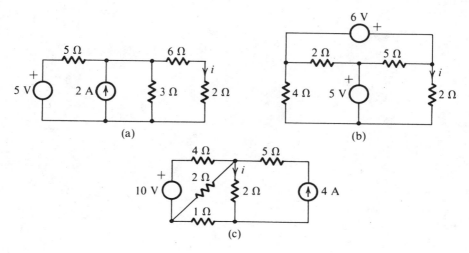

(a)   (b)

(c)

Figure P2.7-3

2.7-5. Repeat Problem 2.7-4 using the Norton theorem.

2.8-1. Find the current *i* for the circuits shown in Figure P2.8-1 using the superposition theorem.

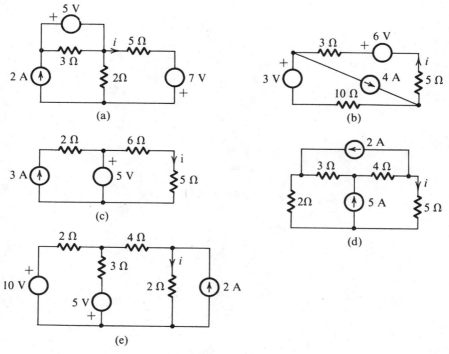

(a)   (b)

(c)   (d)

(e)

Figure P2.8-1

Chapter Three

System Response —
Time Domain Considerations

The Kirchhoff laws applicable to electric circuits lead to sets of integro-differential equations. Once the equations which describe the interconnected system are established, then it is possible to determine the response of the system to a wide variety of excitation functions. We shall here limit ourselves to the important features of solving system equations represented by linear differential equations with constant coefficients. A number of methods exist for carrying out the details of such solutions, including analytic methods and numerical methods that might involve the use of digital computers.

FIRST ORDER SYSTEMS

3.1 GENERAL FEATURES OF SOLUTIONS OF DIFFERENTIAL EQUATIONS

Refer to Figure 3.1-1 which shows a series RL circuit subject to an excitation function $v(t)$. The problem is to determine the current $i(t)$, which is related to $v(t)$ by the differential equation (Kirchhoff's voltage law)

$$L\frac{di(t)}{dt} + Ri(t) = v(t) \tag{3.1-1}$$

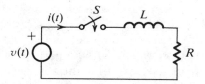

Figure 3.1-1. Electric circuit involving R and L

The specific problem we wish to consider here is concerned with the details of solving Equation (3.1-1) when $v(t)$ is a known time function. In principle, $v(t)$ may be any analytic function of time. From a practical point of view, however, there is a relatively limited number of excitation functions that form the basis for most of our subsequent analysis. Typical of these are the waveforms illustrated in Figure 3.1-2. Observe that all of these have been drawn to indicate a discontinuity, which is to denote that the wave is switched into the system at a given time t_o usually taken as $t=0$. From an analytic point of view, even though these waveforms may be continuous after $t=0$, nevertheless, they must be considered to be discontinuous in time. This is important since it emphasizes the need for *initial* statements of the state of the system, which, together with specified switching conditions, will be used to specify completely the subsequent behavior of the system.

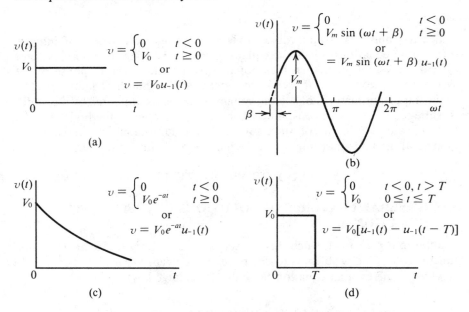

Figure 3.1-2.   Typical waveforms for through or across time functions

We shall begin our considerations with Equation (3.1-1) since the pattern that is employed in studying this equation is typical of that for linear differential equations in general. We proceed by noting that the solution to an equation of this type consists of two parts. One part of the solution is entirely dependent on the nature of the network in the absence of any excitation. The second part is determined by the character of the applied excitation function. The part of the solution that is due to the nature of the network alone is obtained from the homogeneous or *complementary equation*, which is the original equation with the right hand or driving terms set to zero

$$L\frac{di_t}{dt} + Ri_t = 0 \tag{3.1-2}$$

The solution to this equation is known as the *complementary solution*, and will be written as i_t, where the subscript denotes that this is the *transient* portion of the total solution, as we shall see later.

The *particular integral solution* will be designated i_s and is often called the *steady state* solution, although in general, this term will be time varying. The particular integral solution depends explicitly on the form of the excitation function $v(t)$. We shall discuss below important techniques for finding i_s. The complete solution is then

$$i(t) = i_t(t) + i_s(t) \tag{3.1-3}$$

and explicitly shows it to be made up of the complementary solution and the particular integral solution.

The essential features of systems described by linear, time invariant differential equations can be displayed graphically as shown in Figure 3.1-3. As discussed above for linear systems and employing classical methods for the solution of ordinary differential equations, the sequence is precisely that illustrated, with each step being separately accomplished. When using Laplace

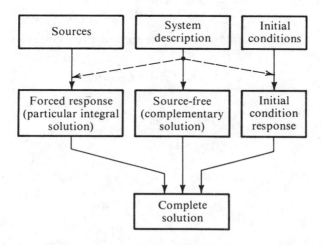

Figure 3.1-3.   The factors involved in determining the response of a system

transform methods, as we shall do in Chapter 5, the several steps are accomplished together. Whatever the method, the complete solution is the superposition of the continuously action-forced response; the response of the originally relaxed system (zero initial conditions, also referred to as the normal mode response) to the suddenly applied (switched) sources; and excitations caused by energies stored within the system itself.

We shall limit our discussion to passive physical systems for which the output response is zero for $t < t_o$, if the input excitation is zero for $t < t_o$. This means that if

$$v(t) = 0 \qquad \text{for } t < t_o$$

then

$$i(t) = [\text{Linear operation on}] \ v(t) = 0 \qquad \text{for } t < t_o$$

Systems which satisfy these conditions are called *causal* systems. In general, a function $f(t)$ is called causal if it has zero value for $t < 0$; that is, $f(t) = 0$ for $t < 0$. It can be shown that all physically realizable systems are causal.

The complementary solution and the particular integral solution satisfy the respective equations

$$L\frac{di_t}{dt} + Ri_t = 0 \qquad\qquad \text{(a)} \quad (3.1\text{-}4)$$

$$L\frac{di_s}{dt} + Ri_s = v(t) \qquad\qquad \text{(b)}$$

then the differential equation which is the sum of these equations

$$L\frac{d}{dt}(i_t + i_s) + R(i_t + i_s) = v(t)$$

is satisfied by the complete solution

$$i(t) = i_t(t) + i_s(t) \qquad\qquad (3.1\text{-}5)$$

This result is possible because *differentiation is a linear process*

$$\frac{d}{dt}[f_1(t) + f_2(t)] = \frac{df_1(t)}{dt} + \frac{df_2(t)}{dt}$$

3.2   THE COMPLEMENTARY SOLUTION

It is customary to adopt as a tentative solution to the complementary equation an exponential function of the form e^{st}, since the form of this function does not change with repeated differentiations or integrations. Thus we shall use as a test function

$$i_t(t) = Be^{st} \qquad (3.2\text{-}1)$$

with the thought that it may be possible to choose the constant B and the value of s to satisfy the equation. If we combine Equation (3.2-1) with Equation (3.1-2)

$$L\frac{di_t}{dt} + Ri_t = 0$$

we find that

$$LsBe^{st} + RBe^{st} = 0 \qquad (3.2\text{-}2)$$

It follows from this that

$$s = -\frac{R}{L} \qquad (3.2\text{-}3)$$

and this is independent of the value of B. This root is known as the *normal mode* or the *eigenvalue* (characteristic value) of the system. The complementary function is

$$i_t(t) = Be^{-Rt/L} = Be^{-t/(L/R)} \qquad (3.2\text{-}4)$$

where L/R has the units of time, s. Since the value of L/R determines how fast the complementary function decays, it is called the *time constant* of the circuit (system). We observe that only one arbitrary, unknown, constant is present. If the differential equation is of higher order than the first, the number of eigenvalues and the number of arbitrary constants in the solution would equal the highest order of the derivative that appears in the differential equation, as we shall see.

EXAMPLE 3.2-1. Find the complementary solution for the system shown in Figure 3.2-1.

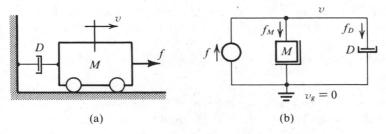

(a)   (b)

**Figure 3.2-1.   (a) Dynamical system
(b) Circuit-type representation of the system**

SOLUTION. We follow the procedure outlined in Section 2.3. We obtain the system equation

$$-f + f_M + f_D = 0$$

or equivalently,

$$M\frac{dv(t)}{dt} + Dv(t) = f(t) \tag{3.2-5}$$

Assuming the function $v_t = Be^{st}$ as the tentative solution of the homogeneous equation

$$M\frac{dv_t}{dt} + Dv_t = 0$$

we obtain the complementary function

$$v_t = Be^{-(D/M)t} \tag{3.2-6}$$

for this physical system.

□ □ □

3.3 THE PARTICULAR INTEGRAL SOLUTION

As already noted, the particular integral solution will depend on the particular form of the excitation function $v(t)$. No acceptable general method exists for finding this function. However, we shall adopt a rather heuristic viewpoint; we shall try to find a solution by whatever means may appear reasonable, recognizing that the validity of the solution is readily checked by direct recourse to the differential equation. We then rely on the uniqueness theorem to support the fact that such a solution is a unique solution. For most problems that arise in systems with linear coefficients, one of the following methods can usually be used:

1. EXCITATION FUNCTION A POLYNOMIAL IN t. Suppose that the voltage $v(t)$ applied to the circuit of Figure 3.1-1, is a polynomial of the form [see Equation (1.5-2)]

$$v(t) = a_0 + a_1 t + a_2 t^2 + \ldots + a_n t^n \tag{3.3-1}$$

A usual procedure in finding an expression for the current $i(t)$ is to adopt as a trial solution a similar power series. Hence we write tentatively

$$i(t) = c_0 + c_1 t + c_2 t^2 + \ldots + c_n t^n \tag{3.3-2}$$

Equation (3.3-2) is combined with Equation (3.1-4b). This involves differentiation of the power series, which can be done on a term by term basis. Next the series are added in the manner called for in Equation (3.1-4b). The result of such an operation is a power series in t. This leads to a power series appropriate to the left hand member of Equation (3.1-4b) which is equal to the power series expression for $v(t)$ given in Equation (3.3-1). For equality, the coefficients of like powers of t must be equal. This leads to a set of algebraic equations involving the coefficients, and these can be solved for the various c-s in terms of known a-factors.

EXAMPLE 3.3-1. Suppose that the force applied to the physical system shown in Figure 3.2-1a is of the form $f(t) = 1 + 2t^2$. Find the particular integral solution.

SOLUTION. Set

$$v_s(t) = c_0 + c_1 t + c_2 t^2$$

and introduce this function into Equation (3.2-5). We obtain

$$M(c_1 + 2c_2 t) + D(c_0 + c_1 t + c_2 t^2) = 1 + 2t^2$$

or

$$(Dc_0 + Mc_1) + (Dc_1 + 2Mc_2)t + Dc_2 t^2 = 1 + 2t^2$$

Equating coefficients of like powers of t, we deduce the following set of equations

$$Dc_0 + Mc_1 = 1$$
$$Dc_1 + 2Mc_2 = 0$$
$$Dc_2 = 2$$

We solve for c_0, c_1 and c_2, and obtain the following

$$c_2 = 2/D$$
$$c_1 = -4M/D^2$$
$$c_0 = \frac{D^2 + 4M^2}{D^3}$$

The particular solution is then written

$$v_s(t) = \frac{D^2 + 4M^2}{D^3} - \frac{4Mt}{D^2} + \frac{2t^2}{D}$$

The reader should substitute this equation into Equation (3.2-5) and verify that this is the particular solution.

☐ ☐ ☐

2. EXCITATION FUNCTION, AN EXPONENTIAL FUNCTION OF t. In this case, suppose that the applied force to the mechanical circuit shown in Figure 3.2-1 is

$$f(t) = Ae^{\alpha t}$$

where α is a real number. We shall assume a trial solution of the same form, namely

$$v_s(t) = Be^{\alpha t}$$

Combine these with Equation (3.2-5) to find

$$\alpha MBe^{\alpha t} + Be^{\alpha t}D = Ae^{\alpha t}$$

This equation is solved for B, and yields the value

$$B = \frac{A}{\alpha M + D}$$

The particular solution is given by

$$v_s(t) = \frac{A}{\alpha M + D}e^{\alpha t}$$

Observe that the form for $v_s(t)$ has precisely the same form as the excitation $f(t)$ except that the amplitude will differ, in general.

3. EXCITATION FUNCTION, A SINE OR COSINE FUNCTION OF t. In this case, a trial function of the form

$$v_s = A \cos t + B \sin t$$

is assumed, where A and B are unknown constants. By combining this trial function with Equation (3.2-5) relations arise that permit an evaluation of A and B.

As an example, suppose that $f(t) = 4 \sin t$ is the assumed excitation function in Equation (3.2-5). By introducing the suggested form for $v(t)$ in this equation we will obtain

$$(MB + DA) \cos t + (DB - MA) \sin t = 4 \sin t$$

By equating coefficients of like terms yields the equation set

$$\left. \begin{array}{r} -MA + DB = 4 \\ MB + DA = 0 \end{array} \right\} \quad \text{or} \quad A = \frac{-4M}{M^2 + D^2}; \quad B = \frac{AD}{M^2 + D^2}$$

A second approach to this type of excitation function will be studied in detail in Chapter 4.

4. EXCITATION FUNCTION, A CONSTANT. This is an important case, and it is the excitation function corresponding to the dc excitation. The desired result is the dc response. Actually, the solution is just a special case under (1) and (2). Case (1) applies by setting $c_0 \neq 0$ and all other c-s $= 0$. Case (2) applies by setting $\alpha = 0$.

5. EXCITATION FUNCTION, A COMBINATION OF THE ABOVE CASES. Under these conditions, we create a set of differential equations by splitting the input function into its separate parts, and solving each part; the result will be the superposition of the separate solutions. For example, suppose that $f(t) = (1 + \sin t + e^{\alpha t})u_{-1}(t)$ in Equation (3.2-5). We separate the driving function, and write the set of differential equations

$$M\frac{dv_1}{dt} + Dv_1 = 1$$

$$M\frac{dv_2}{dt} + Dv_2 = \sin t$$

$$M\frac{dv_3}{dt} + Dv_3 = e^{\alpha t}$$

The complete particular solution will be

$$v_s = v_1 + v_2 + v_3$$

3.4 EVALUATION OF INTEGRATION CONSTANTS – INITIAL CONDITIONS

Once the complementary solution and the particular integral solution have been deduced for a particular example, the next step is to determine the constants of integration that arise in the complementary solution. These constants must be chosen to yield a response function that satisfies all conditions of the particular problem. These conditions, as previously discussed, are the known charges on all capacitors (usually given as initial voltages across the capacitors), and known current through all inductors at some specified initial time, usually taken as $t = 0$. In the more general case, the initial conditions would be specified by initial through and across variables pertinent to the system elements. If these initial voltages and currents are zero, the system is said to be *initially relaxed.* In all cases, the specified initial conditions must be applied to the complete solution to determine the constants of integration. In this way the character of the system disturbance is taken into account. Of course, if the system disturbance involves more than the switching of excitation functions, as, for example, the switching of system elements, such changes must also be taken into account.

A variety of switching operations is possible:

1. The most common switching operation is that of introducing an excitation source into a circuit. The more common input waveforms are given in Figure 3.1-2. The excitation function establishes the form of the particular solution. For example, the specification that the circuit is initially relaxed, meaning that initial voltages across capacitors and initial currents through inductors are zero, provides sufficient relations to evaluate the constants of integration.

2. If initial voltages across capacitors are not zero, and if, during the switching operation, the total system capacitance remains unchanged, then the voltage across the capacitor will be the same before and after the instant of switching. This condition assumes the absence of switching impulses to the capacitor or capacitors. This result follows from the fact that for the capacitor, $i = C \, dv/dt$, and in the switching operation during the interval from $t = 0-$ to $t = 0+$ when C is a constant

$$\int_{v(0-)}^{v(0+)} C \, dv = \int_{0-}^{0+} i \, dt \tag{3.4-1}$$

The value of the integral on the right is zero unless i is an impulse function. This is a statement of conservation of charge (conservation of momentum in mechanics) and says that if no current impulse is applied during the switching interval, then

$$Cv(0+) - Cv(0-) = 0 \tag{3.4-2}$$

3. If initial currents exist in inductors, and if, during the switching operation, the total system inductance remains unchanged, then the current through the inductor will remain unchanged over the switching instant. This condition is the dual of that for the voltage across the capacitor, and assumes the absence of switching voltage impulses. This result follows directly from the fact that the terminal relation for the inductor is $v = L \, di/dt$, and with L constant over the switching interval

$$\int_{i(0-)}^{i(0+)} L \, di = \int_{0-}^{0+} v \, dt$$

The right hand side will be zero in the absence of voltage impulses. This is a statement of conservation of flux linkages, and says that in the absence of voltage impulses during the switching interval

$$Li(0+) - Li(0-) = 0 \qquad (3.4\text{-}3)$$

4. In light of the discussion in (2) and (3), for circuits with constant excitation:

    a. capacitors behave as open circuits in the steady state in networks with constant excitation.

    b. inductors behave as short circuits in the steady state in networks with constant excitation.

5. In the event that L or C or both are changed instantaneously during a switching operation, and in the absence of switching impulses, Equations (3.4-2) and (3.4-3) must be modified in form to the following:

for capacitors,   conservation of charge $q(0+) = q(0-)$

for inductors,   conservation of flux linkages $\psi(0+) = \psi(0-)$

As a practical matter, circuits with switched L or C are easily accomplished in electrical circuits by placing switches across all or part of the L or C of a circuit.

More will be said about initial conditions in Chapter 5 in connection with the Laplace transform.

3.5   THE SERIES RL CIRCUIT AND ITS DUAL

We wish to carry out the solutions in detail of a number of important problems. We again consider the simple series RL circuit and its dual, as illustrated in Figure 3.5-1. That is, the circuit and its dual are described by similar differential equations. The excitation function is a step function, and as before, we write this $Vu_{-1}(t)$, where the symbol $u_{-1}(t)$ denotes the unit step function which is defined as

$$u_{-1}(t) = \begin{cases} 0 & t < 0 \\ 1 & t \geqslant 0 \end{cases} \qquad (3.5\text{-}1)$$

The dynamic equation for Figure 3.5-1a is given by Equation (3.1-1) which is rewritten here

$$L\frac{di}{dt} + Ri = v(t) \qquad \text{For the dual circuit:} \quad C\frac{dv}{dt} + Gv = i(t) \qquad (3.5\text{-}2)$$

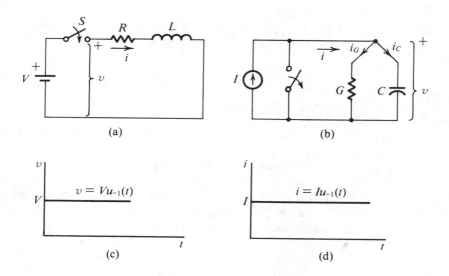

Figure 3.5-1. The series RL circuit and its dual with step function excitation

We note that except for a change of symbols, the solution in the present case applies for both the circuit and its dual. To find the complementary solution, we choose an exponential function of the form, as discussed in Section 3.2,

$$i_t = Be^{st} \qquad\qquad (3.5\text{-}3)$$

as a trial solution. This leads to the complementary solution given in Equation (3.2-4), namely

$$i_t = Be^{-Rt/L} \qquad\qquad (3.5\text{-}4)$$

The particular integral solution, based on the discussion in Section 3.3, form 4, is found to be

$$i_s = A = \frac{V}{R} \qquad\qquad (3.5\text{-}5)$$

by choosing the trial solution

$$i_s = A = \text{constant}$$

This form, which is the steady dc current, is consistent with the fact that when $i = $ constant the inductor has no effect; i.e., $L\, di/dt = 0$. The complete solution is then

$$i = i_s + i_t = \frac{V}{R} + Be^{-(R/L)t} \qquad\qquad (3.5\text{-}6)$$

To evaluate the constant B in this equation, we require the availability of one initial condition. We shall assume that the initial current through the inductor is zero; i.e., $i(0-)=0$; that is, we assume that the switch in the series circuit had been open for a long time prior to $t=0$. In the dual circuit, the corresponding condition is that the switch across the parallel circuit had been closed for a long time prior to $t=0$, and that the voltage across the capacitor is zero, or $v(0-)=0$. Now we invoke the conservation laws discussed in Section 3.4, which require, respectively, that $i(0+)=0$ for the series circuit and $v(0+)=0$ for the dual circuit. We thus write from Equation (3.5-6) for $t=0$

$$0=\frac{V}{R}+B$$

from which

$$B=-\frac{V}{R} \tag{3.5-7}$$

The final solution for the current given by Equation (3.5-6) is thus

$$i=\frac{V}{R}(1-e^{-Rt/L}) \tag{3.5-8}$$

The nature of this function is illustrated in Figure 3.5-2. This figure shows that the current rises from zero, the value imposed by the condition $i(0-)=i(0+)$ $=0$, with a decreasing slope as time progresses, and ultimately attains its asymptotic value or steady state value V/R.

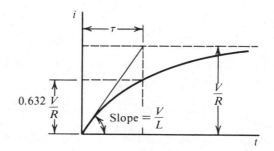

**Figure 3.5-2. The response of an initially relaxed RL circuit
to a step function excitation**

The initial slope is an important feature of the exponential function. The slope of the current curve at any point is

$$\frac{di}{dt}=\frac{V}{L}e^{-Rt/L} \tag{3.5-9}$$

which has the value V/L at the origin $t=0$. We shall use this initial slope to calculate the intercept at τ the point that the tangent to the response curve at the origin makes with the final value of the current. This is

$$\tau = \frac{V/R}{\text{slope}} = \frac{L}{R} \qquad (3.5\text{-}10)$$

The quantity $\tau = L/R$ is known as the *time constant* of the circuit (τ is in seconds when L is in henry and R is in ohm). This shows that the time constant can be interpreted as the time that it would take the current to reach its final steady state value if it were to continue at its original rate. The time constant can also be interpreted from Equation (3.5-8) to show that for $t = \tau$ the current will reach 0.632 of its final value. It is of interest to note that the current will reach 99 percent of its final value in 5 time constants. We shall find that these interpretations apply even when the initial current is not zero.

Equation (3.5-9) can be given another interesting interpretation. This stems from the inherent property of linear differential equations. Begin with the differential equation

$$Ri + L\frac{di}{dt} = v(t)$$

which is written operationally as

$$\left(R + L\frac{d}{dt}\right)i = v(t)$$

or

$$O\{i\} = v(t)$$

where O denotes a linear operator, in this case equal to $Z(p) = R + Lp$. From a mathematical viewpoint we can now write that

$$i = O^{-1}\{v(t)\}$$

where O^{-1} is another linear operator that is different from O. By differentiation it follows that

$$\frac{di}{dt} = \frac{d}{dt}\left\{O^{-1}\{v(t)\}\right\} = O^{-1}\left\{\frac{dv(t)}{dt}\right\}$$

because the operations are linear. This sequence can be shown graphically (see Figure 3.5-3). These two equations show that if an input v produces an output i, then an input dv/dt will produce an output di/dt. This sequence of operations can be extended to further orders of differentiation.

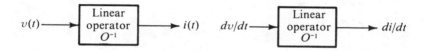

Figure 3.5-3.   Features of linear differential operators

Consider now the particular case when $v(t) = u_{-1}(t)$, with its corresponding output current $i(t)$, as specified by Equation (3.5-8). It follows, therefore, that if the input is $dv(t)/dt = du_{-1}(t)/dt = u_0(t)$, then the corresponding response is $di(t)/dt$. Hence Equation (3.5-9) specifies the response of the RL circuit to the impulse input $u_0(t)$.

EXAMPLE 3.5-1. Find the current in a series RL circuit with zero initial conditions (initially relaxed) when the excitation function has the form

$$v(t) = 2u_{-1}(t) + 0.5 \sin 100t \; u_{-1}(t)$$

SOLUTION. From the discussion above, the complementary solution is again

$$i_t = Be^{-Rt/L}$$

where B is an unknown constant. The particular integral solution for the excitation $2u_{-1}(t)$ is

$$i_{s1} = \frac{2}{R}$$

To find the particular integral solution for the excitation $0.5 \sin 100t \; u_{-1}(t)$, we assume a solution of the form

$$i_{s2} = A \cos 100t + D \sin 100t$$

where A and D are unknown constants. This assumed solution is combined with the differential equation

$$L\frac{di_{s2}}{dt} + Ri_{s2} = 0.5 \sin 100t$$

This leads to the equation set

$$-100LA + RD = 0.5$$

$$RA + 100LD = 0$$

From this set we find that

$$A = -\frac{50L}{R^2 + (100L)^2}$$

$$D = \frac{0.5R}{R^2 + (100L)^2}$$

The total solution is,

$$i = Be^{-Rt/L} + \frac{2}{R} - \frac{50L}{R^2 + (100L)^2} \cos 100t + \frac{0.5R}{R^2 + (100L)^2} \sin 100t \qquad t \geqslant 0$$

The initial condition $i = 0$ at $t = 0$, when applied to these solutions yields equations from which B can be obtained. Thus finally

$$i = \left(-\frac{2}{R} + \frac{50L}{\sqrt{R^2 + (100L)^2}} \right) e^{-Rt/L} + \frac{2}{R} - \frac{50L}{R^2 + (100L)^2} \cos 100t$$

$$+ \frac{0.5R}{R^2 + (100L)^2} \sin 100t \qquad t \geqslant 0$$

□ □ □

EXAMPLE 3.5-2. A mass M of nitroglycerine is secured as shown in Figure 3.5-3. If the box is dropped from a height of 2 m, determine its velocity, if no rebound occurs.

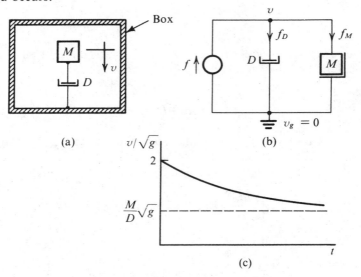

Figure 3.5-4.   (a) Mechanical system
(b) Equivalent circuit representation   (c) The velocity function

SOLUTION. The equation of motion is written as follows

$$-f + f_M + f_D = 0 \quad \text{or} \quad M\frac{dv}{dt} + Dv = f$$

The force f is due only to the gravitational pull and is equal to the constant Mg where g is the gravitational constant. At the impact time, $t = 0$, the velocity is equal to $v(0) = \sqrt{2gh} = 2\sqrt{g}$. From the previous discussion the complementary function is

$$v_t = Be^{-Dt/M}$$

Since f is constant, the particular solution is easily found if we set $v_s = A$ in the equation. Hence

$$DA = Mg \quad \text{or } A = Mg/D$$

and the complete solution is equal to

$$v = Be^{-Dt/M} + \frac{Mg}{D}$$

Apply the initial conditions to the last equation to obtain

$$v(o) = 2\sqrt{g} = B + \frac{Mg}{D}$$

The solution is given by

$$v(t) = \left(2\sqrt{g} - \frac{Mg}{D}\right)e^{-Dt/M} + \frac{Mg}{D}$$

If we select the values of M or D such that $2 \gg (M/D)\sqrt{g}$, then the velocity function has the form shown in Figure 3.5-3c. Under these conditions the velocity will not become negative, and hence no rebound will occur.

◻ ◻ ◻

3.6 THE SERIES RL CIRCUIT WITH AN INITIAL CURRENT

We wish to examine the features of the circuit behavior when an initial current exists and is subject to a variety of switching conditions. This is best done by examining specific examples. These examples will illustrate some of the more common procedures used to solve such problems.

EXAMPLE 3.6-1. Consider the circuit shown in Figure 3.6-1a which shows the switching of the circuit resistance. Observe that the total circuit resistance is

$R_1 + R_2$ before switching and becomes R_1 after switching at $t = 0$. Find $i(t)$ for $t > 0$.

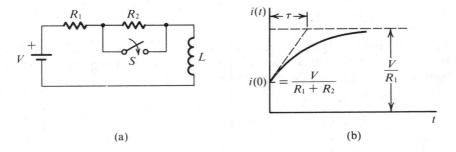

(a)   (b)

Figure 3.6-1.   (a) Switching of R in a circuit with an initial current
(b) The response of the circuit in (a)

SOLUTION. The initial current prior to the switching time is assumed to be constant since the source was assumed to be on for a long time and any transient effect has disappeared. The initial current has the value

$$i_0 = i(0-) = \frac{V}{R_1 + R_2} \tag{3.6-1}$$

After switching, the controlling differential equation is given by Equation (3.5-2), with the general solution [see Equation (3.5-6)]

$$i = \frac{V}{R_1} + B e^{-R_1 t/L} \tag{3.6-2}$$

To evaluate the constant B we must impose the initial condition, which is that $i(0-) = i(0+)$ since by Equation (3.4-3) no instantaneous change in current will occur. We now write

$$\frac{V}{R_1 + R_2} = \frac{V}{R_1} + B$$

from which we find that

$$B = V \left(\frac{1}{R_1 + R_2} - \frac{1}{R_1} \right) = \frac{-VR_2}{R_1(R_1 + R_2)} \tag{3.6-3}$$

The final solution is given by the expression

$$i = \frac{V}{R_1} \left(1 - \frac{R_2}{R_1 + R_2} e^{-R_1 t/L} \right) \tag{3.6-4}$$

The nature of this function is illustrated in Figure 3.6-1b. The meaning of the time constant here remains precisely as in Section 3.5, but current changes are now measured from the initial value of current rather than from zero, which was previously the initial value.

□ □ □

EXAMPLE 3.6-2. Refer to Figure 3.6-2a which shows the switching of L in a circuit with an initial current. Prior to switching, the inductance is L_1, and after switching the total circuit inductance becomes $L_1 + L_2$. Switching occurs at $t = 0$. Find the current in the circuit.

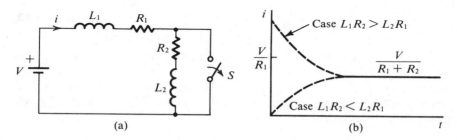

(a)   (b)

Figure 3.6-2.   (a) Switching of L in a circuit with initial current
(b) Response of the RL circuit when L is switched

SOLUTION. The current in the circuit prior to switching, for assumed steady conditions, is

$$i(0-) = \frac{V}{R_1} \tag{3.6-5}$$

To find the current after switching, we must employ the law of conservation of flux linkages discussed in Section 3.4. We can write, over the switching period,

$$L_1 i(0-) = (L_1 + L_2) i(0+) \tag{3.6-6}$$

from which

$$i(0+) = \frac{L_1}{L_1 + L_2} i(0-) = \frac{L_1}{L_1 + L_2} \frac{V}{R_1} \tag{3.6-7}$$

Now, because there has been a change in the circuit parameters, a transient current will result. Again the circuit dynamics is described by Equation (3.5-2) with the general solution

$$i(t) = \frac{V}{R_1 + R_2} + B e^{-(R_1+R_2)t/(L_1+L_2)} \tag{3.6-8}$$

But it is required that at the switching instant $t = 0$

$$\frac{V}{R_1 + R_2} + B = \frac{L_1}{L_1 + L_2} \frac{V}{R_1}$$

from which

$$B = V\left[\frac{L_1}{R_1(L_1 + L_2)} - \frac{1}{R_1 + R_2}\right] = \frac{(L_1 R_2 - L_2 R_1)V}{R_1(R_1 + R_2)(L_1 + L_2)} \qquad (3.6\text{-}9)$$

Thus the final solution is given by the expression

$$i = \frac{V}{R_1 + R_2}\left[1 + \frac{L_1 R_2 - L_2 R_1}{R_1(L_1 + L_2)} e^{-(R_1 + R_2)t/(L_1 + L_2)}\right] \qquad (3.6\text{-}10)$$

The nature of this function is illustrated in Figure 3.6-2b. This figure shows that at the switching instant the current may rise or fall, depending on the relative values $L_1 R_2$ and $L_2 R_1$, with or without a time delay until the circuit current assumes its final changed value. Observe that if $R_2 = 0$, the current will recover to its original value.

□   □   □

3.7   THE SERIES RC CIRCUIT AND ITS DUAL

This section is the counterpart of Section 3.5; the circuits under survey are shown in Figure 3.7-1. We shall assume that there is an initial charge on the capacitor so that an initial voltage V_o exists thereon. Conversely, in the dual case, it is assumed that an initial current I_o exists in the inductor.

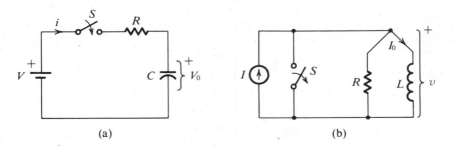

(a)   (b)

Figure 3.7-1.   The series RC circuit and its dual

The controlling system equation for the circuit, after switching, is

$$Ri + \frac{1}{C}\int i\, dt = V \qquad (3.7\text{-}1)$$

As before, a simple exponential form is assumed for the complementary solution $i_t = Be^{st}$. This leads to the requirement on s that

$$R + \frac{1}{Cs} = 0$$

which establishes the value for s

$$s = -\frac{1}{RC} \tag{3.7-2}$$

Since the capacitor cannot support a dc current through it, the steady state or particular solution is zero. This can be seen by differentiating both sides of Equation (3.7-1), where no excitation function appears on the right. Hence the complete solution is only due to the complementary function

$$i = Be^{-t/RC} \tag{3.7-3}$$

To find the value of B requires an appropriate initial condition, $i(0+)$. This can be found from the fact that the voltage across the capacitor cannot change instantaneously, hence $v_c(0+) = v_c(0-) = V_o$, and the initial current is then

$$I_o = i(0+) = \frac{V - V_o}{R} \tag{3.7-4}$$

This value is combined with Equation (3.7-3) to yield $B = (V - V_o)/R$, and the final expression for the current is

$$i = \frac{V - V_o}{R} e^{-t/RC} \tag{3.7-5}$$

The nature of this function is shown in Figure 3.7-2a. Here, as in Figure 3.5-2, the time constant $= RC$ (τ is in seconds when R is in ohm and C is in farad) can

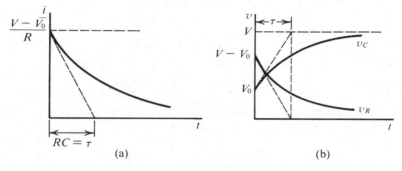

Figure 3.7-2. (a) The current in an RC circuit
(b) The voltages in an RC circuit

be related both to the initial slope of the curve and to the 0.632 value of the change in current, or the time to reach $1/e^{th}$ of its final value.

Often the voltage across the capacitor is of interest, rather than the current in the circuit. This may be found in several different ways. If the current is known, as in the present case, then the voltage across the capacitor is given by the equation

$$v_c = \frac{1}{C} \int i\, dt + K$$

The constant of integration K that arises is evaluated from a knowledge of v_c when $t=0$. This is, by performing the indicated integration,

$$v_c = \frac{1}{C} \int \frac{V-V_o}{R} e^{-t/RC}\, dt + K = -(V-V_o)e^{-t/RC} + K \tag{3.7-6}$$

But at the time $t=0$

$$V_o = -(V-V_o) + K$$

and Equation (3.7-6) becomes

$$v_c = V - (V-V_o)e^{-t/RC} \tag{3.7-7}$$

Another approach would be to write the dynamics of the system in terms of v_c, recalling that $i = C\, dv_c/dt$. Thus Equation (3.7-1) would be written in the form

$$RC\frac{dv_c}{dt} + v_c = v(t) \tag{3.7-8}$$

which defines the system conditions in terms of v_c as the dependent variable. The solution proceeds precisely as before, with the complementary solution being an exponential provided that s satisfies the equation

$$RCs + 1 = 0 \tag{3.7-9}$$

which again leads to Equation (3.7-2) for the system time constant. The particular integral solution of Equation (3.7-8) is the steady state value of v_c, which is V, as seen from an inspection of the circuit (no dc current can be supported by the capacitor) or from Equation (3.7-8) since in the steady state $dv_c/dt = 0$. The general solution to Equation (3.7-8) is

$$v_c = V + Be^{-t/RC} \tag{3.7-10}$$

B is evaluated using the initial condition $v_c(0-) = v_c(0+) = V_o$; thus

$$V_o = V + B$$

which leads again to Equation (3.7-7). A sketch of the solution for v_c is given in Figure 3.7-2b. Also shown in this figure is the value v_R, the voltage across the resistor. This can be immediately written down, since from Equation (3.7-1) we have that

$$V = v_c + v_R$$

Therefore, v_R has the analytic description

$$v_R = (V - V_o)e^{-t/RC} \tag{3.7-11}$$

which can be written from Equation (3.7-5).

EXAMPLE 3.7-1. The switch S that has been closed for a long time is opened at time $t = 0$ in the circuit shown in Figure 3.7-3. Find $i(t)$, assuming that C_1 was fully charged when the switch is opened.

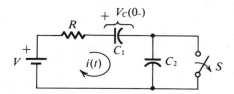

Figure 3.7-3. Switching of capacitors

SOLUTION. From Equation (3.7-5), $I_o = 0$ when $V_C(0-) = V$. Upon opening the switch, an application of conservation of charge [see Equation (3.4-1)] requires that

$$C_1 v(0-) = \frac{1}{\dfrac{1}{C_1} + \dfrac{1}{C_2}} v(0+) = \left(\frac{C_1 C_2}{C_1 + C_2} \right) v(0+)$$

or

$$v(0+) = \left(\frac{C_1 + C_2}{C_2} \right) v(0-) = \left(\frac{C_1 + C_2}{C_2} \right) V$$

Observe that the switching operation reduces the total capacitance of the circuit, with a resulting increase in the instantaneous voltage. The current in the circuit is, by an adaptation of Equation (3.7-5),

$$i(t) = \frac{V - \dfrac{C_1 + C_2}{C_2} V}{R} e^{-t/R(C_1 C_2 / C_1 + C_2)}$$

$$i(t) = -\frac{C_1 V}{C_2 R} e^{-t/R(C_1 C_2 / C_1 + C_2)}$$

This shows that

$$i(0+) = -\frac{C_1 V}{C_2 R}$$

$\square$ $\square$ $\square$

SECOND ORDER SYSTEMS

3.8   THE SERIES RLC CIRCUIT AND ITS DUAL

A detailed study of the series RLC circuit or its dual is of interest because it introduces some additional ideas. Thus we now consider Figure 3.8-1. The

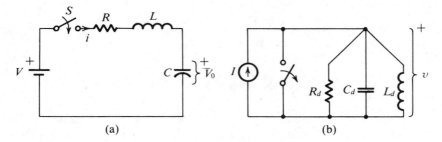

(a)   (b)

Figure 3.8-1.   The series RLC circuit and its dual

dynamic description of this circuit is the equation (KVL)

$$L\frac{di}{dt} + Ri + \frac{1}{C}\int i\, dt = v \tag{3.8-1}$$

To obtain the complementary solution we introduce a trial solution of the form

$$i_t = Be^{st} \tag{3.8-2}$$

If Equation (3.8-2) is combined with Equation (3.8-1), we find that

$$\tau_n^2 sBe^{st} + 2\zeta\tau_n Be^{st} + \frac{1}{s}Be^{st} = 0 \qquad \text{(a)} \quad (3.8\text{-}3)$$

where

$$\tau_n = \text{characteristic time} = \sqrt{LC} \qquad \text{(b)}$$

$$\zeta = \text{damping ratio} = \sqrt{\frac{R^2C}{4L}} = \frac{R}{2}\sqrt{\frac{C}{L}} \qquad \text{(c)}$$

It follows that

$$\tau_n^2 s^2 + 2\zeta\tau_n s + 1 = 0 \qquad (3.8\text{-}4)$$

This shows that s must satisfy a quadratic function. There are two roots to this equation, namely

$$s_1 = -\frac{\zeta}{\tau_n} + \frac{1}{\tau_n}\sqrt{\zeta^2 - 1} \qquad \text{(a)} \quad (3.8\text{-}5)$$

$$s_2 = -\frac{\zeta}{\tau_n} - \frac{1}{\tau_n}\sqrt{\zeta^2 - 1} \qquad \text{(b)}$$

The complete solution is

$$i = i_s + i_t = i_s + B_1 e^{s_1 t} + B_2 e^{s_2 t} \qquad (3.8\text{-}6)$$

The form of the solution depends on the relation among the parameters of the system. We wish to consider each case in some detail, subject to the following initial conditions

$$i(0-) = 0 \qquad \text{(a)} \quad (3.8\text{-}7)$$

$$v_i(0-) = V_o \qquad \text{(b)}$$

That is, there is zero initial current through the inductor, but the capacitor is assumed to have an initial charge.

From the conservation laws, the initial conditions after closing the switch are

$$i(0+) = 0 \qquad \text{(a)} \quad (3.8\text{-}8)$$

$$v_c(0+) = V_o \qquad \text{(b)}$$

Since our solution is in $i(t)$, we must translate the second of these conditions into an equivalent initial condition involving a function of i. This is done by making use of the integrodifferential equation, Equation (3.8-1), which is valid, of course, from $t=0$ for all time. We use this equation for the instant $t=0+$. This yields directly

$$L\frac{di(0+)}{dt}+0+v_c(0+)=V$$

from which we write

$$\frac{di(0+)}{dt}=\frac{V-V_o}{L} \tag{3.8-9}$$

To carry out the solution, we use the known fact that i_s must be zero, since dc is applied to a circuit containing a series capacitor C. Thus we must study the equation

$$i=B_1e^{s_1t}+B_2e^{s_2t} \tag{3.8-10}$$

subject to the initial conditions specified by Equations (3.8-8) and (3.8-9). We proceed by evaluating the constants B_1 and B_2. At $t=0+$ Equation (3.8-10) becomes

$$i(0+)=0=B_1+B_2 \qquad\qquad \text{(a)} \quad (3.8\text{-}11)$$

and

$$\frac{di(0+)}{dt}=s_1B_1+s_2B_2=\frac{V-V_o}{L} \qquad\qquad \text{(b)}$$

The simultaneous solution of these two equations yields

$$B_1=-B_2=\frac{V-V_o}{L(s_1-s_2)}=\frac{V-V_o}{\dfrac{2L}{\tau_n}\sqrt{\zeta^2-1}} \tag{3.8-12}$$

The final solution for the current is

$$i(t)=-\frac{V-V_o}{\dfrac{2L}{\tau_n}\sqrt{\zeta^2-1}}e^{-\zeta t/\tau_n}\left[\exp\left(\sqrt{\zeta^2-1}\,\frac{t}{\tau_n}\right)-\exp\left(-\sqrt{\zeta^2-1}\,\frac{t}{\tau_n}\right)\right] \tag{3.8-13}$$

We now examine the details of Equation (3.8-13) for the three ranges of values for ζ^2.

(1) $\zeta^2 > 1$. In this case, the final solution has the form

$$i(t) = \frac{V - V_o}{\dfrac{L}{\tau_n}\sqrt{\zeta^2 - 1}} e^{-\zeta t/\tau_n} \sin h\sqrt{\zeta^2 - 1}\,\frac{t}{\tau_n} \qquad (3.8\text{-}14)$$

The form of this equation is illustrated in Figure 3.8-2, which also includes representations of Equation (3.8-13), for which $|s_1| < |s_2|$, so that $e^{s_1 t}$ has a longer time constant than $e^{s_2 t}$. We observe that as C becomes very large in value, the circuit approaches the series RL case, and Figure 3.8-2 approaches Figure 3.5-2 in form. Likewise, if L becomes very small, the circuit approaches the series RC case, and Figure 3.8-2 approaches Figure 3.7-2a in form.

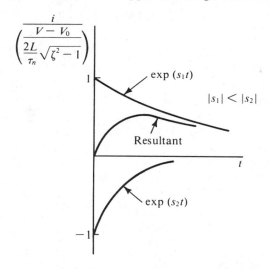

Figure 3.8-2. Graphs of Equations (3.8-14) and (3.8-13)

(2) $\zeta^2 = 1$. This is a special case, and it requires a special selection of system parameters to meet this condition. However, it is a form that is often achieved. In this case, Equation (3.8-5) shows that the two roots are equal. This common value is written as s_o, with

$$s_o = -\frac{1}{\tau_n} \qquad (3.8\text{-}15)$$

Now, however, the two transient terms of Equation (3.8-6) reduce to a single term, and we must seek a second solution in order to satisfy the required conditions for two arbitrary constants in the solution.

The approach in this case is to examine as a trial function

$$i_t = Bte^{s_o t} \tag{3.8-16}$$

It is necessary to show that this expression is a solution to our differential equation. Introduce Equation (3.8-16) into Equation (3.8-1) and obtain

$$LBe^{s_o t} + LBts_o e^{s_o t} + RBte^{s_o t} + \frac{Bt}{Cs_o}e^{s_o t} - \frac{B}{C}\frac{1}{s_o^2}e^{s_o t} = 0$$

or

$$\left(LC - \frac{1}{s_o^2}\right) + t\left(LCs_o + RC + \frac{1}{s_o}\right) = 0 \tag{3.8-17}$$

The first quantity on the left is identically zero since $1/s_o^2 = \tau_n^2 = LC$. The second quantity on the left is also zero since $s_o = -1/\sqrt{LC}$ and $R = 2\sqrt{L/C}$. Hence Equation (3.8-1) is satisfied by the trial solution Equation (3.8-16), and the complementary function is then

$$i_t = (B_1 + B_2 t)e^{s_o t} = (B_1 + B_2 t)e^{-t/\tau_n} \tag{3.8-18}$$

where B_1 and B_2 are arbitrary constants.

The complete form for the current is, in this case,

$$i = \frac{V - V_o}{\dfrac{L}{\tau_n}} te^{-\zeta t/\tau_n} \tag{3.8-19}$$

The general form of the variation shown in Figure 3.8-2 is valid in this case, but because the circuit is now *critically damped*, the time for decay is a minimum, without overshoot.

(3) $\zeta^2 < 1$. This is the underdamped case, and the solution is

$$i = \frac{V - V_o}{\dfrac{L}{\tau_n}\sqrt{1 - \zeta^2}} e^{-\zeta t/\tau_n} \sin\sqrt{1 - \zeta^2}\,\frac{t}{\tau_n} \tag{3.8-20}$$

This expression is easily found since the quantity $\sqrt{\zeta^2 - 1}$ is imaginary and Euler's expression $e^{\pm jx} = \cos x \pm j \sin x$ gives $e^{jx} - e^{-jx} = 2j \sin x$. Equation (3.8-20) can exhibit rather different variations depending on the quantities ζ and τ_n. When ζ/τ_n is large and $\sqrt{1 - \zeta^2}/\tau_n$ is small, there will be an overshoot of the current curve, and the sinusoidal variation specified by the equation will be masked. For intermediate values there will be a generally sinusoidal character, but with a noticeable decrement from one cycle to the next. For very light damping, the function begins to resemble a true sinusoid over a short time interval. These variations are illustrated in Figure 3.8-3.

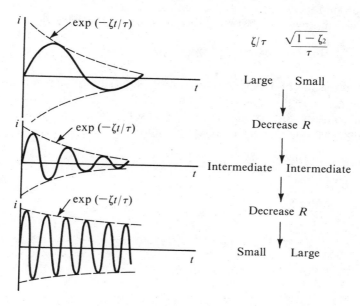

Figure 3.8-3. The damped sinusoid, with decreasing damping

From Figures 3.8-2 and 3.8-3, if R is considered as an adjustable parameter, (1) corresponds to large R. As R decreases, the quantity $\zeta = R\sqrt{C/L}/2$ decreases, with the curve approaching the axis in shorter and shorter times. A point is reached, Case (2), when the time is a minimum without overshoot. The continued reduction of R results in overshoot, with the results as shown in Figure 3.8-3. Often a circuit of the type here studied is used to generate finite groups of lightly damped sine waves by applying a square pulse instead of the step function, and arranging, when the excitation is removed to add heavy damping to the circuit to cause the waves to damp rapidly to zero. Such a circuit is often referred to as a shock-excited oscillator.

3.11 POSTLUDE

The work of this chapter shows that relatively straightforward procedures exist for the solution of the special class of differential equations that arise in linear systems analysis. However, these procedures become progressively more difficult to apply as the order of the differential equation increases. Fortunately, more powerful methods exist for solving linear differential equations. One method involves the use of the Laplace transform, and this will be studied in Chapter 5.

If the differential equation is nonlinear, then the classical methods introduced in this chapter will generally fail. Moreover, general methods for the solution of nonlinear differential equations do not exist. Often numerical methods are employed to find solutions to specific problems.

SUMMARY

- The total solution of a differential equation is the sum of its complementary function i_t, where the subscript denotes that this is the transient portion of the total solution, and its particular integral solution, often called the steady state. For example, for the differential equation

$$a\frac{di(t)}{dt} + bi(t) = f(t),$$

$i_t(t)$ is a solution of

$$a\frac{di(t)}{dt} + bi(t) = 0,$$

$i_s(t)$ is a solution of

$$a\frac{di(t)}{dt} + bi(t) = f(t),$$

and the total solution is $i(t) = i_t(t) + i_s(t)$. The unknown constant is associated with the complementary solution (two unknown constants for second order differential equation) and for a specific case can be found if the initial conditions are applied to the total solution.

- To determine the constants of integration, the initial conditions for inductors and capacitors are:
  (a) The voltage across a constant capacitor remains the same during switching operations in the absence of current impulses, or

$$\int_{v(0-)}^{v(0+)} C\, dv = \int_{0-}^{0+} i\, dt$$

or

$$Cv(0+) - Cv(0-) = 0.$$

  (b) The current through a constant inductor remains the same during switching operations in the absence of voltage impulses, or

$$\int_{i(0-)}^{i(0+)} L\, di = \int_{0-}^{0-} v\, dt$$

or

$$Li(0+) - Li(0-) = 0$$

- For a series RLC circuit we distinguish the three response cases shown below.

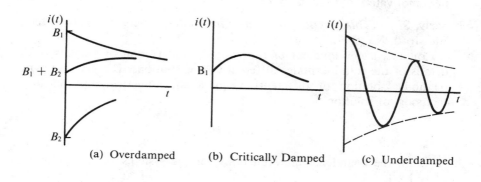

(a) Overdamped   (b) Critically Damped   (c) Underdamped

REVIEW QUESTIONS

1. Write a second order linear differential equation with constant coefficient. Write the corresponding homogeneous equation.
2. What is the general character of the solution of a homogeneous differential equation?
3. What is meant by the particular integral solution of a differential equation?
4. Is differentiation a linear process? Is integration a linear process?
5. Define the characteristic value or eigenvalue of a dynamical system.
6. If the solution of a first order differential equation is of the form $i = A + Bte^{-t}$ separate it into its complementary and particular functions.
7. What do we mean when we say that a system is initially relaxed?
8. A capacitor that has been charged to an initial voltage is switched into a circuit. Does the voltage across the capacitor change within the time interval $t(0-) < t < t(0+)$? Explain.
9. If an initial current exists through an inductor which is switched into a network, does the current in the inductor change within the time interval $t(0-) < t < t(0+)$? Explain.
10. A battery is switched across a capacitor at $t = 0$. How long will it take for the voltage across the capacitor to reach the battery voltage?
11. If a battery is switched across a pure inductor, describe what will happen.
12. What do we mean by the "time constant" of a system?
13. What are the zero input and the zero state responses of a system?

REFERENCES

1. Finizio, N. and G. Ladas, *Ordinary Differential Equations with Modern Applications*, Wadsworth Publishing Co., Belmont, CA, 1978.

   A clear and methodical presentation of ordinary differential equations. Numerous examples from many fields provide pertinent illustrations to help motivate the student.

2. Seely, S., *An Introduction to Engineering Systems*, Pergamon Press, Inc., Elmsford, NY, 1972.

   Contains a development of time domain description of systems, with details of the solution under different type excitations. Discusses analytic methods (solution of differential equations), numerical and machine methods, of solution.

PROBLEMS

3.2-1. Find the complementary functions for the systems shown in Figure P3.2-1.

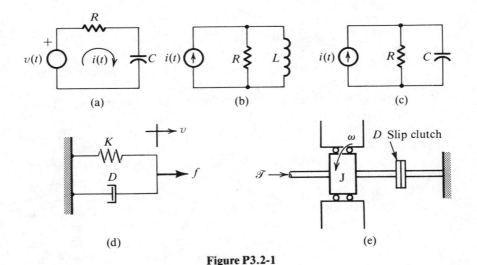

Figure P3.2-1

3.3-2. Find the particular solution to the systems given in Problem 3.2-1 for each of the following forcing functions which are switched on at $t = 0$:

   (a) 3
   (b) $1 + \sin t$
   (c) $1 + t^2 + e^{-\alpha t}$
   (d) $2 + t + 2t^2 + \cos t + e^{-\alpha t}$.

3.5-1. Find the velocity of the system shown in Figure P3.5-1 with zero initial condition and excitation function of the form:

(a) $f = 2e^{-t}u_{-1}(t)$

(b) $f = (2 + 3t + \cos t)u_{-1}(t)$

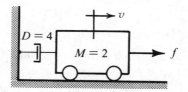

Figure P3.5-1

3.5-2. Find the current in a series RL circuit with zero initial conditions when the excitation function has the form:

(a) $v(t) = 3u_{-1}(t)$;

(b) $v(t) = (\cos t + e^{-t})u_{-1}(t)$;

(c) $v(t) = (1 + t + 3t^2 + \cos t)u_{-1}(t)$.

The values of the circuit components are: $R = 1$ ohm, $L = 2$ henry.

3.6-1. (a) Consider the circuit shown in Figure P3.6-1a. Find the current if the switch is opened at $t = 0$, assuming that it had been closed for a long time before this instant.

(b) Repeat for the circuit shown in Figure P3.6-1b.

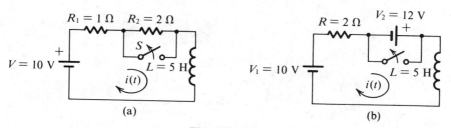

Figure P3.6-1

3.6-2. (a) Find the current in the circuit of Figure P3.6-2 if the source is an impulse function $u_o(t)$. [Hint: During the impulse appearance at

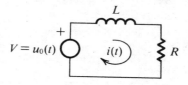

Figure P3.6-2

$t=0$ the inductance acts as an open circuit and all the voltage appears across it. Hence

$$i(0+) = \frac{1}{L}\int_{0-}^{0+} u_o(t)\, dt = \frac{1}{L}$$

which is the initial current.]
   (b) Relate this solution to Equation (3.5-9).

3.6-3. The circuit shown in Figure P3.6-3 is initially in its quiescent steady state when the switch is opened, say at $t=0$.

   (a) Deduce an expression for the inductor currents for $t>0$.
   (b) Determine an expression for v as a function of time for $t>0$.

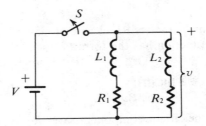

Figure P3.6-3

3.6-4. An ac source is switched into an initially relaxed RL circuit shown in Figure P3.6-4. Obtain an expression for the current $i(t)$.

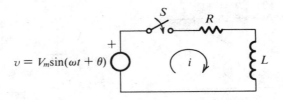

Figure P3.6-4

3.7-1. The capacitor is charged to a voltage V_o. Find the current in the circuit shown in Figure P3.7-1 if at $t=0$ the switch is closed.

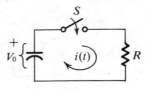

Figure P3.7-1

3.7-2. Find the voltage across the parallel RC network:

  (a) if an impulse $u_o(t)$ current source is applied as shown in Figure P3.7-2a,
  (b) for an initially charged capacitor.

  Note: This is the dual of Problem 3.6-2. [Hint: At $t=0$ when the impulse source appears the capacitor acts as a short circuit. During the time $0-<t<0+$ there is a current into the capacitor and charges it to

$$v_c(0+) = \frac{1}{C}\int_{0+}^{0+} u_o(t)\, dt = \frac{1}{C}.$$

  For $t>0$ the circuit shown in Figure P3.7-2b applies.]

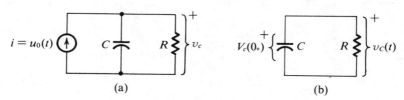

(a)   (b)

Figure P3.7-2

3.7-3. In the circuit shown in Figure P3.7-3 the capacitor is charged to 10 V. Find the current in the circuit after the switch is closed.

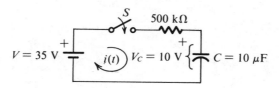

Figure P3.7-3

3.7-4. The initially relaxed RC series circuit shown in Figure P3.7-4 has a pulse excitation applied to it. Obtain expressions for the current $i(t)$ and the voltage $v_C(t)$. [Hint: Do this on a piecewise time basis: (a) find $i(t)$ and $v_C(t)$ for $t \le T$, (b) determine $v_C(T)$, (c) use this as the initial condition for $t \ge T$.]

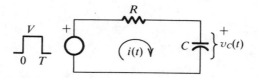

Figure P3.7-4

3.7-5. A series RLC initially relaxed circuit with $L = R = C = 1$ is excited by $v(t) = 1 + t^2$. Find the complete solution.

Chapter Four

System Response to Sinusoidal Excitation Functions

The properties of system response to sinusoidal excitation functions are of considerable importance in practical problems and will receive careful consideration in this chapter. There are several reasons for this: (a) sinusoidal sources and appropriate instrumentation (over wide ranges of frequency) are readily available; (b) many of our further studies (for example, electronic, communications and power systems) will be carried out using sinusoidal excitation; and (c) the method of solution will be of importance in providing the particular integral solution to the system differential equation for a switched sinusoidal source, a subject already noted in Chapter 3. This chapter will be concerned with certain aspects of system response and the special techniques that are peculiar to sinusoidal excitation.

4.1 FEATURES OF SINUSOIDS

Ordinarily, the electric voltage supplied by the electric utilities is very closely sinusoidal in time. In fact, the alternator, the rotating machine that generates the power, has been carefully designed both mechanically and electrically to insure that the voltages that are produced are almost pure sinusoids. As a result, almost all electrical appliances and electrical instruments operate from sinusoidal voltage sources. Signal generators for engineering and scientific purposes often are basically sinusoidal sources with high purity of waveform over wide ranges of frequency, though not all signal sources are necessarily designed to produce sinusoidal signals.

We shall have occasion to use various properties of the sinusoid. Refer to Figure 4.1-1 which illustrates the simple sinusoidal waveform. These are described analytically, respectively, as $I_m \sin \omega t$ and $I_m \sin (\omega t + \theta)$, where I_m denotes the peak value of the wave, and θ denotes the phase angle with respect to time $t = 0$. Among the important characteristics of the sinusoid are the time average value (the time duration must be indicated) and the so-called rms (root mean square) value. These are discussed in the following examples.

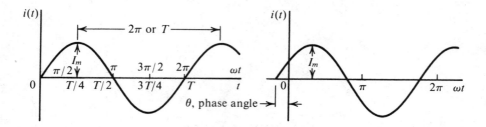

Figure 4.1-1.   The sinusoidal waveform

EXAMPLE 4.1-1. Show that the full-cycle time average value of the sine wave is zero.

SOLUTION. By definition, the full cycle time average is

$$I_{avg} = <i(t)> = \frac{1}{T}\int_0^T i(t)\,dt = \frac{1}{2\pi}\int_0^{2\pi} i(\omega t)\,d(\omega t) \qquad (4.1\text{-}1)$$

The current waveform is written explicitly

$$i = I_m \sin \omega t = I_m \sin\left(\frac{2\pi}{T}t\right) = I_m \sin(2\pi f t)$$

where $f = 1/T$ is the frequency in cycles per second or hertz (Hz). Then

$$<i(t)> = \frac{1}{2\pi}\int_0^{2\pi} I_m \sin \omega t\, d(\omega t) = \frac{1}{2\pi}[-\cos \omega t]_0^{2\pi} = 0$$

If it is recognized that the average value, as defined by Equation (4.1-1), is a measure of the net area under the curve over one cycle, and since the sinusoid will have as much area above the zero axis as below it, then the result is obvious. In fact, the time average value of a sinusoid will be zero independent of any phase angle θ. For $\theta = 90°$ the wave will be a cosine function, but the net area under the curve over a complete cycle remains zero.

☐ ☐ ☐

Consider now that a sinusoidal voltage source is applied across a resistor having a resistance R. We write directly, since

$$v = iR$$

that

$$i = \frac{V_m \sin \omega t}{R} = I_m \sin \omega t$$

where $I_m = V_m/R$. Furthermore, the *instantaneous power* to the resistor is

$$p = vi = i^2 R \qquad \text{watt}$$

The question is what is the full-cycle average value of the power? To answer this, we write, in accordance with "time average" definition, Equation (4.1-1),

$$P = <p(t)> = \frac{1}{T}\int_0^T (i^2 R)\, dt = \frac{1}{2\pi}\int_0^{2\pi} [i^2(\omega t)R]\, d(\omega t) \qquad (4.1\text{-}1)$$

We write this

$$P = <p(t)> = R\left[\frac{1}{T}\int_0^T i^2\, dt\right] = R\left[\frac{1}{2\pi}\int_0^{2\pi} i^2\, d(\omega t)\right] \qquad (4.1\text{-}2)$$

We define the quantity I_{rms} from these expressions

$$I_{rms} = \sqrt{\frac{1}{2\pi}\int_0^{2\pi} i^2\, d(\omega t)} \qquad (4.1\text{-}3)$$

Observe that it is actually the root-mean-square value of the current, deduced from the mean value of the current squared. Based on this definition, we see that we may write

$$P = <p(t)> = I_{rms}^2 R \qquad (4.1\text{-}4)$$

EXAMPLE 4.1-2. Deduce the value of I_{rms} in terms of I_m for the sinusoidal current wave.

SOLUTION. We proceed directly from Equation (4.1-3) and write

$$I_{rms} = \left[\frac{1}{2\pi}\int_0^{2\pi} I_m^2 \sin^2 \omega t\, d(\omega t)\right]^{1/2}$$

Carrying out the details of the integration

$$I_{rms} = \left[\frac{I_m^2}{2\pi}\int_0^{2\pi} \frac{1 - \cos 2\omega t}{2}d(\omega t)\right]^{1/2} = \left[\frac{I_m^2}{2\pi}\left(\frac{\omega t}{2} + \frac{\sin 2\omega t}{4}\right)\Big|_0^{2\pi}\right]^{1/2}$$

$$= \left[\frac{I_m^2}{2\pi}\frac{2\pi}{2}\right]^{1/2} = \frac{I_m}{\sqrt{2}} = 0.707 I_m$$

Observe from the foregoing examples that the full cycle average value of a sinusoidal wave is zero, whereas the rms value is a constant value equal to 0.707 of the peak value of the sinusoid. Moreover, these results are *independent of any time phase displacement* with, say $i = I_m \sin (\omega t + \theta)$ replacing $I_m \sin \omega t$ in the foregoing examples.

□ □ □

An important feature of the sinusoid is that the sum of two sinusoids of the same period but of different amplitudes and different phase will also be a sine wave. This same idea is valid for any number of sine waves of equal period. Another important feature of the sinusoid is that the derivative and the integral of the function are also sinusoidal. This means that any linear operation on a sinusoid does not change the waveshape.

Examining the matter of combining sine waves of the same period provides us with the opportunity to introduce some important notation for sinusoids. Suppose that we add the two sinusoids

$$v_1 = V_1 \sin \omega t \qquad\qquad v_2 = V_2 \sin (\omega t + \theta) \qquad\qquad (4.1\text{-}5)$$

We consider

$$v = v_1 + v_2 = V_1 \sin \omega t + V_2 \sin (\omega t + \theta) \qquad\qquad (4.1\text{-}6)$$

By direct trigonometric expansion we have that

$$v = V_1 \sin \omega t + V_2 (\sin \omega t \cos \theta + \cos \omega t \sin \theta)$$

which may be combined as follows

$$v = (V_1 + V_2 \cos \theta) \sin \omega t + V_2 \sin \theta \cos \omega t \qquad\qquad (4.1\text{-}7)$$

This is written in the form

$$v = [(V_1 + V_2 \cos \theta)^2 + (V_2 \sin \theta)^2]^{1/2} \left[\frac{(V_1 + V_2 \cos \theta) \sin \omega t}{[(V_1 + V_2 \cos \theta)^2 + (V_2 \sin \theta)^2]^{1/2}} \right.$$
$$\left. + \frac{V_2 \sin \theta \cos \omega t}{[(V_1 + V_2 \cos \theta)^2 + (V_2 \sin \theta)^2]^{1/2}} \right] \qquad\qquad (4.1\text{-}8)$$

Since $\cos^2 \psi + \sin^2 \psi = 1$, we may define the quantities

$$\cos \psi = \frac{V_1 + V_2 \cos \theta}{[(V_1 + V_2 \cos \theta)^2 + (V_2 \sin \theta)^2]^{1/2}} \qquad (a) \quad (4.1\text{-}9)$$

$$\sin \psi = \frac{V_2 \sin \theta}{[(V_1 + V_2 \cos \theta)^2 + (V_2 \sin \theta)^2]^{1/2}} \qquad (b)$$

Equation (4.1-8) becomes, in the light of these

$$v = [(V_1 + V_2 \cos \theta)^2 + (V_2 \sin \theta)^2]^{1/2} (\sin \omega t \cos \psi + \cos \omega t \sin \psi)$$

which is

$$v = [V_1^2 + V_2^2 + 2 V_1 V_2 \cos \theta]^{1/2} \sin (\omega t + \psi) \qquad\qquad (4.1\text{-}10)$$

This development verifies that the resultant of the two sinusoids of the same period is also a sine wave. Clearly, because of the phase angle θ, the amplitude of the resultant may vary over wide limits.

Now let us reconsider the same problem but using the exponential forms for the sinusoids. Here we begin with the two sine functions which are written

$$v_1 = \text{Im}(V_1 e^{j\omega t}) \qquad\qquad v_2 = \text{Im}(V_2 e^{j(\omega t + \theta)}) \qquad\qquad (4.1\text{-}11)$$

where Im( ) means the imaginary part of the complex quantity inside the parenthesis. This stems from the Euler relation

$$e^{\pm jx} = \cos x \pm j \sin x$$

Similarly, Re( ) will denote the real part of the complex quantity. The sum of these is

$$v = \text{Im}(V_1 e^{j\omega t}) + \text{Im}(V_2 e^{j(\omega t + \theta)}) = \text{Im}(V_1 e^{j\omega t} + V_2 e^{j(\omega t + \theta)}) \qquad (4.1\text{-}12)$$

or

$$v = \text{Im}[(V_1 + V_2 e^{j\theta}) e^{j\omega t}] \qquad\qquad (4.1\text{-}13)$$

Observe that each wave is defined by complex numbers $\mathbf{V}_1 = V_1 e^{j0}$ and $\mathbf{V}_2 = V_2 e^{j\theta}$ which specify the respective amplitude and phase factors. Further, the sum of these two sinusoids has the amplitude $\mathbf{V}_1 + \mathbf{V}_2 = V_1 e^{j0} + V_2 e^{j\theta}$, which is also a complex algebraic quantity, independent of time. Except for the implied time factor, only the amplitude and phase factors are important in algebraic operations (see Appendix 1). It is convenient to emphasize the amplitude and phase features by referring to the complex number representation as *phasors* or *sinors*. To see the phasor combination appropriate to Equation (4.1-11), refer to Figure 4.1-2. From the figure we write directly that

$$V = |\mathbf{V}| = [(V_1 + V_2 \cos \theta)^2 + (V_2 \sin \theta)^2]^{1/2}$$
$$= [V_1^2 + V_2^2 + 2V_1 V_2 \cos \theta]^{1/2} \qquad\qquad \text{(a)} \quad (4.1\text{-}14)$$

$$\psi = \tan^{-1} \frac{V_2 \sin \theta}{V_1 + V_2 \cos \theta} \qquad\qquad \text{(b)}$$

$$\mathbf{V} = V e^{j\psi} \qquad\qquad \text{(c)}$$

which corresponds exactly to the results contained in Equation (4.1-13).

Some discussion about Equation (4.1-13) is important. To arrive at this equation, the amplitude and phase information of each sinusoid (the phase information must be specified relative to the same reference point in time) was extracted. These phasor quantities were then combined according to simple algebraic rules of complex numbers to give the phasor of the resultant. To

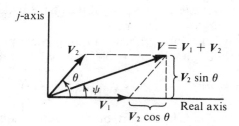

Figure 4.1-2.   Combination of two phasors

complete the result, the resultant phasor quantity must be combined with the time function that is implicit in our work. This means that the phasor or sinor quantities here discussed do not have physical reality in themselves — one does not measure these complex numbers directly; it is the time function that has physical reality. Actually, not all of the phasor quantities relating to sinusoidal problems involve the time factor explicitly or implicitly. The impedance and admittance functions are of these types. Because of this, there have been suggestions in the past that two different phasor quantities must be distinguished in such problems. This is not necessary during intermediate operations that are concerned only with finding quantities which utlimately are combined to yield time information. In both cases the phasors are merely complex numbers which satisfy the rules of complex number arithmetic. Care must be exercised, of course, in the ultimate steps relating such complex numbers to time functions. But in no case is the phasor quantity synonymous with the final time function. It is a mathematical algebraic procedure for ultimately determining amplitude and phase information.

The procedure involving the use of complex number arithmetic for sinusoids can be simplified somewhat if some basic rules are established. Thus we choose *always* to write sinusoids in terms of sinusoidal time functions; thus a cosine function is written in equivalent sine form, with explicit designation of the appropriate phase angle. This allows us to drop the designation Im, since the imaginary part of the resulting function will always be implied. Now if we were to proceed from Equation (4.1-11) we would write the quantities

$$\mathbf{V}_1 = V_1 e^{j0} \qquad\qquad \mathbf{V}_2 = V_2 e^{j\theta} \qquad\qquad (4.1\text{-}15)$$

and the result obtained by adding these two phasors is

$$\mathbf{V} = \mathbf{V}_1 + \mathbf{V}_2 = V_1 e^{j0} + V_2 e^{j\theta} = V e^{j\psi}$$

which is precisely the situation illustrated in Figure 4.1-2.

4.2 STEADY STATE RESPONSE OF THE SYSTEM ELEMENTS TO SINUSOIDAL EXCITATION FUNCTIONS

To find the response of the electrical elements to sinusoidal excitation let $i = I_m \cos \omega t = \text{Re}[I_m e^{j0} e^{j\omega t}] = \text{Re}[\mathbf{I} e^{j\omega t}]$. Consider each of the systems of Figure 4.2-1. We obtain

$$v_R = \text{Re}(\mathbf{V}_R e^{j\omega t}) = Ri = \text{Re}(R\mathbf{I} e^{j\omega t})$$

or

$$\mathbf{V}_R = R\mathbf{I} \tag{4.2-1}$$

$$v_L = \text{Re}(\mathbf{V}_L e^{j\omega t}) = L\frac{di}{dt} = \text{Re}\left(LI_m \frac{de^{j\omega t}}{dt}\right) = \text{Re}(LI_m j\omega e^{j\omega t})$$

or

$$\mathbf{V}_L = j\omega L I_m e^{j0} = jX_L\mathbf{I} = X_L e^{j(\pi/2)}\mathbf{I} = \mathbf{Z}_L\mathbf{I} \tag{4.2-2}$$

$$v_c = \text{Re}(\mathbf{V}_c e^{j\omega t}) = \frac{1}{C}\int i \, dt = \text{Re}\left(\frac{1}{C}\mathbf{I}\int e^{j\omega t} \, dt\right) = \text{Re}\left(\frac{1}{j\omega C}\mathbf{I} e^{j\omega t}\right)$$

or

$$\mathbf{V}_c = \frac{1}{j\omega C}\mathbf{I} = -jX_C\mathbf{I} = X_c e^{-j(\pi/2)}\mathbf{I} = \mathbf{Z}_c\mathbf{I} \tag{4.2-3}$$

where $X_L = \omega L$ is the *inductive reactance*, $X_C = 1/\omega C$ is the *capacitive reactance*, $\mathbf{Z}_L$ and $\mathbf{Z}_C$ are the impedances of the inductor and capacitor, respectively, and Re( ) means the real part of the complex quantity inside the parentheses.

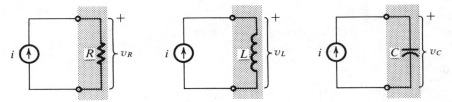

Figure 4.2-1.   One-element electrical system

The representation of the impedances in the complex plane are shown in Figure 4.2-2a. If we assume the current phasor to be $\mathbf{I} = I e^{j0}$ in Figure 4.2-2, then the voltages in phasor form are shown in Figure 4.2-2b.

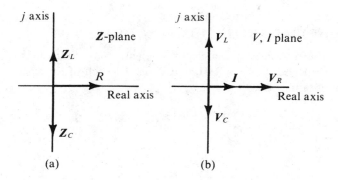

**Figure 4.2-2. The impedances and voltages in the complex plane
(a) Impedance plane   (b) Voltage and current plane**

EXAMPLE 4.2-1. Determine the impedance of the mechanical system shown in Figure 4.2-3a.

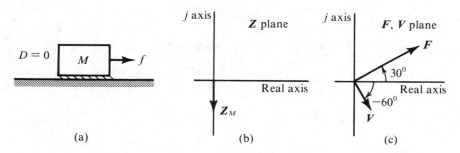

Figure 4.2-3.   The impedance concept of a mechanical system

SOLUTION. Using Table S1.1 the relation between force and velocity is $v = (\int f\, dt)/M$. Therefore we write

$$v = \mathrm{Re}(Ve^{j\omega t}) = \mathrm{Re}\left(\frac{1}{M}F \int e^{j\omega t}\, dt\right) = \mathrm{Re}\left(\frac{1}{j\omega M}Fe^{j\omega t}\right)$$

or

$$V = \frac{1}{j\omega M}F = Z_M F \qquad \left(Z_M = \frac{1}{j\omega M} = \frac{1}{\omega M}e^{-j(\pi/2)}\right)$$

If in addition we take $F = 2e^{j30°}$ and $1/\omega M = 0.5$ then the phasor representations of the different variables are shown in Figure 4.2-3c.

□ □ □

The *admittances*, which are the reciprocal of impedances, for the simple electrical elements are

$$\mathbf{Y}_R = G = \frac{1}{R}, \qquad \mathbf{Y}_L = \frac{1}{\mathbf{Z}_L} = \frac{1}{j\omega L}, \qquad \mathbf{Y}_C = \frac{1}{\mathbf{Z}_C} = j\omega C$$

Both the impedances and admittances are collectively called *immittances*.

4.3 STEADY STATE SYSTEM RESPONSE TO SINUSOIDAL EXCITATION FUNCTIONS

We proceed by considering the more general case of a simple series RLC circuit through which there is a current $i(t) = I_m \sin \omega t$ — the assumed steady state response to an applied sinusoidal forcing function. We are interested in determining the corresponding voltage $v(t)$ which produces the current $i(t)$. We begin with the general equation (KVL)

$$Ri + L\frac{di}{dt} + \frac{1}{C}\int i\, dt = v(t) \qquad (4.3\text{-}1)$$

which arises from the circuit shown in Figure 4.3-1a. We proceed by writing

$$i(t) = \text{Im}(I_m \underline{/0^\circ}\, e^{j\omega t}) = \text{Im}(\mathbf{I}e^{j\omega t})$$

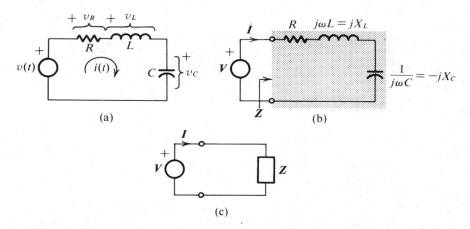

(a)

(b)

(c)

Figure 4.3-1. The simple series RLC circuit and its equivalent frequency model

Combine this with Equation (4.3-1) to obtain

$$\text{Im}(R\mathbf{I}e^{j\omega t} + j\omega L\mathbf{I}e^{j\omega t} + \frac{1}{j\omega C}\mathbf{I}e^{j\omega t}) = \text{Im}(\mathbf{V}e^{j\omega t})$$

or

$$\left(R + j\omega L + \frac{1}{j\omega C}\right) I = V$$

which we write

$$ZI = V \qquad\qquad \text{(a)} \quad \text{(4.3-2)}$$

where

$$Z = R + j\omega L + \frac{1}{j\omega C} = R + j\left(\omega L - \frac{1}{\omega C}\right) = R + j(X_L - X_C) \qquad \text{(b)}$$

specifies the impedance of the network viewed from the input terminals. This is a complex quantity which can be written

$$Z = |Z|\underline{/\theta} = \left[R^2 + \left(\omega L - \frac{1}{\omega C}\right)^2\right]^{1/2} \underline{/\tan^{-1}\left(\dfrac{\omega L - \dfrac{1}{\omega C}}{R}\right)}$$

which is represented in Figure 4.3-1b which is called the phasor circuit, with ctual elements being replaced by the appropriate resistance or reactance values. The corresponding voltage is

$$V = IZ = I\underline{/0}|Z|\underline{/\theta} = |ZI|\underline{/\theta + 0} = |ZI|\underline{/\theta} = |Z||I|\underline{/\theta}$$

which leads directly to the time function

$$\text{Im}(Ve^{j\omega t}) = \text{Im}(|Z||I|\underline{/\theta}\, e^{j\omega t}) = \text{Im}(|Z|I_m e^{j\theta} e^{j\omega t})$$

or

$$v(t) = |Z|I_m \sin(\omega t + \theta) \qquad\qquad \text{(4.3-3)}$$

where θ is the *phase angle* of the circuit.

The impedance function Z which here relates the response (the output, the current) to the excitation (the input, the applied voltage) is the *system* function (or *transfer* function) for the specified output/input ratio. Specifically, if the output were to be V_c, the voltage across the capacitor, rather than the current through the circuit, then we would write

$$V_c = -jX_C I = \frac{1}{j\omega C} I = \frac{V}{Z}\frac{1}{j\omega C} = \frac{V}{j\omega C\left(R + j\omega L + \dfrac{1}{j\omega C}\right)}$$

If we designate the output/input ratio as the *system function* $H(j\omega)$ for this ratio, then

$$H(j\omega) = \frac{\mathbf{V}_c}{\mathbf{V}} = \frac{1}{j\omega C \left(R + j\omega L + \dfrac{1}{j\omega C} \right)} \tag{4.3-4}$$

is the corresponding system function.

We again consider Equation (4.3-1) which is written in operational form

$$\left(R + Lp + \frac{1}{pC} \right) i(t) = v(t)$$

Note specifically that we obtain the system function $H(j\omega)$ from the system operator $H(p)$ by the simple process

$$H(p)v(t) = i(t); \qquad H(j\omega) = H(p)|_{p=j\omega} = \frac{\mathbf{I}}{\mathbf{V}} = \frac{1}{R + j\omega L + \dfrac{1}{j\omega C}}$$

That is, the system function $H(j\omega)$ is found by substituting $j\omega$ in the place of p in the expression for $H(p)$. This is exactly the same system function which is found using Equation (4.3-2a).

EXAMPLE 4.3-1. Find the impedance of the mechanical system shown in Figure 4.3-2a.

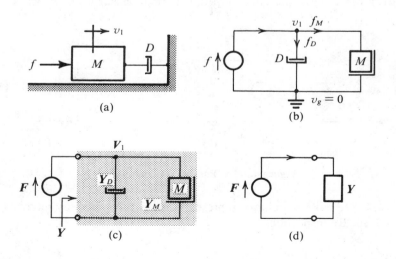

Figure 4.3-2. **The response of a mechanical system to sinusoidal force excitation**

SOLUTION. From the equivalent circuit shown in Figure 4.3-2b we write

$$M\frac{dv_1}{dt} + Dv_1 = f$$

or

$$Mj\omega V_1 + DV_1 = F \qquad (4.3\text{-}5)$$

But we have defined the impedance as the ratio of the across variable to the through variable, with admittance being the inverse ratio. Equation (4.3-5) is written

$$(Y_M + Y_D)V_1 = YV_1 = F$$

and hence the input impedance is

$$\mathbf{Z} = \frac{1}{\mathbf{Y}} = \frac{1}{\mathbf{Y}_M + \mathbf{Y}_D} = \frac{1}{j\omega M + D} = \frac{1}{\dfrac{1}{\mathbf{Z}_M} + \dfrac{1}{\mathbf{Z}_D}} = \frac{\mathbf{Z}_M \mathbf{Z}_D}{\mathbf{Z}_M + \mathbf{Z}_D} \qquad (4.3\text{-}6)$$

The two elements, D and M, are connected in parallel, and we observe that the total admittance $\mathbf{Y}$ is equal to the sum of the individual admittances.

□ □ □

EXAMPLE 4.3-2. Find the input impedance of the electric system shown in Figure 4.3-3.

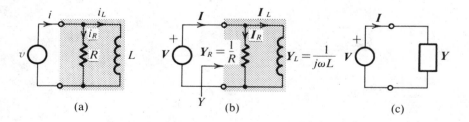

(a)   (b)   (c)

Figure 4.3-3.   Parallel RL circuit

SOLUTION. We write the phasor representation of the system by referring to Figure 4.3-3b. By inspection

$$\mathbf{V} = \mathbf{IZ} = \mathbf{I}\frac{1}{\mathbf{Y}} = \frac{\mathbf{I}}{(\mathbf{Y}_R + \mathbf{Y}_L)} = \frac{\mathbf{I}}{\left(\dfrac{1}{R} + \dfrac{1}{j\omega L}\right)} = \mathbf{I}\left(\frac{j\omega LR}{R + j\omega L}\right)$$

or

$$Z = \frac{j\omega LR}{R + j\omega L} = \frac{Z_L Z_R}{Z_L + Z_R} = \frac{1}{\dfrac{1}{Z_L} + \dfrac{1}{Z_R}}$$

Observations that follow from the above examples are:

1. The total impedance of a circuit of impedances in series:

$$Z = Z_1 + Z_2 + \ldots \tag{4.3-7}$$

2. The total admittance of a circuit with admittances in parallel:

$$Y = Y + Y_2 + \ldots \qquad \text{(a)} \quad (4.3\text{-}8)$$

or

$$\frac{1}{Z} = \frac{1}{Z_1} + \frac{1}{Z_2} + \ldots \qquad \text{(b)}$$

3. For circuits with series and parallel combinations we use the appropriate equations to reduce the circuit to an equivalent impedance or admittance. Similar conclusions were discussed in Section 2.3 in terms of immittance operators.

□ □ □

EXAMPLE 4.3-3. Find the input impedance, the voltage across each element, and the current through each element of the circuit shown in Figure 4.3-4a. Plot the voltages and currents in the complex plane and write the instantaneous values of all the varying variables. Given: $v(t) = 10\sqrt{2} \sin (400t + 45°)$, $R_1 = \frac{2}{5}$ ohm, $R_2 = 2$ ohm, $L = 10^{-2}$ henry, $C = 0.5 \times 10^{-3}$ farad.

SOLUTION. Using the equivalent phasor network of Figure 4.3-4b we have

$$Z = Z_{R_1} \frac{1}{3} Z_p \tag{4.3-9}$$

but

$$\frac{1}{Z_p} = \frac{1}{Z_{R_2}} + \frac{1}{Z_s} = \frac{1}{Z_{R_2}} + \frac{1}{Z_L + Z_C}$$

and hence Equation (4.3-9) becomes

$$Z = Z_{R_1} + \frac{1}{\dfrac{1}{Z_{R_2}} + \dfrac{1}{Z_L + Z_C}} = Z_{R_1} + \frac{Z_{R_2}(Z_L + Z_C)}{Z_{R_2} + Z_L + Z_C} = \frac{2}{5} + \frac{2(j4 - j5)}{2 + j4 - j5}$$

$$\tag{4.3-10}$$

$$= \frac{2}{5} + \frac{-j2}{2 - j} = \frac{4}{5}(1 - j) = \frac{4}{5}\sqrt{2}\underline{/-45°}$$

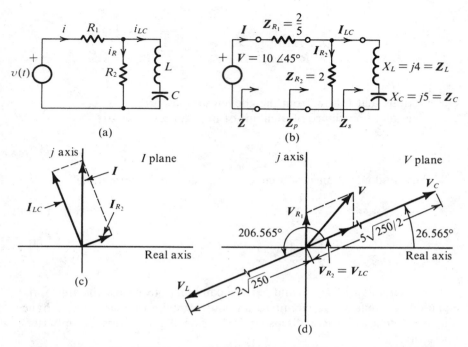

Figure 4.3-4. Circuit diagram with its current- and voltage-phasor diagrams

The other unknowns are, using the rms value $\mathbf{V} = (V_m/\sqrt{2})\underline{/45°} = 10\underline{/45°}$ instead of $V_m\underline{/45°}$,

$$\mathbf{I} = \frac{\mathbf{V}}{\mathbf{Z}} = \frac{10\underline{/45°}}{\frac{4}{5}\sqrt{2}\underline{/-45°}} = \frac{50}{4\sqrt{2}}\underline{/90°} = \frac{25\sqrt{2}}{4}\underline{/90°}$$

$$\mathbf{V}_{R_1} = \mathbf{I}\mathbf{Z}_{R_1} = \frac{50}{4\sqrt{2}}\underline{/90°} \times \frac{2}{5}\underline{/0°} = \frac{5\sqrt{2}}{2}\underline{/90°}$$

$$\mathbf{V}_{R_2} = \mathbf{V} - \mathbf{V}_{R_1} = \left(10\frac{\sqrt{2}}{2} + j10\frac{\sqrt{2}}{2}\right) - j\frac{5\sqrt{2}}{2} = \frac{\sqrt{250}}{2}\underline{/26.565°}$$

$$\mathbf{V}_{LC} = \mathbf{V}_{R_2}$$

$$\mathbf{I}_{R_2} = \frac{\mathbf{V}_{R_2}}{\mathbf{Z}_{R_2}} = \frac{\sqrt{250}}{4}\underline{/26.565°}$$

$$\mathbf{I}_{LC} = \frac{\mathbf{V}_{LC}}{\mathbf{Z}_L} = \frac{(\sqrt{250}/2)\underline{/26.565°}}{1\underline{/-90°}} = \frac{\sqrt{250}}{2}\underline{/116.565°}$$

$$\mathbf{V}_L = \mathbf{I}_{LC}\mathbf{Z}_L = \frac{\sqrt{250}}{2}\underline{/116.565°} \times 4\underline{/90°} = 2\sqrt{250}\underline{/206.565°} = 31.6\underline{/206.565°}$$

$$\mathbf{V}_C = \mathbf{I}_{LC}\mathbf{Z}_C = \frac{\sqrt{250}}{2}\underline{/116.565°} \times 5\underline{/-90°} = \frac{5\sqrt{250}}{2}\underline{/26.565°} = 39.5\underline{/26.565°}$$

Notice the interesting fact that both V_L and V_C exceed the input rms magnitude $V = 10$, as illustrated in Figure 4.3-4d.

□   □   □

EXAMPLE 4.3-4. Repeat Example 4.3-3 using general loop equations.

SOLUTION. The loop equations are (see Figure 4.3-5)

$$\left(\frac{2}{5}+2\right)\mathbf{I}_1 - 2\mathbf{I}_2 = 10\underline{/45°} = \frac{10}{\sqrt{2}}(1+j1)$$

$$-2\mathbf{I}_1 + (2-j1)\mathbf{I}_2 = 0$$

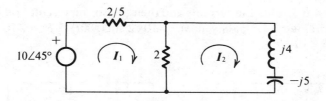

Figure 4.3-5.   Two-loop circuit diagram

Using Cramer's rule (see Appendix III), or direct substitution may also be used

$$\mathbf{I}_1 = \frac{\begin{vmatrix} \dfrac{10}{\sqrt{2}}(1+j1) & -2 \\ 0 & 2-j1 \end{vmatrix}}{\begin{vmatrix} 2.4 & -2 \\ -2 & (2-j1) \end{vmatrix}} = \frac{\dfrac{10}{\sqrt{2}}(1+j1)(2-j1)}{2.4(2-j1)-4} = \frac{\dfrac{10}{\sqrt{2}}(3+j1)}{0.8-j2.4} = \frac{12.5}{\sqrt{2}}\underline{/90°}$$

$$\mathbf{I}_2 = \frac{\begin{vmatrix} 2.4 & \dfrac{10}{\sqrt{2}}(1+j1) \\ -2 & 0 \end{vmatrix}}{\begin{vmatrix} 2.4 & -2 \\ -2 & (2-j1) \end{vmatrix}} = \frac{\dfrac{20}{\sqrt{2}}(1+j1)}{0.8(1-j3)} = \frac{\dfrac{20}{\sqrt{2}}(1+j1)(1+j3)}{0.8 \times 10}$$

$$= \frac{5}{\sqrt{2}}(-1+j2) = 5\sqrt{\frac{5}{2}}\underline{/116.6°}$$

Then

$$\mathbf{Z}_{in} = \frac{\mathbf{V}}{\mathbf{I}_1} = \frac{10\underline{/45°}}{\dfrac{12.5}{2}\underline{/90°}} = \frac{4}{5}\sqrt{2}\underline{/-45°}$$

$$\mathbf{V}_{R1} = \frac{2}{5}\mathbf{I}_1 = \frac{2}{5} \times \frac{12.5}{\sqrt{2}} \underline{/90°} = \frac{5}{\sqrt{2}} \underline{/90°}$$

$$\mathbf{V}_{R2} = 2(\mathbf{I}_1 - \mathbf{I}_2) = 2 \left[\frac{12.5}{\sqrt{2}}(0 + j1) - \frac{5}{\sqrt{2}}(-1 + j2) \right] = \frac{2 \times 2.5}{\sqrt{2}}(2 + j1)$$

$$= 5\sqrt{\frac{5}{2}} \underline{/26.6°}$$

$$\mathbf{V}_L = 4j\mathbf{I}_2 = j4 \times 5\sqrt{\frac{5}{2}} \underline{/116.6°} = 20\sqrt{2.5} \underline{/206.6°}$$

$$\mathbf{V}_C = -j5\mathbf{I}_2 = -j5 \times 5\sqrt{2.5} \underline{/116.6°} = 25\sqrt{2.5} \underline{/26.6°}$$

□ □ □

EXAMPLE 4.3-5. Find the currents and their phasor representation for the circuit shown in Figure 4.3-6. Given: $v(t) = 10\sqrt{2} \sin(500t)V$, $R_1 = 2\ \Omega$, $L = 10^{-3}$ H and $C = 0.8 \times 10^{-3}$ F.

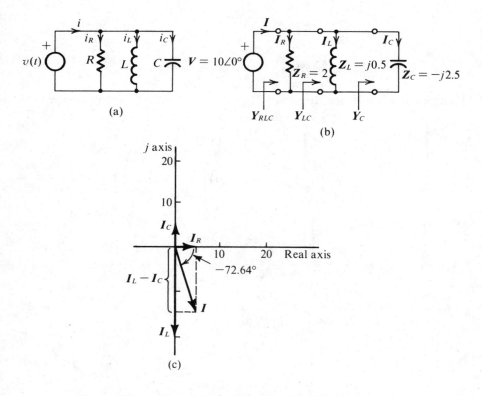

Figure 4.3-6.   A parallel circuit and its current-phasor diagram

SOLUTION. Follow the same procedure as above.

$\mathbf{I} = \mathbf{V}\mathbf{Y}_{RLC} = 10\underline{/0^\circ} \times (0.5 - j1.6) = 10\sqrt{2.81}\ \underline{/-\tan^{-1} 3.2} = 10\sqrt{2.81}\ \underline{/-72.64^\circ}$

$\mathbf{I}_R = \mathbf{V}\mathbf{Y}_R = 10\underline{/0^\circ} \times 0.5\underline{/0^\circ} = 5\underline{/0^\circ}$

$\mathbf{I}_L = \mathbf{V}\mathbf{Y}_L = 10\underline{/0^\circ} \times 2\underline{/-90^\circ} = 20\underline{/-90^\circ}$

$\mathbf{I}_C = \mathbf{V}\mathbf{Y}_C = 10\underline{/0^\circ} \times 0.4\underline{/90^\circ} = 4\underline{/90^\circ}$

□ □ □

From our discussion and the foregoing examples, the following steps may be followed in carrying out ac circuits problems:

1. Transform time functions to phasors.
2. Transform the parameter values of each element to impedances (ohm) and/or admittances (mho). Be sure that due account is taken of the time phase by including factors $+j$ for inductors and $-j$ for capacitors.
3. Draw the equivalent phasor-circuit diagram.
4. Proceed to solve for the circuit dependent variables using Kirchhoff's laws.
5. Draw the current and the voltage phasors carefully so that you can check your answers. The phasor sum of current (or voltage) phasor must constitute a closed polygon.

4.4 POWER

The instantaneous power to a one-port system is defined by:

$$p(t) = v(t)i(t) \tag{4.4-1}$$

When the voltage and current are sinusoidal functions of time, say

$$v(t) = V_m \sin(\omega t + \alpha)$$

$$i(t) = I_m \sin(\omega t + \beta)$$

then

$$p = V_m I_m \sin(\omega t + \alpha) \sin(\omega t + \beta) \tag{4.4-2}$$

Consider initially the case when the two waves are in phase, with $\alpha = \beta = 0$. Under these conditions

$$p = V_m I_m \sin^2 \omega t = \frac{V_m I_m}{2}(1 - \cos 2\omega t) \tag{4.4-3}$$

The time average value of the power during one period of the sinusoidal function is

$$P_{av} = \frac{V_m I_m}{2} \left[\frac{1}{2\pi} \int_0^{2\pi} (1 - \cos 2\omega t) \, d(\omega t) \right] = \frac{V_m I_m}{2} \qquad (4.4\text{-}4)$$

Figure 4.4-1 contains the significant information given above. It is observed that the power curve is a double frequency curve, with the axis of symmetry displaced by the average power

$$\frac{V_m I_m}{2} = \frac{V_m}{\sqrt{2}} \times \frac{I_m}{\sqrt{2}} = V_{rms} I_{rms}$$

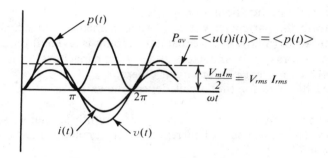

Figure 4.4-1. The power curve in a sinusoidally excited system

In the more general case the phase angles will be different from zero. To find the average power, we proceed somewhat differently from the above. We write

$$v(t) = V_m \sin (\omega t + \alpha) = \text{Im}(V_m e^{j\alpha} e^{j\omega t})$$
$$i(t) = I_m \sin (\omega t + \beta) = \text{Im}(I_m e^{j\beta} e^{j\omega t}) \qquad (4.4\text{-}5)$$

Suppose that the phasor amplitudes of v and i are written

$$\mathbf{V} = \frac{V_m}{\sqrt{2}} e^{j\alpha} = a + jb \qquad\qquad \mathbf{I} = \frac{I_m}{\sqrt{2}} e^{j\beta} = c + jd \qquad (4.4\text{-}6)$$

We write

$$p = [\text{Im}(\sqrt{2}(a + jb)e^{j\omega t})][\text{Im}(\sqrt{2}(c + jd)e^{j\omega t})] \qquad (4.4\text{-}7)$$

This expression expands to

$$p = [\text{Im}(\sqrt{2}(a + jb)(\cos \omega t + j \sin \omega t))][\text{Im}(\sqrt{2}(c + jd)(\cos \omega t + j \sin \omega t))]$$

from which

$$p = 2(a \sin \omega t + b \cos \omega t)(c \sin \omega t + d \cos \omega t)$$
$$= 2(ac \sin^2 \omega t + (bc + ad) \sin \omega t \cos \omega t + db \cos^2 \omega t) \qquad (4.4\text{-}8)$$

The time average value of this expression is

$$<p> = P_{av} = (ac + bd) = \frac{1}{2} V_m I_m (\cos \alpha \cos \beta + \sin \alpha \sin \beta)$$

$$= \frac{V_m I_m}{2} \cos (\alpha - \beta) = \frac{V_m I_m}{2} \times p.f. = V_{rms} I_{rms} \times p.f. \qquad (4.4\text{-}9)$$

The angular difference $(\alpha - \beta)$ is called the *power factor angle*, and is the difference in angle between the voltage and the current. The factor $\cos (\alpha - \beta)$ is known as the *power factor*.

We may relate P to the phasors $\mathbf{V}$, $\mathbf{V}^*$, $\mathbf{I}$, $\mathbf{I}^*$. We write

$$\mathbf{VI}^* = (a + jb)(c - jd) = (ac + bd) + j(bc - ad) \qquad (a) \quad (4.4\text{-}10)$$

Also

$$\mathbf{V}^*\mathbf{I} = (a - jb)(c + jd) = (ac + bd) - j(bc - ad) \qquad (b)$$

Note from these expressions that the average power may be written in several different forms, namely,

$$P_{av} = \text{Re}(\mathbf{VI}^*) = \text{Re}(\mathbf{V}^*\mathbf{I}) = \frac{1}{2}(\mathbf{VI}^* + \mathbf{V}^*\mathbf{I}) \qquad (4.4\text{-}11)$$

Moreover, since $\mathbf{V} = \mathbf{ZI}$ and $\mathbf{I} = \mathbf{YV}$ for the one-port, then it follows that

$$P_{av} = \text{Re}(\mathbf{V}^*\mathbf{I}) = \text{Re}(|\mathbf{I}|^2 \mathbf{Z}_1^*) = |\mathbf{I}|^2 \text{Re}(\mathbf{Z}_1^*) = |\mathbf{I}|^2 R \qquad (a) \quad (4.4\text{-}12)$$

$$P_{av} = \text{Re}(\mathbf{VI}^*) = \text{Re}(|\mathbf{V}|^2 \mathbf{Y}^*) = |\mathbf{V}|^2 \text{Re}(\mathbf{Y}^*) = |\mathbf{V}|^2 G \qquad (b)$$

These equations are related to the phasor diagram of Figure 4.4-2.

Let us examine critically the situation that exists when the circuit element is a pure inductor with the current lagging the voltage across the element by 90°. By Equation (4.4-9), the average power is zero; i.e., an inductor absorbs or dissipates no average power. In a similar way it follows, since the current in a capacitor leads the voltage by 90°, that the average power is also zero. Reference to Figure 4.4-1 when drawn for the inductor or the capacitor will show that energy is supplied to the element over one half cycle, but the element returns this energy during the second half cycle. This means that in any circuit, however complicated, it is only the resistors that are absorbing average power.

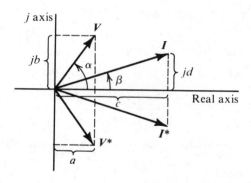

Figure 4.4-2. Phasor diagram of a one-port network

The power absorbed can be found, in addition to the equations given above, by finding the $|I|^2R$ for each resistor in the circuit and summing these.

EXAMPLE 4.4-1. Refer to the circuit shown in Figure 4.4-3. Find the current **I** and $i(t)$. Draw the phasor diagram. Determine the power delivered by the source.

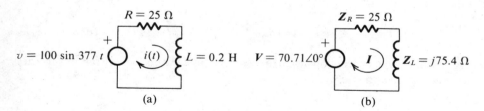

Figure 4.4-3. A simple series electric circuit
(a) Time diagram   (b) Phasor representation

SOLUTION. For the specified ω and the designated circuit parameters, we write:

$$X_L = \omega L = 377 \times 0.2 = 75.4 \ \Omega$$

$$V \doteq 70.71 \ \text{rms}, \quad \text{or} \quad V = 70.71 \underline{/0°} \ V$$

From Figure 4.4-3b, the equilibrium equation (KVL) is

$$70.71 \underline{/0°} = 25I + j75.4I = (25 + j75.4)I$$

or

$$\mathbf{I} = \frac{70.71\underline{/0^\circ}}{25 + j75.4} = \frac{70.71\underline{/0^\circ}}{79.436\underline{/71.656^\circ}} = 0.89\underline{/-71.656^\circ} \text{ A}$$

From this we write

$$i(t) = 0.89\sqrt{2} \sin (377t - 71.656^\circ)$$

The average circuit power is therefore given by

$$P_{av} = \text{Re}(\mathbf{VI^*}) = \text{Re}(70.71 \times 0.89 e^{j71.656^\circ})$$

$$\text{Re}[70.71 \times 0.89(\cos 71.656^\circ + j \sin 71.656^\circ)] = 19.8 \qquad \text{watt}$$

$$= \text{Re}\left[(70.71 + j0)\left(\frac{70.71 + j0}{25 + j75.4}\right)\right] = \left(\frac{70.71^2 \times 25}{25^2 + 75.4^2}\right) = 19.8 \quad \text{watt}$$

The phasor diagram is shown in Figure 4.4-4a and it is obtained from the following relations:

$$\mathbf{V} = 70.71\underline{/0^\circ}$$

$$\mathbf{V}_R = 25 \times 0.89\underline{/-71.656^\circ}$$

$$\mathbf{V}_L = 75.4\underline{/90^\circ} \times 0.89\underline{/-71.656^\circ} = 67.106\underline{/18.344^\circ}$$

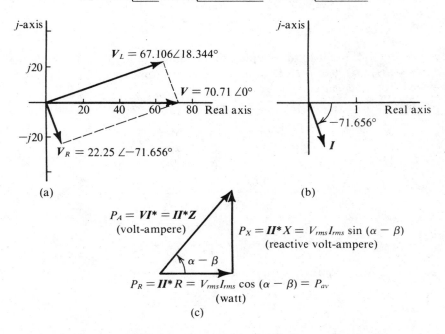

Figure 4.4-4. (a) Voltage phasor diagram (b) Current phasor diagram
(c) Power phasor diagram

Since

$$P_R = \mathbf{II}^* \operatorname{Re}(\mathbf{Z}_R) = |\mathbf{I}|^2 R = (0.89)^2 \times 25 = 19.802 \qquad \text{watt}$$

and

$$P_X = \mathbf{II}^* \operatorname{Im}(\mathbf{Z}_L) = |\mathbf{I}|^2 X_L = (0.89)^2 \times 75.4 = 59.724 \qquad \text{RVA}$$

we can draw the *power triangle*, which is shown in Figure 4.4-4c. The hypotenuse of the power triangle, which is the product of the amplitudes of voltage and current, and is volt-amperes (VA), is known as the *apparent power*. In our problem, this is

$$P_A = V_{rms} I_{rms} \underline{/\alpha - \beta} = V_{rms} I_{rms} \cos(\alpha - \beta) + jVI \sin(\alpha - \beta)$$

$$= 70.71 \times 0.89 \underline{/0 - (-71.656^\circ)} = 62.932 \underline{/71.656^\circ} = 19.806 + j59.734$$

$$= P_R + jP_X \qquad \text{(volt-ampere)}$$

P_R is the real power and P_X is the reactive power, often called *reactive volt-amperes* (RVA). When the current lags the voltage, the phase displacement between the voltage and current $(\alpha - \beta)$ is positive; and when the current leads the voltage, $(\alpha - \beta)$ is negative.

□ □ □

EXAMPLE 4.4-2. Refer to the coupled circuit shown in Figure 4.4-5. Find the currents $\mathbf{I}_1$, $\mathbf{I}_2$, $i_1(t)$, and $i_2(t)$. Draw the phasor diagram. Determine the power absorbed from the source.

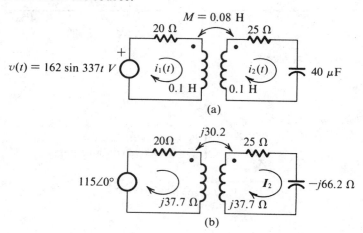

Figure 4.4-5. (a) A coupled electrical circuit
(b) The equivalent phasor representation

SOLUTION. From the specified ω and the designated circuit parameters, we write:

$$X_L = \omega L = 377 \times 0.1 = 37.1 \ \Omega$$

$$X_C = \frac{1}{\omega C} = \frac{1}{40 \times 10^{-6} \times 377} = 66.2 \ \Omega$$

$$X_m = \omega M = 377 \times 0.08 = 30.2 \ \Omega$$

$$V = 162 \text{ peak} = 115 \text{ rms, V}$$

From the figure, the equilibrium equations (KVL) are

$$115 = (20 + j37.7)\mathbf{I}_1 - j30.2\mathbf{I}_2$$

$$0 = -j30.2\mathbf{I}_1 + (25 + j37.7 - j66.2)\mathbf{I}_2$$

The reader should observe carefully the current directions with respect to the dots [see also Equation (1.9-4)] when writing the equilibrium equations. Dividing the first equation by $(20 + j37.7)$ and the second by $j30.2$ and then adding the two resulting equations, we find

$$\mathbf{I}_2 = \cfrac{\cfrac{115}{20 + j37.7}}{\cfrac{25 + j(37.7 - 66.2)}{j30.2} - j\cfrac{30.2}{20 + j37.7}} = 1.385\underline{/81.5°}$$

Dividing next the first equation by $j30.2$ and the second by $[25 + j(37.7 - 66.2)]$ and adding the two resulting equations, we obtain

$$\mathbf{I}_2 = \cfrac{\cfrac{115}{j30.2}}{\cfrac{20 + j37.7}{j30.2} - j\cfrac{30.2}{25 + j(37.7 - 66.2)}} = 1.73\underline{/-57.3°}$$

From these we write the explicit time functions

$$i_1(t) = 1.73\sqrt{2} \ \sin \ (377t - 57.3°)$$

$$i_2(t) = 1.385\sqrt{2} \ \sin \ (377t + 81.5°)$$

The phasor diagram is given in the accompanying figure (Figure 4.4-6). The average power absorbed is

$$P_{av} = V_{rms} I_{rms} \cos \ (\alpha - \beta) = 115 \times 1.73 \cos \ (57.3°) = 107.48 \qquad \text{watt}$$

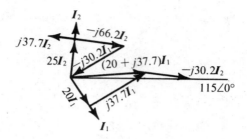

Figure 4.4-6.   Phasor representation for the circuit of Figure 4.4-5

As a check we also write

$$P_{av} = (1.73)^2 \times 20 + (1.385)^2 \times 25 = 107.81$$

The apparent power is

$$P_A = 115 \times 1.73 \underline{/57.3°} = 107.48 + j167.42 \qquad \text{volt-ampere}$$

□ □ □

4.5   THE SYSTEM FUNCTION (TRANSFER FUNCTION)

We shall extend the system function considerations of Section 4.3 to the more general form that exists in the notation of the Laplace transform (to be studied in Chapter 5). Much of this results from some notational changes.

In this chapter we began our considerations using the sinusoidal excitation function which was written in exponential form $e^{j\omega t}$. Suppose now that we consider the function e^{st} where, for the sinusoidal or frequency domain, $s = j\omega$. If we look upon s as a complex number in general, then s may take on different values corresponding to different excitation functions; e.g., $s = 0$ for a constant or dc excitation function. Observe that e^{st} can be handled with the same ease as $e^{j\omega t}$, and if e^{st} were used in Section 4.3, all considerations would remain essentially unchanged except that s will now replace $j\omega$. Thus we will find for the circuit shown in Figure 4.5-1a that the input impedance **Z** is

$$\mathbf{Z} = \mathbf{Z}_R + \mathbf{Z}_L = R + j\omega L = R + sL|_{s=j\omega} \qquad (4.5\text{-}1)$$

where, of course, **Z** is defined by the ratio **V/I**, and so

$$\mathbf{I} = \frac{\mathbf{V}}{\mathbf{Z}} \qquad (4.5\text{-}2)$$

As already discussed in Section 4.3, it is convenient to introduce the concept of a system function $H(s)$ which specifies the output or another desired function

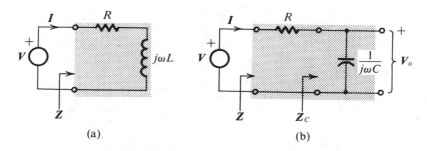

Figure 4.5-1. An electrical RL and RC circuit

in its relation to a specified input function. For the simple case above, we would write

$$I(s) = H(s)V(s) \qquad (4.5\text{-}3)$$

where, of course, $H(s) = 1/Z(s)$.

Suppose that the ratio of the output voltage $\mathbf{V}_o$ to the voltage input $\mathbf{V}$ is to be found in the circuit of Figure 4.5-1b. The procedure would be to find the current $\mathbf{I}$,

$$\mathbf{I} = \frac{\mathbf{V}}{\mathbf{Z}} = \frac{\mathbf{V}}{R + \dfrac{1}{sC}}$$

and then the output voltage is

$$\mathbf{V}_o = \mathbf{I}\mathbf{Z}_c = \frac{\mathbf{V}}{R + \dfrac{1}{sC}} \times \frac{1}{sC} = \frac{\mathbf{V}}{RCs + 1} \qquad (4.5\text{-}4)$$

The voltage transfer function or system function for this situation is

$$H(s) = \frac{\mathbf{V}_o}{\mathbf{V}} = \frac{\dfrac{1}{RC}}{s + \dfrac{1}{RC}} \qquad (4.5\text{-}5)$$

As noted above, s is a general complex number. For this reason, we can associate with $H(s)$ a complex s-plane of the form shown in Figure 4.5-2. The point $-1/RC$ is the *pole* of the system function (shown by an x on the s-plane), that is, the point at which the function becomes ∞. In the more general case where the system function might be of the form

$$H(s) = K\frac{(s+a)}{(s+b)} \qquad (4.5\text{-}6)$$

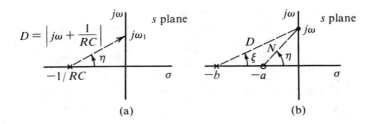

Figure 4.5-2.   The s-plane representations of $H(s)$

one distinguishes the *zeros*, the points where $H(s)$ becomes zero ($s = -a$ in the case considered), and the poles ($s = -b$), the points where the denominator becomes zero, or where $H(s)$ becomes ∞. K is called the *amplitude factor*. The pole-zero configuration or constellation is shown for this case in Figure 4.5-2b.

To find the value of $H(s)$ when s assumes the value $s = j\omega$ appropriate to a sinusoidal input of frequency ω, two procedures are possible. In one, s is replaced by $j\omega$ and the results corresponding to Equations (4.5-5) and (4.5-6) are then written

$$H(j\omega) = H(s)\big|_{s=j\omega} = \frac{\dfrac{1}{RC}}{j\omega + \dfrac{1}{RC}} \qquad\qquad \text{(a)} \quad (4.5\text{-}7)$$

$$H(j\omega) = H(s)\big|_{s=j\omega} = K\frac{(j\omega + a)}{(j\omega + b)} \qquad\qquad \text{(b)}$$

which are complex numbers, thus permitting immediate determination of magnitude and angle. The second method is a graphical one that follows directly from Figure 4.5-3. Here we consider a general point a in the complex s-plane (it might be a zero or a pole), and consider specifically $(s_r - a)$, where s_r is a designated value for s. The construction in Figure 4.5-3 shows the phasor $(s_r - a)$ which points from a to s_r with magnitude $|s_r - a|$ and angle η. Clearly, therefore, for a specified $H(s_r)$, each zero and each pole would be replaced by its appropriate magnitude and angle, and then the prescribed complex arithmetic would be completed.

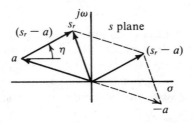

Figure 4.5-3.   To examine the graphical representation of $(s + a)$

A particularly important case is for $s_r = j\omega$, the value of $H(s)$ for a specified frequency ω. The constructions are those shown in Figure 4.5-2. For $H(j\omega)$ appropriate to Equation (4.5-4), the result is

$$H(j\omega) = H(s)|_{s=j\omega} = \frac{\dfrac{1}{RC}}{s + \dfrac{1}{RC}}\Bigg|_{s=j\omega} = \frac{\dfrac{1}{RC}}{De^{j\eta}} \qquad \text{(a)} \quad (4.5\text{-}8)$$

where

$$D = \left| j\omega + \frac{1}{RC} \right| = \left[\omega^2 + \left(\frac{1}{RC} \right)^2 \right]^{1/2}; \quad \eta = \tan^{-1}\left(\frac{\omega}{\dfrac{1}{RC}} \right) \qquad \text{(b)}$$

Both D and η are real functions of the frequency ω. The magnitude of $H(s)$ is given by

$$|H(j\omega)| = H(s)|_{s=j\omega} = K\frac{1}{D} \qquad (4.5\text{-}9)$$

since $|e^{j\eta}| = 1$ (show it!).

When the frequency ω assumes different values, the corresponding values of $H(j\omega)$ can be obtained from Equation (4.5-7). The same results will follow, of course, by allowing s_r to take on different values of $j\omega$, which means moving s_r along the $j\omega$ axis. When this is done and the magnitude and angle functions are plotted versus ω, the curves are somewhat as shown in Figure 4.5-4. Such frequency response curves are particularly important in signal processing studies.

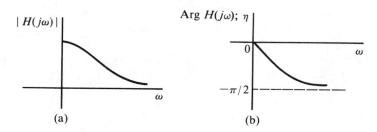

Figure 4.5-4. **Frequency response of $H(j\omega)$ for Equation (4.5-8)**

From the plot we observe that when a dc battery ($\omega = 0$) is applied, its voltage will appear across the capacitor, that is, $V_o = V$. However, if the source frequency is very large (approaching infinity), the output voltage approaches zero. Comparing the plots in Figures 4.5-4a and b with that in Figure 4.5-2a, we can trace mentally the two curves as the frequency varies and s takes values along the imaginary axis.

EXAMPLE 4.5-1. Find the current-voltage transfer function for the circuit shown in Figure 4.5-5 and plot its frequency characteristics.

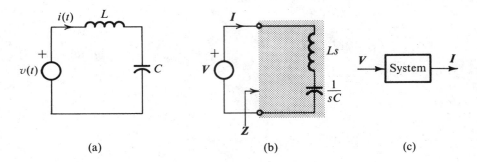

(a)   (b)   (c)

Figure 4.5-5.   An electrical LC circuit

SOLUTION. Since the current in the circuit is

$$I = \frac{V}{Z} = \frac{V}{sL + \dfrac{1}{sC}}$$

then

$$H(s) = \frac{I}{V} = \frac{I}{I\left(sL + \dfrac{1}{sC}\right)} = \frac{1}{L}\frac{s}{s^2 + \dfrac{1}{LC}} \tag{4.5-10}$$

$$= \frac{1}{L}\frac{s}{\left(s - j\dfrac{1}{\sqrt{LC}}\right)\left(s + j\dfrac{1}{\sqrt{LC}}\right)}$$

For this particular case the function has two poles located on the $j\omega$ axis, and one zero at the $(0,0)$ point. Equation (4.5-10) can also be written in the form

$$H(j\omega) = \frac{1}{L}\frac{j\omega}{j^2\left(\omega^2 - \dfrac{1}{LC}\right)} = -\frac{j}{L}\frac{\omega}{\left(\omega^2 - \dfrac{1}{LC}\right)} = \begin{cases} \dfrac{\omega}{L\left(\omega^2 - \dfrac{1}{LC}\right)}e^{-j(\pi/2)} & \omega^2 > \dfrac{1}{LC} \\[4mm] \dfrac{\omega}{L\left(\dfrac{1}{LC} - \omega^2\right)}e^{j(\pi/2)} & \omega^2 < \dfrac{1}{LC} \end{cases} \tag{4.5-11}$$

The frequency characteristic for the transfer function $H(s)|_{s=j\omega} = I/V = Y(s)|_{s=j\omega}$ is shown in Figure 4.5-6. We observe that at the frequency $1/\sqrt{LC}$, $|H(j\omega)|$

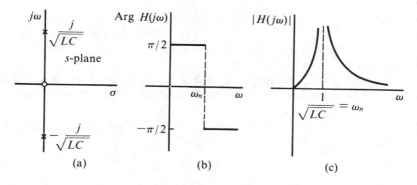

Figure 4.5-6.   Transfer function characteristics of a series LC circuit

goes to infinity. This often observed physical phenomenon is called *resonance* and the frequency ω_n is called the *resonant frequency*. Resonance, and some of its features, will be discussed in greater detail in what follows.

□ □ □

* The Series Circuit

Let us now investigate the somewhat more complicated circuit by adding a resistor in series with the series LC circuit discussed in the example above. The required current-voltage transfer function is given by

$$\frac{\mathbf{I}}{\mathbf{V}} = \mathbf{Y}(s) = \frac{1}{\mathbf{Z}(s)} = \frac{1}{Ls + R + \dfrac{1}{Cs}} = \frac{1}{L}\frac{s}{\left(s^2 + \dfrac{Rs}{L} + \dfrac{1}{CL}\right)} \qquad (4.5\text{-}12)$$

This is written in a form that can be displayed on the s-plane

$$\mathbf{Y}(s) = \frac{1}{L}\frac{s}{(s - s_a)(s - s_a^*)} \qquad (4.5\text{-}13)$$

where

$$s_a, s_a^* = -\frac{R}{2L} \pm j\sqrt{\frac{1}{LC} - \frac{R^2}{2L}}$$

The roots are written

$$s_a, s_a^* = -\zeta\omega_n \pm j\omega_n\sqrt{1 - \zeta^2} \qquad \text{(a)} \quad (4.5\text{-}14)$$

where

$$\omega_n = \frac{1}{\sqrt{LC}} \qquad \zeta = \frac{R}{2}\sqrt{\frac{C}{L}} \qquad \text{(b)}$$

ω_n is the *natural undamped frequency* of the system; ζ is the dimensionless *damping ratio*. We shall show below the influence of these factors on the response. In the form shown in Equation (4.5-14) we are assuming that $\zeta^2 < 1$, which is the *underdamped* case.

The variation of the pole locations of $Y(s)$ for constant ω_n and adjustable ζ are shown in Figure 4.5-7. The locus of the poles is a circle. In addition, there

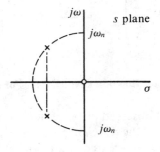

Figure 4.5-7.   The locus of the poles of $Y(s)$ versus the damping ratio ζ

is a zero at the origin. We wish to study the variation of this function with frequency. The details of the construction are contained in Figure 4.5-8. The

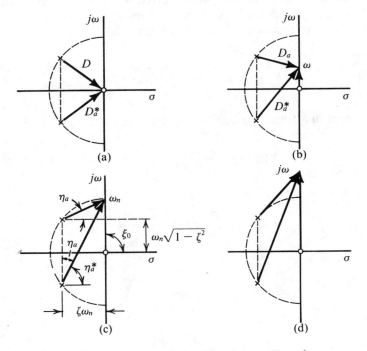

Figure 4.5-8.   *s*-plane construction for different frequencies

resulting value of the function can be put in the form

$$\mathbf{Y}(j\omega) = \frac{1}{L} \frac{N_o e^{j\xi_o}}{D_a e^{j\eta_o} D_a^* e^{j\eta_a^*}} = \frac{1}{L} \frac{N_o}{D_a D_a^*} e^{j(\xi_o - \eta_a - \eta_a^*)} \qquad (4.5\text{-}15)$$

The frequency response characteristic has the form illustrated in Figure 4.5-9. (Compare these with Figures 4.5-4a and b.) Note from Equation (4.5-10) that $\mathbf{Y}(j\omega)$ will be maximum near the frequency at which D_a or D_a^* is a minimum, actually when D_a is a minimum for positive frequency. This occurs at that frequency at which the pole D_a is the shortest distance from the $j\omega$ axis. Moreover, the smaller the distance to the $j\omega$ axis, the larger will be the value of $\mathbf{Y}(j\omega)$ at this frequency, since this factor appears in the denominator of the expression for $\mathbf{Y}(j\omega)$. Further, both N_o and D_a^* will be slowly varying in the range when D_a is changing rapidly. The frequency at which $\mathbf{Y}(j\omega)$ is a maximum is defined as the *resonant* frequency.

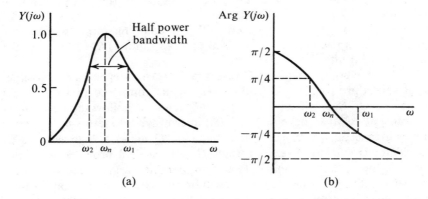

Figure 4.5-9. The frequency response characteristic of the series RLC circuit

Certain features of the shape of the curves in Figure 4.5-9 are better discussed analytically. We examine the magnitude function

$$|\mathbf{Y}(j\omega)| = \frac{1}{[R^2 + (\omega L - 1/\omega C)^2]^{1/2}} \qquad (4.5\text{-}16)$$

Observe that this function has a maximum value $= 1/R$ when the quantity

$$\omega_n L - \frac{1}{\omega_n C} = 0$$

or when

$$\omega_n = \frac{1}{\sqrt{LC}} \qquad (4.5\text{-}17)$$

This shows that resonance occurs when $\omega = \omega_n$, the situation shown in Figure 4.5-8c. When resonance occurs, $\eta_a + \eta_a^* = 90°$, and the total phase angle is

$$\xi_o - (\eta_a + \eta_a^*) = 0 \qquad (4.5\text{-}18)$$

Resonant circuits are often discussed in terms of the circuit Q, sometimes called the *"quality"* of the circuit. The Q of a series RLC circuit is defined by the relation

$$Q = \frac{\omega_n L}{R} = \frac{1}{2}\frac{\omega_n}{R/2L} = \frac{1}{2}\frac{\omega_n}{\zeta\omega_n} = \frac{1}{2\zeta} \qquad (4.5\text{-}19)$$

We make the following observations, noting from Figure 4.5-8c that ω_n is the radius of the semicircle of the poles, and $\zeta\omega_n$ is the distance from the pole to the $j\omega$ axis. Note that:

1. Shorter distances $\zeta\omega_n$ from the poles s_a and s_a^* to the $j\omega$ axis result in higher values of Q.

2. The value of Q varies inversely with the damping ratio ζ. Thus low damping is accompanied by high values of Q. In the limit as $R \to 0$, the Q of the circuit will be infinite.

In the real world, completely lossless passive circuits are not possible. Typical values are roughly the following: circuits composed of wire-wound coils may have Q values from 10 to 100; coils made of hollow tubing, as used radio transmitters, may have a Q of 1000; microwave resonators may have Q values as high as 50,000; crystal filters may have Q values as high as 100,000. An oscillator circuit possesses an infinite Q value since it provides an output without an input. These circuits are of considerable importance but involve active devices. Some further comments will be made in Chapter 13 on the relation of stability and the location of the poles of the system function. The effects of $\zeta = 1/(2Q)$, the damping ratio, on the frequency response curve of the series RLC network are shown in Figure 4.5-10.

It is clear from Figure 4.5-10 that the amplitude of $|\mathbf{Y}(j\omega)|$ increases with reduced damping or with higher Q. We can use this feature to describe additional properties of the series RLC circuit. We begin with the expression for $\mathbf{Y}(j\omega)$ in the form

$$\mathbf{Y}(j\omega) = \frac{1}{R + j\left(\omega L - \dfrac{1}{\omega C}\right)} \qquad (4.5\text{-}20)$$

Observe that the phase angle of this function will be $\pm 45°$ when

$$\omega_p L - \frac{1}{\omega_p C} = \mp R \qquad (4.5\text{-}21)$$

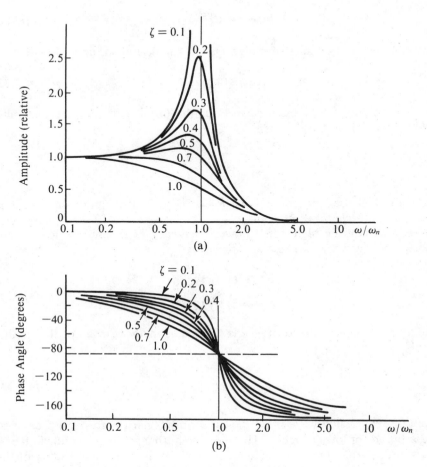

Figure 4.5-10. Amplitude and phase plots of $\dfrac{1}{1+\dfrac{2j\zeta\omega}{\omega_n}-\left(\dfrac{\omega}{\omega_n}\right)^2}$

This equation may be written

$$\omega_p^2 \pm \frac{R}{L}\omega_p - \frac{1}{LC} = 0$$

from which it is found that

$$\omega_p = \mp\frac{R}{2L} \pm \sqrt{\left(\frac{R}{2L}\right)^2 + \frac{1}{LC}}$$

This may be written

$$\omega_p = \omega_n(\mp\zeta \pm \sqrt{\zeta^2 + 1}) \qquad (4.5\text{-}22)$$

But in the case of circuits with high Q, ζ is small, and so, approximately,

$$\omega_p = \omega_n(1 \mp \zeta) \qquad (4.5\text{-}23)$$

Further, for the values specified in Equation (4.5-21), $|Y(j\omega)|$ has the value $0.707\, R$. But since $\mathbf{I} = \mathbf{V}Y$, then

$$\mathbf{I} = \frac{\mathbf{V}}{\sqrt{2}R} = 0.707\frac{\mathbf{V}}{R} \qquad (4.5\text{-}24)$$

From the fact that the power is $|\mathbf{I}|^2 R = 0.5|\mathbf{V}|^2/R$, these points are also referred to as the *half-power* points.

We designate the higher half-power frequency as ω_1 and the lower half-power frequency as ω_2. These are, repectively,

$$\omega_1 = \omega_n(1 + \zeta)$$
$$\omega_2 = \omega_n(1 - \zeta) \qquad (4.5\text{-}25)$$

The total frequency spread $\omega_1 - \omega_2$ is defined as the *bandwidth* of the circuit. Then

$$B_w = \omega_1 - \omega_2 = 2\zeta\omega_n = \frac{\omega_n}{Q} \qquad (4.5\text{-}26)$$

From this expression we see that the bandwidth is narrow for high Q circuits, and is broad for low Q circuits. This means that to increase the bandwidth of a series circuit, the Q must be reduced, or correspondingly, the loading of the circuit must be increased. The relation of B_w to $|Y(j\omega)|$ is shown in Figure 4.5-10a.

Another interpretation of Q is possible. Begin with Equation (4.5-19) and multiply and divide by πi^2. This is rearranged slightly to the following

$$Q = \frac{\omega_n L}{R} = \frac{(2\pi)\frac{1}{2}Li^2}{\dfrac{\pi i^2 R}{\omega_n}} = \frac{2\pi\left(\frac{1}{2}Li^2\right)}{\dfrac{i^2 R}{2}\dfrac{2\pi}{\omega_n}} \qquad (4.5\text{-}27)$$

Observe that the numerator is the peak stored energy (multiplied by 2π), and the denominator is the energy dissipated per cycle. Thus

$$Q = 2\pi\frac{\text{peak stored energy}}{\text{energy dissipated per cycle}} \qquad (4.5\text{-}28)$$

As a final feature of the series RLC circuit under resonant conditions, we note that

$$\mathbf{V} = \mathbf{V}_R \qquad \mathbf{V}_L = \mathbf{V}_C$$

from which it follows that

$$\mathbf{V}_L = \omega_n L \mathbf{I} = \frac{\omega_n L}{R} R \mathbf{I} = Q\mathbf{V} \qquad (4.5\text{-}29)$$

This shows that the voltage across the inductor and the capacitor can be many times the input voltage, and in this sense, the series RLC circuit under resonant or near resonant conditions will act as a voltage transformer with a step-up ratio equal to the circuit Q.

* The Parallel Circuit

Many of the ideas that were developed from considerations of the series RLC circuit apply to the parallel GCL circuit. There are several aspects of these dual situations that warrant specific attention. Refer to Figure 4.5-11

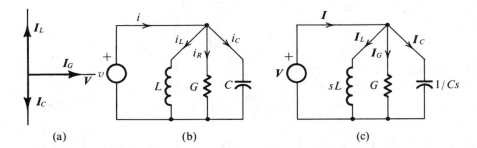

Figure 4.5-11.   A simple parallel GCL circuit

which shows the simple parallel GCL circuit (G = conductance = $1/R$). We write directly that

$$\mathbf{Y}(s) = \mathbf{Y}_R + \mathbf{Y}_C + \mathbf{Y}_L = G + Cs + \frac{1}{sL} \qquad (4.5\text{-}30)$$

We proceed with considerations of the inverse of this function

$$\mathbf{H}(s) = \frac{\mathbf{V}}{\mathbf{I}} = \mathbf{Z}(s) = \frac{1}{\mathbf{Y}(s)} = \frac{1}{C} \frac{s}{\left(s^2 + \frac{G}{C}s + \frac{1}{CL}\right)} \qquad (4.5\text{-}31)$$

We define the quantities

$$\omega_n = \frac{1}{\sqrt{LC}} \qquad\qquad \zeta = \frac{G}{2}\sqrt{\frac{L}{C}} \qquad\qquad (4.5\text{-}32)$$

Note that the discussion previously relating to $Y(j\omega)$ for the series RLC circuit applies to $Z(j\omega)$ for the parallel GCL circuit. While $Y(j\omega)$ for the *series resonant* circuit is a maximum $Z(j\omega)$ for the *parallel anti-resonant* circuit (often referred to as the "shunt" resistance) is a maximum $= 1/G$. Antiresonant circuits are also discussed in terms of the circuit Q, which is defined by the relation

$$Q = \frac{1}{\omega_n LG} = \frac{1}{G}\sqrt{\frac{C}{L}} = \frac{1}{2\zeta} \qquad\qquad (4.5\text{-}33)$$

The bandwidth considerations are as above, and Equation (4.5-26) remains valid for the antiresonant circuit.

As a final feature of the parallel GCL circuit under resonant conditions, refer to Figure 4.5-11b. Also shown is a phasor diagram of the currents. The currents I_L and I_C are equal and opposite at antiresonance and the driving point current is a minimum $= I_G$; thus

$$I = I_G \qquad I_L = I_C$$

from which it follows that

$$I_L = \frac{V}{\omega_n L} = \frac{VG}{\omega_n LG} = QI_G \qquad\qquad (4.5\text{-}34)$$

This shows that the current through the inductor and capacitor can be many times the input current. In this sense, the parallel QCL circuit under resonant or near resonant conditions will act as a current transformer with a step-up ratio equal to the circuit Q.

4.6* THE $H(j\omega)$ PLANE

The discussion in the foregoing section has shown that the system function $H(j\omega)$ varies with frequency and with variations for special systems being shown in Figures 4.5-4 and 4.5-6. In these figures the magnitude $|H(j\omega)|$ and the angle arg $H(j\omega)$ are plotted versus ω to show explicitly the variation with frequency. Often it is convenient to combine these figures into a polar plot of the results. Such a polar plot is called an $H(j\omega)$-plane diagram, the general features being somewhat as shown in Figure 4.6-1. Observe that in this diagram the phasor value of $H(j\omega)$ is plotted, with the angular frequency ω being shown as a parameter.

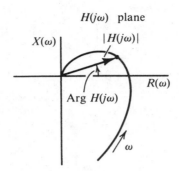

Figure 4.6-1. The polar $H(j\omega)$ diagram

As ω varies, $H(j\omega)$ will change its magnitude and argument. This means that if $H(j\omega)$ is written in the form

$$H(j\omega) = R(\omega) + jX(\omega) \qquad (4.6\text{-}1)$$

where $R(\omega)$ denotes the real part and $X(\omega)$ denotes the imaginary part of the system function, then, in general, as ω varies, both $R(\omega)$ and $X(\omega)$ will vary. This accounts for the labeling of the polar diagram of Figure 4.6-1. Since, as already discussed, $H(j\omega)$ is appropriate to the variations of a point at ω along the $j\omega$-axis in the s-plane, it is known as the image of the axis of imaginaries of the complex s-plane for the function $H(s)$. It is also known as the *Nyquist diagram*.

The $H(j\omega)$ locus possesses some special characteristics when $H(s)$ denotes a *driving point* impedance or admittance function. Now $R(\omega)$ is proportional to the active power dissipated in the network under sinusoidal conditions (see Section 4.4). For the system to remain passive, the absorbed power must be positive, which requires that the locus must always lie to the right of the $X(\omega)$ axis.

4.7* BODE DIAGRAMS

Refer again to Figures 4.5-4 and 4.5-6 which show the magnitude and phase of the system function as the frequency is varied. Often, instead of plotting $|H(j\omega)|$ and φ to linear scales, as was done in these figures, it is convenient to plot these data on a logarithmic scale, in the following manner,

$$\text{decibels (db)} = 20 \log_{10} |H(j\omega)| \text{ vs } \omega \text{ (on a logarithmic scale)}$$

$$\varphi = \arg H(j\omega) \qquad \text{vs } \omega \text{ (on a logarithmic scale)} \qquad (4.7\text{-}1)$$

Specifically for the circuit of Figure 4.5-1a, where $H(j\omega)$ denotes the driving point admittance, we readily find that

$$H(j\omega) = \frac{1}{L}\left(\frac{1}{j\omega + \frac{R}{L}}\right) = \frac{1}{R}\left(\frac{1}{j\omega\frac{L}{R} + 1}\right) = \frac{1}{R}\left(\frac{1}{j\omega\tau + 1}\right) \qquad (4.7\text{-}2)$$

where $\tau = L/R$ is the time constant of the circuit. This expression is written

$$H(j\omega) = |H(j\omega)|e^{j\varphi(\omega)} = \frac{1}{R}\frac{1}{\sqrt{1 + \omega^2\tau^2}}e^{j\,\tan^{-1}\,(-\omega\tau)} \qquad (a) \quad (4.7\text{-}3)$$

where

$$|H(j\omega)| = \text{gain} = \frac{1}{R}\frac{1}{\sqrt{1 + \omega^2\tau^2}} \qquad (b)$$

$$\varphi(\omega) = \text{phase} = -\tan^{-1}(\omega\tau) \qquad (c)$$

The corresponding figures plotted in accordance with Equation (4.7-1) are called the *Bode diagrams*. Setting $R = L = 1$, for example, Equations (4.7-3b) and (4.7-3c) are shown graphically in Figure 4.7-1. Observe from Equation

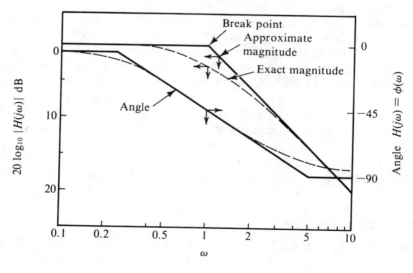

Figure 4.7-1. Bode diagram for first order system, $H(j\omega) = \dfrac{1}{1 + j\omega}$

(4.7-3) that for the first order system: (a) when $\omega\tau$ is small so that $\omega\tau \ll 1$, then $20\,\log_{10}|H(j\omega)| = 0$; (b) when $\omega\tau$ is large so that $\omega\tau \gg 1$, $H(j\omega) \propto 1/\omega\tau$. Thus when $\omega\tau$ is increased by a factor of 10, $20\,\log_{10}|H(j\omega)|$ falls at the rate of 20 db/decade; (c) at the break point when $\omega\tau = 1$, the function $20\,\log_{10}|H(j\omega)|$ is 3 db down from the zero db line. This construction shows that the actual frequency response curve is established by two straight line segments which are the asymptotic curves for the actual variation, there being a 3-db drop at the break point. The complete Bode plot for a given function will include the term $\log_{10}(1/R)$. For $R \neq 1$, this will shift the Bode variation up or down by the appropriate amount to account for the gain factor.

To examine the asymptotes of the phase angle, we observe that for $\omega\tau \ll 1$ ($\omega \ll 1$ in our example)

$$\varphi(\omega) = -\tan^{-1}(\omega\tau) = 0°$$

and for $\omega\tau \gg 1$ ($\omega \gg 1$ in our example)

$$\varphi(\omega) = -\tan^{-1}(\omega\tau) = -90°$$

The phase angle asymptotes are shown in Figure 4.7-1.

In the more general case when the system function might be of the form

$$H(s) = K_1\frac{(s+s_1)(s+s_2)+\ldots+(s+s_m)}{s^p(s+s_1')(s+s_2')+\ldots+(s+s_n')} = K\frac{(1+s/s_1)(1+s/s_2)\ldots(1+s/s_m)}{s^p(1+s/s_1')(1+s/s_2')\ldots(1+s/s_n')}$$

$$= K\frac{(1+j\omega\tau_1)(1+j\omega\tau_2)\ldots(1+j\omega\tau_m)}{(j\omega)^p(1+j\omega\tau_1')(1+j\omega\tau_2')\ldots(1+j\omega\tau_n')} \tag{4.7-4}$$

where $K = K_1(s_1 s_2 \ldots s_m/s_1' s_2' \ldots s_n')$, $\tau_k = 1/s_k$, $\tau_k' = 1/s_k'$, and p is a positive integer or zero. The db form of Equation (4.7-4) is given by

$$20\log_{10}|H(j\omega)| = 20\log_{10}K + 20\log_{10}|1+j\omega\tau_1| + 20\log_{10}|1+j\omega\tau_2| + \ldots$$

$$- 20\log|(j\omega)^p| - 20\log_{10}|1+j\omega\tau_1'| - 20\log_{10}|\omega+j\omega\tau_2'| - \ldots$$

$$= 20\log_{10}K - 20\log|(j\omega)^p| + 20\sum_{k=1}^{m}\log_{10}|1+j\omega\tau_k| \tag{a}$$

$$- 20\sum_{k=1}^{n}\log_{10}|1+j\omega\tau_k'|$$

and $\tag{4.7-5}$

$$\arg H(j\omega) = \arg K + \arg(1+j\omega\tau_1) + \ldots + \arg(1+j\omega\tau_m)$$

$$+ \arg\left(\frac{1}{(j\omega)^p}\right) + \arg\left(\frac{1}{1+j\omega\tau_1'}\right) + \ldots \tag{b}$$

$$+ \arg\left(\frac{1}{1+j\omega\tau_n'}\right)$$

EXAMPLE 4.7-1. Plot the asymptotic Bode plots for the transfer function

$$H(j\omega) = \frac{5(1+j\omega)}{(j\omega)^2(1+j0.25\omega)}$$

SOLUTION. Using Equations (4.7-5a) and (4.7-5b), we have, respectively

$$20 \log_{10}|H(j\omega)| = 20 \log_{10}5 + 20 \log_{10}|1 + j\omega| - 20 \log_{10}|(j\omega)^2|$$
$$- 20 \log_{10}|1 + j0.25\omega|$$
$$= 20 \log_{10}5 + 20 \log_{10}(1 + \omega^2)^{1/2} - 20 \log_{10}\omega^2$$
$$- 20 \log_{10}(1 + (0.25\omega)^2)^{1/2}$$
$$= 20 \times 0.6989 + 10 \log_{10}(1 + \omega^2) - 40 \log_{10}\omega$$
$$- 10 \log_{10}(1 + (0.25\omega)^2)$$

$$\arg H(j\omega) = \arg (1 + j\omega) + \arg \left(\frac{1}{j\omega}\right)^2 + \arg \left(\frac{1}{1 + j0.25\omega}\right)$$
$$= \tan^{-1} \omega - 180° - \tan^{-1} 0.25\omega$$

The asymptotic forms of these equations are plotted in Figures 4.7-2 and 4.7-3 respectively. The phase errors at the break points are about 11°.

□   □   □

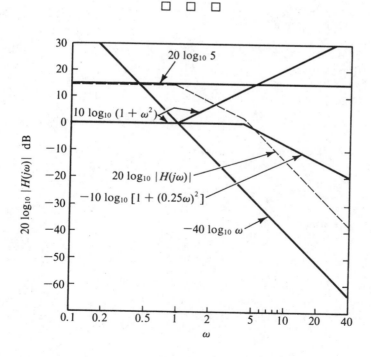

Figure 4.7-2. Bode amplitude plots of Example 4.7-1

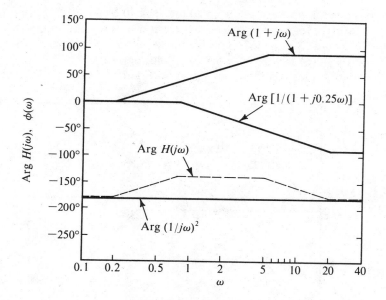

Figure 4.7-3.   Bode phase plots of Example 4.7-1

EXAMPLE 4.7-2. The system function of a particular system is

$$H(s) = \frac{10s(s+2)}{(s+5)(s^2+2s+3)}$$

Draw the overall characteristic from considerations of the symptotic plots.

SOLUTION. The function $H(s)$ is rewritten to make the constant term of each factor equal to unity. This leads to

$$H(s) = \frac{10}{5} \times \frac{2}{3} \times \frac{s(0.5s+1)}{(0.2s+1)(0.33s^2+0.67s+1)}$$

or

$$H(j\omega) = \frac{20}{15} \times \frac{(j\omega)(1+j0.5\omega)}{(1+j0.2\omega)(1+j0.67\omega-0.33\omega^2)}$$

The break frequencies are:
   Break up at 20 db/decade at $\omega = 1/0.5 = 2$, due to factor $(1+j0.5\omega)$.
   Break down at 20 db/decade at $\omega = 1/0.2 = 5$, due to factor $(1+j0.2\omega)$.
   Gain factor 20/15 introduces a constant $20 \log_{10}(20/15) = 2.5$.
   The 20 db/decade rise due to the factor $j\omega$ intersects 0 db at $\omega = 1$.

To find the break point of the term $20 \log_{10}(1 + j0.67\omega - 0.33\omega^2)$, first write this in the form $20 \log_{10}(1 + j2\zeta\tau\omega - \tau^2\omega^2)$ from which we obtain the two factors $\tau = \sqrt{0.33}$ and $2\zeta\tau\omega = 0.67$. The break point occurs at $\omega = 1/\tau = 1/0.574 = 1.74$, and the slope is $-20 \log_{10}(\omega^2\tau^2) = -40 \log_{10}\tau\omega$.

The asymptotic plot has the form shown in Figure 4.7-4.

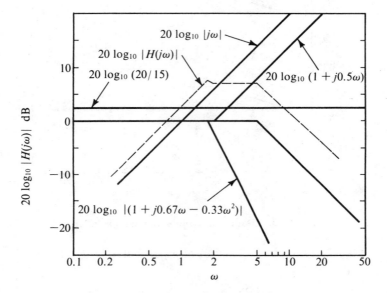

Figure 4.7-4.   Bode plots for Example 4.7-4

4.8   POSTLUDE

This chapter has introduced to the student a number of basic concepts in systems theory: behavior of systems to sinusoidal signals; the concept of the system function in system behavior; the description of system functions in terms of their pole-zero constellation; resonance, bandwidth and Q, the Nyquist diagram and Bode diagrams. These provide the background for further development of systems theory, important in studies in communications, feedback control, electronics, and others. We shall develop these concepts in the work that follows.

SUMMARY

- The full cycle time average of a sinusoidal wave is zero and its root-mean-square is equal to $I_m/\sqrt{2} \doteq 0.707 I_m$, where I_m is its maximum value.

- The impedance of an inductor and a capacitor are given, respectively, by

$$\mathbf{Z}_L = j\omega L = jX_L; \qquad \mathbf{Z}_C = \frac{1}{j\omega C} = -j\frac{1}{\omega C} = -jX_c$$

where $X_L = \omega L$ is the inductive reactance, and $X_c = 1/\omega C$ is the capacitive reactance.

- The reciprocals of the impedances are called admittances and are:

$$\mathbf{Y}_R = G = 1/R, \qquad \mathbf{Y}_L = 1/\mathbf{Z}_L = 1/j\omega L, \qquad Y_c = 1/\mathbf{Z}_c = j\omega C \qquad \text{mho}$$

- The input or driving-point impedance of a series RLC circuit is

$$Z = |\mathbf{Z}| \underline{/\theta} = \left[R^2 + \left(\omega L - \frac{1}{\omega C} \right)^2 \right]^{1/2} \underline{/ \tan^{-1} \left(\frac{\omega L - \dfrac{1}{\omega C}}{R} \right)} \qquad \text{ohm}$$

where θ is the phase angle of the circuit.

- The total impedance of a circuit having n impedances in series is

$$\mathbf{Z} = \mathbf{Z}_1 + \mathbf{Z}_2 + \ldots + \mathbf{Z}_n$$

The total admittance of a circuit with n impedances in parallel is

$$\mathbf{Y} = \mathbf{Y}_1 + \mathbf{Y}_2 + \ldots + \mathbf{Y}_n \qquad \left(\text{or } \frac{1}{\mathbf{Z}} = \frac{1}{\mathbf{Z}_1} + \frac{1}{\mathbf{Z}_2} + \ldots + \frac{1}{\mathbf{Z}_n} \right)$$

- The instantaneous power is defined by

$$p(t) = v(t)i(t)$$

The time average power where $v(t)$ and $i(t)$ are sinusoidal functions which have no phase difference is

$$P = \frac{V_m I_m}{2} = \frac{V_m}{\sqrt{2}} \frac{I_m}{\sqrt{2}} = V_{rms} I_{rms}$$

The time average value of the power with arbitrary phases α and β for the voltage and current, respectively, is

$$P_{av} = \frac{V_m I_m}{2} \cos (\alpha - \beta) = V_{rms} I_{rms} \cos (\alpha - \beta)$$

where $(\alpha - \beta)$ is the power factor angle and $\cos (\alpha - \beta)$ is known as the power factor. The average power is also written as follows:

$$P_{av} = \text{Re}(\mathbf{VI}^*) = \text{Re}(\mathbf{V}^*\mathbf{I}) = \frac{1}{2}(\mathbf{VI}^* + \mathbf{V}^*\mathbf{I})$$

$$P_{av} = \text{Re}(\mathbf{V}^*\mathbf{I}) = \text{Re}(|\mathbf{I}|^2\mathbf{Z}^*) = |\mathbf{I}|^2 \text{Re}(\mathbf{Z}^*)$$

$$P_{av} = \text{Re}(\mathbf{VI}^*) = \text{Re}(|\mathbf{V}|^2\mathbf{Y}^*) = |\mathbf{V}|^2 \text{Re}(\mathbf{Y}^*)$$

The apparent power is defined by

$$\mathbf{P}_A = V_{rms} I_{rms} \underline{/\alpha - \beta} = V_{rms} I_{rms} \cos (\alpha - \beta) + j V_{rms} I_{rms} \sin (\alpha - \beta)$$

- The ratio of the output of a system to its input is called the transfer or system function $H(j\omega)$. The frequency at which the $|H(j\omega)|$ assumes its largest value is called the resonant frequency and the phenomenon is known as resonance.

- In general, the system function $H(s)$ is expressed in a form to display the zeros and the poles on the complex s-plane. For any specified value of $s = s_r$, $H(s)|_{s=s_r} = H(s_r)$ is a complex number. Of special interest is $H(j\omega)$ when $s = j\omega$, which specifies the amplitude and phase of the function as ω is varied.

- Resonant circuits are often discussed in terms of the circuit Q, often called the quality of the circuit. Q determines the frequency selectivity of the circuit, and is defined by

$$Q = 2\pi \times \frac{\text{Maximum energy stored in inductors or capacitors}}{\text{Energy dissipated per cycle}}$$

The Q of a series LC circuit is defined by the relation

$$Q = \frac{\omega_n L}{R} = \frac{1}{2}\frac{\omega_n}{R/2L} = \frac{1}{2}\frac{\omega_n}{\zeta\omega_n} = \frac{1}{2\zeta}$$

where

$$\omega_n = \frac{1}{\sqrt{LC}} \quad \text{and} \quad \zeta = \frac{R}{2}\sqrt{\frac{C}{L}}$$

The total frequency spread $\omega_1 - \omega_2$ is defined as the bandwidth of the series circuit and is given by

$$B_w = \omega_1 - \omega_2 = 2\zeta\omega_n = \frac{\omega_n}{Q}$$

- While $Y(j\omega)$ for the series resonant circuit is a maximum, for the parallel antiresonant circuit $Z(j\omega)$ is a maximum.

- The system function $H(j\omega)$ when plotted on the $H(j\omega)$-plane as phasors with frequency ω as a parameter is known as a Nyquist diagram.

- A plot of $20\log_{10}|H(j\omega)|$ versus ω on a logarithmic scale, and arg $H(j\omega)$ versus ω on a logarithmic scale are called Bode diagrams. A feature of the Bode plot is that the magnitudes can be approximated by the asymptotic lines for each factor in $H(j\omega)$, as discussed in Equations (4.7-5a) and (4.7-5b).

REVIEW QUESTIONS

1. Write expressions for two sinusoidal voltages which differ by 35 degrees.
2. Give the definition of instantaneous power.
3. How much power is delivered to a resistor by a sinusoidal voltage source?

4. If two sinusoidal voltage sources are added in series, is the resulting voltage sinusoidal? If your answer is yes, what additional characteristics appear in the waveform?
5. Explain the features of phasors or sinors.
6. Define the terms: inductive reactance, impedance, capacitive reactance, admittance, immittance.
7. Specify the transfer function $\mathbf{H}(j\omega) = \mathbf{V}/\mathbf{I}$ of a series RLC circuit.
8. What is the impedance of n circuit elements in series? What is the impedance of these same elements when all are connected in parallel?
9. What is the significance of the power factor of a circuit?
10. Electrical energy is sold on the basis of kilowatt-hours (kWh). Does the primary source have to provide the reactive power also?
11. Describe the significance of the pole locations in the complex plane for systems with sinusoidal excitation.
12. Describe five different physical resonant systems.
13. Explain why soldiers must break step when crossing small bridges.
14. What must be the characteristics of a wind to destroy a physical structure such as a bridge, which might be of faulty design?
15. What is the difference between Nyquist and Bode plots?

REFERENCES

See references to Chapter 2.

PROBLEMS

4.1-1. Find the average and rms values of the voltage signals shown in Figure P4.1-1.

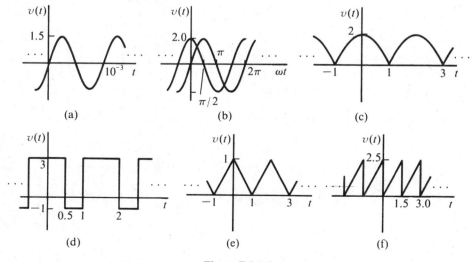

Figure P4.1-1

4.1-2. Write the instantaneous current $i(t)$ if:
   (a) $\mathbf{I} = 3e^{j25°}$ A, $f = 30$ Hz,
   (b) $\mathbf{I} = e^{-j135°}$ A, $T = 3$ ms,
   (c) $\mathbf{I} = -2e^{j145°}$ A, $\omega = 377$ rad/s.

4.1-3. Assume that three voltages have phasor description $\mathbf{V}_1 = V_1 e^{j\theta_1}$, $\mathbf{V}_2 = V_2 e^{j\theta_2}$, and $\mathbf{V}_3 = V_3 e^{j\theta_3}$. If $\mathbf{V} = Ve^{j\theta} = \mathbf{V}_1 + \mathbf{V}_2 + \mathbf{V}_3$, find V and θ.

4.1-4. Suppose that $\mathbf{V}_1 = 10e^{j30}$ V and $\mathbf{V}_2 = 15e^{-j(\pi/4)}$ V. If $\mathbf{V} = Ve^{j\theta} = 3\mathbf{V}_1 + (2 - j3)\mathbf{V}_2$, find V and θ.

4.2-1. (a) Find the instantaneous voltage $v(t)$ across an inductor if:
      (1) $L = 1$ H, $\omega = 2$ rad/s, and $\mathbf{I} = 2e^{-j30°}$ A;
      (2) $L = 1$ H, $\omega = 10^5$ rad/s, and $\mathbf{I} = 2e^{j30°}$ A;
      (3) $L = 10^{-3}$ H, $\omega = 10^5$ rad/s, and $\mathbf{I} = 2e^{j30°}$ A.
   (b) Find the instantaneous current $i(t)$ through a capacitor if:
      (1) $C = 10^{-12}$ F, $f = 60$ Hz, and the voltage across the capacitor $\mathbf{V} = 2 \times 10^{-3} e^{j30°}$ V;
      (2) $C = 10^{-12}$ F, $f = 10$ GHz, and the voltage across the capacitor is $\mathbf{V} = 2 \times 10^{-3} e^{j30°}$ V (1 GHz $= 10^9$ Hz).

4.2-2. Find the impedances and admittances for all the translational and rotational mechanical elements.

4.3-1. For the series RLC circuit of Figure 4.3-1 find the transfer functions
   (a) $H(j\omega) = \mathbf{V}_R / \mathbf{V}$;
   (b) $H(j\omega) = \mathbf{V}_L / \mathbf{V}$.

4.3-2. Find the impedance $\mathbf{Z}$ for the series RLC circuit of Figure 4.3-1 if $R = 1$ Ω, $L = 10^{-3}$ H, $C = 2 \times 10^{-6}$ F and $f = 10^5$ Hz.

4.3-3. Find all the currents and voltages in phasor form and draw the phasor diagram (complex plane) for the circuits shown in Figure P4.3-3.

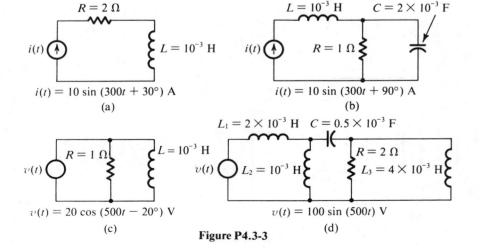

(a) $R = 2$ Ω, $L = 10^{-3}$ H, $i(t) = 10 \sin(300t + 30°)$ A

(b) $L = 10^{-3}$ H, $C = 2 \times 10^{-3}$ F, $R = 1$ Ω, $i(t) = 10 \sin(300t + 90°)$ A

(c) $R = 1$ Ω, $L = 10^{-3}$ H, $v(t) = 20 \cos(500t - 20°)$ V

(d) $L_1 = 2 \times 10^{-3}$ H, $C = 0.5 \times 10^{-3}$ F, $R = 2$ Ω, $L_2 = 10^{-3}$ H, $L_3 = 4 \times 10^{-3}$ H, $v(t) = 100 \sin(500t)$ V

Figure P4.3-3

4.3-4. Find the phasor representation of the forces and velocities for the system shown in Figure P4.3-4.

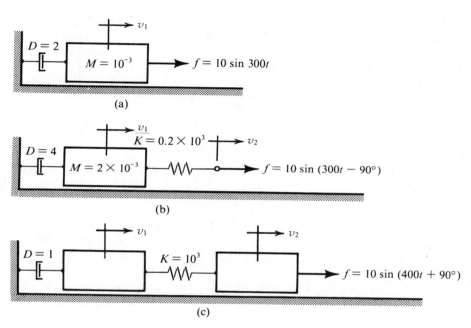

(a)

(b)

(c)

Figure P4.3-4

4.3-5. Repeat Problems 4.3-3c and d when the input voltages are, respectively,

(a) $v(t) = 20 \cos (500t - 20°) + 14 \sin (1000t - 45°)$
(b) $v(t) = 100 \sin 500t + 60 \sin (1500t + 30°)$

4.4-1. Plot the instantaneous power into an inductor and a capacitor. Explain the observed phenomena.

4.4-2. Determine the power factor, the average power, and the apparent power for the circuits shown in Figure P4.4-2.

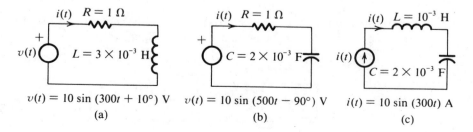

$v(t) = 10 \sin (300t + 10°)$ V $v(t) = 10 \sin (500t - 90°)$ V $i(t) = 10 \sin (300t)$ A
(a)   (b)   (c)

Figure P4.4-2

4.5-1. Determine the voltage transfer function and plot $|H(s)|$ and arg $H(s)$ versus ω for the circuits shown in Figure P4.5-1.

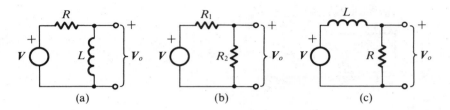

Figure P4.5-1

4.5-2. Find the voltage transfer function for the circuits shown in Figure P4.5-2.

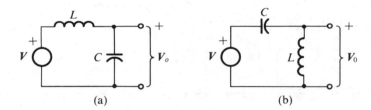

Figure P4.5-2

4.5-3. Determine the voltage-current transfer function for the circuit shown in Figure P4.5-3 and plot its frequency response characteristic.

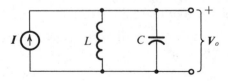

Figure P4.5-3

4.5-4. Determine the transfer function $H(s) = V_2/F(v_1$ is known) and plot its frequency response for the system shown in Figure P4.5-4.

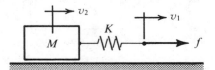

Figure P4.5-4

4.5-5. Determine the transfer function $H(s) = V/F$ and find the Q of the system shown in Figure P4.5-5.

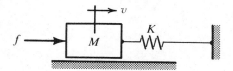

Figure P4.5-5

4.5-6. Refer to the simple series RLC circuit with circuit constants as follows: $R = 10\ \Omega$, $L = 7$ mH, $v = 2\cos 2\pi 10^4 t$ V.

(a) Calculate the value of C for series resonance.
(b) Calculate the current through the circuit under these conditions.
(c) Calculate the voltage (amplitude and phase) across each element of the circuit.
(d) Determine the bandwidth of the circuit.

4.5-7. The parallel combination shown in Figure P4.5-7 is in parallel (anti-resonant) resonance.

(a) Calculate the value of C for parallel resonance.
(b) What is the voltage across the parallel resonant circuit?
(c) Determine the current through each element of the circuit. Comment on the current through the series R and that through the elements in the parallel circuit.
(d) Determine the bandwidth of the circuit.

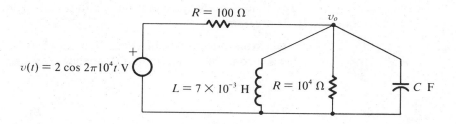

Figure P4.5-7

4.5-8. For the circuit in Problem 4.5-7 adjusted to anti-resonance at 10^4 Hz, the input is changed to

$$v(t) = 2\cos 2\pi 10^4 t + 2\sin(2\pi 3 \times 10^4 t - 45°)\text{ V}$$

(a) What is the voltage across the parallel circuit?
(b) Discuss the frequency discrimination of the circuit.

4.5-9. The pole-zero pattern of Butterworth filters of orders 3, 4, 5 are shown in Figure P4.5-9.

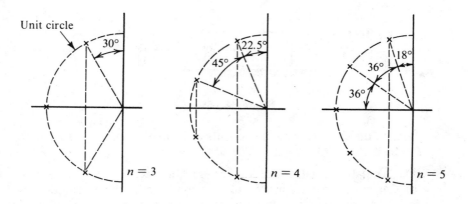

Figure P4.5-9

(a) Deduce the analytic form for $H(s)$ for each.
(b) Sketch $H(j\omega)$ for each, and discuss the filtering properties as the order increases.

4.6-1. Deduce the frequency variation of networks that have the following specified pole-zero patterns by graphical construction:

(a) poles $-2 \pm j5$;
(b) poles $-2 \pm j5$, zero -4;
(c) poles $-2 \pm j5$, zero -1.

Plot the results on a polar diagram (Nyquist plot); magnitude and angle versus frequency; Bode diagram.

4.7-1. Figures P4.7-1 show the asymptotic amplitude characteristics of $Z(j\omega)$ of a number of systems. From these determine the analytic form of $Z(s)$.

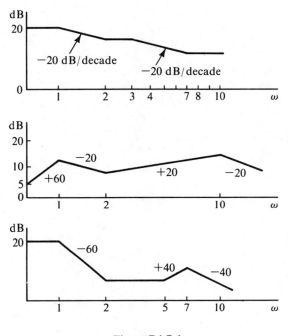

Figure P4.7-1

Chapter Five

The Laplace Transform

Chapters 3 and 4 were concerned with the time domain solution of system equations. Time domain techniques, except for the very simple cases, are not particularly convenient for closed form hand solutions, even for linear problems, and are almost impossible for nonlinear problems. With the general availability of the digital computer, the burdensome calculations are transferred to the machine, and time domain methods are of renewed importance.

Linear time invariant systems constitute a very important part of systems analysis. Where hand solutions are required, it has become customary to effect a mathematical transformation of the integrodifferential equations that describe the dynamics of the system from the time domain to a convenient algebraic domain. Such a transformation technique makes possible many algebraic manipulations as part of the solution process. Ultimately, the time response is desired since the time domain is of particular interest. Thus it is essential that an inverse transformation be effected back to the time domain from the algebraic domain of the transformation. Clearly, with increasing use of the digital computer, such transformation techniques are of lesser importance in providing time solutions to linear systems problems. However, such transformation techniques remain very important methods of analysis and synthesis, and we shall devote considerable time to their study.

The Laplace transform permits, in a formal way, the transformation of an integrodifferential equation whose dependent variable is a function of time to an algebraic equation whose dependent variable is a function of a complex variable of the form $s = \sigma + j\omega$ which is called the s-domain. σ and ω may take values from $-\infty$ to $+\infty$. There are many subtle aspects that concern the convergence of the Laplace transform, a study of which requires an understanding of the theory of functions of a complex variable. Because of this, we shall limit ourselves to the simpler aspects of the Laplace transform methods. These are usually sufficient in our level of presentation to carry out analyses of network behavior.

5.1   THE LAPLACE TRANSFORM

This is one of a family of integral transforms; the Fourier integral is another of the family. The general class of integral transforms here being considered is defined by the integral

$$F(s) = \int_a^b f(x)K(s,x)\,dx \qquad (5.1\text{-}1)$$

where $F(s)$ is the integral transform of $f(x)$, with $f(x)$ being any transformable function of the real variable x. $K(s,x)$ is known as the *kernel* of the transform. Here s is the same parameter mentioned above. In particular, we distinguish between the one-sided Laplace transform which is written

$$F(s) = \int_0^\infty f(x)e^{-sx}\,dx \qquad \text{(a)} \quad (5.1\text{-}2)$$

and the two-sided Laplace transform

$$F(s) = \int_{-\infty}^\infty f(x)e^{-sx}\,dx \qquad \text{(b)}$$

For our purposes the one-sided Laplace transform is adequate, but in certain communication theory applications one must use the two-sided transform. The Fourier transform defined by the integral

$$F(j\omega) = \int_{-\infty}^\infty f(x)e^{-j\omega x}\,dx \qquad (5.1\text{-}3)$$

is seen to be a two-sided transform. The Fourier transform of $f(x)e^{-\sigma x}$ is identical with the two-sided Laplace transform of $f(x)$.

Since we normally operate primarily in the time domain in dynamic systems problems, our basic functions are time functions, and the Laplace transform, which is generally abbreviated as the £-transform of $f(t)$, is written

$$\pounds[f(t)] = \int_0^\infty f(t)e^{-st}\,dt = F(s) \qquad (5.1\text{-}4)$$

For Laplace transformability, $f(t)$ must satisfy the Dirichlet conditions, which are sufficient although not necessary conditions:

1. $f(t)$ must be piecewise continuous; i.e., it must be single-valued but can have a finite number of finite isolated discontinuities for $t \geq 0$.

2. $f(t)$ must be of exponential order; i.e., $f(t)$ must remain less than $Me^{a_o t}$ as t approaches $+\infty$, where M is a positive constant, and a_o is a real number. This is equivalent to $e^{-at}|f(t)| \to 0$ as $t \to +\infty$.

For example, such functions as $\tan \beta t$, $\cot \beta t$, e^{t^2}, do not possess Laplace transforms.

There is the inherent assumption in Equation (5.1-4) that $f(t)$ must remain as defined for all of time. From a practical viewpoint, one may have some skepticism about meeting this requirement, although hypothetically this causes no difficulty.

5.2 LAPLACE TRANSFORMS OF ELEMENTARY FUNCTIONS

Laplace transforms do exist for most functions that are of interest in our studies. We shall evaluate a number of such functions.

EXAMPLE 5.2-1. Find the Laplace transform of the unit step function $f(t) = u_{-1}(t)$.

SOLUTION. By Equation (5.1-4)

$$\text{£}[u_{-1}(t)] = \int_0^\infty u_{-1}(t)e^{-st}\, dt = \int_0^\infty e^{-st}\, dt = -\frac{e^{-st}}{s}\Big|_0^\infty = \frac{1}{s}$$

This result shows the basis for designating the unit step as $u_{-1}(t)$.

□   □   □

EXAMPLE 5.2-2. Find the Laplace transform of the unit impulse function $f(t) = u_o(t)$ $[u_o(t) \triangleq \delta(t)$ delta function].

SOLUTION. This evaluation requires care since $u_o(t)$ does not satisfy the Dirichlet conditions. Since $u_o(t)$ is nonzero only at the origin $t = 0$, then in general for any continuous function $\psi(t)$

$$\int_{-\infty}^\infty \psi(t)u_o(t)\, dt = \int_{0-}^{0+} \psi(t)u_o(t)\, dt = \psi(o)\int_{0-}^{0+} u_o(t)\, dt = \psi(o)$$

since the integral of a delta function by definition is equal to one. If we choose $\psi = e^{-st}$, which equals unity for $t = 0$, then for $t \geqslant 0$

$$\int_{0-}^\infty u_o(t)e^{-st}\, dt = \int_{0-}^\infty u_o(t)e^{-st}\, dt = e^{-s0}\int_{0-}^{0+} u_o(t)\, dt = 1$$

since, by definition, the area under the unit impulse is unity.

□   □   □

EXAMPLE 5.2-3. Find the Laplace transform of the exponential function $e^{-at}u_{-1}(t)$ for any real a.

SOLUTION. We write directly

$$\mathcal{L}[e^{-at}] = \int_0^\infty e^{-at}e^{-st}\,dt = \frac{e^{-(s+a)t}}{-(s+a)}\bigg|_0^\infty = \frac{1}{s+a} \qquad \text{for } \mathrm{Re}\{s\} > -a$$

□   □   □

EXAMPLE 5.2-4. By direct application of the results of Example 5.2-3, deduce the Laplace transform of $\sin \omega t u_{-1}(t)$ and $\cos (\omega t)u_{-1}(t)$.

SOLUTION. From the fact that

$$\sin \omega t = \frac{e^{j\omega t} - e^{-j\omega t}}{2j}$$

$$\cos \omega t = \frac{e^{j\omega t} + e^{-j\omega t}}{2}$$

and noting that

$$\mathcal{L}[e^{j\omega t}] = \frac{1}{s - j\omega} \qquad \mathcal{L}[e^{-j\omega t}] = \frac{1}{s + j\omega}$$

then

$$\mathcal{L}[\sin \omega t] = \frac{1}{2j}\left(\frac{1}{s - j\omega} - \frac{1}{s + j\omega}\right) = \frac{\omega}{s^2 + \omega^2}$$

$$\mathcal{L}[\cos \omega t] = \frac{1}{2}\left(\frac{1}{s - j\omega} + \frac{1}{s + j\omega}\right) = \frac{s}{s^2 + \omega^2}$$

The same results would have been obtained by using $\sin \omega t$ and $\cos \omega t$ as the function $f(t)$ in the Laplace integral.

□   □   □

We can proceed in this way to develop a table of Laplace transform pairs. Such a table can be extended using the properties of the Laplace transform described in the next section. Table 5.2-1 contains some very useful transform pairs.

5.3   PROPERTIES OF THE LAPLACE TRANSFORM

We wish now to examine a number of important properties of the Laplace transform.

Table 5.2-1. Elementary Laplace Transform Pairs

	$f(t)$	$F(s)$
1	$u_o(t)$	1
2	$u_{-1}(t)$	$\dfrac{1}{s}$
3	t^n for $n>0$	$\dfrac{n!}{s^{n+1}}$
4	e^{-at}	$\dfrac{1}{s+a}$
5	te^{-at}	$\dfrac{1}{(s+a)^2}$
6	$\dfrac{t^{n-1}e^{-at}}{(n-1)!}$	$\dfrac{1}{(s+a)^n}$
7	$\dfrac{1}{b-a}(e^{-at}-e^{-bt})$	$\dfrac{1}{(s+a)(s+b)}$
8	$-\dfrac{1}{b-a}(ae^{-at}-be^{-bt})$	$\dfrac{s}{(s+a)(s+b)}$
9	$\sin \omega t$	$\dfrac{\omega}{s^2+\omega^2}$
10	$\cos \omega t$	$\dfrac{s}{s^2+\omega^2}$
11	$e^{-at}\sin \omega t$	$\dfrac{\omega}{(s+a)^2+\omega^2}$
12	$e^{-at}\cos \omega t$	$\dfrac{s+a}{(s+a)^2+\omega^2}$
13	$\sinh \omega t$	$\dfrac{\omega}{s^2-\omega^2}$
14	$\cosh \omega t$	$\dfrac{s}{s^2-\omega^2}$
15	$\dfrac{\sqrt{a^2+\omega^2}}{\omega}\sin(\omega t+\varphi),\ \varphi=\tan^{-1}\dfrac{\omega}{a}$	$\dfrac{s+a}{s^2+\omega^2}$
16	$\dfrac{\omega_n}{\sqrt{1-\zeta^2}}e^{-\zeta\omega_n t}\sin \omega_n\sqrt{1-\zeta^2}\,t,\ \zeta<1$	$\dfrac{\omega_n^2}{s^2+2\zeta\omega_n s+\omega_n^2}$
17	$\dfrac{1}{a^2+\omega^2}+\dfrac{1}{\omega\sqrt{a^2+\omega^2}}e^{-at}\sin(\omega t-\varphi),$ $\varphi=\tan^{-1}\dfrac{\omega}{-a}$	$\dfrac{1}{s[(s+a)^2+\omega^2]}$

18        $1 - \dfrac{1}{\sqrt{1-\zeta^2}} e^{-\zeta\omega_n t} \sin(\omega_n\sqrt{1-\zeta^2}\,t + \varphi),$ $\dfrac{\omega_n^2}{s(s^2 + 2\zeta\omega_n s + \omega_n^2)}$

           $\varphi = \cos^{-1}\zeta,\ \zeta < 1$

Linearity

If the functions $f_1(t)$ and $f_2(t)$ are Laplace transformable and with K_1 and K_2 being constants, then

$$\pounds[K_1 f_1(t) + K_2 f_2(t)] = K_1 F_1(s) + K_2 F_2(s) \qquad (5.3\text{-}1)$$

This result follows directly from Equation (5.1-4) since

$$\pounds[K_1 f_1(t)] = \int_0^\infty [K_1 f_1(t) + K_2 f_2(t)] e^{-st}\, dt$$

$$= \int_0^\infty K_1 f_1(t) e^{-st}\, dt + \int_0^\infty K_2 f_2(t) e^{-st}\, dt$$

$$= K_1 F_1(s) + K_2 F_1(s)$$

Note that this property was used in carrying out Example 5.2-4.

Differentiation

The transform of the derivative of a time function is important in the solution of differential equations. If the function $f(t)$ and its derivative $df(t)/dt$ are Laplace transformable, then from the basic definition of the Laplace transform we can write

$$\pounds\left[\dfrac{df(t)}{dt}\right] = \int_0^\infty \dfrac{df(t)}{dt} e^{-st}\, dt \qquad (5.3\text{-}2)$$

Integrate by parts, by writing

$$u = e^{-st} \qquad\qquad du = -se^{-st}\, dt$$

$$dv = \dfrac{df}{dt}dt \qquad\qquad v = f$$

then

$$\pounds\left[\dfrac{df(t)}{dt}\right] = f(t)e^{-st}\Big|_0^\infty + s\int_0^\infty f(t)e^{-st}\, dt$$

The limit of $f(t)e^{-st}$ as $t \to \infty$ must be zero, otherwise the transform would not exist. Thus

$$\pounds \left[\frac{df(t)}{dt} \right] = s\pounds[f(t)] - f(0+) = sF(s) - f(0+) \qquad (5.3\text{-}3)$$

In this expression $f(0+)$ denotes the value of the function $f(t)$ at the time $t=0+$, but by entry 1 in Table 5.2-1 this represents an impulse of strength $f(0+)$. This is a very important result in network problems since it shows that initial conditions associated with derivative functions are automatically included as series impulse functions in the network description. In particular, if $f(t)$ denotes the current through an inductor, then terms of the form $v = L\,di/dt$ are included in the network equations. In this case, when such a term is Laplace transformed, there will be terms of the form

$$\pounds \left[L \frac{di(t)}{dt} \right] = LsI(s) - Li(0+)$$

where $i(0+)$ denotes the initial current through the inductor. This result means that an inductor with an initial current can be regarded in subsequent calculations as the equivalent of an initially relaxed inductor plus an impulse current source at initial time $t=0$.

To find the transform of the second time derivative, we use Equation (5.3-3) plus induction. We note that

$$\frac{d^2f(t)}{dt^2} = \frac{d}{dt}\left(\frac{df(t)}{dt} \right)$$

then

$$\pounds \left[\frac{d^2f(t)}{dt^2} \right] = \pounds \left[\frac{d}{dt}\left(\frac{df(t)}{dt} \right) \right] = s\pounds \left[\frac{df(t)}{dt} \right] - \frac{df(0+)}{dt}$$

Again using Equation (5.3-3)

$$\pounds \left[\frac{d^2f(t)}{dt^2} \right] = s^2F(s) - sf(0+) - f^{(1)}(0+) \qquad (5.3\text{-}4)$$

where, for convenience in writing, $f^{(1)}(0+)$ denotes df/dt at $t=0+$.

The Laplace transform of the nth time derivative follows as a direct extension of the foregoing development. The result is found to be

$$\pounds \left[\frac{d^nf(t)}{dt^n} \right] = s^nF(s) - s^{n-1}f(0+) - s^{n-2}f^{(1)}(0+) - \ldots - f^{(n-1)}(0+) \qquad (5.3\text{-}5)$$

where $f^{(k)}(0+)$ denotes the kth derivative $d^k f(0+)/dt^k$ at $t=0+$. If all initial values are zero, this expression reduces to the form

$$\pounds\left[\frac{d^n f(t)}{dt^n}\right]=s^n F(s) \qquad\qquad (5.3\text{-}6)$$

EXAMPLE 5.3-1. Find the Laplace transform of the current in the circuit shown in Figure 5.3-1.

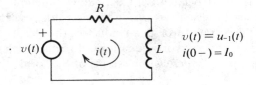

Figure 5.3-1. Transient behavior of an electric circuit

SOLUTION. The Kirchhoff voltage law gives

$$L\frac{di(t)}{dt}+Ri(t)=v(t)=u_{-1}(t)$$

Take the Laplace transform of both sides of the equation. This yields

$$L\pounds\left[\frac{di(t)}{dt}\right]+R\pounds[i(t)]=\pounds[u_{-1}(t)]$$

or

$$LsI(s)-Li(0+)+RI(s)=\frac{1}{s}$$

or

$$I(s)=\frac{1}{s(Ls+R)}+\frac{Li(0+)}{Ls+R}=\frac{1}{s(Ls+R)}+\frac{LI_o}{Ls+R}$$

where the linearity and differentiation properties were used. The conservation of flux linkage theorem allows us to write $i(0-)=I_o=i(0+)$ (see Section 3.4).

□ □ □

Integration

The transform of a time integral proceeds in a straightforward manner from the definition of the Laplace transform. If the function $f(t)$ is Laplace transformable, then its integral is written

$$\pounds\left[\int_{-\infty}^{t} f(t')\,dt'\right] = \int_{0}^{\infty}\left[\int_{-\infty}^{t} f(t')\,dt'\right] e^{-st}\,dt$$

This is integrated by parts by setting

$$u = \int_{-\infty}^{t} f(t')\,dt' \qquad\qquad du = f(t)\,dt$$

$$dv = e^{-st}\,dt \qquad\qquad v = -\frac{1}{s}e^{-st}$$

Then

$$\pounds\left[\int_{-\infty}^{t} f(t')\,dt'\right] = \left[-\frac{e^{-st}}{s}\int_{-\infty}^{t} f(t')\,dt'\right]\Big|_{0}^{\infty} + \frac{1}{s}\int_{0}^{\infty} f(t)e^{-st}\,dt$$

$$= \frac{1}{s}\int_{0}^{\infty} f(t)e^{-st}\,dt + \frac{1}{s}\int_{-\infty}^{0} f(t')\,dt'$$

from which

$$\pounds\left[\int_{-\infty}^{t} f(t')\,dt'\right] = \frac{1}{s}F(s) + \frac{1}{s}f^{(-1)}(0+) \qquad\qquad (5.3\text{-}7)$$

where

$$\frac{f^{(-1)}(0+)}{s}$$

is the initial value of the integral of $f(t)$ at $t = 0+$ and

$$f^{(-1)}(0+) = \int_{-\infty}^{0} f(t')\,dt'$$

Note by entry 2 in Table 5.2-1 that this term denotes a step function of amplitude $f^{(-1)}(0+)$. This also is a very important result in network problems since it shows that initial conditions associated with integral functions are automatically included as step functions in the Laplace transform development. In particular, if $f(t)$ denotes a current $i(t)$ through a capacitor, then the voltage across the capacitor is expressed by the relation

$$v(t) = \frac{q(t)}{C} = \frac{1}{C}\int_{-\infty}^{t} i(t')\,dt'$$

The Laplace transform of such a term then becomes

$$\pounds\left[\frac{q(t)}{C}\right] = \pounds\left[\frac{1}{C}\int_{-\infty}^{t} i(t')\,dt'\right] = \frac{I(s)}{Cs} + \frac{q(0+)}{Cs}$$

where $q(0+)$ is the charge on the capacitor at initial time $t=0+$. This result means that an initially charged capacitor can be regarded, in so far as the subsequent action in a circuit is concerned, as an initially relaxed capacitor plus a series step function voltage source; or equivalently (because of source transformation — see Section 2.6), a shunting step-function current source.

EXAMPLE 5.3-2. Find the Laplace transform of the current in the circuit shown in Figure 5.3-2.

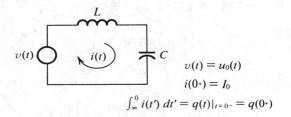

$$v(t) = u_0(t)$$
$$i(0+) = I_0$$
$$\int_{\infty}^{0} i(t')\,dt' = q(t)|_{t=0-} = q(0+)$$

Figure 5.3-2.   Transient behavior of an electric circuit

SOLUTION. Apply the Kirchhoff voltage law. We find the equation

$$L\frac{di(t)}{dt} + \frac{1}{C}\int_{-\infty}^{t} i(t')\,dt' = u_o(t)$$

Take the Laplace transform of both sides of this equation and introduce the initial conditions. We obtain, since $i(0-) = i(0+) = I_o$,

$$LsI(s) - LI_o + \frac{1}{s}I(s) + \frac{1}{Cs}q(0+) = 1$$

or

$$I(s) = \frac{s}{Ls^2+1} - \frac{q(0+)}{C(Ls^2+1)} + \frac{LI_o s}{Ls^2+1} = \frac{s}{Ls^2+1} - \frac{V(0+)}{Ls^2+1} + \frac{LI_o s}{Ls^2+1}$$

where $V(0+)$ is the initial voltage across the capacitor due to the initial current in the circuit.

□   □   □

Time Translation

We shall find occasion to express the transform of a function that has been translated along the time axis. This is the situation illustrated in Figure 5.3-3, which shows the translation of a function $f(t)$ to the right by λ units of time. Upon introducing the translated function into Equation (5.1-4) we obtain

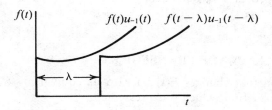

Figure 5.3-3.   A function $f(t)u_{-1}(t)$ and the same function delayed by a time $t = \lambda$

$$\pounds[f(t-\lambda)u_{-1}(t-\lambda)] = \int_0^\infty f(t-\lambda)u_{-1}(t-\lambda)e^{-st}\, dt$$

Next, introducing a new variable $\tau = t - \lambda$, we obtain: $d\tau = dt$, $\tau = 0 - \lambda = -\lambda$ and $\tau = \infty - \lambda = \infty$. This equation takes the form

$$
\begin{aligned}
\pounds[f(\tau)u_{-1}(\tau)] &= e^{-s\lambda}\int_{-\lambda}^\infty f(\tau)u_{-1}(\tau)e^{-s\tau}\, d\tau \\
&= e^{-s\lambda}\int_0^\infty f(\tau)e^{-s\tau}\, d\tau = e^{-s\lambda}F(s)
\end{aligned}
\tag{5.3-8}
$$

since $u_{-1}(\tau) = 0$ for $-\lambda \leqslant \tau \leqslant 0$. Similarly, we find that

$$\pounds[f(t+\lambda)u_{-1}(t+\lambda)] = e^{s\lambda}F(s) \tag{5.3-9}$$

EXAMPLE 5.3-3. Find the Laplace transform of the pulse function shown in Figure 5.3-4.

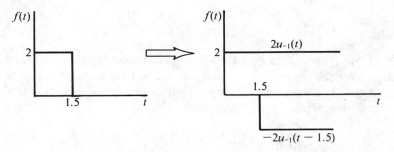

Figure 5.3-4.   Pulse function and its equivalent representation

SOLUTION. Since the pulse function can be decomposed into two step functions as shown in the figure, its Laplace transform is given by

$$\pounds[2(u_{-1}(t) - u_{-1}(t-1.5))] = 2\left(\frac{1}{s} - \frac{1}{s}e^{-s1.5}\right) = \frac{2}{s}(1 - e^{-1.5s})$$

where the shift property was invoked.

□   □   □

5.4   INVERSE LAPLACE TRANSFORM

The operation that changes $F(s)$ back to its equivalent $f(t)$ is the inverse Laplace transformation, which is expressed as

$$\pounds^{-1}[F(s)] = f(t) = \frac{1}{2\pi j}\int_{a-j\infty}^{a+j\infty} F(s)e^{st}\,ds \qquad (5.4\text{-}1)$$

A rigorous proof of the inverse Laplace transform is rather involved and is beyond the scope of this book. Likewise, the evaluation of the line integral is also beyond the scope of this book because it involves contour integration in the complex plane, a study involving complex function theory. However, we shall present a few examples which will show that this formal mathematical procedure can be circumvented by recognizing that the transform pairs given in Table 5.2-1 satisfy Equation (5.4-1).

EXAMPLE 5.4-1. Find the inverse Laplace transform of the function

$$F(s) = \frac{s-2}{s^2 + 3s + 2} \qquad (5.4\text{-}2)$$

SOLUTION. We observe that the denominator can be factored into the product of the terms $(s+1)(s+2)$ since -1 and -2 are roots of the second order algebraic equation $s^2 + 3s + 2$. We next split Equation (5.4-2) into partial fractions in the following manner

$$F(s) = \frac{s-2}{(s+1)(s+2)} = \frac{A}{s+1} + \frac{B}{s+2} \qquad (5.4\text{-}3)$$

where A and B are constants that must be determined, and the first term is the principal part for the pole at -1 and the second term is the principal part for the pole at -2. To evaluate A, we multiply both sides of Equation (5.4-3) by $(s+1)$ and then set $s = -1$. This gives

$$A = F(s)(s+1)\bigg|_{s=-1} = \frac{s-2}{s+2}\bigg|_{s=-1} = -3$$

since

$$\frac{B(s+1)}{s+2}\bigg|_{s=-1}$$

is identically zero. Similarly, for the constant B we have

$$B = F(s)(s+2)\bigg|_{s=-2} = \frac{s-2}{s+1}\bigg|_{s=-2} = 4$$

Hence, the inverse transform is given by

$$\pounds^{-1}[F(s)] = -3\pounds^{-1}\left[\frac{1}{s+1}\right] + 4\pounds^{-1}\left[\frac{1}{s+2}\right] = -3e^{-t} + 4e^{-2t}$$

where Table 5.2-1 was used.

□   □   □

EXAMPLE 5.4-2. Find the inverse Laplace transform of the function

$$F(s) = \frac{s+2}{[(s+1)^2 + 2](s+3)}$$

SOLUTION. This function can be cast into the following form

$$F(s) = \frac{A}{s+3} + \frac{Bs+C}{(s+1)^2 + 2} = \frac{s+2}{[(s+1)^2 + 2](s+3)}$$

Observe the use of functions of s one lower order in the numerator than in the denominator.

We follow the procedure of the previous example. That is, we evaluate A by multiplying both sides by $(s+3)$ and then set $s = -3$; hence

$$A = (s+3)F(s)\bigg|_{s=-3} = \frac{-3+2}{(-3+1)^2 + 2} = -\frac{1}{6}$$

To evaluate B and C we combine the two fractions and equate the coefficients of like powers of s of the numerators. We obtain

$$\frac{-\frac{1}{6}[(s+1)^2 + 2] + (s+3)(Bs+C)}{(s+3)[(s+1)^2 + 2]} = \frac{s+2}{[(s+1)^2 + 2](s+3)}$$

and therefore

$$-\frac{1}{6}[s^2+1+2s+2]+s^2B+sC+3Bs+3C=s+2$$

or equivalently

$$\left(-\frac{1}{6}+B\right)s^2+\left(-\frac{1}{3}+C+3B\right)s+\left(-\frac{1}{2}+3C\right)=s+2$$

From this we deduce that

$$-\frac{1}{6}+B=0, \qquad -\frac{1}{3}+C+3B=1, \qquad -\frac{1}{2}+3C=2$$

From the last three equations we obtain

$$B=\frac{1}{6} \quad \text{and} \quad C=\frac{5}{6}$$

Therefore, we have that

$$F(s)=-\frac{1}{6}\frac{1}{s+3}+\frac{\frac{1}{6}s+\frac{5}{6}}{(s+1)^2+2}=-\frac{1}{6(s+3)}+\frac{1}{6}\frac{s+1}{(s+1)^2+2}+\frac{2\sqrt{2}}{(s+1)^2+(\sqrt{2})^2}\frac{\sqrt{2}}{}$$

and its inverse is easily obtained by using Table 5.2-1. The result is

$$f(t)=-\frac{1}{6}e^{-3t}+\frac{1}{6}e^{-t}\cos\sqrt{2}\,t+2\sqrt{2}e^{-t}\sin\sqrt{2}\,t$$

□   □   □

EXAMPLE 5.4-3. Find the inverse Laplace transform of the function

$$F(s)=\frac{s+3}{(s+2)(s+1)^3}$$

SOLUTION. In this case there exists a first-order pole at $s=-2$ and a third-order pole at $s=-1$. We expand $F(s)$ as follows

$$F(s)=\frac{s+3}{(s+2)(s+1)^3}=\frac{A}{s+2}+\underbrace{\frac{B_1}{s+1}+\frac{B_2}{(s+1)^2}+\frac{B_3}{(s+1)^3}}_{\text{principal part for pole at }-1}$$

We first evaluate A as before, or

$$A = (s+2)F(s)|_{s=-2} = \frac{-2+3}{(-2+1)^3} = -1$$

The coefficients B_n are found by applying the following formula

$$B_n = \left\{ \frac{1}{(k-n)!} \frac{d^{k-n}}{ds^{k-n}}[(s+a)^k F(s)] \right\}\bigg|_{s=-a} \qquad n = 1, 2, \ldots, k \qquad (5.4\text{-}4)$$

where k is the order of the pole in question. In our case we have

$$B_1 = \frac{1}{2!} \frac{d^2}{ds^2}[(s+1)^3 F(s)]\bigg|_{s=-1} = \frac{1}{2}\frac{2s+4}{(s^2+4s+4)^2}\bigg|_{s=-1} = \frac{1}{2}\frac{-2+4}{(1-4+4)^2} = 1$$

$$B_2 = \frac{1}{1!} \frac{d}{ds}[(s+1)^3 F(s)]\bigg|_{s=-1} = -\frac{1}{(s+2)^2}\bigg|_{s=-1} = -1$$

$$B_3 = \frac{1}{0!} \frac{d^\circ}{ds^\circ}[(s+1)^3 F(s)]\bigg|_{s=-1} = \frac{s+3}{s+2}\bigg|_{s=-1} = 2$$

Our function has the final form

$$F(s) = -\frac{1}{s+2} + \frac{1}{s+1} - \frac{1}{(s+1)^2} + \frac{2}{(s+1)^3}$$

The inverse transform is obtained using Table 5.2-1, which is

$$f(t) = -e^{-2t} + e^{-t} - te^{-t} + \frac{2t^2 e^{-t}}{2!} = -e^{-2t} + e^{-t} - te^{-t} - t^2 e^{-t} = e^{-t}(1+t-t^2-e^{-t})$$

$$\square \quad \square \quad \square$$

We call attention to the fact that the functions with which we are concerned are rational functions of s, that is, they are the ratio of two polynomials. Ordinarily these are *proper fractions* since the degree of the numerator polynomial is less than the degree of the denominator polynomial. If these are not rational fractions, the numerator polynomial is divided by the denominator polynomial, with the long division being carried to the point where the resulting fraction is of one degree less than the denominator polynomial. This results in power terms plus a proper fraction. Each power term and the resulting proper fraction are handled directly.

EXAMPLE 5.4-4. Find the inverse transform of the function

$$F(s) = \frac{s^2 + 3s + 4}{s+1}$$

SOLUTION. By long division, this function is written

$$F(s) = s + 2 + \frac{2}{s+1}$$

The inverse transform is

$$f(t) = u_1(t) + 2u_o(t) + 2e^{-t}$$

where $u_1(t)$ is a doublet impulse at $t = 0$, and $u_o(t)$ is the impulse function.

□ □ □

5.5   PROBLEM SOLVING BY LAPLACE TRANSFORMS

We shall consider several examples which will show the manner of employing the Laplace transform in the solution of network problems, and also the relationship of the results to those using the time domain methods already discussed.

EXAMPLE 5.5-1. Find an expression for the current in the simple RL series circuit shown in Figure 5.5-1. Assume that an initial current $i(0-)$ exists in the inductor at the time when the switch S is closed.

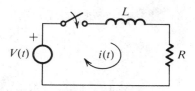

**Figure 5.5-1.   A simple circuit excited by a step voltage source
(a battery switched on)**

SOLUTION. The system differential equation is seen to be

$$L\frac{di}{dt} + Ri = Vu_{-1}(t)$$

By taking the Laplace transform of each term in this differential equation, then

$$L[sI(s) - i(0+)] + RI(s) = \frac{V}{s}$$

In this case we readily see that $i(0+) = i(0-)$, the specified value. This is re-arranged to

$$(Ls + R)I(s) = \frac{V}{s} + Li(0+)$$

We solve for $I(s)$

$$I(s) = \frac{V}{L}\frac{1}{s\left(s + \dfrac{R}{L}\right)} + \frac{i(0+)}{\left(s + \dfrac{R}{L}\right)} = \frac{V}{L}\left[\frac{L}{R}\frac{1}{s} - \frac{L}{R}\frac{1}{\left(s + \dfrac{R}{L}\right)}\right] + \frac{i(0+)}{s + \dfrac{R}{L}}$$

and write this as

$$I(s) = \frac{V}{R}\left(\frac{1}{s} - \frac{1}{s + \dfrac{R}{L}}\right) + i(0+)\frac{1}{s + \dfrac{R}{L}}$$

Observe that the expression for $I(s)$ is made up of three terms: one is due to the applied excitation or forcing function (this leads to the particular solution) $Vu_{-1}(t)$ which appears in its transformed form V/s; the second arises from the network owing to the excitation applied suddenly (the transient or complementary function); the third is also a transient term that is due to the initial current, and appears as an impulse excitation of strength $i(0+)$. We observe also that the nature of the network appears in the function $1/(s + R/L)$, which is the system function $H(s)$, the network for input voltage and output current. To find $H(s)$ we simply disregard any initial conditions and set the input function equal to a delta excitation $u_o(t)$.

Upon taking the inverse Laplace transform of the last equation, we get the result

$$i(t) = \frac{V}{R}u_{-1}(t) - \frac{V}{R}e^{-(R/L)t}u_{-1}(t) + i(0+)e^{-(R/L)t}u_{-1}(t)$$

which, at $t = \infty$, becomes $i(t) = V/R$. This result is expected since all the currents corresponding to transient excitations decay to zero.

□ □ □

EXAMPLE 5.5-2. Find the velocity of the mechanical system shown in Figure 5.5-2 if there is an initial spring deformation of 2 unit lengths. It is assumed that an impulse force is applied at $t = 0$, $f = u_o(t)$.

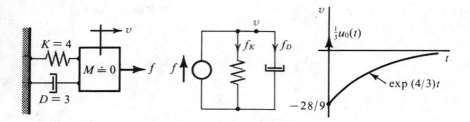

Figure 5.5-2.   Response of a mechanical system

SOLUTION. From Figures 5.5-2a and 5.5-2b the equilibrium equation is

$$Dv + K\int v\,dt = u_o(t)$$

Laplace this equation, noting that $v(0+) = v(0-)$, $D = 3$, $K = 4$. This yields

$$3V(s) + \frac{4}{s}V(s) + 4\frac{2}{s} = 1$$

from which

$$V(s) = \frac{1}{3}\frac{s-8}{s+\frac{4}{3}} = \frac{1}{3}\left(1 - \frac{28}{3}\frac{1}{s+\frac{4}{3}}\right) = -\frac{28}{9}\frac{1}{s+\frac{4}{3}} + \frac{1}{3}$$

The inverse transform is easily found to be (see Table 5.2-1)

$$v(t) = -\frac{28}{9}e^{-(4/3)t}u_{-1}(t) + \frac{1}{3}u_o(t)$$

□   □   □

EXAMPLE 5.5-3. Find the current in the circuit shown in Figure 5.5-3. The source is an impulse function and no initial currents or charges exist.

SOLUTION. Apply the Kirchhoff voltage law to obtain

$$\frac{di(t)}{dt} + \int i(t)\,dt = u_o(t)$$

The Laplace transform of this equation yields

$$sI(s) + \frac{I(s)}{s} = 1 \qquad \text{or} \qquad I(s) = \frac{s}{s^2 + 1}$$

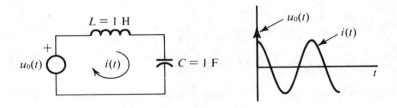

Figure 5.5-3. An RL circuit excited by an impulse function

and its inverse is given (see Table 5.2-1) by

$$i(t) = \cos t$$

We observe that the current never dies out but continues to oscillate. The phenomenon can be easily explained if we consider that the energy which was supplied instantaneously by the source had been constituted as a magnetic field about the coil and as an electric field between the plates of the capacitor. At the moment when $i(t) = 0$ the total energy is present in the associated electric field in space. At the instant when $i(t) = 1$ all of the energy has been transformed to the magnetic field. This exchange of these two energy forms continues forever because the circuit is without the dissipation element, the resistor.

□   □   □

EXAMPLE 5.5-4. Find the transformed expressions for the currents $i_1(t)$ and $i_2(t)$ for the coupled circuit shown in Figure 5.5-4.

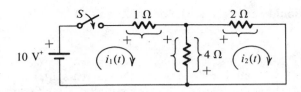

Figure 5.5-4. A two-loop all resistor electrical circuit

SOLUTION. The KVL equations for the two loops are

$$\text{loop 1:} \quad 10 - 1i_1(t) - 4i_1(t) + 4i_2(t) = 0$$

$$\text{loop 2:} \quad -2i_2(t) - 4i_2(t) + 4i_1(t) = 0$$

which are

$$5i_1(t) - 4i_2(t) = 10$$
$$4i_1(t) - 6i_2(t) = 0$$

The Laplace transforms of these equations are:

$$5I_1(s) - 4I_2(s) = \frac{10}{s}$$
$$4I_1(s) - 6I_2(s) = 0$$

The currents $I_1(s)$ and $I_2(s)$ are obtained by an application of Cramer's rule (see Appendix III), or by substitution, and are

$$I_1(s) = \frac{\begin{vmatrix} \dfrac{10}{s} & -4 \\ 0 & -6 \end{vmatrix}}{\begin{vmatrix} 5 & -4 \\ 4 & -6 \end{vmatrix}} = \frac{-\dfrac{60}{s} + 4 \times 0}{-30 + 16} = \frac{30}{7}\frac{1}{s}$$

$$I_2(s) = \frac{\begin{vmatrix} 5 & \dfrac{10}{s} \\ 4 & -6 \end{vmatrix}}{-30 + 16} = \frac{5 \times 0 - 4 \times \dfrac{10}{s}}{-30 + 16} = \frac{20}{7}\frac{1}{s}$$

From Table 5.2-1 the inverse Laplace transforms of these currents are

$$i_1(t) = \frac{30}{7} u_{-1}(t) \qquad\qquad i_2(t) = \frac{20}{7} u_{-1}(t)$$

The reader should verify the KVL for any time $t > 0$.

☐ ☐ ☐

EXAMPLE 5.5-5. Find expressions for the currents $i_1(t)$ and $i_2(t)$ for the coupled circuit shown in Figure 5.5-5, for initially relaxed conditions.

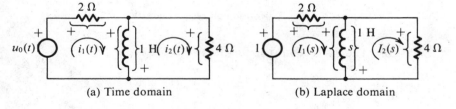

(a) Time domain   (b) Laplace domain

Figure 5.5-5.   A two-loop electrical circuit

SOLUTION. An application of the KVL equations to the two loops yields

loop 1: $\quad u_o(t) - 2i_1(t) - 1\dfrac{di_1(t)}{dt} + 1\dfrac{di_2(t)}{dt} = 0$

loop 2: $\quad -4i_2(t) - 1\dfrac{di_2(t)}{dt} + 1\dfrac{di_1(t)}{dt} = 0$

Laplace transform these equations to find

$$1 - 2I_1(s) - sI_1(s) + sI_2(s) = 0$$
$$-4I_2(s) - sI_2(s) + sI_1(s) = 0$$

or

$$(s+2)I_1(s) - sI_2(s) = 1$$
$$sI_1(s) - (s+4)I_2(s) = 0$$

Use Cramer's rule to find $I_1(s)$

$$I_1(s) = \frac{\begin{vmatrix} 1 & -s \\ 0 & -(s+4) \end{vmatrix}}{\begin{vmatrix} (s+2) & -s \\ s & -(s+4) \end{vmatrix}} = \frac{-(s+4) + s \times 0}{-(s+2)(s+4) + s^2} = \frac{1}{6}\frac{s+4}{s+\dfrac{4}{3}}$$

To find $I_2(s)$, the value for $I_1(s)$ is combined with the second equation in the set

$$I_2(s) = \frac{sI_1(s)}{s+4} = \frac{s}{s+4} \times \frac{1}{6} \times \frac{s+4}{s+\dfrac{4}{3}} = \frac{1}{6} \times \frac{s}{s+\dfrac{4}{3}}$$

To find the corresponding time functions requires that we take the inverse Laplace transforms of $I_1(s)$ and $I_2(s)$. Consider $I_1(s)$ which is expanded to the form

$$I_1(s) = \frac{1}{6}\frac{s+4}{s+\dfrac{4}{3}} \triangleq \frac{1}{6}\left(A + \frac{B}{s+\dfrac{4}{3}}\right) = \frac{1}{6}\frac{As + \dfrac{4}{3}A + B}{s+\dfrac{4}{3}}$$

Equate terms of equal powers of s to find: $A = 1$ and $4/3A + B = 4$, from which $A = 1$, $B = 8/3$. Hence the expression for $I_1(s)$ is

$$I_1(s) = \frac{1}{6}\left(1 + \frac{8}{3}\frac{1}{s+\dfrac{4}{3}}\right)$$

The inverse Laplace transform is, from Table 5.2-1

$$i_1(t) = \frac{1}{6}\left[u_o(t) + \frac{8}{3}e^{-(4/3)t} \right]$$

By following the same procedure for $I_2(s)$, the expression for $i_2(t)$ is

$$i_2(t) = \frac{1}{6}\left[u_o(t) - \frac{4}{3}e^{-(4/3)t} \right]$$

Note that for any time greater than $t = 0$ the value of $u_o(t) = 0$, and the currents are then

$$i_1(t) = \frac{8}{18}e^{-(4/3)t} \qquad\qquad i_2 = -\frac{4}{18}e^{-(4/3)t}$$

It is interesting to substitute these two equations in the loop equation 2. This yields

$$-4\left(-\frac{4}{18}e^{-(4/3)t} \right) - \left[-\frac{4}{18}\left(-\frac{4}{3}e^{-(4/3)t} \right) + \frac{8}{18}\left(-\frac{4}{3} \right)e^{-(4/3)t} \right] = 0$$

or

$$e^{-(4/3)t}\left[\frac{16}{18} - \frac{16}{54} - \frac{72}{54} \right] = 0 \qquad \text{or} \qquad 0 = 0$$

This shows that the KVL is satisfied at any time $t > 0$, as it must.

□ □ □

5.6 POSTLUDE

The importance of the Laplace transform in system studies is two-fold: (a) it introduces the concept of solving differential equations in time by transforming from the time-domain to the algebraic s-domain, carrying out algebraic manipulations in the s-domain and then inverting the result to obtain the time-domain solution; and (b) it introduces the concept of an integral transformation into continuous time systems theory. We shall employ other integral transforms in our later studies. Of special importance in the Laplace transform development is that the system function $H(s)$, which will be discussed in some detail in Chapter 6, automatically appears in the solution, and initial conditions are automatically provided for in the solution rather than having to include them in the solution through separate steps. The method involves the use of tables of Laplace transforms; a short table is included, with more extensive tables available.

The inversion integral, which was not introduced because it involves a background in the theory of functions of a complex variable, is a topic for future study. The inversion process is accomplished by table lookup, and meets most present needs.

SUMMARY

- The Laplace transform of a time function $f(t)$ is defined by the equation

$$\pounds[f(t)] = \int_0^\infty f(t)e^{-st}\, dt$$

where $f(t)$ must be piecewise continuous and of exponential order; i.e., $f(t)$ must remain less than Me^{at} as $t \to \infty$, where M is a positive constant and a is a real number.

- Some of the main properties of the Laplace transform are:

Linearity: $\pounds[K_1 f_1(t) + K_2 f_2(t)] = K_1 F_1(s) + K_2 F_2(s)$

Differentiation: $\pounds\left[\dfrac{df(t)}{dt}\right] = sF(s) - f(0+)$

$\pounds\left[\dfrac{d^2 f}{dt^2}\right] = s^2 F(s) - sf(0+) - \dfrac{df(0+)}{dt}$

Integration: $\pounds\left[\displaystyle\int_{-\infty}^t f(t')\, dt'\right] = \dfrac{F(s)}{s} + \dfrac{1}{s}\int_{-\infty}^0 f(t')\, dt'$

Time translation: $\pounds[f(t-\lambda)u_{-1}(t-\lambda)] = e^{-s\lambda}F(s)$

- The advantage in solving differential equations using Laplace transforms is that we transform them from the time domain to an algebraic domain. It is easy to find the unknown function in its transformed state. We then find the response in the time domain by taking the inverse Laplace transform.

REVIEW QUESTIONS

1. State the Laplace transform. What type of functions are Laplace transformable?
2. What is the Laplace transform of the functions: $u_o(t)$; $u_{-1}(t)$?
3. What do we mean when we say that the Laplace transform operation is linear?
4. When we take the Laplace transform of a derivative or integral do we need to know the initial conditions?
5. Where do we use the partial fraction expansion of a function?

REFERENCES

1. Aseltine, J. A., *Transform Methods in Linear Systems Analysis*, McGraw Hill Book Co., New York, NY, 1958.

   A number of transform methods are discussed, including Laplace transforms, in a variety of engineering problems. Attention is directed at an understanding of the physical phenomena.

2. Papoulis, A., *The Fourier Integral and Its Applications*, McGraw Hill Book Co., New York, NY, 1962.

   An advanced text that contains an excellent development of the use of Fourier and Laplace transforms.

3. LePage, W. R., *Complex Variables and the Laplace Transform for Engineers*, McGraw Hill Book Co., New York, NY, 1961.

   A very complete discussion of Laplace transforms and their applications. Written for senior first-year graduate level students.

4. Seely, S., *An Introduction to Engineering Systems*, Pergamon Press, Inc., Elmsford, NY, 1972.

   This text contains the essential features of the Laplace transform and the application to problem solving. Written for lower division students, and includes detailed procedures for its use.

PROBLEMS

5.2-1. Find the Laplace transform of the following functions:

   (a) $f(t) = e^{bt} u_{-1}(t)$
   (b) $f(t) = e^{-at}[\sin (\omega t)] u_{-1}(t)$
   (c) $f(t) = e^{-at}[\cos (\omega t)] u_{-1}(t)$

5.3-1. Find the Laplace transform of the displacement x if the input force $f(t)$ to the mass M is $[\sin (\omega t)] u_{-1}(t)$ (see Figure P5.3-1). Assume zero initial conditions.

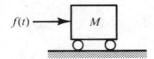

Figure P5.3-1

5.3-2. Find the Laplace transform of the voltages of the systems shown in Figure P5.3-2 if the input current source is a pulse function, $i(t) = u_{-1}(t - 1) - u_{-1}(t - 2)$ and the initial conditions are zero.

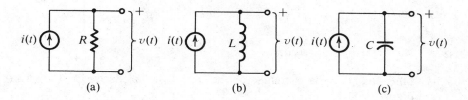

Figure P5.3-2

5.3-3. Find the Laplace transform of the velocity of the system shown in Figure P5.3-3. The applied force is an impulse function, $f(t) = 2u_o(t)$ and the initial conditions are zero.

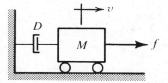

Figure P5.3-3

5.3-4. Find the Laplace transform of the current for the circuit shown in Figure P5.3-4. Assume zero initial conditions.

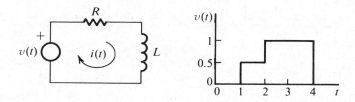

Figure P5.3-4

5.4-1. Find the inverse Laplace transforms of the following functions:

(a) $F(s) = \dfrac{1}{s} - \dfrac{e^{-2.5s}}{s}$

(b) $F(s) = \dfrac{1}{s+1} + \dfrac{2}{(s+2)^2}$

(c) $F(s) = \dfrac{3}{s^2+2} + \dfrac{s}{s^2+1}$

(d) $F(s) = \dfrac{3(s+2)}{(s+1)^2(s+3)^3}$

(e) $F(s) = \dfrac{1}{(s+1.5)^4}$ $\qquad$ (f) $F(s) = \dfrac{1}{(s+1)(s+2)(s+3)}$

(g) $F(s) = \dfrac{s^3+s+1}{s^3+2s^2-s-2}$ $\qquad$ (h) $F(s) = \dfrac{1}{s^2-1} + \dfrac{s}{s^2+4}$

5.5-1. Find and plot the currents for the initially relaxed circuits shown in Figure P5.5-1.

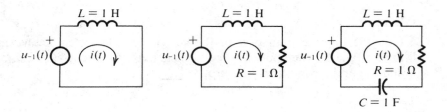

Figure P5.5-1

5.5-2. Find and plot the currents for the circuits of Problem 5.5-1 with initial current for each circuit $i(0-) = 1$ A and no initial charge present.

5.5-3. Find the velocity $v(t)$ for the systems shown in Figure P5.5-3. Given: $M=2$, $K=3$, $D=2$, $v(0-)=1$, $f=u_{-1}(t)-u_{-1}(t-1)$.

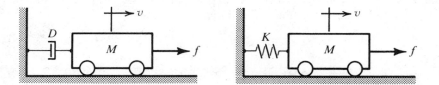

Figure P5.5-3

5.5-4. Find the currents $i_1(t)$ and $i_2(t)$ for the circuit shown in Figure P5.5-4. Assume zero initial conditions. The voltage source is a delta pulse $u_o(t)$.

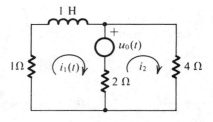

Figure P5.5-4

Chapter Six

Signal Flow Graphs, Block Diagrams and Transfer Functions

Our discussion of system interconnections was a mathematical one which employed fundamental laws of Kirchhoff, D'Alembert and others to write the description of the interconnections of the components of a system by means of differential equations. A second procedure is one which graphically displays the interconnected models and then employs techniques of graphical reductions to write the circuit operations. Two important graphical methods exist: the signal flow graph (SFG) and the block diagram. The two are closely related representations.

These graphical portrayals possess the important feature that the signal paths from input to output are placed in sharp focus without displaying the hardware of the system. Furthermore, they provide tools of analysis which often possess advantages over other methods. The SFG also provides a means for easily establishing the program for analog computer studies of interconnected systems.

We shall show the similarities and differences between the signal flow graph and block diagram representations. To do this, we shall provide separate discussions initially. The relationships between the two will be obvious.

While we shall proceed in the development through a series of mathematical equations which are then given graphical portrayal, we must stress that it is possible to proceed by means of an interconnection pattern and then deduce the equations for the connected system. In fact, this second method is often advantageous since it makes unnecessary some of the steps in the indirect development. Further, by retaining the graphical presentation, system changes are often more readily accommodated in the analysis than through equations. However, since the equation approach has been so extensively studied, it does provide a very convenient way to introduce the graphical presentations.

6.1 PROPERTIES OF SFG

The variables in a signal flow graph are represented by points called *nodes*. Connections between nodes are by directed lines which specify the direction of signal flow; these are called *transmittances*. Generally the independent variables (real or assumed) are viewed as system inputs. The dependent variables, representing the unknown quantities, are viewed as system responses. The paths of interaction and the value of the transmittances along them portray the system interconnection and the effect of one quantity on another.

The rules which exist for the SFG allow algebraic transformations to be effected readily, and a given graph can be rapidly transformed into a form which may have some special attribute for subsequent study. Often, in fact, the SFG makes apparent combinations or transformations that might lead to specially desirable forms. But it should be realized that the SFG technique is involved with the manipulation of the mathematical model of an interconnected physical system. It is less useful in studying the physical system itself.

The rules for drawing a signal flow graph are the following:

1. Signals travel along branches only in the direction of the arrows.

2. The value of a node is the value of the node from which a signal arises multiplied by the transmittances of the branch connecting the nodes.

3. The value of the variable represented by any node is the sum of all signals entering that node.

4. The value of the variable represented by any node is transmitted to all branches leaving that node.

5. The node with only outgoing branches is an input node (or source), and the node with only incoming branches is an output node (or sink).

These rules will be illustrated by several examples.

EXAMPLE 6.1-1. Draw the SFG of the following equations

$$x_4 = t_{14}x_1 + t_{24}x_2 + t_{34}x_3 \quad \text{(the addition rule)}$$

$$x_1 = t_{01}x_0, \ x_2 = t_{02}x_0, \ x_3 = t_{03}x_0 \quad \text{(the transmission rule)}$$

$$x_1 = t_{01}x_0, \ x_2 = t_{12}x_1, \ x_3 = t_{23}x_2 \quad \text{(the multiplication rule)}$$

SOLUTION. The graphs are drawn in Figures 6.1-1a, b and c, respectively.

□   □   □

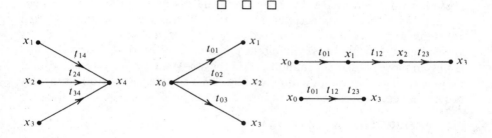

Figure 6.1-1.   The SFG-s of the specified equations

EXAMPLE 6.1-2. Draw the SFG of the equation

$$x_1 = t_{01}x_0 + t_{11}x_1$$

SOLUTION. The graph is drawn according to the specified rules. It is shown in Figure 6.1-2.

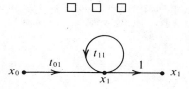

Figure 6.1-2.   The SFG of the specified equation

EXAMPLE 6.1-2. Draw the SFG of the following related equations

$$x_1 = t_{o1}x_o + t_{11}x_1 + t_{21}x_2$$

$$x_2 = t_{o2}x_o + t_{12}x_1 + t_{22}x_2$$

SOLUTION. The graph is the shown in Figure 6.1-3.

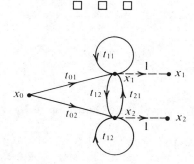

Figure 6.1-3.   The graph of the given pair of equations

Ordinarily a SFG is drawn with no branches entering an input node or leaving an output node. If such branches are desired, this can be accomplished by introducing additional nodes with unit transmittances. Such additional nodes are shown in Figure 6.1-3 to isolate the outputs x_1 and x_2.

6.2   GRAPHING DIFFERENTIAL EQUATIONS

Differential equations can be graphed in a direct manner when the operational symbols p and $1/p$ are used in the equations. The rules are those prescribed above. To examine the procedure, consider the following differential equation:

$$2\frac{dy(t)}{dt} + 5y(t) = 3x(t) \qquad (6.2\text{-}1)$$

This differential equation relates the dependent variable $y(t)$ to the input variable $x(t)$. Clearly, the output variable is y. The procedure is to write this differential equation in a form that shows y explicitly, as follows:

$$y = \frac{3}{5}x - \frac{2}{5}\frac{dy}{dt} \qquad (6.2\text{-}2)$$

In operational form this is

$$y = \frac{3}{5}x - \frac{2}{5}py \qquad (6.2\text{-}3)$$

This equation can be graphed directly as shown in Figure 6.2-1a. Observe that this SFG has been modified to include implicit relations between a variable and its derivative.

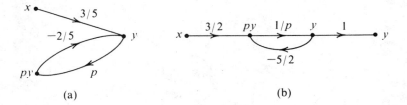

(a)   (b)

Figure 6.2-1.   The SFG-s of Equations (6.2-3) and (6.2-4)

A more interesting and a more useful form of the graph is one which arranges the nodes in such a way that a clear signal path extends from the source node to the output node, the dependent node at which the response is observed. For the present case, this is most conveniently obtained by writing the differential equation in the form

$$py = \frac{3}{2}x - \frac{5}{2}y \qquad (6.2\text{-}4)$$

The graph of this equation is given in Figure 6.2-1b.

We shall later find that in this form the SFG provides the scheme for programming an analog computer (or for using a digital computer provided with an equivalent simulation program, such as CSMP — continuous system modeling program).

EXAMPLE 6.2-1. Find the SFG for the circuit shown in Figure 6.2-2a, where the dependent variable is the charge.

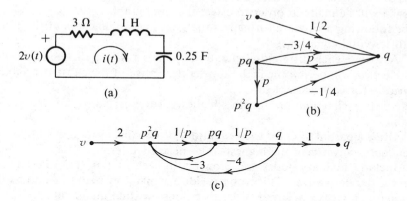

(a)

(b)

(c)

Figure 6.2-2.   The SFG-s of Equations (6.2-6a) and (6.2-6b)

SOLUTION. By an application of the KVL we write

$$\frac{di(t)}{dt} + 4\int i(t)\ dt + 3i(t) = 2v(t)$$

or

$$\frac{d^2q(t)}{dt^2} + 3\frac{dq(t)}{dt} + 4q(t) = 2v(t) \tag{6.2-5}$$

We follow the procedure outlined above to write this equation in the following two forms

$$q = \frac{2}{4}v - \frac{3}{4}pq - \frac{1}{4}p^2q \qquad\qquad \text{(a)} \quad (6.2\text{-}6)$$

$$p^2q = 2v - 3pq - 4q \qquad\qquad \text{(b)}$$

These are graphed in Figures 6.2-2b and 6.2-2c, respectively

□ □ □

6.3 SIMULTANEOUS DIFFERENTIAL EQUATIONS

The procedure in graphing a set of differential equations is a logical extension of the procedure discussed above. Specifically, the procedure calls for each differential equation of the set to be solved for the highest order derivative of the different variables existing in the set. For example, if two related differential equations in x and y exist, one of these will be written in terms of the highest order derivative in x and the second will be written in terms of the highest order derivative in y. Appropriate connections of the SFG for each will be made in order to effect the final graph.

The following procedure formalizes the steps in graphing a set of simultaneous differential equations:

1. Associate each differential equation of the set with a different variable. The selection will permit the highest order derivative of the chosen variable to be written for each variable.

2. Solve each equation for the highest order derivative of the chosen variable.

3. Draw a partial SFG for each equation, proceeding as though all terms are dependent terms except the highest order derivative term.

4. Include auxiliary nodes and branches in each partial SFG to relate successive order derivatives. This is to provide a signal flow path to all nodes that represent derivatives of lower order than those written under rule 2.

5. Combine the partial SFG-s and interconnect identically labeled nodes.

6. Redraw the final graph in a form which clearly displays the transmission paths from the source node to the response node.

EXAMPLE 6.3-1. Graph the following set of differential equations

$$\frac{dy}{dt} + 2y + x = f(t) \qquad \text{(a)} \quad \text{(6.3-1)}$$

$$\frac{dy}{dt} + 4y + \frac{dx}{dt} = 0 \qquad \text{(b)}$$

SOLUTION. The rules given above are followed. The equations are written in operational form with y selected as the variable in the first equation, and x selected as the variable in the second equation:

$$py = f(t) - 2y - x \qquad \text{(a)} \quad \text{(6.3-2)}$$

$$px = -py - 4y \qquad \text{(b)}$$

The partial graphs for each equation are shown in Figures 6.3-1a and 6.3-1b, respectively. The partial graphs are combined into a single SFG, as shown in Figure 6.3-2a, with a rearrangement to show the direct signal flow paths being given in Figure 6.3-2b.

□   □   □

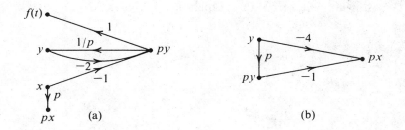

Figure 6.3-1.   SFG-s of the specified equations

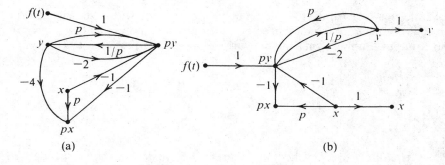

Figure 6.3-2.   SFG representation of Equation (6.3-2)

EXAMPLE 6.3-2. An electrical network is shown in Figure 6.3-3. Draw a SFG in a form that shows the signal flow characteristics through the network from input to output.

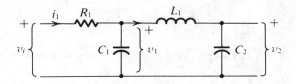

Figure 6.3-3.   The network under survey

SOLUTION. The following equations are written, from an inspection of the circuit:

$$v_i = R_1 i_1 + v_1 \qquad\qquad v_1 = L_1 p i_2 + v_2$$

$$v_1 = \frac{1}{C_1 p}(i_1 - i_2) \qquad\qquad v_2 = \frac{1}{C_2 p} i_2$$

A SFG is drawn directly from these equations in Figure 6.3-4.

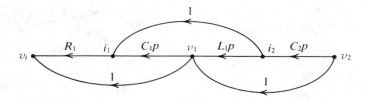

Figure 6.3-4.   A graph of the network equations

While this is a valid SFG, it is not in a form that shows the signal flow through the network from input to output. Rather, it shows the flow from output to input. Suppose that the network equations are rewritten as follows:

$$i_1 = \frac{1}{R_1}(v_i - v_1) \qquad\qquad i_2 = \frac{1}{L_1 p}(v_1 - v_2)$$

$$v_1 = \frac{1}{C_1 p}(i_1 - i_2) \qquad\qquad v_2 = \frac{1}{C_2 p} i_2$$

These equations are graphed in Figure 6.3-5, and this shows the desired properties.

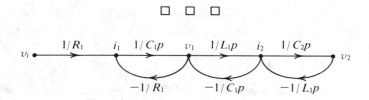

Figure 6.3-5.   The graph showing the signal flow through the network

It is clear from Example 6.3-2 that the form of the SFG will depend upon how the equations relating selected variables are chosen. This lack of a single unique SFG for a given set of equations is both the strength and the weakness of the SFG portrayal. The strength lies in the fact that the system interconnection can be selected from a number of alternatives, allowing selection of the form which will best meet the needs of a given situation. The weakness lies in the fact that it may be necessary to examine a number of alternatives. This versatility is often a real advantage.

EXAMPLE 6.3-3. Draw the signal flow graph for the system given in Figure 6.3-6.

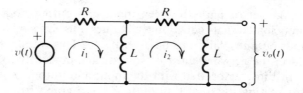

Figure 6.3-6.   The network for this example

SOLUTION. The equations governing the system are

$$Ri_1 + L\frac{d}{dt}(i_1 - i_2) = v(t) \qquad \text{(a)} \quad \text{(6.3-3)}$$

$$Ri_2 + L\frac{d}{dt}(i_2 - i_1) + L\frac{di_2}{dt} = 0 \qquad \text{(b)}$$

$$L\frac{di_2}{dt} = v_o(t) \qquad \text{(c)}$$

Now these equations are rearranged as follows, using the operator p to denote differentiation

$$i_1 = \frac{1}{R+Lp}v + \frac{Lp}{R+Lp}i_2 \qquad \text{(a)} \quad \text{(6.3-4)}$$

$$i_2 = \frac{Lp}{R+2Lp}i_1 \qquad \text{(b)}$$

$$v_o = Lpi_1 \qquad \text{(c)}$$

We arrange the 4 nodes in a convenient array, and use branches appropriate to Equations (6.3-4). The result is that shown in Figure 6.3-7.

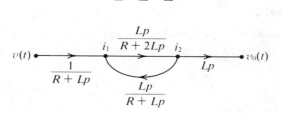

Figure 6.3-7.   The SFG for the circuit of Figure 6.3-6

6.4   THE ALGEBRA OF SFG-s

The examples of Section 6.3 show that sets of simultaneous differential equations lead to a complicated interconnection pattern among the nodes of the SFG, but the set of paths between input and output nodes are clearly shown. It is anticipated that reduction techniques must be available which will permit an input-output relation to be determined. This means that the equations involved in the network must be solved simultaneously to eliminate all variables except those associated with the input and output. A formal set of rules exists for writing the total transmittance of a graph from the transmittances of the individual branches of the graph. The important reduction rules will now be developed.

1. Cascade branches

The reduction follows without difficulty — shown in Figure 6.4-1.

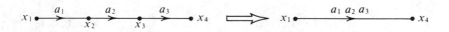

Figure 6.4-1.   Cascaded branches

2. Parallel branches

This reduction follows, according to rule 1, and otherwise without difficulty. The graphs are shown in Figure 6.4-2.

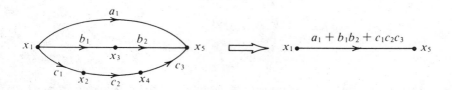

Figure 6.4-2.   Combined parallel and cascaded branches

3. Simple feedback

Refer to Figure 6.4-3 which shows a graph containing a closed loop. The equations appropriate to this graph are written by inspection of the figure. These are

$$x_2 = ax_1 + cx_3$$

$$x_3 = bx_2$$

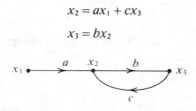

Figure 6.4-3.   A graph involving a feedback loop

These are combined to yield

$$\frac{x_3}{b} = ax_1 + cx_3$$

The total transmittance, which is the ratio x_3/x_1, is

$$\frac{x_3}{x_1} = \frac{ab}{1-bc} \qquad (6.4\text{-}1)$$

This result can be interpreted as follows:

1. If the feedback path c is absent, the signal path from x_1 to x_3 has a direct transmittance ab.

2. The feedback loop introduces the factor $1/(1-bc)$ which is 1 minus the product of the branches of the loop (and this is the loop transmittance).

The above, plus a number of additional SFG transformations and properties, are contained in Table 6.4-1.

Table 6.4-1. Signal Flow Graph Properties

System Diagram	Equivalent Diagram	Observations
$u_1 \xrightarrow{\ T_{12}\ } u_2$		$u_2 = T_{12}u_1$
$u_1 \xrightarrow{T_{13}} u_3 \xleftarrow{T_{23}} u_2$		$u_3 = T_{13}u_1 + T_{23}u_2$
$u_1 \overset{T_{12}}{\underset{T'_{12}}{\rightleftarrows}} u_2$	$u_1 \xrightarrow{\ T_{12}+T'_{12}\ } u_2$	Superposition $u_2 = (T_{12} + T'_{12})u_1$
$u_1 \xrightarrow{T_{12}} u_2 \xrightarrow{T_{23}} u_3$	$u_1 \xrightarrow{\ T_{12}\,T_{23}\ } u_3$	Cascade nodes $u_3 = T_{12}T_{23}u_1$

System Diagram	Equivalent Diagram	Observations
		$u_3 = u_1 T_{13} + u_2 T_{23}$ $u_4 = T_{13} T_{34} u_1 + T_{23} T_{34} u_2$
		Feedback loop $u_3 = \left(\dfrac{T_{12} T_{23}}{1 - T_{23} T_{32}} \right) u_3$
		$u_3 = \dfrac{T_{12} T_{23}}{1 - T_{22}} u_1$
		$u_2 = \dfrac{T_{12}}{1 - T_{12} T_{21}} u_1$
		Absorption of a node
		$u_3 = \dfrac{T_{12} T_{23}}{1 - T_{22}} u_1$

4. Touching and Non-touching Loops

In the case of more complicated graphs the results are dependent on whether feedback loops may be touching other loops. To develop the results, refer to statement 2 in connection with Equation (6.4-1). It is now convenient to discuss the results in terms of a loop that shares nodes with a path, thereby modifying the transmittance of the path. This situation is expressed in the following notation that will be used later; namely,

$$T = \frac{P}{1-L} \tag{6.4-2}$$

where P denotes the path transmittance and L denotes the loop transmittance.

Refer to Figure 6.4-4 which shows two different graphs. For Figure 6.4-4a, the transmittance is written

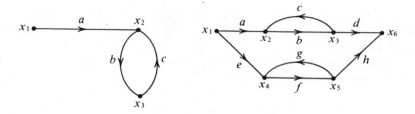

Figure 6.4-4. (a) Single isolated loop   (b) Two isolated loops

$$T = \frac{x_2}{x_1} = \frac{a}{1-bc} = \frac{P}{1-L} \tag{6.4-3}$$

For the two isolated loops shown in Figure 6.4-4b, the result is readily shown to be

$$T = \frac{abd}{1-bc} + \frac{efh}{1-fg} \tag{6.4-4}$$

which can be written as

$$T = \frac{x_6}{x_1} = \frac{P_1}{1-L_1} + \frac{P_2}{1-L_2} \tag{6.4-5}$$

where the path transmittances P_1 and P_2 and the loop transmittances L_1 and L_2 are directly identifiable.

Consider now Figure 6.4-5 which shows two non-touching loops on a single transmission path. This graph is conveniently divided into two cascaded parts, as shown. The total transmittance is the product of the transmittance of each subgraph, or

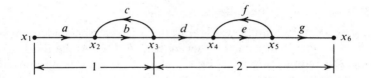

Figure 6.4-5.   Two non-touching loops on a single transmission path

$$T = \frac{x_6}{x_1} = \frac{P_1}{1-L_1} \cdot \frac{P_2}{1-L_2} = \frac{P_1 P_2}{1-L_1-L_2+L_1 L_2} = \frac{P}{1-L_1-L_2-L_1 L_2} \qquad (6.4\text{-}6)$$

which is

$$T = \frac{x_6}{x_1} = \frac{abdeg}{1-bc-ef+bcef} \qquad (6.4\text{-}7)$$

Refer now to Figure 6.4-6 which is similar to Figure 6.4-5 but which shows touching or interacting loops, with two loops sharing a single node. The isolated loop procedure used in conjunction with Figure 6.4-5 cannot be used in this case. Hence detailed attention is given to the SFG. By inspection, the following set of equations is obtained:

$$x_2 = ax_1 + cx_3 \qquad \text{(a)} \quad (6.4\text{-}8)$$

$$x_3 = bx_2 + ex_4 \qquad \text{(b)}$$

$$x_4 = dx_3 \qquad \text{(c)}$$

$$x_5 = fx_4 \qquad \text{(d)}$$

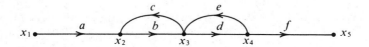

Figure 6.4-6.   A SFG with interacting loops

A systematic elimination of x_2, x_3 and x_4 from this set of equations yields for the transmittance from x_1 to x_5

$$T = \frac{x_5}{x_1} = \frac{abdf}{1-bc-de} \qquad (6.4\text{-}9)$$

which, in terms of our general notation, is

$$T = \frac{P}{1-L_1-L_2} \qquad (6.4\text{-}10)$$

A comparison of this expression with that in Equation (6.4-6) shows that because of the interaction of the loops the product term $L_1 L_2$ is missing from the equation.

To generalize these results, refer to Figure 6.4-7 which shows a more complicated situation. The total transmittance of this graph can be written on the basis of prior discussion. The result is

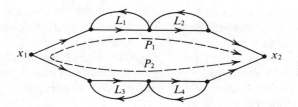

Figure 6.4-7.   A SFG of two sets of interacting loops

$$T = \frac{x_2}{x_1} = \frac{P_1}{1 - L_1 - L_2} + \frac{P_2}{1 - L_3 - L_4} \qquad (6.4\text{-}11)$$

This expression is expanded to the form

$$T = \frac{P_1(1 - L_3 - L_4) + P_2(1 - L_1 - L_2)}{1 - (L_1 + L_2 + L_3 + L_4) + (L_1 L_3 + L_1 L_4 + L_2 L_3 + L_2 L_4)} \qquad (6.4\text{-}12)$$

This expression is written in the form

$$T = \frac{P_1 \Delta_1 + P_2 \Delta_2}{\Delta} \qquad (6.4\text{-}13)$$

This shows that the total transmittance is the sum of the individual path transmittances P_k which have been weighted by path factors Δ_k, the sum being divided by a quantity Δ which involves all of the loops. Note, however, that Δ reflects the manner of the interconnection.

In its general form, the transmittance of a SFG can be written as

$$T = \sum_k \frac{P_k \Delta_k}{\Delta} \qquad (6.4\text{-}14)$$

where P_k denotes the path transmittance from input to output for every possible direct path through the network. In selecting the direct paths P_k, no node should be encountered more than once along path k. The quantity Δ which is called the graph determinant, involves only the closed loops of the graph and their interconnections, if any [refer to Equation (6.4-11)]. The rule for evaluating Δ in terms of the loop transmittances $L_1, L_2, \ldots$ is

$\Delta = 1 -$ (sum of all separate loop transmittances)
  $+$ (sum of all transmittance products of all possible pairs of non-touching loops)
  $-$ (sum of transmittance products of all possible triples of non-touching loops)
  $+ \ldots$

The path factor Δ_k, which is a weighting factor for each path transmittance, involves all of the loops in the graph which are isolated from path k. When a path touches all of the loops of a graph, the path factor is 1. Also, the path factor is 1 when the path contains no loops. In general, the path factor Δ_k is the value of the graph determinant with path k removed from the network. This form is known as the Mason rule. A general proof of this theorem is rather involved, and will not be given here.

EXAMPLE 6.4-1. Specify the path factors P_k, Δ_k and Δ for the SFG shown in Figure 6.4-8.

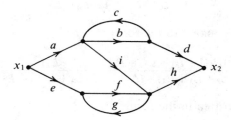

Figure 6.4-8.   An interconnected SFG

SOLUTION. The required quantities are obtained by an inspection of the graph in accordance with the Mason rules. These are

$$P_1 = abd \qquad\qquad P_2 = efh \qquad\qquad P_3 = aih$$

$$\Delta_1 = 1 - fg \qquad\qquad \Delta_2 = 1 - bc \qquad\qquad \Delta_3 = 1$$

$$\Delta = 1 - (bc + fg) + bcfg$$

□ □ □

EXAMPLE 6.4-2. Specify the path factors: P_k, Δ_k and Δ for the SFG shown in Figure 6.4-9.

SOLUTION. From an inspection of the graph, we write the following:

$$P_1 = t_{o2}t_{21} \qquad\qquad P_2 = t_{o1}$$

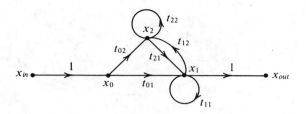

Figure 6.4-9.   An interconnected SFG

$$\Delta_1 = 1 \qquad\qquad\qquad \Delta_2 = 1 - t_{22}$$

$$\Delta = 1 - (t_{11} + t_{22} + t_{12} + t_{21}) + t_{11}t_{22}$$

□   □   □

EXAMPLE 6.4-3. Apply the Mason rule to find the transfer function for the SFG shown in Figure 6.4-10a.

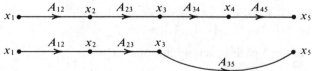

(a)   The system SFG

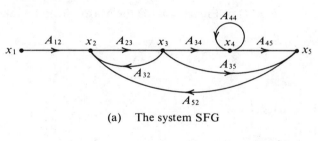

(b)   Two forward loops: $P_1 = A_{12}A_{23}A_{34}A_{45}$, $P_2 = A_{12}A_{23}A_{35}$

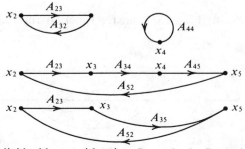

(c)   Four individual loops with gains: $P_{11} = A_{23}A_{32}$, $P_{22} = A_{44}$
$P_{31} = A_{23}A_{34}A_{45}A_{52}$, $P_{41} = A_{23}A_{35}A_{52}$

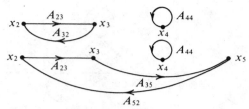

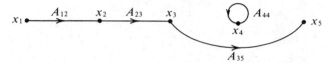

(d)   Two possible combinations of two non-touching loops with loop gain products: $P_{12} = A_{23}A_{32}A_{44}$, $P_{22} = A_{23}A_{35}A_{52}A_{44}$

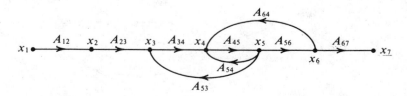

(e)   One forward path which is no in touch with one loop

Figure 6.4-10.   An application of the Mason formula

SOLUTION. For the SFG of Figure 6.4-10a the Mason formula takes the form

$$T = \frac{x_5}{x_1} = \frac{P_1\Delta_1 + P_2\Delta_2}{\Delta}$$

where

$P_1 = A_{12}A_{23}A_{34}A_{45}$

$P_2 = A_{12}A_{23}A_{35}$

$\Delta = 1 - (A_{23}A_{32} + A_{44} + A_{23}A_{34}A_{45}A_{52} + A_{23}A_{35}A_{52})$
$\quad + (A_{23}A_{32}A_{44} + A_{23}A_{35}A_{52}A_{44}) + 0 + \ldots$

$\Delta_1 =$ First forward path touches all loops $= 1$

$\Delta_2 =$ Second forward path does not touch one loop $= 1 - A_{44}$

□   □   □

EXAMPLE 6.4-4. Find the transfer function for the SFG shown in Figure 6.4-11.

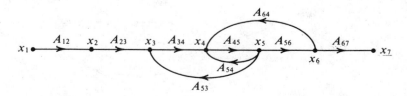

Figure 6.4-11.   Signal flow graph with one forward path and three feedback loops

SOLUTION. There is one forward path with gain

$$P_1 = A_{12}A_{23}A_{34}A_{45}A_{56}A_{67}$$

There are three feedback loops with gains

$$P_{11} = A_{45}A_{54} \qquad P_{21} = A_{34}A_{45}A_{53} \qquad P_{31} = A_{45}A_{56}A_{64}$$

No non-touching loops exist, thus

$$\Delta = 1 - (P_{11} + P_{21} + P_{31})$$

The loops all touch the path, then

$$\Delta_1 = 1$$

Therefore

$$T = \frac{P_1 \Delta_1}{\Delta} = \frac{A_{12}A_{23}A_{34}A_{45}A_{56}A_{67}}{1 - (A_{45}A_{54} + A_{34}A_{45}A_{53} + A_{45}A_{56}A_{64})}$$

□ □ □

EXAMPLE 6.4-5. Find the transmittance of the thermal system shown in Figure 6.4-12.

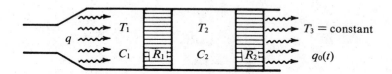

Figure 6.4-12. The features of a thermal system

SOLUTION. Application of the Fourier heat equation yields the equations

$$\frac{dT_1}{dt} = \frac{1}{C_1}\left[q(t) - \frac{1}{R_1}(T_1 - T_2) \right] \qquad \text{(a)} \quad (6.4\text{-}15)$$

$$\frac{dT_2}{dt} = \frac{1}{C_2}\left[\frac{1}{R_1}(T_1 - T_2) - \frac{1}{R_2}(T_2 - T_3) \right] \qquad \text{(b)}$$

$$q_o(t) = \frac{1}{R_2}(T_2 - T_3) \qquad \text{(c)}$$

These equations are recast into the following form, noting that $T_3 = \text{const}$ and so $dT_3/dt = 0$.

$$\frac{d}{dt}(T_1 - T_3) = \frac{1}{C_1}\left[q(t) - \frac{1}{R_2}[(T_1 - T_3) - (T_2 - T_3)] \right] \qquad \text{(a)} \quad \text{(6.4-16)}$$

$$\frac{d}{dt}(T_2 - T_3) = \frac{1}{C_2}\left[\frac{1}{R_1}[(T_1 - T_3) - (T_2 - T_3)] - \frac{1}{R_2}(T_2 - T_3) \right] \qquad \text{(b)}$$

$$q_o(t) = \frac{1}{R_2}(T_2 - T_3) \qquad \text{(c)}$$

For convenience, define the quantities

$$T_1 - T_3 = T_a \qquad\qquad T_2 - T_3 = T_b$$

Equations (6.4-16) become

$$\frac{dT_a}{dt} = \frac{1}{C_1}\left[q(t) - \frac{1}{R_1}(T_a - T_b) \right] \qquad \text{(a)} \quad \text{(6.4-17)}$$

$$\frac{dT_b}{dt} = \frac{1}{C_2}\left[\frac{1}{R_1}(T_a - T_b) - \frac{1}{R_2}T_b \right] \qquad \text{(b)}$$

$$q_o(t) = \frac{1}{R_2}T_b \qquad \text{(c)}$$

Write these equations in operational form, and rearrange them to the following

$$\left(p + \frac{1}{C_1 R_1} \right) T_a = \frac{1}{C_1}q(t) + \frac{1}{C_1 R_1}T_b \qquad \text{(a)} \quad \text{(6.4-18)}$$

$$p + \frac{1}{C_2}\left(\frac{1}{R_1} + \frac{1}{R_2} \right) T_b = \frac{1}{C_2 R_1}T_a \qquad \text{(b)}$$

$$q_o = \frac{1}{R_2}T_b \qquad \text{(c)}$$

The SFG for this set of equations is given in Figure 6.4-13. By an application of the Mason rule, it is found that the transmittance is

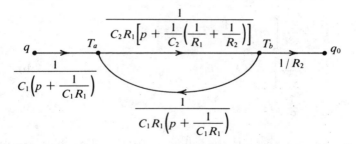

Figure 6.4-13. The SFG for the thermal circuit of Figure 6.4-12

$$T = \frac{q_o}{q} = \frac{\dfrac{1}{R_1 C_1 C_2}}{p^2 + \left(\dfrac{1}{R_1 C_1} + \dfrac{1}{R_1 C_2} + \dfrac{1}{R_2 C_2}\right)p + \dfrac{1}{R_1 R_2 C_1 C_2}}$$

□ □ □

6.5 BLOCK DIAGRAMS

Block diagrams serve much the same purpose as the signal flow graph, and they both serve to display the interconnection among the elements that make up a system. A significant difference between the two is that no relationship between system variables, such as the Mason rule for the SFG, exists for block diagrams. As a result, determining the system transmittance from a block diagram requires the application of a reduction procedure, and this proves to be more cumbersome and often quite difficult to complete. However, block diagrams are extensively used in control system engineering.

Figure 6.5-1 shows a typical block diagram representation of a system, with symbols appropriately defined.

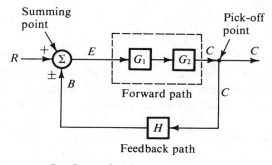

R = Input signal
E = Error signal
$G = C/E$ = Forward transfer function
$H = B/C$ = Feedback transfer function
C = Output signal
$GH = B/E$ = Loop transfer function
$T = C/R$ = Transfer function

Figure 6.5-1. A block diagram representation of a system with feedback

To gain an understanding of a block diagram, consider the system shown in Figure 6.5-2a and b. The KVL gives

$$v(t) = L\frac{di}{dt} + Ri \qquad \text{(a)} \quad (6.5\text{-}1)$$

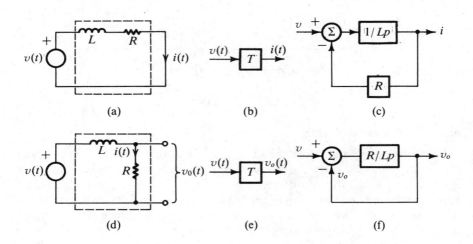

Figure 6.5-2.   Two elementary systems and their block diagram representation

From this we write

$$i = \frac{1}{Lp}(v - Ri) \tag{b}$$

Figure 6.5-2c represents Equation (6.5-1b) in block diagram form.

Let us now use the same circuit but with a different output variable, as shown in Figure 6.5-2d and e. The equations describing the system are

$$v(t) = L\frac{di}{dt} + Ri \qquad\qquad v = Lpi + Ri \qquad\qquad \text{(a)} \quad (6.5\text{-}2)$$

$$v_o(t) = Ri \qquad\qquad v_o = Ri \qquad\qquad \text{(b)}$$

Eliminate i in Equations (6.5-2a) and (6.5-2b) to find

$$v_o = \frac{R}{Lp}(v - v_o) \tag{6.5-3}$$

The block diagram of this equation is shown in Figure 6.5-2f.

The representative block diagram symbols and a number of the basic reduction rules are contained in Table 6.5-1. A block diagram representation of a given system can often be reduced by block diagram reduction techniques to achieve a simplified block diagram with fewer blocks than the original diagram.

Table 6.5-1. Properties of Block Diagrams

System Diagram	Equivalent Diagram	Observations
$u \longrightarrow \boxed{a} \longrightarrow \boxed{b} \longrightarrow y$	$u \longrightarrow \boxed{a\,b} \longrightarrow y$	Two blocks in cascade
$u \longrightarrow \overset{+}{\underset{+}{\Sigma}} \xrightarrow{\;y = u + v\;}$ $\uparrow$ v		Summation point
$u \longrightarrow \overset{+}{\underset{-}{\Sigma}} \xrightarrow{\;y = u - v\;}$ $\uparrow$ v		Subtraction point
$u \longrightarrow \bullet \begin{array}{l} \xrightarrow{\;u\;} \\ \xrightarrow{\;u\;} \\ \xrightarrow{\;u\;} \end{array}$		Pickoff point
$u \longrightarrow \overset{+}{\underset{\pm}{\Sigma}} \longrightarrow \boxed{1} \longrightarrow y$, $\boxed{a}$ feedback	$u \longrightarrow \boxed{\dfrac{1}{1 \mp a}} \longrightarrow y$	Feedback loop
$u \longrightarrow \overset{+}{\underset{\pm}{\Sigma}} \longrightarrow \boxed{a} \longrightarrow y$	$u \longrightarrow \boxed{\dfrac{a}{1 \mp a}} \longrightarrow y$	Special case of unit feedback loop
$u \longrightarrow \overset{+}{\underset{\pm}{\Sigma}} \longrightarrow \boxed{a} \longrightarrow y$, $\boxed{b}$	$u \longrightarrow \boxed{\dfrac{a}{1 \mp ab}} \longrightarrow y$	Complete feedback loop

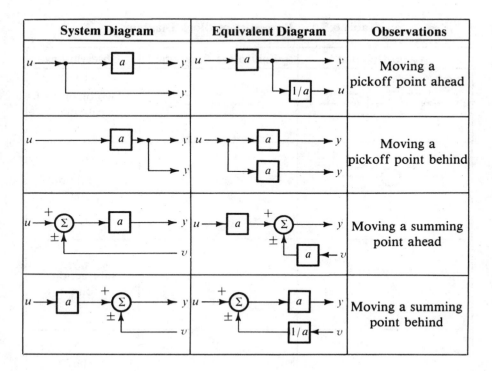

System Diagram	Equivalent Diagram	Observations
		Moving a pickoff point ahead
		Moving a pickoff point behind
		Moving a summing point ahead
		Moving a summing point behind

EXAMPLE 6.5-1. A multiple loop system is shown in Figure 6.5-3. Employ block diagram reduction techniques to obtain the system function of the connected system.

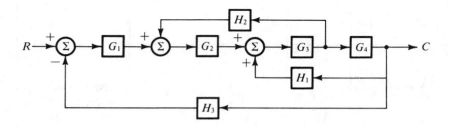

Figure 6.5-3.   A multiple loop system

SOLUTION. The steps in the reduction are shown in the following series of block diagrams.

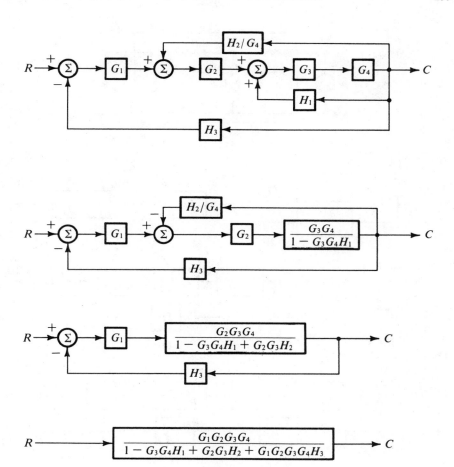

□ □ □

EXAMPLE 6.5-2. Find the block diagram representation of the network shown in Figure 6.5-4a.

SOLUTION. Write the controlling KVL equations in operational form

$$(R + Lp)i_1 - Lpi_2 = v \qquad \text{(a)} \quad (6.5\text{-}4)$$

$$- Lpi_1 + (R + 2Lp)i_2 = 0 \qquad \text{(b)}$$

$$Lpi_2 = v_o \qquad \text{(c)}$$

These equations are shown in block diagram form in Figures 6.5-4b, c and d, respectively. When the parts are combined, the feedback representation of the

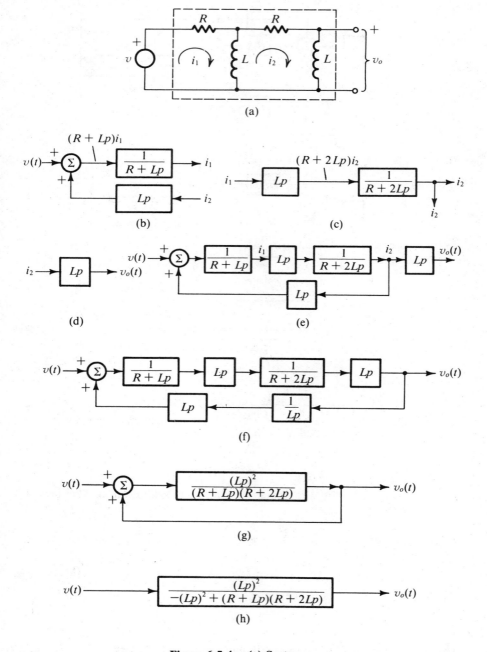

Figure 6.5-4.   (a) System
(b, c, d) Parts of the system developed from Equations (6.5-4a, b, and c)
(e) Assembly of the parts   (f, g, h) Development of the transmittance

network is shown in Figure 6.5-4e. Now with the help of Table 6.5-1 we are able, by successive transformations, shown in Figures 6.5-4f and g to arrive at the final result given in Figure 6.5-4h.

◻ ◻ ◻

EXAMPLE 6.5-3. Refer to the system shown in block form in Figure 6.5-5a. Find the system transmittance.

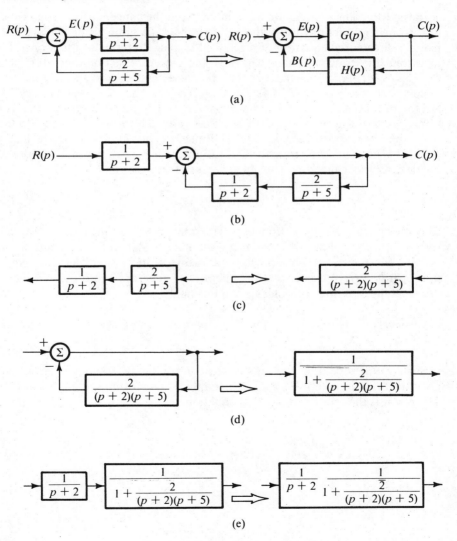

(a)

(b)

(c)

(d)

(e)

Figure 6.5-5 A simple feedback system

SOLUTION. With the help of entries in Table 6.5-1 the transformations shown in Figures 6.5-5b through e are easily found. The final block diagram gives the transmittance. The student should verify the transmittance using Table 6.5-1 entry 7 only.

□   □   □

6.6   SYSTEM FUNCTIONS

In the foregoing sections we have emphasized the concept of a system function (transfer function) using the SFG or block diagram to depict the controlling differential equation of a physical system. In terms of the p operator notation, the transmittance, which is the system function operator, was defined as $H(p)x_i(t) = x_o(t)$. This concept was extended, in the sinusoidal frequency domain in Chapter 4 as $H(j\omega) = H(p)|_{p \to j\omega} = \mathbf{X}_o/\mathbf{X}_i$, where $\mathbf{X}_o$ and $\mathbf{X}_i$ are the phasors appropriate to the sinusoids. In Chapter 5 we found that the Laplace transform of multiple differentiation introduces the factor s, s^2, etc., times the transformed variable, and multiple integration introduces the factor $1/s$, $1/s^2$, etc., times the transformed variable in accordance with the order of the derivatives or integral. Thus in general the result is

$$\pounds\{H(p)x_i(t)\} = H(s)X_i(s)$$

This means that the system function $H(s)$ appears through the Laplace transform of the controlling differential equation of the system for zero initial conditions. Moreover, $H(s)$ has precisely the same form as the differential equation operator $H(p)$ except that the operator p transforms into the variable s. We shall illustrate this through several examples.

EXAMPLE 6.6-1. Find the system function of the thermal system of Example 6.4-5.

SOLUTION. Proceed by determining the controlling differential equations, as given in Equations (6.4-17) and then Laplace transforming these equations. The result is the set of transformed equations:

$$\left(s + \frac{1}{C_1 R_1}\right) T_a(s) = \frac{1}{C_1} Q(s) + \frac{1}{C_1 R_1} T_b(s) \qquad \text{(a)} \quad \text{(6.6-1)}$$

$$\left[s + \frac{1}{C_2}\left(\frac{1}{R_1} + \frac{1}{R_2}\right)\right] T_b(s) = \frac{1}{C_2 R_1} T_a(s) \qquad \text{(b)}$$

$$Q_o(s) = \frac{1}{R_2} T_b(s) \qquad \text{(c)}$$

The corresponding SFG is given in Figure 6.6-1 (compare with Figure 6.4-13) Using the Mason rule, or otherwise solving this set of equations for $Q_o(s)/Q(s)$, it will be found that

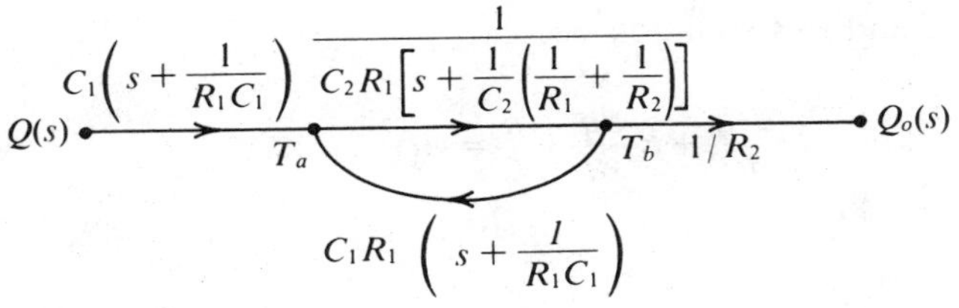

$$Q(s) \xrightarrow{\quad C_1\left(s+\dfrac{1}{R_1C_1}\right) \quad \overbrace{\dfrac{1}{C_2R_1\left[s+\dfrac{1}{C_2}\left(\dfrac{1}{R_1}+\dfrac{1}{R_2}\right)\right]}}} \quad \xrightarrow{\quad T_b \quad 1/R_2 \quad} Q_o(s)$$

with lower branch $C_1R_1\left(s+\dfrac{1}{R_1C_1}\right)$

Figure 6.6-1.   The SFG for the thermal circuit of Figure 6.4-12

$$H(s) = \cfrac{\dfrac{1}{R_1C_1C_2}}{s^2 + \left(\dfrac{1}{C_1R_1}+\dfrac{1}{C_2R_1}+\dfrac{1}{C_2R_2}\right)s + \dfrac{1}{R_1R_2C_1C_2}}$$

□ □ □

EXAMPLE 6.6-2. Find the system function for the network shown in Figure 6.6-2a and b. The input is $v(t)$ and the output is to be the charge $q(t)$.

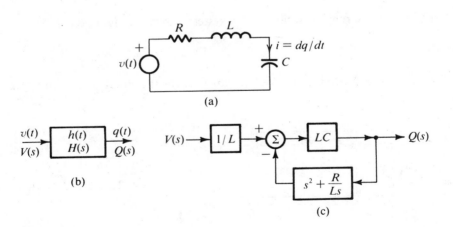

(a)

(b)

(c)

**Figure 6.6-2.   Second order system   (a) Circuit
(b) Schematic representations   (c) Block representation**

SOLUTION. An application of the KVL yields the differential equation

$$L\frac{di}{dt} + Ri + \frac{1}{C}\int i\,dt = v(t) \tag{6.6-2}$$

But $i = dq/dt$, and this equation becomes

$$L\frac{d^2q}{dt^2} + R\frac{dq}{dt} + \frac{q}{C} = v(t) \qquad \text{(a)} \quad \text{(6.6-3)}$$

or

$$\frac{d^2q}{dt^2} + \frac{R}{L}\frac{dq}{dt} + \frac{1}{LC}q = \frac{1}{L}v(t) \qquad \text{(b)}$$

Laplace transform this differential equation, for initially relaxed conditions, which yields

$$s^2Q(s) + \frac{R}{L}sQ(s) + \frac{1}{LC}Q(s) = \frac{1}{L}V(s)$$

The system function is

$$H(s) = \frac{Q(s)}{V(s)} = \frac{1}{L}\frac{1}{s^2 + \frac{R}{L}s + \frac{1}{LC}} \tag{6.6-4}$$

Verify the block representation of the system shown in Figure 6.6-2c.

□   □   □

EXAMPLE 6.6-3. Deduce the system function for the circuit shown in Figure 6.6-3.

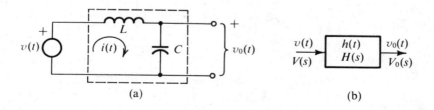

(a)

(b)

Figure 6.6-3. A second order system
(a) Circuit diagram (b) Block representation

SOLUTION. By an application of the KVL, we write

$$L\frac{di}{dt} + \frac{1}{C}\int i\,dt = v(t) \qquad (6.6\text{-}5)$$

This equation becomes, after being Laplace transformed,

$$LsI(s) + \frac{1}{Cs}I(s) = V(s)$$

so that

$$\frac{I(s)}{V(s)} = \frac{1}{Ls + \dfrac{1}{Cs}} \qquad (6.6\text{-}6)$$

However, $V_o(s) = I(s)Z_C(s) = I(s)(1/Cs)$. Combine this with Equation (6.6-6) to find

$$H(s) = \frac{V_o(s)}{V(s)} = \frac{I(s)}{CsV(s)} = \frac{1}{LCs^2 + 1} = \frac{1}{LC}\frac{1}{\left(s + j\dfrac{1}{\sqrt{LC}}\right)\left(s - j\dfrac{1}{\sqrt{LC}}\right)} \qquad (6.6\text{-}7)$$

□ □ □

EXAMPLE 6.6-4. Deduce the system function $\Theta(s)/V(s)$ for the electro-mechanical system given in Figure 6.6-4.

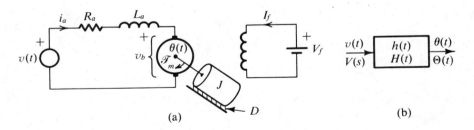

(a)   (b)

Figure 6.6-4. (a) Armature controlled dc motor   (b) Block representation

SOLUTION. In control applications involving dc machines, the linear portion of the magnetization curve is used, thereby indicating that the airgap flux is proportional to the field current,

$$\Phi = K_1 I_f \qquad \text{weber} \qquad (6.6\text{-}8)$$

where K_1 is a constant (a machine factor that is assumed known). The torque $\mathcal{T}_m$ developed by the motor is proportional to the product of the armature current and the airgap flux

$$\mathcal{T}_m = (K_1 I_f)K_2 i_a = K_3 i_a \qquad \text{newton-meter} \qquad (6.6\text{-}9)$$

where $K_3 = K_1 K_2 I_f$. Further, the induced voltage (the back emf) in the armature that results from the armature conductors cutting the field flux, is proportional to the angular speed ω, so that

$$V_b = K_4 \frac{d\theta}{dt} \qquad \text{volt} \qquad (6.6\text{-}10)$$

(For more details of the dc machine, refer to Chapter 12.)
The differential equation of the armature circuit is

$$L_a \frac{di_a}{dt} + R_a i_a + v_b = v(t) \qquad (6.6\text{-}11)$$

In addition, there is a torque equation that relates the motor torque to the mechanical system. This is

$$\mathcal{T}_m = K_3 i_a = J \frac{d^2\theta}{dt^2} + D \frac{d\theta}{dt} \qquad (6.6\text{-}12)$$

where $J =$ moment of inertia of the motor armature and coupled load referred to the motor shaft (kg-m^2), and $D =$ viscous friction coefficient (N-m/rad/s).
By Laplace transforming the several equations above we obtain

$$V_b(s) = K_4 s \Theta(s) \qquad \text{(a)} \quad (6.6\text{-}13)$$

$$(L_a s + R_a)I_a(s) = V(s) - V_b(s) \qquad \text{(b)}$$

$$(Js^2 + Ds)\Theta(s) = K_3 I_a(s) \qquad \text{(c)}$$

Solve this set of equations for the system function $H(s) = \Theta(s)/V(s)$ to find

$$H(s) = \frac{\Theta(s)}{V(s)} = \frac{K_3}{s[(L_a s + R_a)(Js + D) + K_3 K_4]} \qquad (6.6\text{-}14)$$

6.6 POSTLUDE

Signal flow graphs and block diagrams play very important parts in subsequent studies of interconnected systems. Often it proves particularly advantageous to use one or the other as tools of analysis, and control systems are usually studied using one or another of these representations. These will appear in future chapters.

SUMMARY

- The rules for drawing SFG-s are the following: (a) Signals travel along branches only in the direction of the arrows; (b) the value of a node is the value of the node from which a signal arises multiplied by the transmittance of the branch connecting the nodes; (c) the value of the variable represented by any node is the sum of all signals entering that node; and (d) the value of the variable represented by any node is transmitted to all branches leaving that node.

- Signal flow graph properties are given in Table 6.4-1.

- The transmittance of a SFG is given by Mason's rule, which is developed in Section 4.

- Block diagram representations serve the same purposes as SFG-s, and the properties of block diagram representations are given in Table 6.5-1.

- The most useful block diagram is the simple feedback loop with its transfer function as shown.

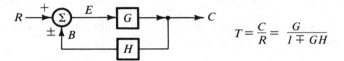

$$T = \frac{C}{R} = \frac{G}{1 \mp GH}$$

- In the Laplace s-domain, the quantities R, E, G, C, H and B are functions of s.

REVIEW QUESTIONS

1. Discuss the general purposes and advantages of a signal flow graph; a block diagram.
2. State the rules for drawing a signal flow graph.
3. Write a third order differential equation, and draw a SFG for this equation.
4. State the Mason rule for the transmittance of a SFG, and explain all terms that appear in this theorem.
5. Discuss the procedure for reducing a block diagram to obtain the total transfer function.

REFERENCES

1. Lynch, W. A., and J. G. Truxal, *Signals and Systems in Electrical Engineering*, McGraw Hill Book Co., New York, NY, 1962.

    This text provides an introduction to electrical engineering with extensive use of signal flow graphs and block-diagram representations of systems.

2. Seely, S., *An Introduction to Engineering Systems*, Pergamon Press, Inc., New York, NY, 1972.

An advanced undergraduate text which includes elements of signal flow graphs and network graph topology.

3. Mason, S. J., "Feedback Theory—Some Properties of Signal Flow Graphs," Proc. IRE, vol. 41, pp. 1144-1156, September 1953; also Proc. IRE, vol. 44, pp. 920-926, July 1956.

These papers present the basic work on signal flow graphs.

PROBLEMS

6.1-1. Generalize the equations of Example 6.1-1 for n branches.

6.1-2. Draw a SFG for the following set of equations

$$x_1 + 2x_2 - x_3 = 0$$
$$2x_2 + x_3 - 3x_4 = 0$$
$$x_3 + 2x_4 = 0$$

(a) When x_1 denotes the input and x_4 denotes the output.
(b) When x_4 denotes the input and x_1 denotes the output.

6.2-1. Deduce the controlling equilibrium equations for the systems shown in Figure P6.2-1 and draw a SFG for each.

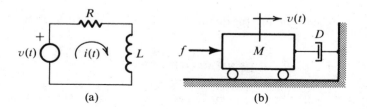

(a)   (b)

Figure P6.2-1

6.2-2. Draw SFG-s for the differential equations listed

$$\frac{d^3y}{dt^3} + 2\frac{d^2y}{dt^2} + 3y = 4$$

$$(p^3 + 3p + 2)y = 11$$

$$(p^2 + 2p + 4)y = 2x + 3$$

6.3-1. Draw the SFG for the systems shown in Figure P6.3-1.

6.3-2. Draw SFG-s for the following sets of differential equations, for zero initial conditions. Both x and y are the outputs of the systems.

$$\begin{cases} (p^2 + 3p + 1)y = x + 4 \\ (p + 3)x = (-2p + 7)y \end{cases} \qquad \begin{cases} (p^2 + 2p + 3)y = 4x + 1 \\ (p^2 + 1)x = 3y + 5 \end{cases}$$

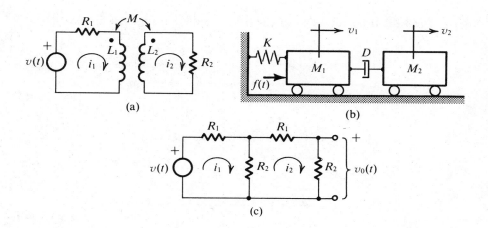

Figure P6.3-1

6.4-1. Write the equations that are portrayed by the SFG-s shown in Figure P6.4-1.

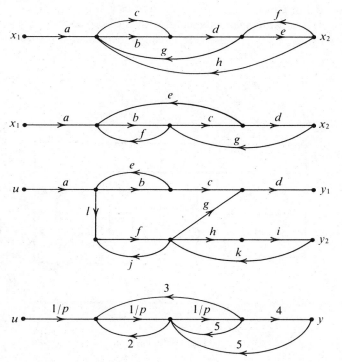

Figure P6.4-1

6.4-2. Find the transmittances of the SFG-s shown in Figure P6.4-2.

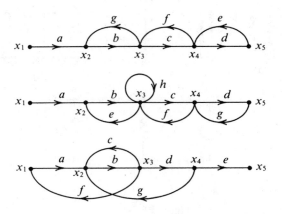

Figure P6.4-2

6.4-3. A model of a human for vibration studies is shown in Figure P6.4-3. As shown, it considers various sections of the body as mass-spring-damper systems. v_1, v_2, v_3, v_4 are referenced velocities with respect to ground.

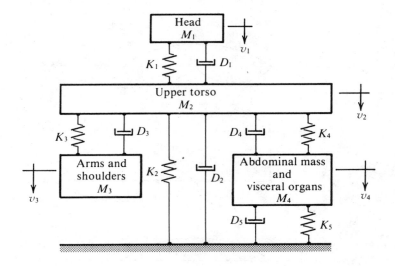

Figure P6.4-3

(a) Obtain a SFG representation of this system.
(b) Write the equations for the system.
(c) Determine the transmittance $v_4(p)/v_3(p)$.

6.5-1. Draw the block diagram representations, and find the transmittance of the systems shown in Figure P6.5-1.

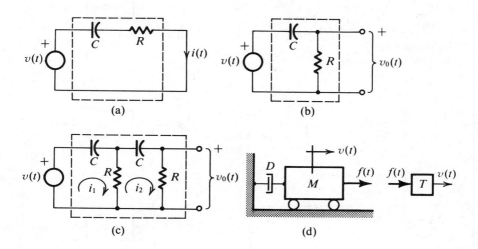

Figure P6.5-1

6.6-1. Verify Equations (6.6-4), (6.6-7) and (6.6-14) by using SFG and block diagram representations of the systems in question.

6.6-2. Find the transfer functions of the systems shown in Figure P6.6-2 and represent them in SFG and in block diagram forms.

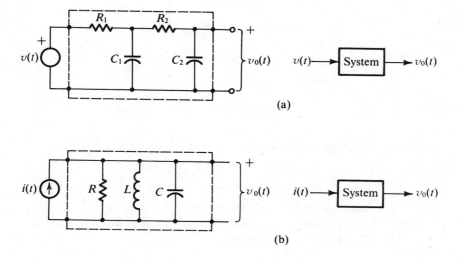

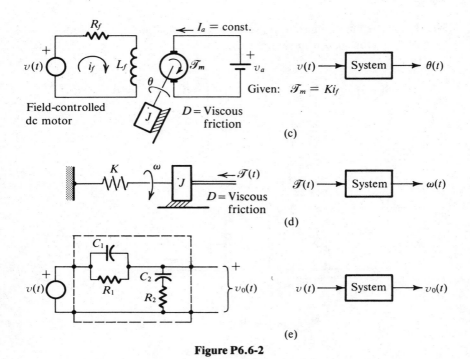

Field-controlled
dc motor

Given: $\mathcal{T}_m = Ki_f$

(c)

(d)

(e)

Figure P6.6-2

6.6-3. (a) A bridged T network is often used in ac control systems as a filter
network.

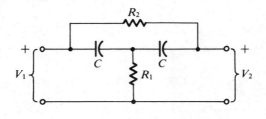

Figure P6.6-3a

(1) Show that the transfer function of this network is

$$\frac{V_2(s)}{V_1(s)} = \frac{1 + 2R_1Cs + R_1R_2C^2s^2}{1 + (2R_1 + R_2)Cs + R_1R_2C^2s^2}$$

(2) Draw the pole-zero diagram when $R_1 = 0.5$, $R_2 = 1$, $C = 0.5$.
(b) Obtain the transfer function of the mechanical accelerometer illustrated. $\dot{x}_m$ and $\dot{y}_m$ are velocities.

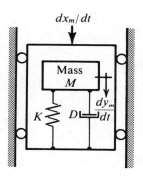

Figure P6.6-3b

(c) Obtain the transfer functions of the two block diagrams shown.

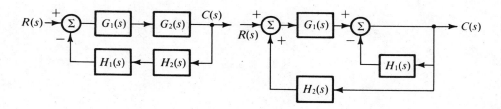

Figure P6.6-3c

Chapter Seven

Electronic Circuits

A tremendous array of electronic circuit elements and devices exists. Some of these are special purpose units, and others have or have had widespread use. Owing to space limitations, this chapter will consider only electronic circuits that involve semiconductor devices. Our study will be limited further to a few classes of the most used devices, including diodes, transistors, and FETs. These are but a fraction of the variety of semiconductors now available commercially in discrete form or in more extensive arrays on integrated circuit chips.

7.1 SEMICONDUCTORS

Conductivity may be chosen as one defining characteristic property of matter. Under such a definition, we can roughly separate the different materials into three broad categories: *conductors* (such as copper, aluminum, mercury); *semiconductors* (germanium, silicon); *insulators* (glass, dry gas). Good conductors have conductivities on the order of 10^7 mho/m; good insulators have conductivities on the order of 10^{-15} mho/m. Semiconductors, because of special treatment, have conductivities in the range between 10 and 10^{-7} mho/m.

An important feature of semiconductors is that their conductivity depends on the number and nature of the impurities that are present in the crystalline material. Temperature affects the electrical characteristics of these materials in ways that are quite different from those of pure conductors. A pure and perfect germanium or silicon crystal at $T = 0°$ K behaves as an insulator. At room temperature the behavior is quite different from that of an insulator. Following is a discussion of the physical basis for these special properties.

Intrinsic Semiconductors

Reference to Group IVa of the periodic table shows that carbon, silicon, and germanium have atomic numbers 6, 14, and 32, respectively. Each of these elements is tetravalent, having four valence electrons that may enter into chemical action. In the crystalline form, each atom is situated at the corner of a basic diamond structure, as shown in Figure 7.1-1a. The binding is by electron-pair or *covalent bonds*. That is, each atom forms an electron pair bond with four other surrounding atoms to form the crystalline structure. A schematic two-dimensional representation of the system is shown in Figure 7.1-1b.

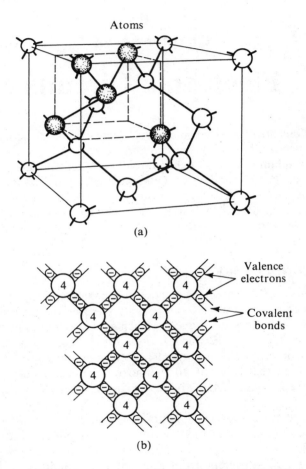

Atoms

(a)

Valence electrons

Covalent bonds

(b)

**Figure 7.1-1.   (a) The crystal structure of diamond (also silicon and germanium)
(b) A two-dimensional representation of the crystalline structure of germanium
showing the electron-pair bonds**

In the diagram, each circle marked +4 is intended to represent the ion consisting of the nucleus surrounded by its cloud of tightly bound electrons with a resultant charge of 4 positive units. The four outer electrons make up the electron pair bonds. Since in this structure every valence electron is tightly bound, appreciable energy is required to release an electron from its bond in the structure. At the temperature 0° K, all of the electrons are in their lowest energy state and are all contained in the *valence band* group of energy levels (see Figure 7.1-2a). The amount of energy required to release an electron from its bond is represented by the width of the forbidden gap E_g, and is about 0.75 eV (electron volt). When such an electron is released from its bond, it constitutes a localized negative charge which can move through the lattice of the crystal under the influence of an electric force. In this case, the electron is said to be in the *conduction band*. This discussion is shown graphically in Figure 7.1-2.

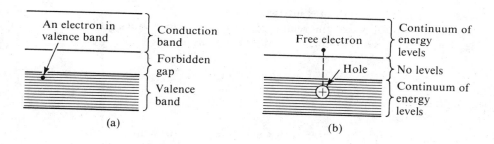

Figure 7.1-2. (a) Pure crystal without broken covalent bond
(b) Pure crystal with one broken covalent bond

Whenever a valence electron is released from its bond, the resultant ion is positively charged. This positive charge (not the ion, only the charge) may also move through the crystal from atom to atom because an electron from a neighboring bond can complete the deficient bond of one ion and leave behind its own positive ion. This positive charge migration in the valence band is referred to as "hole" conduction. In this discussion we have been describing *electron-hole pair generation*.

At higher temperatures there is a finite probability that an electron will acquire enough energy to bridge the forbidden gap. At any particular temperature there is a constant electron-hole pair generation and recombination rate, and an equilibrium condition is attained when the rate of generation is equal to the rate of recombination of these pairs. Under the influence of an applied electric field, the electrons will move in one direction and the holes will move in the opposite direction, since they are of opposite polarity. The resulting motions both contribute to the current. The motion in the electric field is dictated by the mobilities μ_n and μ_p for the negative and positive charges, and the current density J A/cm² is given by

$$J = (n\mu_n + p\mu_p)qE = n_i(\mu_n + \mu_p)qE = \sigma E; \qquad n_i = p_i \qquad (7.1\text{-}1)$$

where:

q = positive value of the electronic charge (1.6×10^{-19} coulomb)

n = free electron concentration, electrons/cm^3

p = hole concentration, holes/cm^3

σ = electrical conductivity, mho/cm

E = electric field intensity, volt/cm

μ_n, μ_p = electron and hole mobilities, cm^2/volt-second

Also, the subscript i indicates intrinsic material.

It has been found that the relation between the concentration of free electrons in intrinsic semiconductors and temperature is given by

$$n_i^2 = A_o T^3 e^{-E_g/kT} \tag{7.1-2}$$

where:

A_o = constant for the material (for Ge, $A_o = 3.1 \times 10^{32}$/cm^6-$^\circ$K^3)

E_g = width of the forbidden gap (eV)

k = Boltzmann constant (1.38×10^{-23} joule/$^\circ$K)

T = absolute temperature, $^\circ$K

E_g is given in units of electron volts, and $kT/1.6 \times 10^{-19}$ is also in eV.

Extrinsic Semiconductors

A very important mechanism for inducing semiconductivity in a material which would otherwise be an insulator is the impurity mechanism. In the n-type impurity, a small mole fraction (10^{-5} to 10^{-3} per cent) of a carefully selected impurity material (one having valence 5), such as phosphorus or arsenic, is added to the silicon melt. Each impurity atom will displace one of the silicon atoms from its regular site in the crystal lattice. Four of its valence electrons will form electron-pair bonds with its neighbors. This leaves the fifth valence electron, which is loosely bound to its parent atom. These loosely bound electrons constitute a ready source of electrons, and such *doped* silicon is *n*-type silicon. The impurity centers which constitute an impurity band just below the normally empty conduction band are called *donors* because they will donate electrons to the conduction band when ionized. The donor levels exist roughly 0.01 eV below the conduction band. This situation is shown in Figure 7.1-3a. At room temperature the thermal energy is roughly 0.025 eV, hence the

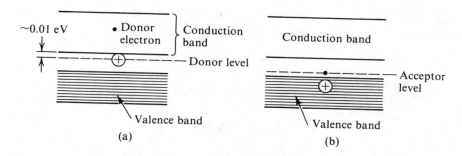

Figure 7.1-3. (a) Energy diagram for *n*-doped material
(b) Energy diagram for *p*-doped material

electrons in the donor levels are completely ionized, and they appear as free conduction electrons in the lower levels of the conduction band of the crystal. The parent atom is a positive ion that is frozen in the crystal lattice. The electron conductivity has been induced in the material without having an equal number of free positive holes appear in the valence band. The conductivity of such an *n*-type impurity semiconductor is dependent on the concentration and atomic species of the impurity atoms in solid solution in the crystal. Since the number of such electrons in the conduction band is far greater than the electrons that are excited from the valence band by the intrinsic process, they are called the *majority carriers* of the *n*-type material.

If N_d is the number of impurity atoms per unit volume, the density of free electrons, for *n*-type material, is

$$n_n \doteq N_d \qquad (7.1\text{-}3)$$

It can be shown that for the *n*-type material

$$n_n p_n = n_i p_i = n_i^2 = p_i^2 = N_d p_n \qquad (7.1\text{-}4)$$

where the quantities n_n denote the concentration of electrons in the *n*-type material, and p_n denotes the concentration of holes in the *n*-type material.

In the *p*-type impurity mechanism, a small concentration of impurity atoms having one valence electron less than the atoms of the crystal material is added during the crystal growing process. Suppose that a trivalent atom such as boron or aluminum is substituted for a normal silicon atom in the crystal lattice. Now, owing to the lack of sufficient electrons in the impurity atom, one of the covalent bonds is not completed and a hole is created in that particular bond. This results in a hole in the valence bond. This will contribute to the conductivity of the material since the holes participate in the charge transport process. The impurity centers are acceptors because they will accept electrons from the valence band. The acceptor levels lie slightly above the valence band within the forbidden band, as shown in Figure 7.1-3b. If N_a denotes the number of acceptors per unit volume, then

$$p_p \doteq N_a \qquad (7.1\text{-}5)$$

For the p-type material we also have the relation

$$n_p p_p = n_i p_i = n_i^2 = p_i^2 = n_p N_a \qquad (7.1\text{-}6)$$

Important properties of Ge and Si are contained in Table 7.1-1.

Table 7.1-1. Properties of Ge and Si at Room Temperature

Property	Ge	Si
Average atomic mass	72.62	28.10
Density, g/cm³	5.32	2.33
Relative permittivity	16.	12.
E_g at 0° K, eV	0.72	1.1
μ_n, cm²/volt-second	3800.	1300.
μ_p, cm²/volt-second	1800.	500.
D_n, cm²/second	99.	34.
D_p, cm²/second	47.	13.
A_o, 1/cm⁶-°K³	3.1×10^{32}	1.5×10^{33}

EXAMPLE 7.1-1. Find the hole concentration in n-type Si semiconductor material for $N_d = 5 \times 10^{16}$ donor atoms/cm³ at room temperature, $T = 300°$ K.

SOLUTION. By Avogadro's law, the concentration of Si atoms is

$$n_{Si} = \frac{6.025 \times 10^{23} \text{ (atoms/g-mole)} \times 2.33 \text{ g/cm}^3}{28.1 \text{ g/g-mole}} = 4.99 \times 10^{22} \text{ atoms/cm}^3$$

Also by Equation (7.1-2) for the intrinsic concentration of electron-hole pairs/cm³

$$n_i^2 = 1.5 \times 10^{33} (300)^3 \exp[-1.1/(1.38 \times 10^{-23} \times 300)/1.6 \times 10^{-19}]$$

where the constant 1.6×10^{-19} in the exponential changes joule into electron volt. From this, $n_i = 1.5 \times 10^{13}$ electron-hole pairs/cm³. Therefore

$$\frac{n_{Si}}{n_i} = \frac{4.99 \times 10^{22}}{1.5 \times 10^{13}} = 3.33 \times 10^9 \qquad \text{Si atoms/electron-hole pair}$$

and

$$p_n = \frac{n_i^2}{N_d} = \frac{2.25 \times 10^{26}}{5 \times 10^{16}} = 4.5 \times 10^9 \qquad \text{holes/cm}^3$$

which is the minority carrier density.

□ □ □

Diffusion

There is an additional factor that arises in a semiconductor when there is a concentration gradient, since now there will be a diffusion of particles towards the region of lower concentration. A current will exist if there is a gradient of charge carriers, and this diffusion current will exist without the presence of an electron field. That is, if a density gradient of holes $\partial p/\partial x$ exists in the x-direction, a hole-diffusion current density J_p A/cm² will be present, where

$$J_p = -qD_p \frac{\partial p}{\partial x} \qquad \text{A/cm}^2 \tag{7.1-7}$$

where D_p is called the *diffusion constant* for holes (cm²/sec). Similarly, there will be a diffusion current for electrons

$$J_n = qD_n \frac{\partial n}{\partial x} \qquad \text{A/cm}^2 \tag{7.1-8}$$

where D_n is the diffusion constant for electrons.

The diffusion constants are related to the mobility by the Einstein equation

$$\frac{D_p}{\mu_p} = \frac{D_n}{\mu_n} = V_T \tag{7.1-9}$$

where $V_T = kT/q = T/11,600$ volt.

7.2 THE p-n JUNCTION DIODE

Open Circuit

The p-n junction consists of a transition from net acceptor to net donor impurity density within a given semiconductor material. The junction may be graded or abrupt by controlling the nature, concentration and distribution of the activating impurities. This depends on whether the junction is prepared through a growing, an alloying or a diffusion process. Several physical processes occur. A diffusion current is present since there is a concentration of holes in the p-side of the junction, with a lesser concentration in the n-side;

and conversely, there is a concentration of electrons in the *n*-side and a lesser concentration in the *p*-side of the junction. In addition, the holes which move to the *n*-side leave negative acceptors in the *p*-side, thereby increasing the negative charge in this region. The reverse happens when the electrons move to the *p*-side of the junction. The general situation is shown in Figure 7.2-1a. Figure 7.2-1b shows the accumulation of charge due to diffusion. This process is limited because, with the separation of the charges, an electric field is produced which creates drifting current in the opposite direction, as shown in Figure 7.2-1a. Eventually, for any given temperature, an equilibrium is attained. By Equations (7.1-7) and (7.1-1) for the diffusion and drift current for

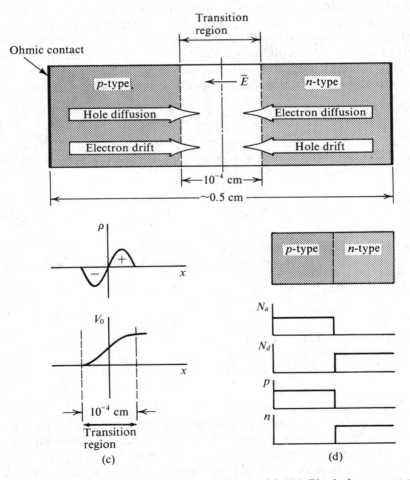

Figure 7.2-1.   A p-n junction with no applied potential   (a) Physical representation (b) Charge density distribution   (c) Electrostatic potential V_o (d) Density distributions

holes in equilibrium and since the net current must be zero on open circuit, we can write

$$J_p = q\left(p\mu_p E - D_p \frac{dp}{dx}\right) = 0 \qquad (7.2-1)$$

A similar expression for the electrons can also be written

$$J_n = q\left(n\mu_n E + D_n \frac{dn}{dx}\right) = 0 \qquad (7.2-2)$$

We combine Equations (7.1-9) and (7.2-1) which yields the equation

$$\frac{dp}{p} = \frac{Eq}{kT} dx \qquad (7.2-3)$$

This is integrated and the boundary condition $x = 0$, $p = p_n$ is applied. There results

$$V_o = \frac{kT}{q} \ln \frac{p_p}{p_n}; \qquad V_o = Ex \qquad (7.2-4)$$

Similarly for the electrons, we find hat V_o is also given by

$$V_o = \frac{kT}{q} \ln \frac{n_n}{n_p} \qquad (7.2-5)$$

By using the reasonable values of $p_p \doteq 10^{16}$ cm^{-3}, $p_n \doteq 10^4$ cm^{-3}, and $kT/q = 0.026$ eV at room temperature, the barrier voltage V_o, also called the *contact potential*, is found to be about 0.72 volt.

Forward Bias

When a battery V is applied to the junction with the polarity shown in Figure 7.2-2a, its voltage opposes the barrier voltage V_o (see Figures 7.2-1b and c) and lowers it, as shown in Figure 7.2-2b. We see that the potential drop across the depletion layer becomes $V_o - V$, neglecting voltage drops in the electrode junctions and in the bulk n-type and p-type regions, since only small currents are assumed. For $V < V_o$, the barrier potential is reduced. Consequently, a larger number of electrons from the n-type region and holes from the p-region will succeed in overcoming the reduced potential barrier, with a substantial increase in the *forward current* I_f. However, the reverse current I_r will remain substantially unchanged since it is the result of minority carriers in the two regions, and is the result of the presence of the electric field. Because $I_f > I_r$, there is a net current in the forward direction.

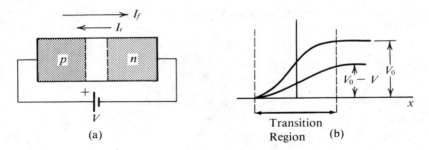

Figure 7.2-2. Forward biased p-n junction diode
(a) Circuit configuration   (b) Potential distribution

Reverse Bias

If we reverse the polarity of the applied voltage source V, the potential barrier will increase to the value $V_o + V$ and the magnitude of the forward and reverse currents will also reverse, with $I_r > I_f$. But the reverse current which results from the intrinsic carriers will be small. As a result, the net current will be very small. Essentially, therefore, the behavior is nonlinear, with potentially large forward currents but very small reverse currents. If the reverse voltage is increased it can exceed the *breakdown voltage*, and the reverse current can become very large. This can result in overheating the diode, with possible permanent damage. There is a class of semiconductor diodes which make use of this breakdown state. These are known as Zener diodes and these have relatively constant breakdown voltage over wide ranges in current.

The Volt-Ampere Characteristics of the *p-n* Diode

The *p-n* junction diode that we have been discussing, and which is shown schematically in Figure 7.2-3a, has a volt-ampere characteristic shown in Figure 7.2-3b. From theoretical considerations, the diode equation is

$$i = I_o(e^{qv/kT} - 1) \tag{7.2-6}$$

where I_o is the reverse current.

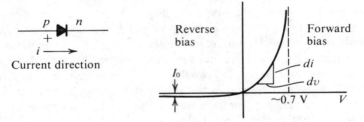

Figure 7.2-3.   (a) Schematic of the junction diode
(b) The volt-ampere characteristic

The slope of the curve at any point is the *dynamic resistance*, and is given by

$$r_D = \frac{dv}{di} \tag{7.2-7}$$

To evaluate this, consider the inverse of r_D. From Equation (7.2-6)

$$g_D = \frac{di}{dv} = \frac{I_o e^{qv/RT}}{kT/q} = \frac{i + I_o}{kT/q}$$

For forward bias conditions

$$\frac{qv}{kT} > 1 \qquad i \gg I_o$$

and so

$$r_D \doteq \frac{kT}{qi} \tag{7.2-8}$$

At room temperature this is

$$r_D = \frac{26}{i(ma)} \qquad \Omega \tag{7.2-9}$$

which shows that the diode resistance is generally small.

If the diode resistance is assumed to be constant, this replaces the diode characteristic of Figure 7.2-3b with that shown in Figure 7.2-4a. Also shown in Figure 7.2-4b is the characteristic for an ideal diode, that is, one with zero internal resistance. Figure 7.2-4c shows a biased ideal diode with a resistor in series, and its *v-i* characteristic.

Figure 7.2-5 shows some circuit configurations incorporating ideal diodes, and the circuit behavior.

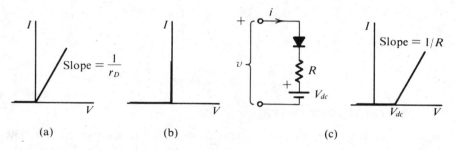

Figure 7.2-4. (a) Linear *v-i* characteristic of a diode
(b) *v-i* characteristic of an ideal diode ($r_D = 0$)
(c) A biased ideal diode and its *v-i* characteristic

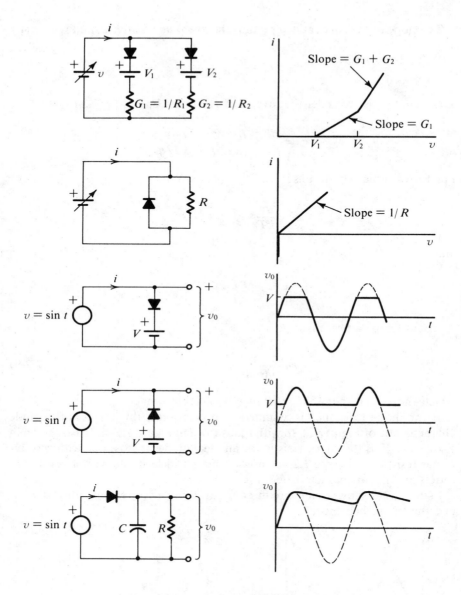

Figure 7.2-5. Circuits with ideal diodes

7.3 THE DIODE RECTIFIER

One of the important uses of a simple diode is as a *rectifier* or *clipper*. The circuit for such an operation is shown in Figure 7.3-1. We shall assume the linear diode characteristic in Figure 7.2-4a, and so, during conduction, the cir-

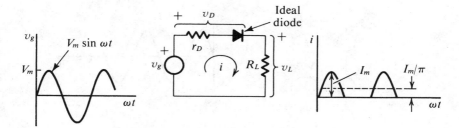

Figure 7.3-1.   Series diode clipper (half-wave rectifier)

cuit consists of r_D and R_L in series. By a direct application of the Kirchhoff voltage law, we write that

$$i = \frac{V_m}{r_D + R_L} \sin \omega t = I_m \sin \omega t \quad \text{during conduction} \qquad \text{(a)} \quad \text{(7.3-1)}$$

$$i = 0 \qquad\qquad\qquad\qquad \text{during the inverse cycle} \qquad \text{(b)}$$

An analytic expression for the output wave is obtained by means of a Fourier series expansion (see Chapter 1), and it is

$$i = I_m \left[\frac{1}{\pi} + \frac{1}{2} \sin \omega t - \sum_{k,\,even} \frac{2}{\pi} \frac{\cos k\omega t}{(k^2 - 1)} \right] \qquad \text{(7.3-2)}$$

If the purpose of the circuit is rectification rather than merely clipping the positive or the negative portion of a waveform, it is possible to combine two half-wave rectifiers back-to-back to achieve full-wave rectification, as illustrated in Figure 7.3-2. The output waveform can be described analytically by superposing or adding Equation (7.3-2) to another similar equation but displaced by π, i.e.,

$$i = i_1 + i_2 = i_1(\omega t) + i_2(\omega t + \pi) \qquad \text{(7.3-3)}$$

which yields

$$i = I_m \left[\frac{2}{\pi} - \frac{4}{\pi} \sum_{k,\,even} \frac{\cos k\omega t}{(k^2 - 1)} \right] \qquad \text{(7.3-4)}$$

It is the purpose of a rectifier to provide a dc output from an ac source of power. What has been achieved, according to Equations (7.3-2) and (7.3-4) are waves which possess a dc component but which also include appreciable varying components. In fact, one defines the *ripple factor* as the ratio of the rms value of the ripple components to the dc value.

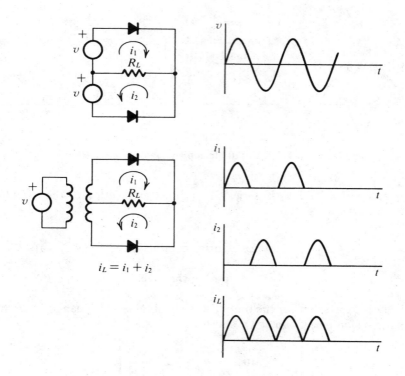

Figure 7.3-2.   Operation of the full-wave rectifier

The ripple factor given by the relation

$$r = \frac{I_{ac}}{I_{dc}} = \frac{V_{ac}}{V_{dc}} = \frac{\text{rms value of ac components}}{\text{dc components}} \qquad (7.3\text{-}5)$$

is an indicator of the effectiveness of the circuit to rectify the alternating excitation.

EXAMPLE 7.3-1. Find the ripple factors for the half- and full-wave rectifier. The two waves are shown in Figure 7.3-3.

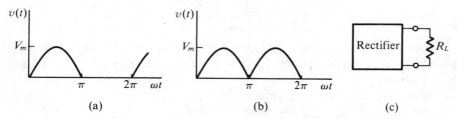

(a)   (b)   (c)

**Figure 7.3-3.   (a) Output of a half-wave rectifier
(b) Output of a full-wave rectifier   (c) Rectifier**

SOLUTION. Since the power dissipated in the load resistor is equal to V_{rms}^2/R and since the total power is equal to the sum of the power due to the dc component, V_{dc}^2/R_L, and due to ac component V_{ac}^2/R_L we have

$$\frac{V_{rms}^2}{R_L} = \frac{V_{ac}^2}{R_L} + \frac{V_{dc}^2}{R_L}$$

or

$$V_{ac} = \sqrt{V_{rms}^2 - V_{dc}^2} \qquad (7.3\text{-}6)$$

Substituting Equation (7.3-6) into Equation (7.3-5) we obtain

$$r = \sqrt{\left(\frac{V_{rms}}{V_{dc}}\right)^2 - 1} \qquad (7.3\text{-}7)$$

The V_{rms} of a half-wave waveform is

$$V_{rms} = \left[\frac{1}{2\pi}\int_0^{2\pi} v^2 d(\omega t)\right]^{1/2} = \left[\frac{1}{2\pi}\int_0^{2\pi} (V_m \sin \omega t)^2\, d(\omega t)\right]^{1/2} = \frac{V_m}{2} \qquad (7.3\text{-}8)$$

From Equation (7.3-2) we observe that $V_{dc} = V_m/\pi$ and thus

$$r_h = \left[\left(\frac{V_m}{2}\frac{\pi}{V_m}\right)^2 - 1\right]^{1/2} = [2.467 - 1]^{1/2} = 1.21 \quad \text{or} \quad 121\% \qquad (7.3\text{-}9)$$

V_{rms} of a full-wave rectified sine function is $V_m/\sqrt{2}$. From Equation (7.3-4) we observe that $V_{dc} = 2V_m/\pi$. Therefore

$$r_f = \sqrt{\left(\frac{V_m}{\sqrt{2}}\frac{\pi}{2V_m}\right)^2 - 1} = \sqrt{1.233 - 1} = 0.4834 \quad \text{or} \quad 48.34\% \qquad (7.3\text{-}10)$$

□   □   □

To reduce the ripple, a filter network of some sort is usually interposed between the rectifier and the load. Properties of important filters are contained in Figure 7.3-4 which shows the filter, the general character of the output, and the approximate ripple factor. If better filtering is required, cascaded filters can be used. More often, however, electronic regulators are employed.

Features to be observed with these filtering systems are that the output voltage with the capacitor filter is approximately V_m, the peak value; whereas with the inductor or L-section, the output is approximately the average value or $2V_m/\pi$. Further, the ripple increases with load (R_L smaller, current larger) for the capacitor filter but decreases with load for the inductor filter. The ripple for the L-section filter is independent of load.

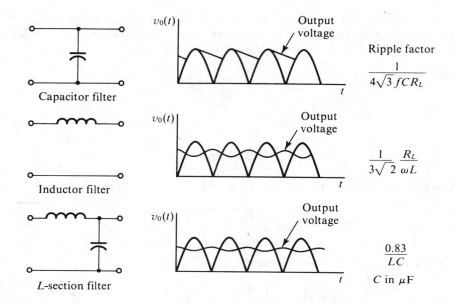

Figure 7.3-4.   General features of rectifier filters

7.4   GRAPHICAL ANALYSIS AND THE LOAD LINE

The discussion in Section 7.2 assumed an ideal diode, thereby permitting an analytic representation of its effect in a simple rectifier circuit. We now wish to study the techniques which involve the actual diode characteristic in its circuit performance. While, for engineering purposes, the approximations made in Section 7.2 are usually adequate, the methods now to be considered are very important since these methods have wide applicability.

Essentially the problem is that the volt-ampere characteristic of a diode is nonlinear. Hence the question is, how can one include such a nonlinear element into a description of the circuit behavior. The approach often involves the use of the Thèvenin theorem to find an equivalent circuit for the linear portion of the circuit. In essence, therefore, the problem should be viewed as a simple linear network plus a diode or other nonlinear element, with the equivalent circuit shown in Figure 7.4-1a. An inspection of Figure 7.4-1 permits us to write

From Kirchhoff's voltage law $v_d = v - iR$ (a)   (7.4-1)

Diode (or nonlinear element) $i = f(v_d)$ (b)

Equation (7.4-1a) refers to the linear portion of the circuit and Equation (7.4-1b) is the graphical functional relationship for the diode. To find the current i and v_d requires that these two expressions be solved simultaneously.

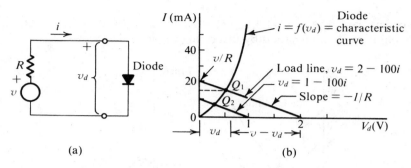

Figure 7.4-1. **(a) A linear circuit driving a diode (or other nonlinear device)**
(b) Graphical solution for finding i and v_d

Since the function $i = f(v_d)$ is ordinarily not given in analytic form, we shall solve the given equations by graphical methods. The solution is given (refer to Figure 7.4-1b) by the point at which the two curves intersect each other. If, for example, we set $v = 2$ V and $R = 100$ Ω, Equation (7.4-1a) becomes

$$v_d = 2 - 100i$$

and defines a straight line which is known as the *dc load line*. The intersection of the dc line and $i = f(v_d)$ gives the point Q_1 which is the operating, the *quiescent* or the Q point. In this particular case the Q point has the coordinates $v_d = 0.55$ V and $i = 16$ mA. If we next set $v = 1$ V, the load line shifts parallel to the $v = 2$ V line and Q_1 moves to point Q_2. This behavior is always true for constant R.

Consider the case when v in Figure 7.4-1a is a sinusoidal voltage of the form $v = V_m \sin \omega t = 2.0 \sin \omega t$. The graphical solution is shown in Figure 7.4-2.

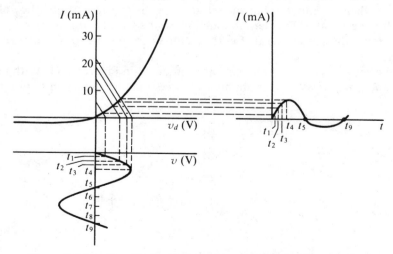

Figure 7.4-2. **Graphical solution for a sinusoidal applied voltage**

For the case when $v = V_{dc} + v_g = V_{dc} + V_m \sin \omega t$ with $V_{dc} > V_m$, the graphical solution is easily understood by inspecting Figure 7.4-3.

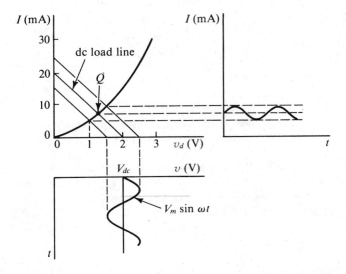

Figure 7.4-3.   Graphical solution for a sinusoidal applied voltage plus a bias source

7.5   DIODE LOGIC

The general functioning of logic gates will be discussed in Chapter 9. We wish to examine here some electronic circuits for achieving these gates. We begin by examining Figure 7.5-1 which is that for a 3 input OR gate. Note that the diodes are normally in the non-conducting state, but conduction occurs in a diode when the input voltage is set at $+5$ volts (assumed to be the voltage level for the 1-state). Further, conduction occurs when 1 or more diodes conduct. Hence the operation satisfies the action or truth table for OR gates and is shown in Figure 7.5-2.

The electronics for an AND gate are contained in Figure 7.5-3. With no inputs, the lower resistor R is shunted by 3 conducting diodes in parallel (the

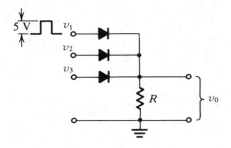

Figure 7.5-1.   The 3 input OR gate

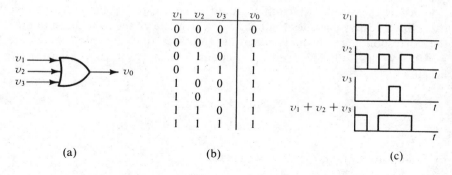

(a)   (b)   (c)

Figure 7.5-2. **(a) Schematic representation of OR gate (b) Truth table for OR gate (c) Possible response for three-input OR gate**

diodes are connected to other logic circuits), thereby setting v_o at about 0.7 volts, the voltage v_o across the diode in the conducting state. When all three terminals have 5 volts applied to them, the diodes cease to conduct and half of the 10 volts will appear at the output $v_o = 5$ volts, the 1-state. The truth table is shown in Figure 7.5-4.

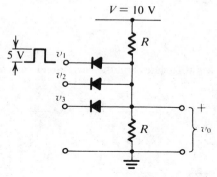

Figure 7.5-3. **The 3 input AND gate**

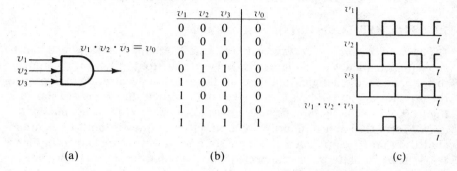

(a)   (b)   (c)

Figure 7.5-4. **(a) Schematic representation of AND gate (b) Truth table for AND gate (c) Possible response for three-input AND gate**

Consider the cases in which the output from one gate is the input to a second gate. Specifically, consider Figure 7.5-5 which shows such a connection and the corresponding schematic diagram. Consider that the input states are: $v_1 = 0$, $v_2 = 1$, $v_3 = 0$. The conducting circuit is then as shown in Figure 7.5-6, because

$$v_1 = 0, \ D1 \text{ is back-biased and } i_{D1} = 0$$

$$v_3 = 0, \ D4 \text{ is back-biased and } i_{D4} = 0$$

by Equation (7.2-9) $i_D r_D \doteq 25$ mV. Then

$$v_o \doteq 5 - 0.7 - 0.025 - 0.7 - 0.025 \doteq 3.55 \text{ V}$$

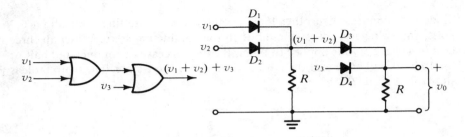

Figure 7.5-5.   Multiple gates and the corresponding schematic diagram

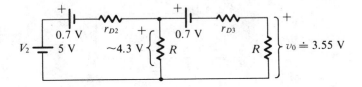

Figure 7.5-6.   The gate circuit of Figure 7.5-5 under specified conditions

7.6   THE BJT TRANSISTOR

The *barrier junction transistor* (BJT) is a 3 terminal device which can be shown schematically as in Figure 7.6-1. Two transistor types exist, the npn and the pnp, and these designations describe the excess concentration of carriers in the 3 regions. The symbols and the essential current directions are shown in Figure 7.6-2. Actually, npn devices are usually easier to fabricate in *integrated circuit* form (IC) and ordinarily are used. Often, however, both types are included on an IC chip. The currents in an npn transistor are shown in Figure 7.6-3. The two batteries are connected with the polarities shown to provide the appropriate bias. The *emitter current* I_E consists of electrons only, and 92 to 99 per cent of these electrons, written αI_E, reach the collector region. The remain-

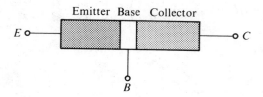

Figure 7.6-1.   A schematic of the BJT transistor

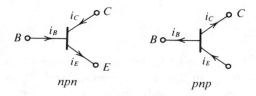

npn   *pnp*

Figure 7.6-2.   The current directions in the npn and the pnp transistors

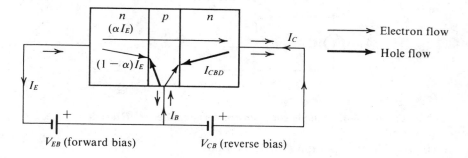

Figure 7.6-3.   Current in the npn junction transistor

ing one to eight per cent of the emitter current is combined with holes in the base-emitter region, as shown. Moreover, a reverse-bias current I_{CBO} exists between the collector and base. The direction of electron flow in the base depends on the magnitude of the currents I_{CBO} and $I_E - \alpha I_E$. The same currents are present in a pnp transistor with the difference that the electron and hole currents are interchanged. Also, the polarities of the biasing batteries are reversed. From Figure 7.6-3 we obtain the following two equations:

$$I_C = \alpha I_E + I_{CBO} \qquad (7.6\text{-}1)$$

$$I_E = I_B + I_c \qquad (7.6\text{-}2)$$

By combining Equation (7.6-1) with Equation (7.6-2) we obtain the base current

$$I_B = (1-\alpha)I_E - I_{CBO} = \left(\frac{1-\alpha}{\alpha}\right)I_C - \frac{I_{CBO}}{\alpha} = \frac{I_C}{\beta} - \frac{I_{CBO}}{\alpha} \qquad (7.6\text{-}3)$$

where

$$\beta = \frac{\alpha}{1-\alpha} \qquad (7.6\text{-}4)$$

Since the current I_{CBO} is extremely small it is usually neglected in Equation (7.6-3) and thus

$$I_C \doteq \beta I_B \qquad (7.6\text{-}5)$$

EXAMPLE 7.6-1. Find I_C, I_E and V_{CE} of a pnp transistor which is connected in the common-emitter (CE) configuration for which $\alpha = 0.98$ and $I_{CBO} = 10^{-11}$ A, as shown in Figure 7.6-4. A 30 μA driving source is applied.

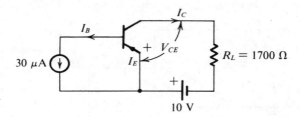

Figure 7.6-4.   Simple common-emitter amplifier configuration

SOLUTION. Using Equation (7.6-4) we find

$$\beta = \frac{0.98}{1-0.98} = 49$$

From Equation (7.6-3) we have that

$$I_C = \beta I_B + \frac{\beta}{\alpha}I_{CBO} = 49 \times 30 \times 10^{-6} + 10^{-11}/0.98$$

$$= 1.47 \times 10^{-3} \text{ A} = 1.47 \text{ mA}$$

The emitter current is found from Equation (7.6-2)

$$I_E = I_B + I_C = 30 \times 10^{-6} + 1.47 \times 10^{-3} = 1.50 \text{ mA}$$

By an application of the KVL around the right hand loop of the circuit, we find that

$$10 - V_{CE} - 1700 \times 1.47 \times 10^{-3} = 0$$

or

$$V_{CE} \doteq 7.50 \text{ V}$$

□ □ □

7.7 GRAPHICAL ANALYSIS OF TRANSISTOR AMPLIFIERS

Consider the common-emitter configuration of an npn transistor amplifier shown in Figure 7.7-1. The I_c, V_{CE} characteristic curves are given in Figure 7.7-1b. These curves should be viewed in the light of Equation (7.6-3) which predicts that

$$I_C = \beta I_B - \frac{\beta}{\alpha} I_{CBO}$$

This formula suggests almost equi-spaced horizontal lines on the I_c, V_{CE} curve, showing independence of V_{CE}. The actual characteristics support the validity of this equation, although deviations occur for low and high values of I_B. Figure 7.7-1c gives the I_B, V_{BE} characteristics. Observe that the emitter junction is for-

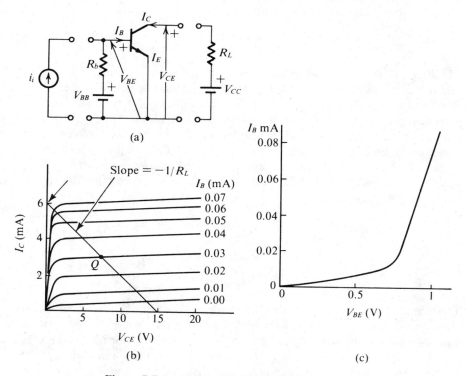

Figure 7.7-1. (a) Common emitter configuration
(b) $I_C - V_{CE}$ dc characteristic of npn transistor (c) $I_B - V_{BE}$ dc characteristic

ward biased and the collector is reverse biased. Because the forward resistance of the emitter junction is very small, the base current, without the input source, is supplied by the source V_{BB}, and is equal to $I_B = V_{BB}/R_b$. Further, since I_{CBO} is very small we can use Equation (7.6-5) which gives the collector current as $I_C \doteq \beta I_B$.

Next apply the KVL to the right hand loop of the circuit. There results

$$V_{CC} - R_L I_C - V_{CE} = 0$$

or

$$\frac{R_L}{V_{CC}} I_C + \frac{1}{V_{CC}} V_{CE} = 1 \tag{7.7-1}$$

which represents a straight line on the $I_C - V_{CE}$ characteristic. For example, for $V_{CC} = 15$ V and $R_L = 2500$ Ω, the straight line is that shown in Figure 7.7-1b. The intersection of the load line with the base current curve $I_B = V_{BB}/R_B$ is the operating point Q. If we select $V_{BB} = 1.2$ V and $R_B = 40 \times 10^3$ $\Omega = 40$ kΩ, the operating point Q is that shown in the figure ($I_B = V_{BB}/R_B = 30$ μA).

To find the circuit performance of Figure 7.7-1 we observe that we have available the functional relationship

$$V_{CE} = f(I_B, I_C) \tag{7.7-2}$$

which describes the transistor curves shown in Figure 7.7-1b, and the circuit relation given by Equation (7.7-1). The simultaneous solution of these equations yields a value for V_{CE}. To carry the solution forward, we adopt a graphical procedure, similar to that in Section 7.4. This is done by first drawing the linear curve specified by Equation (7.7-1) onto the set of curves specified by Equation (7.7-2). This establishes the dc load line, which has the slope $-1/R_L$. A typical plot, assuming idealized common-emitter characteristics is shown in Figure 7.7-2. From this curve we can determine the specific values for the quantities

$I_B(\mu A)$	$V_{CE}(V)$	$I_C(mA)$
$I_{B,min}$	$V_{CE,max}$	$I_{C,min}$
$I_{B,max}$	$V_{CE,min}$	$I_{C,max}$

The current I_{CQ} must be established by properly adjusting V_{BB}, as we have done above, so that as i_B varies sinusoidally from Q to a maximum allowable swing. The V_{CE} variation is also a sinusoid with little or no distortion. The time varying current $i_B = I_B + i_i = I_B + (I_{B,max} - I_{B,min}) \sin \omega t$. Note the significant fact that as the current i_B increases, I_C changes from I_{CQ} to $I_{C,max}$ and V_{CE} varies from

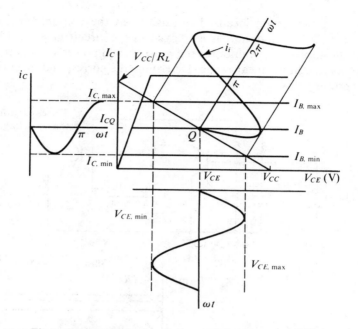

Figure 7.7-2. Deducing the operation from the static curves

$V_{CE,Q}$ to $V_{CE,min}$. That is, there is an inherent phase reversal between input and output. The ratio

$$\frac{\Delta I_C}{\Delta I_B} = \frac{I_{C,max} - I_{C,min}}{I_{B,max} - I_{B,min}} = A_i \tag{7.7-3}$$

is known as the *current gain*. For best operation, the swing should be symmetrical to yield optimum gain.

To determine the *voltage gain* A_v in this configuration, we must take the ratio of change in collector voltage to the change in base voltage, which means

$$A_v = \frac{\Delta V_{CE}}{\Delta V_{BE}} = \frac{\Delta V_{CE}}{r_i \Delta I_B} \tag{7.7-4}$$

where r_i is the input resistance of the transistor between base and emitter. This is found from Figure 7.7-1c, and is

$$r_i = \frac{\Delta V_{BE}}{\Delta I_B} \tag{7.7-5}$$

The *power gain* is the product of the voltage gain and the current gain, and is

$$A_p = A_v A_i \tag{7.7-6}$$

EXAMPLE 7.7-1. A certain idealized transistor has the volt-ampere curves shown in Figure 7.7-3b and c. It is employed in the circuit given in Figure 7.7-3a. Find the appropriate values for the resistors and power sources for the amplifier to operate in its linear range. Determine the corresponding current, voltage and power gains.

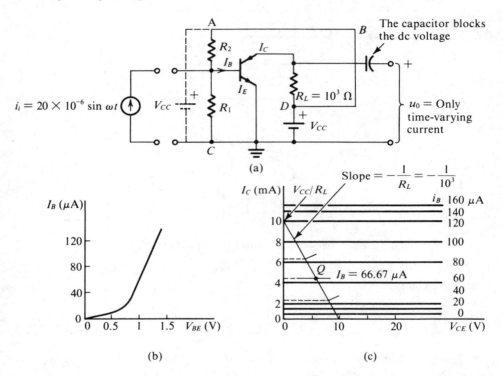

Figure 7.7-3. (a) Common emitter configuration
(b) Collector characteristics (c) Base characteristics

SOLUTION. Observe that V_{CC} provides the excitation for both the collector and the base circuits. The first step is to disconnect the circuit ABD and replace it by an equivalent dc source, as shown by the dotted circuit. We focus attention on this circuit, which is redrawn in Figure 7.7-4a and which is the bias circuit for the base. An application of the Thèvenin theorem permits this circuit to be redrawn to that shown in Figure 7.7-4b, with

$$R_b = \frac{R_1 R_2}{R_1 + R_2} \tag{7.7-7}$$

$$V_{EQ} = V_{BB} = \left(\frac{R_1}{R_1 + R_2} \right) V_{CC} \tag{7.7-8}$$

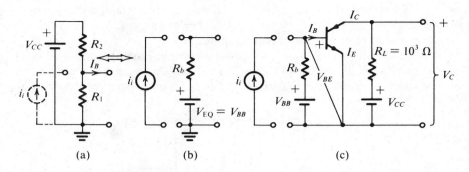

**Figure 7.7-4. (a, b) Thèvenin's equivalent of the bias circuit
(c) Equivalent circuit of Figure 7.7-3a**

We can now redraw Figure 7.7-3a, the original circuit, to the equivalent form given in Figure 7.7-4c, which is exactly the circuit of Figure 7.7-1. For a chosen $V_{CC} = 10$ V, the load line is that shown in Figure 7.7-3b. The next need is to select R_b, and hence R_1 and R_2, so that the operating point lies between the lines $I_B = 100$ μA and 60 μA. This will insure linearity of operation, since the maximum value of the source is (peak value) $i_{i,max} = 20$ μA. If we select $R_1 = 50$ kΩ and $R_2 = 150$ kΩ, then from Equations (7.7-7) and (7.7-8) we find that $R_b = 37.5$ kΩ and $V_{BB} = 2.5$ V. From the expression $I_B = V_{BB}/R_b$, we find that $I_B = 66.67$ μA, which establishes the Q-point shown in Figure 7.7-3c.

For the various gain factors, we find

$$A_i = \frac{(6.4 - 2.4) \text{ mA}}{(86.67 - 46.67) \text{ } \mu\text{A}} = 100$$

$$A_v = \frac{4}{0.15} = 26.6$$

$$A_p = 100 \times 26.6 = 2660$$

□ □ □

7.8 INCREMENTAL MODELS OF TRANSISTORS

When a transistor is used as a small signal amplifier the operation is essentially linear, and in such operations every effort is made to have the output be a replica of the input, except for the voltage or current amplitude levels. The voltage and current excursions away from the quiescent or no-signal levels are small, and the direct use of the transistor curves in the manner discussed in the previous section is not always particularly suitable. It is expedient therefore to examine the operation about the quiescent level by replacing the use of the transistor characteristic curves by a mathematical procedure that considers only the variations about the Q-point. Because of this, the operating supply voltages do not appear in the analysis, but they are assumed to be proper to establish and to maintain the operating point.

As a preliminary to this study, we consider certain general features of two-port networks, as illustrated in Figure 7.8-1. This study can be considered as an extension of the material in Chapter 2. We focus on one pair of terminals as

Figure 7.8-1.   The transistor as a 3-terminal device

input terminals and a second pair of terminals as the output terminals. The considerations parallel, to some extent, those discussed in connection with the Thèvenin theorem. We can establish a variety of descriptions of this 2-port device, depending on which two of the four variables V_1, V_2, I_1, I_2 are chosen as the independent variables. In Table 7.8-1 we define the following often used 2-port transistor sets. We shall confine our discussion only to the hybrid parameter description.

Table 7.8-1.   Two-port Transistor Descriptions

Independent Variables	Parameter Designation
V_1, V_2	y
I_1, I_2	z
I_1, V_2	h, or hybrid parameters
V_1, I_2	g

For that description we select the input current I_1 and the output voltage V_2 as the independent variables; therefore I_2 and V_1 are the dependent variables. We can write

$$V_1 = h_i I_1 + h_r V_2 \qquad \text{(a)} \quad (7.8\text{-}1)$$

$$I_2 = h_f I_1 + h_o V_2 \qquad \text{(b)}$$

The h-parameters are defined from this set as follows

$$h_i = \left. \frac{V_1}{I_1} \right|_{V_2=0} = \text{input impedance with output shorted (ohm)} \qquad (7.8\text{-}2)$$

$$h_o = \frac{I_2}{V_2}\bigg|_{I_1=0} = \text{output admittance with input open (mho)}$$

$$h_f = \frac{I_2}{I_1}\bigg|_{V_2=0} = \text{short-circuit forward current transfer ratio (dimensionless)}$$

$$h_r = \frac{V_1}{V_2}\bigg|_{I_1=0} = \text{open-circuit reverse voltage transfer ratio (dimensionless)}$$

Equations (7.8-1) give the explicit network representation shown in Figure 7.8-2. Observe that this figure precisely represents the network equations.

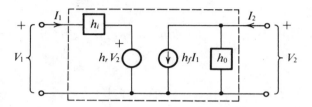

Figure 7.8-2.   Hybrid network representation of a two port network

EXAMPLE 7.8-1. Develop the incremental model of the common-emitter transistor configuration shown in Figure 7.8-3a.

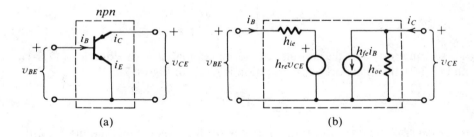

(a)   (b)

**Figure 7.8-3.   (a) Common-emitter configuration
(b) Incremental model of the C-E configuration**

SOLUTION. Reference to Figure 7.7-1 shows that the transistor in the common emitter configuration is described by curves that relate I_C and V_B to I_B and V_C. These interrelationships can be described in functional form as

$$V_B = V_B(I_B, V_C)$$

and

$$I_C = I_C(I_B, V_C)$$

In incremental variations about the established dc levels, the changes will be given by

$$\Delta V_B = \frac{\partial V_B}{\partial I_B} \Delta I_B + \frac{\partial V_B}{\partial V_C} \Delta V_C$$

$$\Delta I_C = \frac{\partial I_C}{\partial I_B} \Delta I_B + \frac{\partial I_C}{\partial V_C} \Delta V_C$$

These equations are written, using small letters to denote incremental variations,

$$v_B = h_i i_B + h_r v_C$$

$$i_C = h_f i_B + h_o v_C$$

where

$$h_i = \frac{\Delta V_B}{\Delta I_B}\bigg|_{\Delta V_C = 0} = \frac{v_B}{i_B}\bigg|_{v_C}$$

$$h_r = \frac{\Delta V_B}{\Delta V_C}\bigg|_{\Delta I_B = 0} = \frac{v_B}{v_C}\bigg|_{i_B}$$

$$h_f = \frac{\Delta I_C}{\Delta I_B}\bigg|_{\Delta V_C = 0} = \frac{i_C}{i_B}\bigg|_{v_C}$$

$$h_o = \frac{\Delta I_C}{\Delta V_C}\bigg|_{\Delta I_B = 0} = \frac{i_C}{v_C}\bigg|_{i_B}$$

These equations and definitions should be compared with Equations (7.8-1) and (7.8-2). The network representation is given in Figure 7.8-3b.

EXAMPLE 7.8-2. An npn transistor is used in a small signal amplifier, with the essential circuit shown in Figure 7.8-4a. Assuming that the amplifier is appropriately dc biased, find the voltage gain of this amplifier.

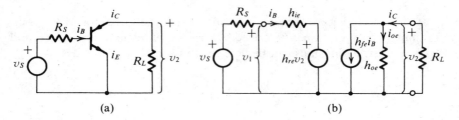

(a)   (b)

Figure 7.8-4. (a) A simple amplifier with the transistor in the common-emitter configuration (b) Incremental model of the amplifier

SOLUTION. The dc supply sources are not shown, but are implied to exist. The circuit equations for this circuit are

$$v_S = (R_S + h_{ie})i_B + h_{re}v_2 \qquad \text{KVL}$$

$$0 = (i_1 + i_{oe} + h_{fe}i_B) = \left(h_{oe} + \frac{1}{R_L} \right) v_2 + h_{fe}i_B \qquad \text{KCL}$$

From these we find that

$$v_S = - \left[\frac{(R_S + h_{ie})(h_{oe} + 1/R_L)}{h_{fe}} - h_{re} \right] v_2$$

The voltage gain is given by

$$A_v = \frac{v_2}{v_S} = \frac{h_{fe}}{(R_S + h_{ie})\left(h_{oe} + \dfrac{1}{R_L} \right) - h_{re}h_{fe}}$$

While the hybrid network assumes that the h-parameters are constants, the transistor parameters vary with the emitter current, as shown in Figure 7.8-5. Typical values for the h-parameters are often given as $h_{ie} = 1.3$ kΩ; $h_{re} = 3 \times 10^{-4}$; $h_{fe} = 50$; $h_{oe} = 25 \times 10^{-6}$ mho. Observe that the forward current gain h_{fe} and the reverse voltage amplification factor h_{re} remain relatively constant over substantial ranges of I_E. However, both the output conductance h_{oe} and the input resistant h_{ie} do vary rather markedly. For best results in general we seek transistors with large current gain $h_{fe} \triangleq \beta$. This quantity is a sensitive measure of transistor quality in the common-emitter configuration.

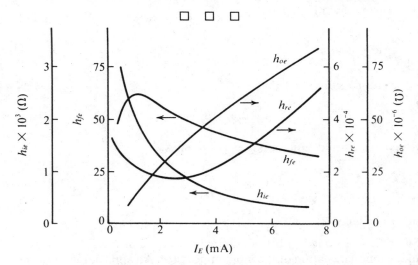

Figure 7.8-5.   **Typical variation of common-emitter h-parameters with emitter current**

7.9   INPUT AND OUTPUT IMPEDANCE

Important considerations in transistor amplifiers are the input and output impedances. The input impedance will indicate the extent to which the circuit may load the source that drives the amplifier. This can be particularly important if the impedance of the driving source is high, since a heavy loading may affect the amplitude or the waveform. If the amplifier is one of a cascaded chain, it can seriously affect the effective R_L of the stage that is driving the amplifier.

The output impedance is of importance if the amplifier is to drive another stage or some output device. If the output impedance is high, then any appreciable loading will cause the output signal to fall, and with much of the power output lost within the amplifier itself.

To examine these matters in detail, refer to Figure 7.9-1. We determine the important features of this amplifier stage.

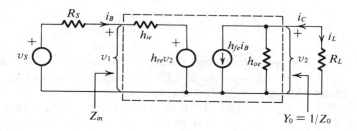

Figure 7.9-1.   Incremental model of the common-emitter amplifier

Current Gain A_i

The current gain is defined by

$$A_i = \frac{i_L}{i_B} = -\frac{i_C}{i_B} \tag{7.9-1}$$

We see from Figure 7.9-1 that

$$i_C = h_{fe} i_B + h_{oe} v_2 \tag{7.9-2}$$

But $v_2 = -i_C R_L$ and Equation (7.9-1) becomes

$$A_i = -\frac{h_{fe}}{1 + h_{oe} R_L} \tag{7.9-3}$$

Input Impedance Z_i

Since R_s is assumed to be the internal resistance of the source, it is not included in the calculation of the input impedance. An application of the KVL to the input loop leads to

$$v_1 = h_{ie} i_B + h_{re} v_2$$

or

$$\frac{v_1}{i_B} = Z_i = h_{ie} + h_{re} \frac{v_2}{i_B} \tag{7.9-4}$$

Since

$$v_2 = -i_C R_L = -\frac{i_C}{i_B} i_B R_L = A_i i_B R_L \tag{7.9-5}$$

Then Equation (7.9-4) becomes

$$Z_i = h_{ie} + h_{re} A_i R_L = h_{ie} - \frac{h_{fe}}{1 + h_{oe} R_L} \tag{7.9-6}$$

where the value of A_i was taken from Equation (7.9-3)

Voltage Gain A_v

We can write directly that

$$A_v = \frac{v_2}{v_1} = \frac{A_i i_B R_L}{v_1} = \frac{A_i i_B R_L}{i_B Z_i} = \frac{A_i R_L}{Z_i} \tag{7.9-7}$$

Output Impedance Z_o

It proves to be more convenient to find the output admittance $Y_o = 1/Z_o$. This requires, from Equation (7.9-2), that we obtain the relation

$$Y_o = \frac{1}{Z_o} = \frac{i_C}{v_2}\bigg|_{v_s = 0} = h_{fe} \frac{i_B}{v_2} + h_{oe} \tag{7.9-8}$$

We set $v_s = 0$ and apply the KVL to the input loop of the circuit. This gives

$$R_S i_B + h_{ie} i_B + h_{re} v_2 = 0$$

or

$$\frac{i_B}{v_2} = -\frac{h_{re}}{h_{ie} + R_S} \tag{7.9-9}$$

This is combined with Equation (7.9-8) to give

$$Y_o = \frac{1}{Z_o} = h_{oe} - \frac{h_{fe} h_{re}}{h_{ie} + R_S} \tag{7.9-10}$$

It is observed that Y_o is a function of the source resistance.

Total circuit voltage gain A_{v_s} including the input resistor R_s

By overall voltage amplification we mean

$$A_{vs} = \frac{v_2}{v_s} = \frac{v_2}{v_1}\frac{v_1}{v_s} = A_v\frac{v_1}{v_s} \qquad (7.9\text{-}11)$$

But $v_1 = v_s Z_i/(Z_i + R_s)$, and so

$$A_{vs} = A_v\frac{Z_i}{Z_i + R_s} = A_i\frac{R_L}{Z_i + R_s} \qquad (7.9\text{-}12)$$

Total system current gain A_{is}, including the resistor R_s

To carry out this calculation, it proves convenient to use the Norton equivalent source theorem and change the series combination of v_s and R_s to an equivalent parallel combination of the current source $i_s = v_s/R_s$ and the resistor R_s.

The total system current gain is defined by

$$A_{is} = -\frac{i_C}{i_s} = -\frac{i_C}{i_B}\frac{i_B}{i_s} = A_i\frac{i_B}{i_s} = A_i\frac{i_s R_s}{R_s + Z_i}\frac{1}{i_s} = A_i\frac{R_s}{R_s + Z_i} \qquad (7.9\text{-}13)$$

EXAMPLE 7.9-1. A transistor circuit having the incremental circuit model shown in Figure 7.9-1 has the following parameter values: $h_{ie} = 1.3 \times 10^3$ Ω; $h_{re} = 3 \times 10^{-4}$; $h_{fe} = 50$; $h_{oe} = 25 \times 10^{-6}$ mho; $R_L = 6 \times 10^3$ Ω; $R_s = 10^3$ Ω. Find the various gain factors and the input and output impedances.

SOLUTION. This requires the numerical values for the quantities derived. These are

$$A_i = -\frac{50}{1 + 25 \times 10^{-6} \times 6 \times 10^3} = -43.48$$

$$Z_i \triangleq R_i = 1.3 \times 10^3 + 3 \times 10^{-4} \times (-43.48) \times 6 \times 10^3 = 1221.74 \ \Omega$$

$$A_v = -\frac{43.48 \times 6 \times 10^3}{1221.7} = -213.53$$

$$A_{vs} = -\frac{43.48 \times 6 \times 10^3}{6 \times 10^3 + 10^3} = -37.27$$

$$A_{is} = -\frac{43.48 \times 10^3}{6 \times 10^3 + 10^3} = -6.21$$

$$Y_o = \frac{1}{R_o} = 25 \times 10^{-6} - \frac{50 \times 3 \times 10^{-4}}{1.3 \times 10^3 + 10^3} = 18.48 \times 10^{-6}, \qquad R_o = 54.11 \times 10^3 \ \Omega$$

$$A_p = A_i A_v = 213.53 \times 43.48 = 9284.28$$

□   □   □

EXAMPLE 7.9-2. Analyze the behavior of the *emitter follower* circuit given in Figure 7.9-2a.

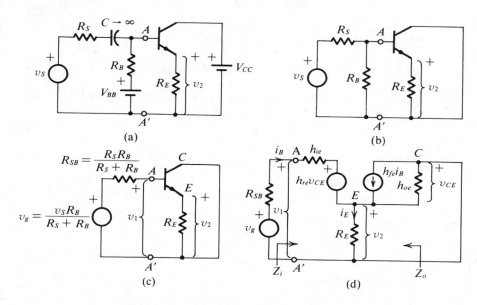

(a)   (b)   (c)   (d)

Figure 7.9-2. (a) Emitter follower circuit   (b) Its ac equivalent circuit
(c) Thèvenin equivalent of the input circuit
(d) Incremental model of the emitter follower

SOLUTION. The figures show the successive steps in developing the incremental equivalent circuit of the emitter follower, recognizing that we are interested in its operation about the fixed dc levels which are established by the bias sources and the circuit elements. Observe that the presence of the capacitor is only to block the dc voltages. Its impedance to ac sources is zero and therefore is neglected in the analysis.

A straightforward application of known laws to Figure 7.9-2d yields

$$v_g = (R_{SB} + h_{ie})i_B + h_{re}v_{CE} + v_2 \qquad \text{KVL, first loop} \qquad \text{(a)} \quad (7.9\text{-}14)$$

$$i_E = h_{fe}i_B + h_{oe}v_{CE} + i_B \qquad \text{KCL, node E} \qquad \text{(b)}$$

$$v_2 = i_E R_E \qquad \text{Ohm's law} \qquad \text{(c)}$$

$$v_2 = -v_{CE} \qquad \text{KVL, second loop} \qquad \text{(d)}$$

Solving these equations for v_2 in terms of $v_1 = v_g - R_{SB}i_B$ yields

$$A_v = \frac{v_2}{v_1} = \frac{(1 + h_{fe})R_E}{h_{ie} + h_{ie}h_{oe}R_E + (1 - h_{re})(1 + h_{fe})R_E} \qquad (7.9\text{-}15)$$

Ordinarily $h_{re} \ll 1$; $h_{fe} \gg 1$; $1 + h_{oe}R_E \doteq 1$, and this equation reduces to

$$A_v \doteq \frac{h_{fe}R_E}{h_{ie} + h_{fe}R_E} = \frac{1}{1 + \dfrac{h_{ie}}{h_{fe}R_E}} \qquad (7.9\text{-}16)$$

This shows that for any reasonable value of R_E the voltage gain is essentially unity.

The input impedance, using similar approximations, is readily found to be

$$Z_i \doteq h_{ie} + (1 + h_{fe})R_E \qquad (7.9\text{-}17)$$

The input impedance can be further approximated to

$$Z_i \doteq h_{fe}R_E \qquad (7.9\text{-}18)$$

A calculation of the output impedance yields the expression

$$Z_o = \frac{h_{ie} + R_{SB}}{1 + h_{fe}} \qquad (7.9\text{-}19)$$

which is very low for normal values of R_{SB}.

The emitter follower has the essential properties of unity gain without phase reversal, high input impedance, and low output impedance. This makes the emitter follower a convenient coupling device for driving a low impedance output from a high impedance source, with little loading.

□   □   □

EXAMPLE 7.9-3. Analyze the behavior of the common-base transistor amplifier given in Figure 7.9-3.

SOLUTION. Apply known laws to Figure 7.9-3c to find

$$v_1 + h_{ie}i_B = 0 \qquad \text{(a)} \quad (7.9\text{-}20)$$

$$i_E = i_B + h_{fe}i_B \qquad \text{(b)}$$

$$v_2 = -h_{fe}i_B R_L \qquad \text{(c)}$$

Use Equations (7.9-20c) and (7.9-20a) to obtain

$$A_v = \frac{v_2}{v_1} = R_L \frac{h_{fe}}{h_{ie}} \qquad (7.9\text{-}21)$$

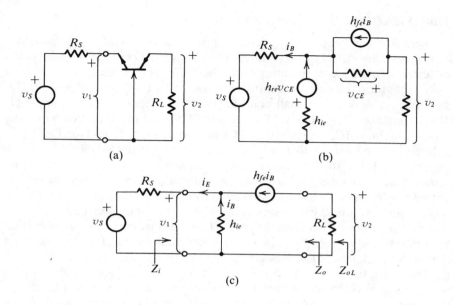

Figure 7.9-3. **(a) Common-base circuit** **(b) Its ac equivalent circuit**
(c) Simplified model

Combine Equations (7.9-20b) and (7.9-20a) to obtain the input impedance

$$Z_i = \frac{v_2}{-i_E} = \frac{h_{ie}}{1 + h_{fe}}$$ (7.9-22)

From Equation (7.9-20c) we find that

$$Z_o = \frac{v_2}{0} = \infty$$ (7.9-23)

when R_L is not connected and

$$Z_{oL} = \frac{v_2}{-h_{fe}i_B} = R_L$$ (7.9-24)

when R_L is present. Finally from Equation (7.9-20b) we obtain

$$A_i = \frac{i_C}{i_E} = \frac{i_B h_{fe}}{i_E} = \frac{h_{fe}}{1 + h_{fe}}$$ (7.9-25)

□ □ □

7.10   FIELD EFFECT TRANSISTORS

There is a very important class of semiconductor devices known as *field effect transistors* (FET) with a variety of subclasses. These are fundamentally different in design and operation from the BJT since the current is mainly a drift of majority carriers, as contrasted with the BJT which is largely a diffusion current device. We shall consider two basic types of FET, the simple JFET (junction FET), UNIFET (unipolar FET) and the *insulated gate field effect transistor*, IGFET or MOSFET (metal-oxide-semiconductor FET).

Illustrated in Figure 7.10-1 are the unipolar FET and the MOSFET. Refer to Figure 7.10-1 for the JFET. This device consists of a heavily doped thin semiconductor channel with large area *p-n* junction on one or both sides of the channel between two electrodes, the *source* and the *drain* respectively. For an *n*-type channel, a positive voltage is applied to the drain electrode. This produces a flow of electrons from the source to the drain and a flow of holes from the drain to the source. The edges of the depletion region of the *p-n* junction define the thickness of the conducting channel in the *n*-type region. Consider the case when the gate is reverse biased relative to the channel. When the bias voltage is low, the junction depletion layer is relatively thin, and a large current exists between the source and drain. Increases in the reverse bias cause the depletion layer to grow until finally the entire channel is pinched off, and no

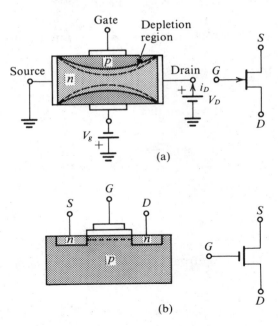

Figure 7.10-1.   Features of field effect transistors and their symbols
(a) The *n*-channel unipolar JFET with appropriate bias sources
(b) The thin film MOSFET

current exists. Suppose now that the drain voltage is increased; the current increases. Also the depletion layer between drain and *gate* grows, thereby constricting the drain end of the channel. Further increases of drain voltage result in less and less current increase until a current saturation value is reached. Saturation is reached when the sum of the gate and drain voltage is equal to the pinchoff voltage. At higher drain voltage, current saturation sets in. The situation is illustrated in Figure 7.10-2a.

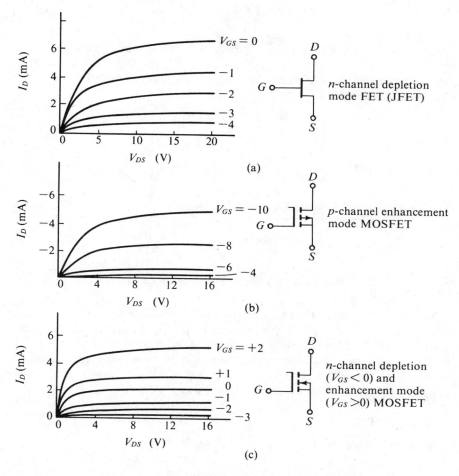

Figure 7.10-2.   Characteristics of typical FETs

In the MOSFET (see Figure 7.10-1b), a thin layer of SiO_2 insulates the gate contact from the channel. Operation of the device is roughly as follows. For zero gate bias voltage with a positive drain voltage, conduction exists in the semiconductor channel which is induced by the electric field that is established between the gate and the substrate. If a negative voltage is applied to the gate, the density of free electrons in the channel is decreased and the drain current is thereby decreased. The reverse is true when the gate voltage is positive, as shown in Figure 7.10-2c, which shows the characteristics of an n-channel MOSFET in the depletion and in the enhancement mode.

The current-voltage relation of the FET is nearly square law, and is of the form

$$I_D = I_{DSS} \left(1 - \frac{V_G}{V_P} \right)^n \qquad (7.10\text{-}1)$$

where V_G is the gate voltage, V_P is the pinchoff voltage (the value of V_G that is necessary to reduce the drain current to zero), I_{DSS} is the drain current when the gate is shorted to the source, and the exponent is approximately $n = 2$. These characteristics are shown in Figure 7.10-3.

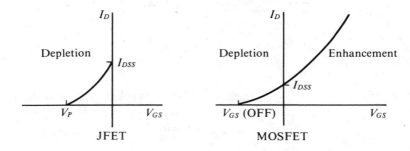

Figure 7.10-3. Transfer characteristics of FETs

The special features of the FET are that as an amplifier they have a very high input resistance (from 1 MΩ to 100 MΩ, the MOSFET being generally higher than the JFET) and a relatively low output impedance (1 kΩ to 100 kΩ). The MOSFET that employs p-type rather than n-type semiconductor material is known as the complementary MOSFET or CMOSFET. Many of the large scale integrated LSI circuits are fabricated using MOSFET-s.

Biasing the JFET

A typical simple amplifier circuit with its volt-ampere characteristics is given in Figure 7.10-4. The procedure for establishing the dc bias levels parallels that for the BJT. Refer to Figure 7.10-4. If we adjust $V_{GG} = -2$ V (the signal v_1 is not considered for the dc behavior) then the point Q is automatically specified by the intersection of the line $V_{GG} = -2$ V and the load line. The dc load line is specified by the equation deduced by the KVL applied to the right hand loop,

$$V_{DD} - i_D R_L - V_{DS} = 0 \qquad (7.10\text{-}2)$$

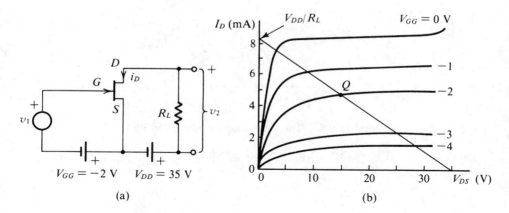

Figure 7.10-4. (a) Simple JFET amplifier
(b) v-i characteristics and the dc load line

Small Signal Analysis

The FETs are described by the functional forms

$$I_G = 0 \qquad\qquad I_D = I_D(V_{GS}, V_{DS}) \qquad\qquad (7.10\text{-}3)$$

In the incremental operation about the established bias levels, the variation of the drain current is

$$\Delta I_D = \frac{\partial I_D}{\partial V_{GS}} \Delta V_{GS} + \frac{\partial I_D}{\partial V_{DS}} \Delta V_{DS} \qquad\qquad (7.10\text{-}4)$$

which permits us to define the quantities

$$\frac{\partial I_D}{\partial V_{GS}} = \frac{\Delta I_D}{\Delta V_{GS}}\bigg|_{V_{DS}=0} = g_m \quad \text{transconductance (mho)} \qquad \text{(a)} \quad (7.10\text{-}5)$$

$$\frac{\partial I_D}{\partial V_{DS}} = \frac{\Delta I_D}{\Delta V_{DS}}\bigg|_{V_{GS}=0} = \frac{1}{r_d} \quad \text{inverse dynamic drain resistance} \qquad \text{(b)}$$

The variational equation can then be written

$$i_D = g_m v_{gs} + \frac{1}{r_d} v_{ds} \qquad\qquad (7.10\text{-}6)$$

These results can be given network representation as shown in Figure 7.10-5. Note specifically that the FET is a voltage driven device, as contrasted with the BJT which was seen to be a current driven device. Typical range for g_m is 10^{-3} to 4×10^{-3} mho and r_d is 20×10^3 to 250×10^3 Ω.

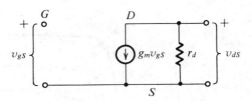

Figure 7.10-5. The small signal model of an FET

EXAMPLE 7.10-1. Evaluate the gain of the simple FET amplifier shown in Figure 7.10-6a.

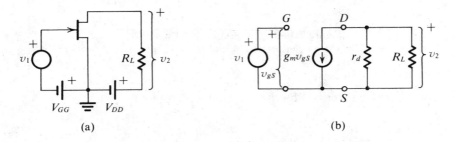

      (a)   (b)

Figure 7.10-6. (a) Simple JFET amplifier   (b) Its incremental model

SOLUTION. An application of the KVL to the left-hand loop yields the equation

$$v_1 = v_{gs} \tag{7.10-7}$$

However, the voltage output is

$$v_2 = -g_m v_{gs} \left(\frac{R_L r_d}{R_L + r_d} \right) \tag{7.10-8}$$

Then, using Equation (7.10-7)

$$A_v = \frac{v_2}{v_1} = -g_m \left(\frac{R_L r_d}{R_L + r_d} \right) \tag{7.10-9}$$

Since usually $r_d \gg R_L$, Equation (7.10-9) assumes the simple form

$$A_v = -g_m R_L \tag{7.10-10}$$

□ □ □

7.11   OPERATIONAL AMPLIFIERS AND THEIR USES

General Information

The *operational amplifier* in its present IC (integrated circuit) form is a direct outgrowth of the linear amplifiers that provided the basic elements in the computational circuits used in analog computers. The characteristics sought in such op-amps are the following:

Voltage gain	$A \doteq \infty$	$(10^6 \leqslant A \leqslant 10^9)$
Bandwidth	$BW \doteq \infty$	
Input impedance	$Z_i \doteq \infty$	$(10^5 \ \text{ohm} \leqslant Z_i \leqslant 10^{10} \ \text{ohm})$
Output impedance	$Z_o \doteq 0$	$(10 \ \text{ohm} \leqslant Z_o \leqslant 100 \ \text{ohm})$

These extreme specifications are not fully met in commercial units, but available IC units approach these characteristics sufficiently closely that the circuits involving them generally operate satisfactorily.

Figure 7.11-1a shows a schematic diagram of an op-amp. The signs of the inputs indicate the relation between the input to that terminal and the resulting output voltage. The output signal is in phase with the signal applied at the plus terminal and is inverted with respect to the signal applied at the minus terminal.

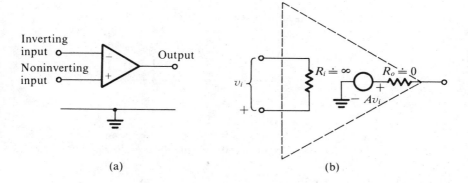

(a)   (b)

**Figure 7.11-1.   (a) Schematic representation of op-amp
(b) The equivalent circuit of the op-amp**

To illustrate the features of an op-amp, consider the circuit shown in Figure 7.11-2a. Its ideal equivalent circuit is shown in Figures 7.11-2b and c. Applying KCL at node 1 and noting that $v_o = -Av_i$, we obtain the equations

$$\frac{v_i - v_s}{R_s} + \frac{v_i + Av_i}{R_f} = 0 \qquad (7.11\text{-}1)$$

$$v_o = -Av_i \qquad (7.11\text{-}2)$$

Upon eliminating v_i from the last two equations, we obtain

$$\frac{v_o}{v_s} = -\frac{AR_f}{R_f + (1+A)R_s} \doteq -\frac{R_f}{R_s} \qquad (7.11\text{-}3)$$

since $A \gg 1$ and $AR_s \gg R_f$. Equation (7.11-3) indicates that the ratio of the output to input voltage depends only on the value of resistors R_s and R_f, given that A is very large.

We shall examine several of the important "analog" circuits which employ the op-amp. These include the inverter (the NOT circuit of Chapter 9), the summer, and the integrator.

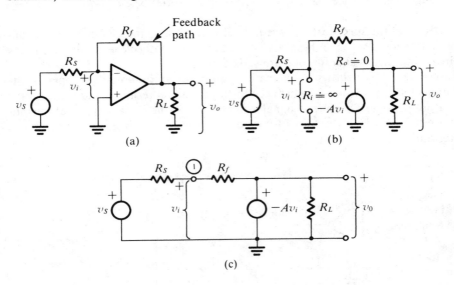

Figure 7.11-2. **(a) An op-amp with its associated connections (b) Equivalent circuit (ideal) (c) circuit (b) redrawn**

Uses of Operational Amplifiers

THE INVERTER CIRCUIT. To find the output voltage of an ideal op-amp shown in Figure 7.11-3a and in its conventional form in Figure 7.11-3b, we incorporate the two approximate rules: (a) Because the nominal gain of the op-amp is very high, then for an output of a few volts the changing voltage at node 1 with respect to the ground is virtually zero; (b) Because of the high input impedance, the current into the op-amp input terminal is zero. Hence, KCL at node 1 is (see Figure 7.11-3c)

$$\frac{0 - v_s}{R_s} + \frac{0 - v_o}{R_f} = 0$$

or

$$v_o = -\frac{R_f}{R_s} v_s \qquad (7.11\text{-}4)$$

which is identical with Equation (7.11-3). Clearly the minus sign shows this to be an inverting amplifier, the output gain being $-R_f/R_s$. This shows that simple voltage scaling is possible.

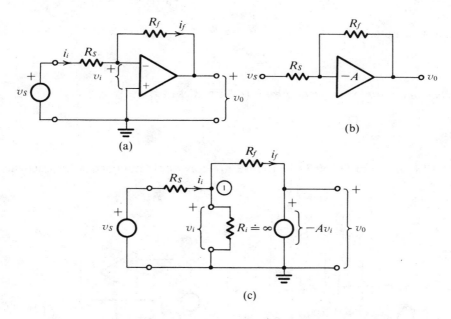

Figure 7.11-3.   The basic inverting circuit

Suppose that we had applied the source and feedback to the terminal marked $+$. If the transistors and components composing the op-amp were exactly the same, then the output-input ratio would be

$$\frac{v_o}{v_s} \doteq \frac{R_f}{R_s} = A$$

This means that if we applied v_{s1} to one terminal and v_{s2} to the second terminal, the output would be

$$v_o = \frac{R_f}{R_s}(v_{s1} - v_{s2}) = A(v_{s1} - v_{s2})$$

For $v_{s1} = v_{s2}$, the so called *common-mode* output should be zero. In general, owing to slight differences in the two channels, the output may be slightly different from zero. It has become customary to define the quantities:

$$\text{difference} \quad v_d = v_{s1} - v_{s2} \qquad \text{mean voltage} \quad v_c = \frac{1}{2}(v_{s1} + v_{s2})$$

and for channel gains A_1 and A_2

$$A_d = \frac{1}{2}(A_1 - A_2) \qquad\qquad A_c = (-A_1 + A_2)$$

For a single output

$$v_o = A_d v_d + A_c v_c$$

The *common mode rejection ratio* is defined as

$$\text{CMRR} = \frac{A_d}{A_c}$$

CMRR of the order of 70 to 100 dB are commonly obtained with practical amplifiers.

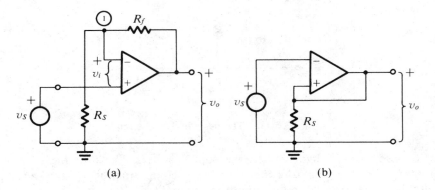

Figure 7.11-4. (a) Non-inverting amplifier
(b) Unity follower circuit (voltage follower)

NON-INVERTING CIRCUIT. The circuit of Figure 7.11-4a shows a non-inverting amplifier. From the figure, with the use of KCL at node 1 we obtain

$$\frac{v_s + v_i}{R_s} + \frac{v_s + v_i - v_o}{R_f} = 0$$

or

$$\frac{v_o}{v_s + v_i} \doteq \frac{v_o}{v_s} = \frac{R_s + R_f}{R_s} = 1 + \frac{R_f}{R_s} \tag{7.11-5}$$

since

$$v_i \doteq 0.$$

UNITY FOLLOWER. If we set $R_f = 0$, then from Equation (7.11-5) we observe that $v_o = v_s$ and the output has the same polarity and magnitude as the input. The circuit of the unity follower is shown in Figure 7.11-4b.

THE SUMMING CIRCUIT. The summing circuit is a modification of Figure 7.11-3 to accommodate multiple inputs. The basic circuit is shown in Figure 7.11-5. Since node 1 is at virtual ground potential an application of the KCL at the same node gives the following equation

$$\frac{0 - v_1}{R_1} + \frac{0 - v_2}{R_2} + \ldots + \frac{0 - v_n}{R_n} + \frac{0 - v_o}{R_f} = 0$$

or

$$\sum_{n=1}^{n} \frac{v_n}{R_n} = -\frac{v_o}{R_f} \tag{7.11-6}$$

This shows the summation property with simultaneous scaling of each separate input as it is reflected in the output. Observe that a signal can be *subtracted* by first passing it through an inverter (scaling factor $R_f/R_1 = 1$) before it is applied to the input of the summer.

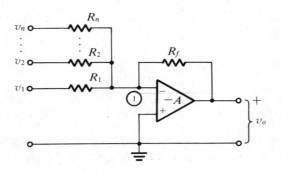

Figure 7.11-5. The summing circuit

INTEGRATOR CIRCUIT. If instead of the feedback resistor R_f, we consider this to be a general operational function $Z_f(p)$ the form of Equation (7.11-4) will remain unchanged, but we can now view the resulting equation

$$v_o = -\frac{Z_f(p)}{R_s} v_s \qquad (7.11\text{-}7)$$

as an operational expression, the character of the operation depending on the specific form of $Z_f(p)$. Of particular importance is the circuit when $Z_f(p)$ is the function $1/Cp$ that results using a capacitor, as shown in Figure 7.11-6a. It is this general property, with the circuit of the integrator being a special example, which was the basis for the term, operational amplifier.

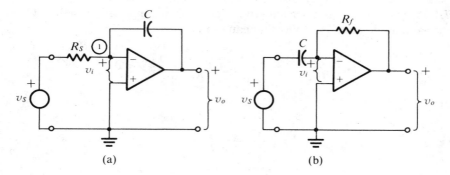

(a)   (b)

Figure 7.11-6.   (a) Integrating circuit   (b) Differentiating circuit

Since no currents enter the op-amp, the KCL at node 1 gives

$$\frac{v_i - v_s}{R_s} + C\frac{d(v_i - v_o)}{dt} = 0 \qquad \text{or} \qquad \frac{dv_o}{dt} = -\frac{1}{R_s C} v_s \qquad (v_i \doteq 0)$$

Solving for v_o we obtain

$$v_o(t) = -\frac{1}{R_s C} \int_{-\infty}^{t} v_s(t)\, dt \qquad (7.11\text{-}8)$$

which shows that the output is the integral of the inverted input signal scaled by $R_s C$.

A simple extension of the summing amplifier of Figure 7.11-5 into a summing integrator requires replacing R_f by a capacitor C. The output is readily shown to be

$$v_o(t) = -\frac{1}{Cp}\left(\frac{v_1}{R_1} + \frac{v_2}{R_2} + \dots + \frac{v_n}{R_n}\right) \qquad (7.11\text{-}9)$$

THE DIFFERENTIATOR. By interchanging C and R_s in Figure 7.11-6a the circuit becomes a differentiator (see Figure 7.11-6b). However, since differentiators have the property of accentuating high frequency components of noise, it is desirable not to use such circuits. Instead, the circuit requirements can be rearranged to use integrators in place of differentiators. This is illustrated in the following example.

EXAMPLE 7.11-1. Deduce a signal flow program graph and the op-amp configuration for an analog computer to solve the differential equation

$$m\frac{d^2y}{dt^2} + c\frac{dy}{dt} + ky = f(t) \tag{7.11-10}$$

This equation describes the motion of a mass m that is supported on a spring with elastic constant k, and with viscous damping cdy/dt.

SOLUTION. The program graph is essentially the signal flow graph which specifies the equation

$$\frac{d^2y}{dt^2} = \frac{1}{m}\left[f(t) - c\frac{dy}{dt} - ky\right] \tag{7.11-11}$$

This program graph, which includes only integrators plus other circuits but no differentiators, is shown in Figure 7.11-7. The function $1/p$ denotes integration (see Chapter 6).

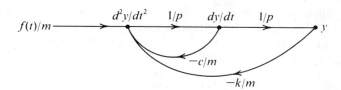

Figure 7.11-7.   The program graph of Equation (7.11-11)

The analog computer circuit is a translation of the program graph, except that the inversion features of the op-amp must be taken into account. Because of this, it is often necessary to include sign-changers in the analog computer circuit to provide appropriately signed quantities. The detailed program is given in Figure 7.11-8. Note that other equivalent programs can be devised.

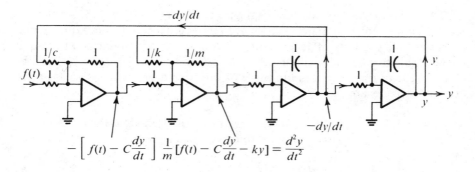

$$-\left[f(t) - C\frac{dy}{dt} \right] \frac{1}{m}[f(t) - C\frac{dy}{dt} - ky] = \frac{d^2y}{dt^2}$$

Figure 7.11-8. The analog computer program

7.12* SWITCHING CIRCUITS FOR LOGIC OPERATIONS

Most present-day computers and electronic equipment are built using integrated circuits. Groups of these circuits are compatible; that is, they can be interconnected to form a complete digital circuit. We have already discussed simple diode logic in Section 7.5. We now wish to examine other families of digital circuits, such as *diode-transistor logic* (DTL) and *transistor-transistor logic* (TTL).

Transistor Switch

Often the transistor is used as a switch. Figure 7.12-1a shows the *v-i* characteristics of an ideal switch, and Figure 7.12-1b includes the *v-i* characteristics of a common emitter npn transistor. That the transistor circuit acts as a switch is evident when we recognize that for a large current i_B, the switch is closed, and $v_{CE} = 0$; when $i_B = 0$, the switch is open, or equivalently, the collector voltage is open-circuited. The conditions on i_C and the relation to i_B describe the several regions

$$\text{in the linear region} \qquad i_C \doteq \beta i_B$$

$$\text{in the saturation region} \quad i_C < \beta i_B$$

EXAMPLE 7.12-1. Refer to the circuit of Figure 7.12-1b, with $i_B = 100$ μA, $\beta = 65$, $V_{cc} = 20$ V. We must find R_L such that the transistor operates in the saturation region.

SOLUTION. Apply the KVL around the right-hand loop, which gives

$$20 - i_C R_L - v_{CE} = 0$$

For the saturation condition

$$i_C = \frac{20 - v_{CE}}{R_L} \doteq \frac{20}{R_L}$$

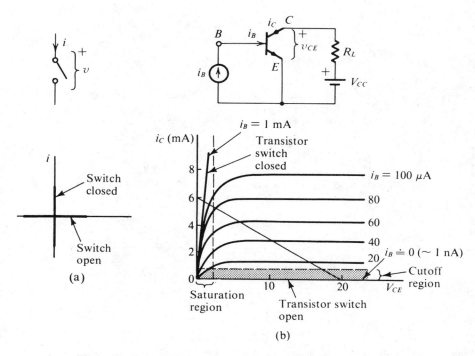

Figure 7.12-1. (a) Switching characteristics of an ideal switch
(b) Switching characteristics of a transistor

But since $i_c < \beta i_B = 100 \times 10^{-6} \times 65 = 6.5$ mA, we can choose $R_L = 3330$ Ω, the value that gives $i_c(\text{max}) = 6$ mA. This load line is shown on Figure 7.12-1b.

□   □   □

Inverter

We know from past discussion that the simple transistor amplifier involves a phase reversal. Using the circuit of Figure 7.12-2a, we observe that the output voltage is the inverse of the input. A characteristic timing signal is shown in Figure 7.12-2c. This type of switch is an inverter or NOT gate.

The Flipflop

It will later be shown that the flipflop is one of the important components in digital circuits. The circuit possesses other applications since it provides one convenient way for generating a square wave. In essence, the flipflop is a two transistor cross-coupled bistable electronic circuit which forces one transistor to be in saturation while the other is cutoff. To understand the operation, refer to Figure 7.12-3. Roughly, the situation involves the following conditions. Suppose that T_1 is in the OFF state and T_2 is in the conducting ON state. As a

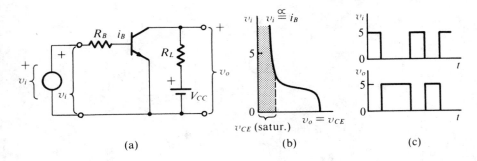

**Figure 7.12-2.   (a) Transistor inverter   (b) v_i-v_o characteristics
(c) Timing diagram**

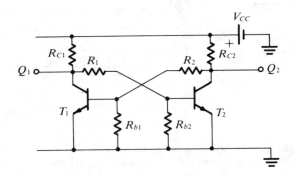

Figure 7.12-3.   A direct-coupled flipflop

result, point Q_1 is at approximately V_{cc}, causing the base of T_2 to be high, and causing T_2 to be conducting, as noted. Simultaneously, because T_2 is conducting, Q_2 is almost at ground potential. This voltage appears on T_1 and is such that T_1 is in the non-conducting state. This is a stable situation and the *FF* can remain in this state indefinitely.

Suppose now that a positive pulse is applied to the base of T_1 (this signal might be applied simultaneously to both bases) so that T_1 begins to conduct. This will cause the potential of Q_1 to begin to fall. This results in a falling potential on the base of T_2. Soon T_2 begins to turn off, which drives Q_2 upward. This appears on the base of T_1 as a rising voltage which causes T_1 to conduct heavily into saturation. This switching is very rapid and is accomplished in nanoseconds. Timing can be influenced by distributed capacitance across R_{b1} and R_{b2}. To compensate for this, small capacitors are often added across R_1 and R_2. Can you explain why?

To analyze the circuit operation, assume that T_2 is in the conducting state and T_1 is off. The circuit is that shown in Figure 7.12-4. Under the conditions

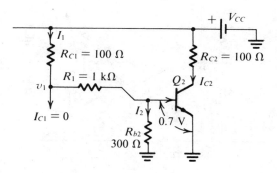

Figure 7.12-4. The circuit when T_2 is conducting

shown $V_{Q2} = 0$, neglecting the voltage v_{CE2}. Also $I_{C1} = 0$ since T_1 is cutoff. Then, assuming $v_{BE} = 0.7$ V

$$I_{C2} = \frac{V_{CC} - V_{CE2}}{R_{C2}} = \frac{5 - 0}{100} = 50 \text{ mA}$$

$$I_2 = \frac{V_{BE2}}{R_{b2}} = \frac{0.7}{300} = 2.33 \text{ mA}$$

Also

$$I_1 = \frac{V_{CC} - V_{BE2}}{R_{C1} + R_1} = \frac{5 - 0.7}{100 + 1000} = \frac{4.3}{1100} = 3.91 \text{ mA}$$

Hence

$$I_{B2} = I_1 - I_2 = 3.91 - 2.33 = 0.58 \text{ mA}$$

For an assumed $\beta = 100$

$$\beta I_{B2} = I_{c2} = 100 \times 0.58 = 58 \text{ mA}$$

This is larger than the value $I_{C2} = 50$ mA above, and T_2 is saturated. The voltage at Q_1 is

$$V_{Q1} = V_{CC} - R_{C1}I_1 = 5 - 0.39 = 4.61 \text{ V}$$

The Transistor Monostable Circuit

A slight modification of the flipflop or bistable circuit is shown in Figure 7.12-5. Observe that a cross-coupling capacitor C_1 is used instead of the resistor R_1. The result of this change is a circuit that produces a single square

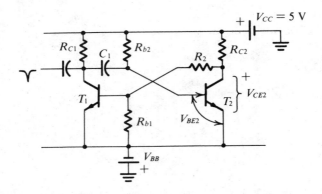

Figure 7.12-5.   The transistor (monostable) circuit

pulse of fixed time duration when a negative triggering pulse is applied. The
stable circuit condition requires that T_1 is OFF (non-conducting) and that T_2 is
ON (conducting). This can be checked by noting that when T_2 is ON

$$V_{B2} \doteq 0.7 \text{ V} \qquad\qquad V_{CE2} \doteq 0.1 \text{ V}$$

Neglecting the small value of V_{CE2}

$$V_{BE1} = \frac{-R_2}{R_2 + R_{b1}} V_{BB}$$

and this must be sufficiently negative to insure that T_1 is off. Then

$$V_{CE1} = V_{cc}$$

If a negative triggering pulse is applied to the collector of T_1 or a positive
trigger is applied to the base of T_1, the circuit undergoes a transition and
becomes quasi-stable, with T_1 on and T_2 off. To confirm that T_1 is in saturation, the base current I_{B1} is determined. To calculate this, refer to Figure 7.12-6
which is the T_1 base circuit. With T_2 off and T_1 on, then

$$I_2 = \frac{V_{cc} - 0.7}{R_{c1} + R_{c2}}$$

$$I_1 = \frac{0.7 + V_{BB}}{R_{b1}}$$

with

$$I_{b1} = I_2 - I_1$$

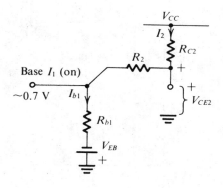

Figure 7.12-6.   The T_1 base circuit

At this time

$$V_{CE2} = V_{CC} - R_{C2}I_1$$

Also at the transition V_{CE1} falls from V_{CC} to the value $\doteq 0.1$ V, and simultaneously V_{BE2} will fall by this same voltage. Thus V_{BE2} will fall to the value

$$V_{BE2} = -(V_{CC} - 0.1) + 0.7 = -V_{CC} + 0.8 \text{ V}$$

The circuit remains in the stable state as long as T_2 remains OFF, with V_{CE1}, V_{CE2} and V_{BE1} at the above values. However, after the switching operation and the consequent (almost simultaneous) changes in level, V_{BE2} reaches the value ~ 0.7 V and T_2 again conducts, and T_1 goes off. There is a slight overshoot in V_{BE2} which decays rapidly as C_1 recharges through the load resistor R_{C1}. The time constant of this overshoot is $R_{C1}C_1$.

To find the duration of the pulse, the circuit is in the quasi-stable state during the time that V_{BE2} varies from the value $-(V_{CC} - 0.8)$ to 0.1 V along the exponential curve from $-(V_{CC} - 0.8)$ toward V_{CC}. The approximate equation for the charging curve is

$$V_{BE2} \doteq V_{CC} - 2V_{CC}e^{-t/R_{b2}C_1}$$

and the pulse duration is thus

$$T = R_{b2}C_1 \ln 2 = 0.69 R_{b2}C_1$$

The appropriate waveforms are given in Figure 7.12-7.

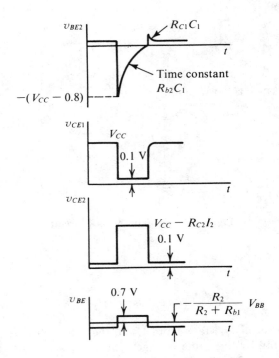

Figure 7.12-7. The waveforms in the monostable circuit

The Astable Multivibrator

The astable multivibrator, which is the third form of the cross-coupled circuit, is a free-running square wave generator. The circuit of a symmetrical multivibrator is shown in Figure 7.12-8. The operation proceeds as follows. Suppose initially that T_1 is off and T_2 is on, then C_1 will charge approximately to V_{CC}. Now suppose that switching occurs, with T_1 on and T_2 off. Assume that V_{CE1} is negligible, then the positive side of C_1 is essentially at ground potential. The base circuit of T_2 now becomes that shown in Figure 7.12-9. At the instant

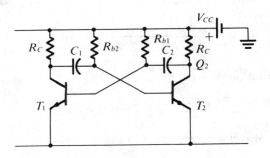

Figure 7.12-8. The astable multivibrator

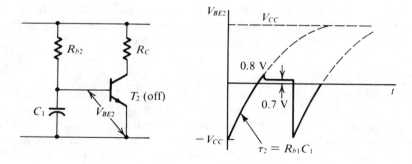

Figure 7.12-9.   The base circuit of T_2

of switching $V_{BE2} = -V_{CC}$ and will charge toward $+V_{CC}$. When the base-emitter voltage reaches a figure slightly above zero, T_2 will switch from off to on. During the interval that V_{BE2} is moving toward zero, C_1 is charging to V_{CC}. When T_2 switches on, this places the base of T_1 at $-V_{CC}$ and T_1 switches off. The cycle then repeats. Sketches of the waveshapes are given in Figure 7.12-10.

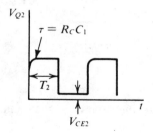

Figure 7.12-10.   The collector waveshape of the multivibrator

To find the period of the multivibrator, we see that

$$V_{BE1} = V_{CC} - 2V_{CC}e^{-t/R_{b1}C_2}$$

The T_1 off period is the time for V_{BE1} to change from $-V_{CC}$ to zero (nearly) or

$$T_1 = R_{b1}C_2 \ln 2 = 0.69R_{b1}C_2$$

Similarly, T_2 is off for the time

$$T_2 = R_{b2}C_1 \ln 2 = 0.69R_{b2}C_1$$

Hence the full cycle period is

$$T = T_1 + T_2 = 0.69(R_{b1}C_2 + R_{b2}C_1)$$

It is quite possible to set the recovery times T_1 and T_2 to be different from each other, thereby yielding an unsymmetrical wave. It is not generally wise to set one of these times more than about 10 times the other.

Diode-Transistor Logic

THE NOR GATE. A diode-transistor circuit for the NOR gate is shown in Figure 7.12-11a, with the truth table given in Figure 7.12-11b. If an input appears at the transistor input, the base-emitter junction will be forward biased, with a base current i_B. As a result, there will be a current i_C such that $i_C R_L \doteq V_{CC}$, and so $v_o \doteq 0$. The only condition that will result in a 1 at v_o is when both inputs are zero.

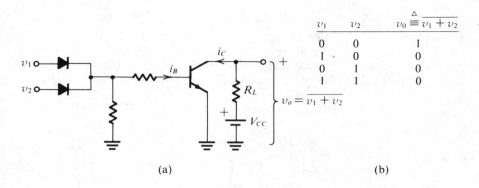

v_1	v_2	$v_0 \overset{\triangle}{\equiv} \overline{v_1 + v_2}$
0	0	1
1	0	0
0	1	0
1	1	0

(a)   (b)

Figure 7.12-11.   (a) Diode-transistor NOR gate   (b) Truth table

THE NAND GATE. The circuit of Figure 7.12-12a is that for a two-input NAND gate. The corresponding truth table is given in Figure 7.12-11b, as is readily checked.

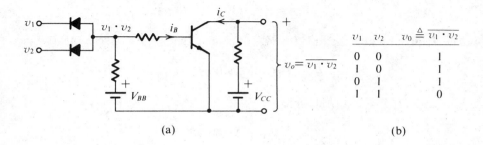

v_1	v_2	$v_0 \overset{\triangle}{=} \overline{v_1 \cdot v_2}$
0	0	1
1	0	1
0	1	1
1	1	0

(a)   (b)

Figure 7.12-12.   (a) Diode-transistor NAND gate   (b) Truth table

7.13* FEEDBACK IN AMPLIFIERS

A feature of feedback in a system (reference to feedback has been made at several points in this text) is that the signal at one point is determined in whole or in part by a signal elsewhere in the system. In the discussion to follow we shall consider a typical feedback system, as shown in Figure 7.13-1 in block diagram and flow graph form. These diagrams show clearly that a part of the output is being combined with the input signal. The arrows call attention to the forward transmission path from input to output, and a reverse transmission or feedback path from output to input.

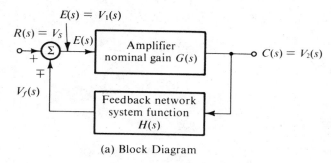

(a) Block Diagram

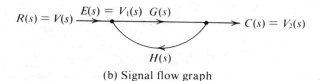

(b) Signal flow graph

Figure 7.13-1.   The elements of a simple feedback system

Feedback may be either positive or negative. If the net effect of the feedback is to increase the effective input signal and thereby increase the magnitude of the change at the output, the feedback is called *positive* or *regenerative*. If the resultant input signal is reduced by the feedback, which causes a reduction in the magnitude of the output, the feedback is *negative* or *degenerative*. We shall not study the many system performance properties that are affected by the presence of feedback. Some of these considerations will be examined in Chapter 13. Our interest here is principally in the influence of feedback on the gain of an amplifier operating principally in the small signal mode.

Suppose that the input to the feedback network is a voltage, here denoted as $C(s) = V_2(s)$, the transformed output controlled signal. Suppose also that the signal injected into the input from the feedback network is a voltage $H(s)C(s)$, where $H(s)$ is the feedback system function. The input to the feedback network may be either a voltage or a current, and correspondingly the output may be either a voltage or current — hence four possibilities exist. By definition we write

$$G(s) = \frac{V_2(s)}{V_1(s)} \qquad\qquad\qquad \text{(a)} \quad (7.13\text{-}1)$$

$$H(s) = \frac{V_f(s)}{V_2(s)} \qquad\qquad\qquad \text{(b)}$$

The input to the forward transmission path is

$$V_1(s) = V_s(s) \mp H(s)V_2(s) \tag{7.13-2}$$

Write this equation, using Equation (7.13-1a) as

$$\frac{V_2(s)}{G(s)} = V_s(s) \mp H(s)V_2(s)$$

from which

$$V_2(s) = \frac{G(s)V_s(s)}{1 \pm G(s)H(s)} \tag{7.13-3}$$

The overall gain of the amplifier with feedback is written $G_f(s)$

$$G_f(s) = \frac{V_2(s)}{V_s(s)} \tag{7.13-4}$$

Therefore it follows that

$$G_f(s) = \frac{G(s)}{1 \pm G(s)H(s)} \tag{7.13-5}$$

This equation expresses the resultant gain of the amplifier with feedback G_f in terms of the nominal gain of the amplifier without feedback G and the feedback fraction H.

The quantity $1 \pm GH$ is generally complex and may have a magnitude that is greater or less than unity. If $|1 \pm GH|$ is greater than unity, then G_f is less than G, and the feedback is negative. The effect of negative feedback in an amplifier results in an extended frequency response characteristic, albeit at the expense of gain: the amplifier performance becomes more stable since it is less dependent on load or circuit parameter variations and is less sensitive to transistor characteristic changes or to changes in voltage; nonlinear and phase distortion are reduced; and the output characteristics can be markedly influenced by the characteristics of the feedback network $H(s)$. The emitter-follower, Example 7.9-2, is an amplifier unity negative feedback.

If $|1 \pm GH|$ is less than unity, then G_f is greater than G, and feedback is positive. The effects of positive feedback are opposite to those of negative feedback, and too much regenerative feedback may cause the amplifier to oscillate. Since both the forward and the reverse transmission paths are generally frequency dependent, the feedback can be negative over one range of frequencies and positive over another range of frequencies.

If $GH = \mp(1 + j0) = 1/\mp180°$, then the gain of the amplifier becomes infinite. This is the condition for oscillation, there being an output in the absence of an input signal. The amplitude of the output signal is limited by the power supply or by nonlinearities which are inherent to the system or have been deliberately introduced to control the amplitude. Usually GH is slightly greater than unity in oscillators in order to allow for any incidental variations that might arise. A tolerance of 5 per cent is sufficient to insure continued oscillation. Feedback in excess of this will be accompanied by distortion of the output waveshape should sinusoidal oscillations be desired. For the production of square waves, as discussed in Section 7.12, the feedback is extreme.

7.14* FEEDBACK OSCILLATORS

Refer to Figure 7.14-1 which shows the details of a tuned-collector oscillator. Observe that this has been drawn in a form that corresponds to Figure 7.13-1, clearly isolating the amplifier G and the feedback network H. In

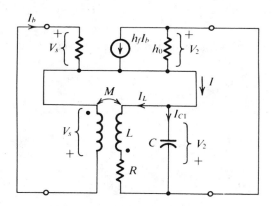

Figure 7.14-1.   A tuned collector oscillator

this figure h_r is chosen to be zero and the coupling transformer winding resistance is assumed to be negligible. From the figure, the base-signal voltage is simply

$$V_s = sMI_L = Z_M I_L \qquad (7.14\text{-}1)$$

Also from the diagram

$$-V_s = Z_L I_L = Z_C I_C \qquad (7.14\text{-}2)$$

Thus the network transfer function is

$$H(s) = \frac{V_s}{V_2} = \frac{Z_M I_L}{-Z_L I_L} = \frac{-Z_M}{Z_L} \tag{7.14-3}$$

For the transistor circuit

$$I = h_f I_b + h_o V_2 \tag{7.14-4}$$

It is convenient to define the transfer impedance $Z_T = -V_s/I$, which is

$$Z_T = \frac{-V_s}{I} = \frac{-Z_M I_L}{I_L + I_C} = \frac{-Z_M Z_C}{Z_C + Z_L} \tag{7.14-5}$$

Also, with good approximation

$$I_b \doteq \frac{V_s}{h_i} \tag{7.14-6}$$

Combine Equations (7.14-6) and (7.14-4) with Equation (7.14-5) and obtain an expression for the gain A

$$A = \frac{V_2}{V_s} = -\left(\frac{h_f}{h_i h_o} + \frac{1}{h_o Z_T} \right) \tag{7.14-7}$$

The conditional equation for sustained oscillation $AH = 1$ can be written in the form

$$1 = \frac{Z_M}{Z_L} \left(\frac{h_f}{h_i h_o} + \frac{1}{h_o Z_T} \right)$$

which is

$$\frac{h_f}{h_i} Z_M Z_C = (Z_L + Z_C) + h_o Z_L Z_C \tag{7.14-8}$$

Include the known forms for the several impedances in this equation, which gives

$$\frac{h_f M}{h_i C} = R + j \left(\omega L - \frac{1}{\omega C} \right) - j \frac{h_o R}{\omega C} + \frac{L h_o}{C} \tag{7.14-9}$$

Equate real and imaginary terms to find two equations

$$\frac{h_f M}{h_i C} = R + \frac{h_o L}{C} \qquad \text{Amplitude condition} \qquad \text{(a)} \tag{7.14-10}$$

$$\omega L - \frac{1}{\omega C} - \frac{h_o R}{\omega C} = 0 \qquad \text{Phase condition} \qquad \text{(b)}$$

The first of these equations can be written in the form

$$\frac{h_f}{h_i} = \frac{RC + h_o L}{M} \qquad (7.14\text{-}11)$$

which really specifies an average h_f/h_i. This expression provides information, at least in principle, concerning the amplitude of the oscillations.

The second equation becomes

$$\omega^2 = \frac{1}{LC}(1 + h_o R)$$

which can be written

$$\omega = \omega_o \sqrt{1 + h_o R} \qquad (7.14\text{-}12)$$

where

$$\omega_o \frac{1}{\sqrt{LC}}$$

Since the factor $h_o R$ is generally small, then the transistor plays only a small part in determining the frequency of the oscillator; the resonant frequency of the tuned circuit is the principal factor in the equation. In fact, as the shunt resistance of the antiresonant circuit increases, that is, for increased Q of the tank circuit, the influence of the transistor decreases. However, the ability to control the frequency over limited amounts by changing the effective R of the circuit is the basis of operation of a number of electronic instruments.

A number of oscillator coupling circuits have been developed. The more common of these are given in Figure 7.14-2.

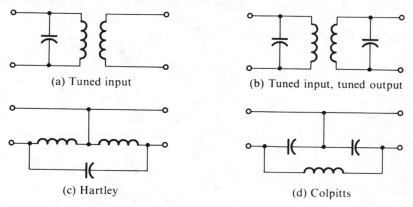

(a) Tuned input   (b) Tuned input, tuned output

(c) Hartley   (d) Colpitts

Figure 7.14-2.   Coupling networks of the more important oscillators

If oscillators of high frequency stability are required, a crystal (often in an oven to maintain a constant temperature and hence a constant electrical characteristic) is often used either to maintain the circuit frequency, or as a substitute for the tuned circuit. With such crystal control, the frequency can be maintained within 1 part in 10^6 or better.

7.15*   RC OSCILLATORS

There is no fundamental reason why a tuned LC circuit must be used to effect the 180 degree phase shift required for the feedback to produce oscillations. RC networks when used appropriately produce phase shifts adequate for a coupling network. Refer to Figure 7.15-1 which is that of a phase-shift oscillator. The operation of this circuit can be understood by considering each RC section as a simple phase-shifting circuit that introduces a 60 degree phase angle at the frequency of operation. The three sections thus introduce the required 180 degree total phase shift through the network.

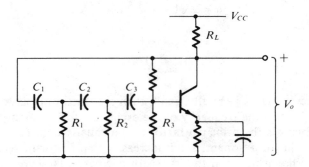

Figure 7.15-1.   Phase shift oscillator

This explanation is not complete because the loading of the RC pairs has been neglected. Further, a substantial attenuation will occur in the network, thus requiring that the gain of the driving element must be high enough to insure an adequate amplitude of feedback.

If it is assumed that each section introduces a 60 deg phase shift, and by selecting $C_1 R_1 = C_2 R_2 = C_3 R_3 = CR$, with $R_3 \gg R_2 \gg R_1$, it follows that

$$\tan \theta = \sqrt{3} = \frac{1}{\omega R C}$$

from which

$$\omega = \frac{1}{\sqrt{3}\, RC} \qquad\qquad (7.15\text{-}1)$$

A more exact calculation for the case where $R_3 = R_2 = R_1 = R$ and $C_3 = C_2 = C_1 = C$ but neglecting the amplifier loading by the phase shift network yields the expression

$$\omega = \frac{1}{\sqrt{6}\,RC} \tag{7.15-2}$$

The corresponding attenuation through the network is found to be 1/29. Thus the driving element must possess a gain of at least 29 for the circuit to operate as an oscillator. A more exact calculation for the transistor-driven circuit shows that the transistor h_f must exceed 45 for oscillations to be possible.

A number of other RC coupling networks exist. One of the more important, and this circuit has been used extensively in laboratory signal generators, is the Wien bridge, which is shown in basic form in Figure 7.15-2. An analysis of the operation of this circuit leads to the amplitude and phase equations

$$\frac{R_3}{R_4} = \frac{R_1}{R_2} + \frac{C_2}{C_1} \qquad\qquad \omega_o^2 = \frac{1}{R_1 R_2 C_1 C_2} \tag{7.15-3}$$

When $R_1 = R_2 = R$ and $C_1 = C_2 = C$, these become

$$\frac{R_3}{R_4} = 2 \qquad\qquad \omega_o = \frac{1}{RC} \tag{7.15-4}$$

For $R_3/R_4 < 2$, the circuit behaves as a frequency selective rejection amplifier. When R_3/R_4 is greater than 2, the circuit acts as an oscillator.

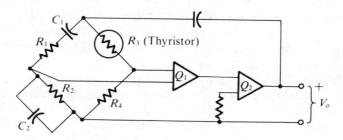

Figure 7.15-2. The basic Wien bridge oscillator, with thermistor stabilization

Continuous variation of the frequency of the Wien bridge oscillator is most easily accomplished by simultaneously varying the two capacitors C_1 and C_2 (these would ordinarily be mounted on a common shaft). Owing to the limited frequency range possible with variable air capacitors, major changes in frequency are accomplished by switching different resistor pairs R_1 and R_2 into the circuit. There is a practical limit to the values of R_1 and R_2 that can be used, and these oscillators have limited number of decades of operation.

Twin-T and bridged-T networks are often used for oscillators. These are shown in Figure 7.15-3.

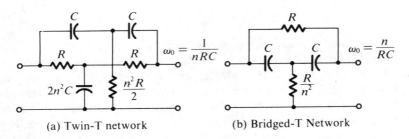

(a) Twin-T network   (b) Bridged-T Network

Figure 7.15-3.   Frequency selective RC networks

7.16   POSTLUDE

This chapter introduces a small but useful part of the enormous area of electronics. It discussed methods for determining the performance of diodes, transistors, and FETs, involving the static curves and the load line and introduced and analyzed typical circuits. For small signal operations, which involve small excursions about the quiescent point, the replacement of the electronic device by a mathematical model allows a straightforward network solution. These methods have become reasonably standardized although more than one model may be selected.

Much research and development work continues in semiconductor materials, and new devices are introduced frequently. More important than discrete devices is the entire range of integrated circuits, about which nothing has been said but which provides a large variety of total operating circuits on semiconductor chips. Several of such chips will be noted in Chapter 9. Presently a significant effort is going into developing microprocessors, large scale integrated circuits which contain the essential elements of a complete digital minicomputer. The application of such microprocessors to widespread uses is absolutely astounding and makes our limited discussion of BJTs and FETs little more than an indication of the essentials of controlled devices and their performance in simple circuits. However, this discussion does serve to distinguish between large signal operation involving the use of the characteristic curves and the load line, and small signal operation involving the use of the hybrid (or other) model of the device.

The op-amp was among circuits considered which have special properties. The op-amp is of importance because it can be used for simple amplifier purposes, and it can be used for operational applications in analog computers. A continuing effort exists to develop circuits which possess special op-amp output characteristics as units for use in analog type computer circuits which are designed for providing special frequency (filter) characteristics. These active filters have the advantage that frequency sensitive circuits are produced using R's, C's and amplifiers instead of using L's and C's.

Feedback in amplifiers results in marked changes in the performance of an amplifier, depending on the character of the feedback. This chapter examined the conditions necessary for an amplifier to produce self-sustained oscillations. The use of feedback to control system performance under prescribed conditions will be studied in some detail in Chapter 13.

SUMMARY

- Materials with large energy gap $E_g = 10$ eV between the valence and conduction bands are classified as insulators; those with $E_g \doteq 1$ eV are semiconductors; those with overlapping bands are conductors.

- In intrinsic semiconductors, hole-electron pairs are generated with electrons into the conduction band and holes in the valence band. Both contribute to conduction in the material.

- Low density doping with pentavalent (trivalent) elements produces an n-type (p-type) semiconductor of increased conductivity.

- The diffusion of localized p-type material into an n-type substrate, or the diffusion of localized n-type material into a p-type substrate, produces a pn junction. The diode equation is

$$I = I_o(e^{qv/kT} - 1)$$

- A "linear" diode is an idealized device with infinite back resistance and constant and small forward resistance.

- A rectifier converts ac into unidirectional current. The dc component in a half-wave rectifier with resistor load is

$$I_{dc} = \frac{1}{\pi} \frac{V_m}{R_L} = \frac{I_m}{\pi}$$

In full-wave rectification with resistor load $I_{dc} = 2I_m/\pi$.

- The ripple factor of a rectifier is

$$r = \frac{V_{rms} \text{ of the ripple components}}{V_{dc}}$$

- A filter reduces the ripple factor by selective discrimination against ac components versus dc components in the output wave.

- Diodes are important elements of digital logic circuits, and are incorporated in AND and OR gates.

- BJT transistors are available both as npn or pnp devices.

- An amplifier is a circuit for raising the level of a signal voltage, current or power.

- The biasing circuit establishes and maintains the operating point at a prescribed value. For an output that is to be a replica of the input, the bias must be such that equal signal swings about the quiescent point can be accepted with the two halves remaining replicas of the input. The bias level is determined from an examination of the static curves of the transistor.

- The small signal performance of electronic devices can be predicted using a linear incremental model of the device in conjunction with the circuit.

- The hybrid model is a convenient representation of the junction transistor. The common-emitter configuration has the form

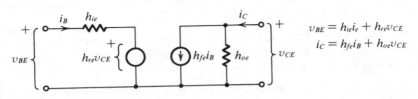

$$v_{BE} = h_{ie}i_e + h_{re}v_{CE}$$
$$i_C = h_{fe}i_B + h_{oe}v_{CE}$$

- The input impedance of a circuit equals the open circuit input modified by the coupled effect of the output circuit and load.

- The output impedance of a circuit equals the open circuit output terminal impedance modified by the coupled effect of the input circuit.

- The input current is negligible for a field effect transistor, and the incremental model has a simple form

$$g_m = \frac{\partial I_D}{\partial V_{GS}}\bigg|_{V_{DS}=0} \; ; \quad r_d = \frac{\partial V_{DS}}{\partial I_D}\bigg|_{V_{GS}=0}$$

- The ideal op-amp has infinite gain, bandwidth, input impedance, and zero output impedance.

- Op-amps are used in a variety of applications: inverting an non-inverting amplifiers, summing circuits, voltage follower, integrators.

- The electronic analog computer is an electrical model of the system being studied, the system operating in continuus time with continuously varying output variables. Programming consists in arranging the op-amps to perform the operations indicated in the equations describing the system.

- Two transistors when cross-coupled with resistors will operate as a bistable flipflop. The resistance values must be selected to insure conduction and cutoff as required.

- When one cross-coupling resistor in the bistable is replaced by a capacitor, the circuit is monostable, and produces a pulse of fixed width when a transition is induced.

- When both cross-coupling resistors in the bistable are replaced by capacitors, the circuit is unstable and oscillates with roughly square-wave output at a rate dictated by the bias resistors and the coupling capacitors.

- Feedback in an amplifier can be positive or negative. Negative feedback extends the frequency response characteristics; it improves the stability of the amplifier; it makes the performance less dependent on the circuit parameters; it can produce marked changes in the output characteristics depending on the feedback network properties; it can alter the input and output impedance characteristics. Positive feedback acts in a manner opposite to that of negative feedback.

- The resulting gain of an amplifier with feedback is expressed in terms of the gain of the amplifier without feedback and the effect of the feedback. The expression is

$$G_f(s) = \frac{G(s)}{1 - G(s)H(s)}$$

where $H(s)$ is the transfer function of the feedback network.

- For positive feedback $G(s)H(s) = +1$, the gain becomes infinite, which means that there is an output without an input, and this is the condition for oscillation.

- A number of tuned LC coupling networks have been devised for coupling output energy back into the input. These oscillators are named according to the network or according to the person who devised the circuit. It includes tuned output, tuned input, tuned output tuned input, Hartley, Colpitts.

- To improve the frequency stability of an oscillator, a crystal is often used. Crystal-controlled oscillators are used extensively where high stability is required.

- A number of RC coupling networks have been devised for oscillator used, including phase shift, Wien bridge, twin-T, and bridged-T.

REVIEW QUESTIONS

1. What is the difference in the band structure between semiconductors and conductors?

2. What is the difference between an intrinsic and extrinsic semiconductor?

3. Name the different energy bands in semiconductors.
4. How are majority carriers and minority carriers produced?
5. How can a diffusion current be produced?
6. Discuss how forward bias and reversed bias are produced in a diode.
7. Sketch the volt-ampere characteristics of a diode and specify approximately the range of their values.
8. What are the v-i characteristics of an ideal diode?
9. What is the purpose of a rectifier?
10. What is meant by a linear network?
11. Is the diode a linear or a nonlinear element?
12. Show how to use diodes to create an OR and an AND gate.
13. Describe the barrier junction transistor (BJT).
14. What is the beta of a transistor?
15. Why is a graphical analysis used with transistor circuits?
16. Under what conditions do we use the h-parameters?
17. Define: h_i, h_o, h_f and h_r.
18. Why is it important to know the input and output impedances of amplifier circuits?
19. What are the significant features of the emitter follower?
20. Discuss the difference between BJT and FET transistors.
21. What are the basic characteristics of an op-amp?
22. Name some op-amp uses.
23. How is a transistor used as a switch?
24. What are the monostable and astable multivibrators?
25. What are the effects in an amplifier of negative feedback; positive feedback?
26. What is the necessary requirement for a feedback oscillator?
27. Can an LC network provide the required phase shift between input and output for a feedback oscillator? Discuss using a tuned LC circuit.
28. Can an RC circuit provide the required phase shift?
29. Discuss the Wien bridge oscillator.

REFERENCES

1. Schilling, D. L. and C. Belove, *Electronic Circuits — Discrete and Integrated*, McGraw Hill Book Co., New York, NY, 1968.

    This text provides an introduction to the analysis and design of electronic circuits at the sophomore-junior level.

2. Millman, J. and H. Taub, *Pulse, Digital and Switching Waveforms*, McGraw Hill Book Co., New York, NY, 1965.

    A comprehensive discussion of electronic circuit theory, and studies a wide range of applications.

3. Seely, S., *Electronic Circuits*, Holt, Rinehart and Winston, Inc., New York, NY, 1969.

   This text includes general electronic circuit theory, and discusses a wide variety of applications.

4. Millman, J. and C. C. Halkias, *Electronic Devices and Circuits*, McGraw Hill Book Co., New York, NY, 1967.

   A comprehensive discussion of electronic circuits and systems.

PROBLEMS

7.1-1. Find the average drift velocity of the electrons in a copper conductor (atomic weight 63.6, density 8.9) with a cross-sectional area of 10^{-5} m^2 carrying a current of 20 A. Assume that there is 1 free electron per atom.

7.1-2. The average energy of a crystal at temperature T is kT.

   (a) Show that eV and kT have the same units. Calculate e/kT for room temperature, $T = 20°C$.

   (b) Sketch a graph of $e^{-eV/kT}$ for $20°C$ and $0.01 < V < 1$ volt. Discuss the relation between thermal generation rate and energy gap.

7.1-3. Determine the relative concentration of Ge atoms and electron-hole pairs at room temperature, $T = 20°C$, and find the intrinsic resistivity. Compare this with the resistivity of Cu ($\varrho = 1.73 \times 10^{-8}$ Ω-m).

7.1-4. Suppose that every 10 millionth Ge atom in the Ge crystal is replaced by Antimony. Calculate the conductivity of this doped material at room temperature, $T = 20°C$.

7.1-5. In a Si diode the density of holes drops from 1.8×10^{18}/m^3 to 1.68×10^{18}/m^3 in 2 μm. Estimate the diffusion current density due to holes across the junction at room temperature, $T = 20°C$.

7.2-1. The reverse current of a Ge diode at room temperature $T = 239°K$ is 100 μA for $V = -1$ volt. Determine the current for $v = -0.3$ V; for $v = +1.10$ V. If the reverse current is assumed the same compare the values of the currents found at these voltages to those corresponding to $T = 315°K$.

7.2-2. A pn diode has a reverse saturation current of 2×10^{-9} A. Draw the diode v-i characteristic for -0.4 V $< v < 0.4$ V at room temperature. Use an expanded scale for negative currents. Find its dynamic resistance at $v = 0.2$ V.

7.2-3. Shown is the characteristic of a power diode.

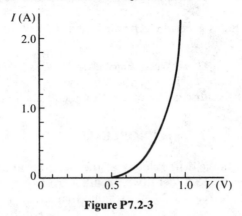

Figure P7.2-3

(a) Represent this by a circuit model consisting of an ideal diode and a voltage source.
(b) Use this model to estimate the current in a circuit consisting of a 1 V battery and a 1.2 Ω resistor.
(c) Compare the value in (b) with that by drawing a load line on the curve.

7.2-4. Plot the *v-i* characteristics of the circuits shown in Figure P7.2-4.

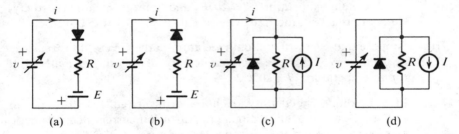

Figure P7.2-4

7.2-5. Sketch $v_2(t)$ for the circuits shown in Figure P7.2-5.

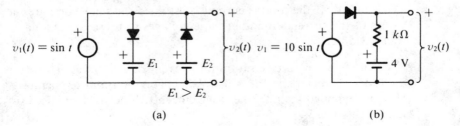

Figure P7.2-5

7.3-1. Find the ripple factor for the waveforms in Figure P7.3-1.

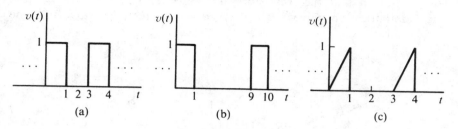

(a)   (b)   (c)

Figure P7.3-1

7.5-1. Find the truth table for the circuit shown in Figure P7.5-1.

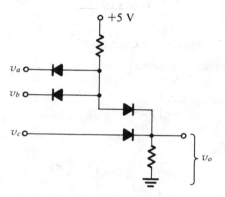

Figure P7.5-1

7.7-1. Using Figures 7.7-3b and c find the various gain factors (A_i, A_v and A_p) for the circuits shown in Figure P7.7-1. Be sure they operate linearly.

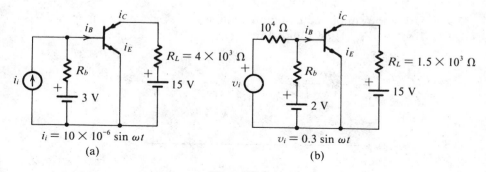

$i_i = 10 \times 10^{-6} \sin \omega t$

(a)

$v_i = 0.3 \sin \omega t$

(b)

Figure P7.7-1

7.8-1. Common-emitter amplifiers are shown in Figure P7.8-1. If it is assumed that the transistors are biased properly find the voltage amplification. Given: $h_{ie} = 1$ kΩ, $h_{re} = 1.8 \times 10^{-4}$, $h_{oe} = 25 \times 10^{-6}$ mho and $h_{fe} = 60$.

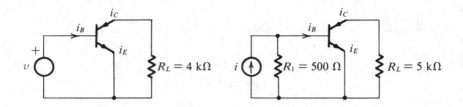

Figure P7.8-1

7.9-1. Verify Equations (7.9-15) through (7.9-19).

7.9-2. Find A_v, Z_i and Z_o for the circuits shown in Figure P7.9-2.

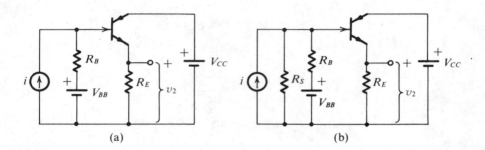

(a)   (b)

Figure P7.9-2

7.9-3. Using the simplified common-emitter model shown in Figure P7.9-3 find A_i, Z_i, A_v, Z_o, and A_{vs}.

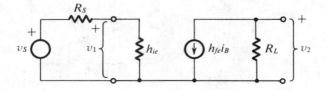

Figure P7.9-3

7.10-1. Evaluate the gain of the FET amplifiers which are appropriately biased and shown in Figure P7.10-1. Given: $g_m = 1500 \times 10^{-6}$ mho, $r_d = 65$ kΩ.

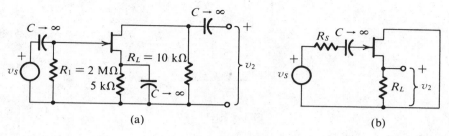

(a)   (b)

Figure P7.10-1

7.10-2. Consider the self-biased circuit employing an FET.

(a) Derive an expression for the midfrequency voltage gain.

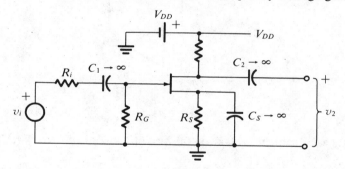

Figure P7.10-2a

(b) Repeat (a) for the high frequency range using the high frequency incremental model for the FET, which is shown.

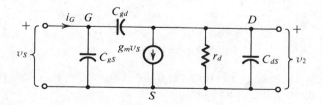

Figure P7.10-2b

(c) For all capacitances assumed "large," $R_i = 1$ kΩ, $R_g = 1$ MΩ, $R_s = 1$ kΩ, $R_L = 5$ kΩ, $g_m = 3000$ μmho, $r_d = 10$ kΩ, determine the midfrequency gain; also the high frequency cutoff (the value of f at which the output gain is 0.707 that at midfrequency).

7.11-1. Shown is a current to voltage converter. Deduce the relation for $v_o = f(i_s)$.

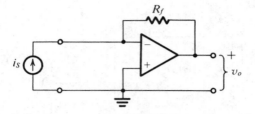

Figure P7.11-1

7.11-2. Find the input-output relation of the op-amp circuit shown in Figure P7.11-2.

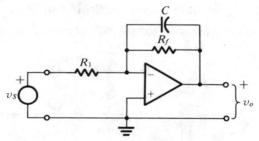

Figure P7.11-2

7.11-3. Repeat Problem 7.11-2 for the circuit shown in Figure P7.11-3.

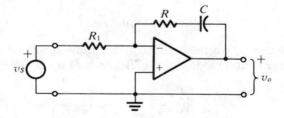

Figure P7.11-3

7.11-4. Draw SFG program graphs and the analog computer setup for solving the differential equations

(a) $\dfrac{d^2 y}{dt^2} + 2y = 3 + 4 \sin \omega t$

(b) $\dfrac{d^3 y}{dt^3} + 2\dfrac{d^2 y}{dt^2} + 4\dfrac{dy}{dt} + y = 8 \, e^{-at} \sin \omega t$

7.12-1. Refer to Figure 7.12-1 for a NOT circuit. If $V_{cc} = 5$ V, $R_B = 10^5$ kΩ find the minimum value of R_L to ensure that the transistor saturates. Assume $\beta = 40$.

7.12-2. A monostable circuit (see Figure 7.12-5) is driven by a 1000 Hz pulse driver. It is desired to produce 50 μs pulses. Show the circuit details, with all circuit parameters specified.

7.12-3. (a) Using R_b and C in the circuit of the astable multivibrator of Figure 7.12-8, with $R_b = 25$ kΩ, $V_{cc} = 5$ V, and $\beta = 50$, show the circuit details for a multivibrator with a symmetrical full cycle period of 460 μs.

(b) For a full cycle period of 460 μs, but with an unsymmetrical wave with one period being 3 times the other, what are the new values of C?

7.13-1. An amplifier has a gain $3000\underline{/0°}$. When negative feedback is applied the gain is reduced to $2000\underline{/0°}$. Determine the feedback network.

7.13-2. An amplifier without feedback gives an output of 46 V when the input is 0.16 V.

(a) If 1 per cent of the output is fed back into the input in a degenerative circuit, what is the output voltage?

(b) If an output of 46 V is required with 2 per cent feedback, what is the input voltage?

7.14-1. Deduce the system function for the Hartley oscillator feedback nework. Does this result show a 180 deg phase shift difference between output and input signals?

7.15-1. Consider the two section RC phase shift oscillator shown in Figure P7.15-1.

(a) Find the roots of the network function $H(s)$.

(b) Show that even though $GH = 1$ that oscillations are not possible if $G > 5$.

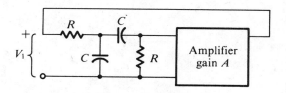

Figure P7.15-1

Chapter Eight

Measurements and Instruments

Reference has been made throughout this text to physical quantities and, by implication, it has been presupposed that means exist for their measurement. In this chapter the discussion will deal directly with measurements and certain instruments for accomplishing specific types of measurements. In addition, a discussion is included of the analysis of the data obtained.

Measurements are made with a purpose—certain data are needed for one reason or another. In general, a number of steps are important in the conduct of the experiment that is to provide information. These include:

1. The design of an efficient measurement setup. This involves care in the selection of the necessary equipment, plus a clear understanding of the measurements that are to be made.

2. The proper and intelligent carrying out of the measurement process.

3. Maintaining a proper record of the data and a total report of all aspects of the conduct of the experiment. These are necessary to insure that the total experiment can be repeated in the future to yield equivalent results.

4. An estimte of the accuracy of the measurements with some estimate of the magnitude of the possible errors.

5. A report which adequately describes the purposes of the experiment, the manner of its conduct, the results obtained, and a discussion of the results and their meaning.

Our concerns here are with only a portion of these five items. We shall address certain classes of measurements, some equipment for carrying out these measurements, and having obtained certain data, we will carry out the operation under item 4.

TECHNIQUES OF MEASUREMENT

8.1 THE CONCEPT OF MEASUREMENTS

The measurement of any given quantity consists in its comparison with another quantity of the same kind that has been chosen as a basic standard unit. In electrical measurements the comparison is usually indirect, two or more measurements being required in passing from the quantity to be measured to the basic unit quantity.

A standard is a concrete representation of a unit. The Bureau of Standards in Washington, D.C., has a complete set of physical measurement standards. Such standards are very expensive to build and offer many difficulties in their use in routine measurements. Because of this, secondary standards form the basis of measurements in engineering and commercial laboratories where the highest possible accuracy is required. Included among the secondary standards are resistors, inductors, capacitors, voltage standards, and indicating instruments.

Electrical measuring instruments or meters can be classified into two classes: the *absolute* and the *secondary*. Absolute instruments, which are very carefully designed and constructed, depend upon their physical design to permit their results to be expressed mathematically in the appropriate system of units. With secondary instruments, which may or may not be critically designed and constructed, the relation between their indications and the quantities under measurements must be established experimentally. Examples of absolute instruments include the tangent galvanometer and the Kelvin current balance. Secondary instruments include portable ammeters and voltmeters.

Electrical measuring instruments or meters can be classified according to the method of operation, or the quantity to be measured. Included among the latter are instruments for measuring current, voltage, charge, power, energy, frequency, power factor, phase, and speed. The principles of operation are varied and depend on the quantity to be measured. For example, the ammeter may depend for its operation on basic electromagnetic principles (refer to Chapter 12 for a discussion of basic force and torque considerations), on electrodynamic principles, or on some thermal principle. The graduations of the scale on each instrument or meter will depend on its principle of operation. Some scales will be uniformly calibrated, others may follow a square law, while others may require no divided scale but might merely have such indications as "slow" and "fast." Some types of meters will be of the integrating type, for example, watthour meters. Important indicating instruments include cathode ray tubes to measure voltage or current produced in all manner of service.

We shall study a wide variety of indicating instruments both in their basic forms and in more sophisticated varieties, often involving digital readout.

8.2   DC INSTRUMENTS

Many electrical meters, especially those that are to read dc current or voltage or any quantity related to one or the other of these, involves a d'Arsonval moving coil mechanism. This device (see Section 12.10) consists of a coil of many turns of fine wire suspended in the field of a permanent magnet. When at rest, the coil is so adjusted that its plane is parallel to the magnetic field. When a current is in the coil, the suspended spring constrained system, which is mounted on bearings, will rotate. The angle through which the coil rotates is indicated by a pointer attached to the coil. The deflection per unit current depends on the spring constant of the restraining spring and the magnetic field strength. Such d'Arsonval movements provide full scale deflection from microampere to ampere levels, depending on the construction.

A multi-range ammeter consists of a basic d'Arsonval movement, usually of high or moderate sensitivity; i.e., ampere per full scale deflection, with a series of shunts across the basic instrument. These shunts will be so selected that a known fraction of the total current will pass through the movement, the balance being diverted through the shunt. Often shunts will be designated as 50 millivolt full scale, e.g., 100 A, 50 mV shunt. This means that 100 ampere through the shunt results in a 50 mV voltage across the shunt terminals. This 50 mV is applied across a 50 mV voltmeter, which is merely a d'Arsonval movement with enough series resistance so that with an applied 50 mV, the instrument will indicate full scale deflection. The situation is illustrated in Figure 8.2-1.

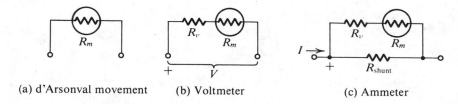

(a) d'Arsonval movement   (b) Voltmeter   (c) Ammeter

Figure 8.2-1.   Schematic representations of indicating instruments incorporating a d'Arsonval movement

With a voltmeter and an ammeter, resistance measurements can be made using Ohm's law. A variety of methods exists and we shall examine some of these, including the voltmeter-ammeter, the voltmeter and the ohmmeter methods. We shall later discuss bridge methods. Care in performing measurements is essential because the actual process of performing the measurements might introduce errors.

EXAMPLE 8.2-1. Determine the error produced by inserting a 1 mA ammeter with meter resistance $R_m = 30\ \Omega$ to measure the current through (a) a 500 Ω resistor, (b) a 2000 Ω resistor, when connected across a 0.5 V source.

SOLUTION. (a) In the absence of the indicating instrument, the current in the 500 Ω resistor is $0.5/500 = 1$ mA. With the instrument in the circuit the current is $0.5/(500 + 30) = 0.943$ mA. The error is

$$\text{Error} = \frac{1.0 - 0.943}{1.0} \times 100 = 5.7\%$$

(b) By following the same procedure for the 2000 ohm resistor, we find that

$$\text{Error} = \frac{0.25 - .246}{0.25} \times 100 = 1.6\%$$

These results show that the error is dependent on relative value of the meter resistance and that of the resistor involved—the error decreases as the meter resistance becomes a smaller fraction of the circuit resistance.

□ □ □

Voltmeter-Ammeter Method

To measure resistance by this method, it is only necessary to measure the voltage across the resistor R_x when a known current is present. Figure 8.2-2 shows two possible connections for this test. Note that in Figure 8.2-2a the

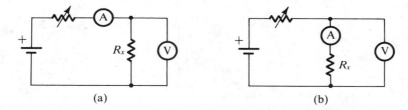

| (a) | (b) |

Figure 8.2-2.   Voltmeter-ammeter method of measuring resistance

voltmeter reads the voltage across the terminals of the resistor but the ammeter reads the sum of the currents through the resistor plus that in the voltmeter. The value of R_x is given by

$$R_x = \frac{V}{I - \dfrac{V}{R_v}} \tag{8.2-1}$$

where a correction for the voltmeter current is made. I is the reading of the ammeter, V is the reading of the voltmeter and R_v is the internal resistance of the voltmeter.

If the circuit is arranged as in Figure 8.2-2b, the current in R_x is being measured, but the voltmeter reads the voltage across the ammeter plus R_x. In this case R_x is given by

$$R_x = \frac{V - IR_A}{I} \tag{8.2-2}$$

where R_A is the internal resistance of the ammeter. Often the correction terms are negligible, but this may not be so in any given example.

Voltmeter Method

The circuit arrangement for this measurement is given in Figure 8.2-3. In this circuit the voltmeter has a resistance R_v. With the short-circuiting switch closed, the voltmeter reads V. With the short-circuiting switch open, the

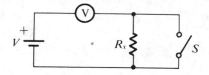

Figure 8.2-3. The voltmeter method of measuring resistance

resistor R_x is introduced into the circuit, and the voltmeter reading will be V_1, with $V_1 < V$. The resistance R_x is given by

$$R_x = R_v \frac{V - V_1}{V_1} \tag{8.2-3}$$

A modification of this method is used in the simple ohmmeter.

The simple ohmmeter circuit is shown in Figure 8.2-4. As usually constructed, the battery (usually a 1.5 V cell), the fixed resistor R_1, and the adjustable R_A for initial adjustment of the voltmeter V setting, are mounted

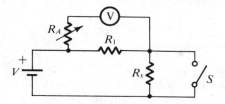

Figure 8.2-4. A simple ohmmeter

within the ohmmeter case. With S closed, that is, with the test probes shorted, R_A is adjusted until the voltmeter reads full scale V_o (usually 1 V). When S is open, that is, when R_x is in the circuit, the voltage read is the voltage across R_1. If the voltmeter resistance R_v is very large compared with R_1, then the reading of the voltmeter is

$$V_x = \frac{R_1}{R_1 + R_x} \times V_o \tag{8.2-4}$$

Observe that when $R_x = R_1$, V_x is at the half-scale position. Consequently, high resistance values are crowded into the lower part of the scale with midscale readings being most precise. Thus to provide reasonable accuracy over wide ranges of resistance values, a selector switch is provided with typical midscale values of 10 Ω, 1 kΩ, and 100 kΩ. Actually, commercial ohmmeters use a more complicated circuit, but the general principles of operation are those discussed.

Attention is called to the fact that these measurements require that the resistor to be measured is passive, otherwise the associated sources would affect the currents in the circuit. Further, as a note of caution, the resistors to be measured must be able to sustain the current without damage. Hence caution is essential if semiconductor devices, fuses, or meter movements are to be measured.

The *rating* of a voltmeter, sometimes called its *sensitivity*, is the voltage required for full scale deflection of the instrument. Often, however, a criterion of sensitivity is the ohm per volt rating of the instrument. For example, if a 1 mA movement is used as the indicating device, this voltmeter is called a $1/10^{-3} = 1000$ ohm/volt instrument. If a 25 μA movement is used, the voltmeter is called a $1/25 \times 10^{-6} = 40,000$ ohm/volt instrument. An ideal voltmeter, one that will not impose any load on the circuit being measured, would have an infinite ohm/volt rating. Typical laboratory dc voltmeters using d'Arsonval meter movements have 20,000 ohm/volt ratings. Electronic voltmeters often have higher ratings, with an input resistance of 10^6 Ω or higher.

8.3 AC INSTRUMENTS

Alternating currents and voltages are measured using a variety of devices, including electrodynamometer, iron-vane, thermocouple, and rectifier instruments.

Electrodynamometer Instruments

These devices will be discussed further in Chapter 12. They consist of a coil structure fixed in position in series with a coil structure mounted on bearings which can move due to the interaction of the magnetic field produced by the current in the fixed structure with the current in the movable structure. The torque is proportional to the square of the current, the inertia of the movable structure is sufficiently large to perform an averaging function, and the indication is a true rms value. If one coil is connected across the lines through a resistor to give a current proportional to the line voltage, and the other coil carries line current as shown schematically in Figure 8.3-1, then the device gives a reading proportional to the average power, and the device is a wattmeter. The frequency range of operation is not large for such instruments, with satisfactory operation over the range to several hundred Hz.

Iron Vane Instruments

In these instruments, which are used extensively for power frequency measurements, the fixed coil structure is replaced by a soft iron vane and the

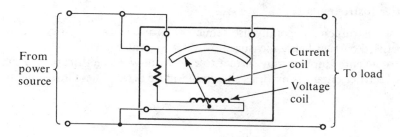

Figure 8.3-1.   Connections of a wattmeter

movable coil is also replaced by a vane. The excitation is by a coil that encloses both vanes, thereby magnetizing them and causing a movement of the movable vane. The general features of the instrument are shown in Figure 8.3-2. The torque produced is proportional to the square of the current since the magnetism in each vane is proportional to the current, with the displacing torque depending on the product of the two fields. Actually, in this device a dc current is equally effective in producing the magnetism, and the instrument may be used to measure dc currents. The d'Arsonval device is preferred for dc measurements because of the linear scale rather than the square law scale of the iron vane meter.

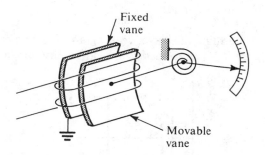

Figure 8.3-2.   The features of the iron vane instrument

Thermocouple Instruments

These devices include a thermocouple and a d'Arsonval movement to measure the emf generated at a junction of dissimilar metals. The dc emf is dependent on the temperature rise of the junction which is nearly proportional to the square of the current. The instruments can be calibrated in terms of rms currents, and can be used over a very wide range of frequencies to measure true rms currents. Thermocouple instruments will operate satisfactorily up to 50 MHz.

Rectifier Instruments

These instruments generally use semiconductor diodes to convert ac to dc, the rectified current being measured by a d'Arsonval movement. To avoid the need for a center-tapped transformer to effect full-wave rectification, a simple bridge rectifier circuit is used, as shown in Figure 8.3-3. These instruments are

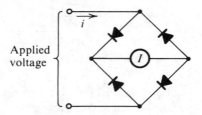

Figure 8.3-3. A rectifier-type instrument

waveshape dependent, and the deflection is proportional to the average current. Ordinarily these instruments are calibrated on sinusoidal waves to read rms values. However, the rms value of the sinusoid is (see Section 4.1) $0.707/0.636 = 1.11$ times the average value, and the instrument actually reads 1.11 times the average value of the rectified current. If the applied waveshape is other than a sinusoid, the instrument reading will not be correct, and an appropriate correction must be made.

EXAMPLE 8.3-1. Determine the meter reading and the true rms value of the wave shown in Figure 8.3-4 if applied to a rectifier instrument.

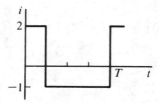

Figure 8.3-4. The applied wave to a rectifier instrument

SOLUTION. The instrument indicates

$$I_{av} = 1.11 \frac{(2 \times 1 + 1 \times 3)}{4} = 1.11 \times \frac{5}{4} = 1.39 \text{ A}$$

The true rms value of this wave is

$$I_{rms} = \frac{2^2 \times 1 + 1^2 \times 3}{4} = 1.32 \text{ A}$$

□   □   □

8.4 BRIDGE MEASUREMENTS

A variety of structures exist for measuring passive elements by comparing their value relative to some "standard or known element. Modified bridge structures allow other measurements to be made including frequency and Q. We shall examine the essential features of a number of types. As shall be shown, the range of measurements using bridges is quite large.

The Wheatstone Bridge

This network for measuring resistance values of resistors is shown in Figure 8.4-1. This is the basic bridge structure for general impedance measurements.

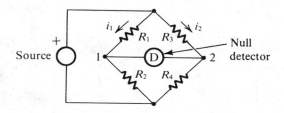

Figure 8.4-1.   The Wheatstone bridge

Measurements may be made using dc excitation with a d'Arsonval movement for null measurement indication. However, the accuracy of the results and the convenience with which the results are obtained are frequently enhanced through the use of ac sources, often at a convenient audio frequency level (say 1000 Hz) and with earphones as a detector. The use of digital instruments in place of the headphones is very common. When the bridge is balanced there is no current through the null detector. This means that the node voltage v_1 is equal to that of node 2, v_2, and so

$$i_1 R_1 = i_2 R_3 \qquad \text{(a)} \qquad \text{(8.4-1)}$$

$$i_1 R_2 = i_2 R_4 \qquad \text{(b)}$$

Divide these two equations to get

$$\frac{R_1}{R_2} = \frac{R_3}{R_4} \qquad (8.4\text{-}2)$$

If $R_1 = R_x$, the resistor being measured, then

$$R_x = \frac{R_3}{R_4} R_2 \qquad (8.4\text{-}3)$$

Often a ratio box is used, with R_3/R_4 being some convenient ratio appropriate to the value of R_x and R_2. These values might be a convenient integral value, e.g., 1, 10, 100, 1000. The ratio box and the resistor R_2 might be high quality devices which are known to 0.01%. If the null point is established precisely, the value of R_x is then known to a high degree of accuracy.

Such a simple bridge structure is not adequate for measuring very low or very high resistance values, but it is suitable for use over a very wide range of resistance values.

Similar Angle AC Bridge Networks

If in Figure 8.4-1 the resistors are replaced by general impedances and with an ac signal source, then when the bridge is balanced, the general result is

$$\frac{Z_1}{Z_2} = \frac{Z_3}{Z_4} \tag{8.4-4}$$

If this is expressed in terms of the magnitudes and angles of the impedances, this specifies that

$$\left|\frac{Z_1}{Z_2}\right| = \left|\frac{Z_3}{Z_4}\right|; \qquad \theta_1 - \theta_2 = \theta_3 - \theta_4 \tag{8.4-5}$$

where $Z_1 = |Z_1|e^{j\theta_1}$, $Z_2 = |Z_2|e^{j\theta_2}$, $Z_3 = |Z_3|e^{j\theta_3}$ and $Z_4 = |Z_4|e^{j\theta_4}$. This indicates that not only must the magnitudes be balanced, but the phase angles of the branches must also be balanced.

The four branch bridge can easily be treated by graphical methods when balance is secured. The following phasor diagram (Figure 8.4-2) for the balanced four-branch impedance bridge of Figure 8.4-1 can be shown to lead to the balance conditions given in Equation (8.4-4). A number of different applications exist for such bridges.

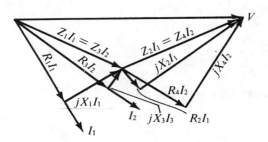

Figure 8.4-2. The phasor diagram of the balanced AC bridge

SIMILAR ANGLE INDUCTOR BRIDGE. A common variety of the simple four-branch network is that for which the impedance arms are those shown in Figure 8.4-3. That is,

$$Z_1 = R_1 + j\omega L_1 \qquad\qquad Z_2 = R_2 + j\omega L_2$$

$$Z_3 = R_3 \qquad\qquad Z_4 = R_4$$

In this case, Equation (8.4-4) under conditions of balance reduces to

$$\frac{R_1}{R_2} = \frac{R_3}{R_4} \qquad\qquad \frac{L_1}{L_2} = \frac{R_3}{R_4} \qquad (8.4\text{-}6)$$

The double conditions for balance is characteristic of ac bridges. The first relation corresponds to an ordinary dc balance and can be established with the use of a constant voltage source and a dc indicator. Generally, however, both the dc balance and the ac balance are made simultaneously by adjusting both R_2 or R_4 and R_3.

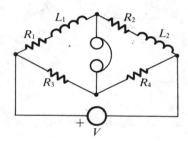

Figure 8.4-3.   The similar angle inductance bridge

THE CAPACITOR BRIDGE. If the reactances of Figure 8.4-4 are capacitive instead of being inductive, then the elements are

$$Z_1 = R_1 - j\frac{1}{\omega C_1} \qquad\qquad Z_3 = R_3$$

$$Z_2 = R_2 - j\frac{1}{\omega C_2} \qquad\qquad Z_4 = R_4$$

and the conditions for balance are

$$\frac{R_1}{R_2} = \frac{R_3}{R_4} \qquad\qquad \frac{C_2}{C_1} = \frac{R_3}{R_4} \qquad (8.4\text{-}7)$$

Suppose that $C_1 = C_x$, the capacitor being measured, has associated with it some series resistance $R_1 = R_x$. Also, suppose that C_2 is a capacitor of high quality with negligible series resistance, but with an external resistor R_2. In this case we can find the apparent power factor of the capacitor C_x to be

$$\cos \theta_x = \frac{1}{\sqrt{1 + \dfrac{1}{\omega^2 R_x^2 C_x^2}}}$$

where $\omega/2\pi$ is the frequency at which the bridge is balanced. Actually $\omega R_x C_x$ is very small compared with unity so that effectively

$$\cos \theta_x = \omega R_x C_x \tag{8.4-8}$$

The power factor of a capacitor furnishes a criterion of quality, the smaller the power factor, the better the capacitor.

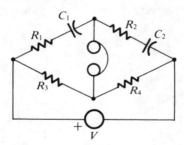

Figure 8.4-4.   The similar angle capacitance bridge

For precisely measuring small capacitances, determining relative permittivity, or determining power losses in capacitors, the simple capacitance bridge discussed here is unsatisfactory because the stray capacitances of the various parts of the bridge are of the same order of magnitude as those to be measured. If attention is paid to shielding and grounding, the range of the simple bridge can be extended to cover a wide range of capacitance measurements.

THE MAXWELL BRIDGE. A simple though effective method by which self-inductance and capacitance are compared is the method of Maxwell, shown in bridge form in Figure 8.4-5. The impedances in the various arms are

$$Z_1 = R_1 + j\omega L_1 \qquad\qquad Z_3 = R_3$$

$$Z_2 = R_2 \qquad\qquad Z_4 = \frac{1}{\dfrac{1}{R_4} + j\omega C_4}$$

The condition for balance reduces to

$$\frac{R_1}{R_2} = \frac{R_3}{R_4} \qquad\qquad \frac{L_1}{R_2} = R_3 C_4 \tag{8.4-9}$$

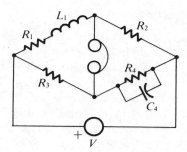

Figure 8.4-5. Maxwell bridge

If either the inductor or the capacitor (or both) is variable, this method is adapted to the measurement of capacitance in terms of inductance, or to the calibration of a variable inductor in terms of known capacitance. However, because of the usual range of inductors and capacitors available, this method is more suitable for measuring inductance in terms of capacitance.

8.5 POTENTIOMETERS

The potentiometer is an instrument for measuring the difference of potential between two points in a circuit. It is one of the few instruments which does not disturb an electrical system when introduced into the circuit and when balanced. Of course, electronic instruments with very high input impedance can be introduced with very little effect on the circuit.

The potentiometer principle can best be understood by referring to Figure 8.5-1a.

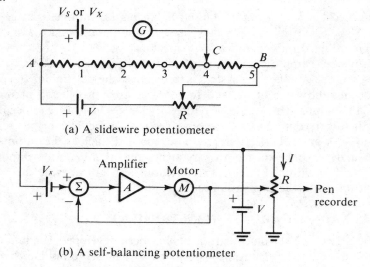

(a) A slidewire potentiometer

(b) A self-balancing potentiometer

Figure 8.5-1.   Basic potentiometer circuits

The Slide Wire Potentiometer

Suppose that AB is a slide wire divided into five equal parts. This wire is paralleled by two battery circuits. One consists of source V, the current from which can be varied by means of the resistor R. The other contains either a standard cell V_s or a Zener diode regulated voltage supply, or the unknown V_x, a sensitive galvanometer, and a movable contact C. Suppose the V_s with a voltage of 4 V is inserted in the circuit. Then C is put on contact 4 and R is adjusted until the galvanometer reads zero. The voltage between A and contact 4 then corresponds to 4 volts, that between A and contact 3 is 3 V, etc. Now suppose that V_s is replaced by V_x. The voltage V_x will be given directly in volts by the contact number at which C must be placed in order to give zero deflection on the galvanometer.

Such a unit permits V_x to be measured only to the nearest volt. However, if the slide wire between two contacts were subdivided into 10 equal parts, the measurement can then be made to tenths of a volt. If it were subdivided into 100 equal parts, then V_x can be measured to hundredths of a volt, etc. Very precise measurements can be made with special instruments. The Leeds & Northrup Type K potentiometer permits measurements to five significant figures when V_s is a calibrated Standard Cell. (A standard cell of the Weston type has a voltage of roughly 1.0813 V.) To measure voltages that have much higher values than V_s, a volt-box can be used. This is simply the equivalent of a calibrated drop wire, usually providing fixed voltage ratios 1/10, 1/100, 1/1000, the output terminals providing a voltage consistent with the calibrating V_s.

Self-Balancing Potentiometer

A simplified block diagram of the self-balancing potentiometer is given in Figure 8.5-1b. Such units are widely used for automatic control and continuous recording. In its operation, the difference between V_x and the potentiometer voltage is amplified, and this amplified difference is used to drive the balancing motor M. When the system is in balance, the position of the motor shaft indicates the value of V_x, and the pen recorder provides a permanent record of the output. This would be desired if changes in V_x were to occur, for example, if V_x is the output of a thermocouple in a furnace. If two voltages corresponding to X and Y deflections are to be recorded, such as the outputs of a spectrum analyzer, one axis denoting frequency the other denoting amplitude, an X-Y recorder with self-balancing potentiometers will provide the deflections appropriate to the two variables being plotted.

8.6 ELECTRONIC INDICATING INSTRUMENTS

A wide variety of electronic instruments has been developed. An important feature common to most electronic instruments is that their input impedance is high. Equivalently, the power required to drive these devices from the system under observation is small, with the power required to drive the indicating or recording instrument being supplied by the amplifier. Another feature of electronic instruments is that the frequency range and the versatility of design permits instruments appropriate to a wide range of general and special purpose measurements.

Instruments can be categorized in terms of their use, and might be listed as voltmeters, ammeters, wattmeters, frequency meters, phase meters, impedance meters, and a wide variety of special purpose instruments. We shall consider selected devices.

Electronic Voltmeters

A large variety of electronic voltmeter types is available. The differences among them are in input impedance level, frequency range, principle of operation, and type of indication. Consequently, care is often important in the selection of the type of instrument for a particular application. Such devices provide a convenient method for accurately measuring dc or ac voltages over high frequency ranges with low loading of the source of the voltage.

RMS VOLTMETER. To provide a voltmeter with an rms indication requires that the input device possess a square law characteristic relating the input voltage and the mean rectified current. Electronic devices that provide a roughly square law characteristic do exist, but they may be of limited accuracy. A thyrite element incorporated in a rectifier bridge circuit has been used, with proper square law behavior within ± 2.5 per cent over a current range of 50:1. A square law diode has been developed, and is used in such rms voltmeter service. As discussed in Section 7.10, the FET is closely square law.

AVERAGE READING VOLTMETERS. In an average reading instrument, the output indication is proportional to the average value of the input voltage. Typical circuits are given in Figure 8.6-1. Figures 8.6-1a and 8.6-1b are simply

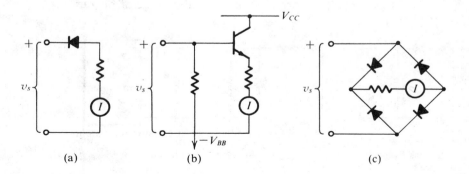

(a)   (b)   (c)

Figure 8.6-1. The circuits of three average reading EVM

basic rectifier circuits. The output will be the half-wave average, the choice of positive or negative excursions being dependent on the input connection. In the form shown in Figure 8.6-1a, the circuit responds to the negative half-cycle of the input voltage; Figure 8.6-1b responds to the positive half-cycle of the input voltage. Clearly, the output from all three circuits depends on the waveform of the input voltage, and if the instrument has been calibrated using a symmetrical sinusoidal input, corrections will be necessary for other waveform inputs. This matter was discussed in Section 8.3-4 for the diode bridge voltmeter. For the other circuits, if the applied voltage is not a sine wave or other symmetrical waveform, a reversal of the polarity of the input wave will change the reading of the instrument. This effect is known as *turnover*.

A rather different approach to such voltmeter operation has also been adopted. In this, the input dc voltage, which may be that of an ac probe plus rectifier and filter, is used to vary the frequency of a voltage sensitive oscillator. The frequency that results is measured using frequency measuring techniques, and this is a measure of the input voltage.

PEAK READING VOLTMETER. As the name implies, the reading in this voltmeter is proportional to the peak value of the applied voltage. The instrument would be independent of the input waveform if it is calibrated in peak volts. Often peak reading instruments are calibrated to read rms values for sinusoidal input voltage, which is 0.707 of the peak voltage. A number of different peak reading instruments are possible, including diode, feedback and slideback types.

The *diode peak* voltmeter is a simple and accurate device, and operates over a wide range of frequencies. A typical circuit is given in Figure 8.6-2a which includes a conventional shunt diode rectifier with capacitor input filter in the output. A resistor and series milliammeter constitutes the load circuit. The time constant of the circuit is large compared with the period of the applied voltage to insure that the reading is at the peak value. A more complete circuit is given in Figure 8.6-2b to provide for a broader range of operation.

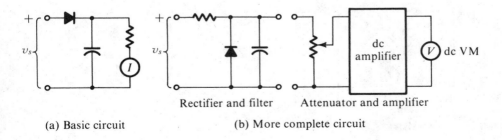

(a) Basic circuit   (b) More complete circuit

Figure 8.6-2.   Diode peak voltmeter

The *slideback* voltmeter is illustated in Figure 8.6-3. Observe that this is essentially a threshold indicator which indicates on a dc voltmeter when a dc voltage is made equal to the peak value of the applied voltage. When the voltmeter is being used, the bias voltage is initially set for a very low reading on the ammeter. The voltage to be measured is then applied to the input terminals and the bias is increased to a point where the ammeter reading is returned to the initial value. The peak value of the voltage being read is given by the change in bias.

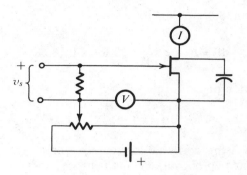

Figure 8.6-3.   A slide back peak voltmeter

LOGARITHMIC VOLTMETER. A direct method for achieving a logarithmic indicating voltmeter (which will have a linear decibel scale) is to use an average reading instrument with the pole pieces of the indicating instrument so shaped that the scale indication is logarithmic. Another direct method is to use a semiconductor diode because the current is known to be of the form $I = I_o(e^{qV/kT} - 1)$ over wide ranges of V. However, the application in such voltmeter service has been limited.

Basically what is required for a logarithmic voltmeter is an element for which the output voltage is related to the signal by an equation of the form

$$V_2 = V_s A e^{aV_c} \tag{8.6-1}$$

where V_c is the dc bias on the element, where a and A are constants. The basic features of such a voltmeter are shown in Figure 8.6-4. When operating, the output is maintained constant by using the output in a control loop. This involves using the output voltage to bias the amplifier. Thus with V_2 constant, from Equation (8.6-1)

$$V_c = K - \frac{1}{a} \ln V_s$$

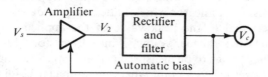

Figure 8.6-4. Block diagram of a logarithmic voltmeter

But from Equation (8.6-1) in dB form

$$dB = 20 \log_{10} \frac{V_2}{V_s} = 20 \log_{10} A + 8.68 a V_c$$

which is an equation of the form

$$dB = k + m V_c \qquad (8.6\text{-}2)$$

This shows that V_c is proportional to the output on a logarithmic scale. Such voltmeters were made using variable-mu pentode tubes.

8.7 ELECTRONIC COUNTER

Electronic counters, which will be discussed in Section 9.10, have been used extensively in instrumentation for counting events. This use requires that the events be transduced into electrical signals. Appropriate transducers must be devised for specific needs. The basic form of an electronic counting system is shown in Figure 8.7-1. The timing generator or clock, which may be a controlled oscillator, establishes a precision time base. The clock pulses are used to open and close a gating circuit to the electronic counter chain conveniently made up of modulo-10 counters (those that read to 10 before reset). In its

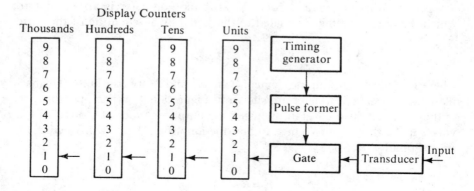

Figure 8.7-1. Elements of an electronic counting system

operation the counting proceeds for a precise fraction of a second, as dictated by the time during which the gating circuit is held open. The gate is then closed and the total count is displayed.

Such a counting circuit can be adapted to measure frequency or elapsed time between similar events. When used in such measurements, the signal or event to be measured is used to open the counter gate allowing the timing generator signals to be passed to the counter until the next event closes the counter gate. For example, if the timing generator operates at a frequency of 10 Mhz with pulses spaced therefore at $1/10^7 = 10^{-7}$ s, and if the successive events that open and close the counter gate allows 500 pulses to be indicated, then the interval between events is 50×10^{-6} s or a frequency of 20 kHz.

8.8 ANALOG/DIGITAL AND DIGITAL/ANALOG CONVERTERS

With the widespread processing of information in digital form, it is often necessary to convert analog data into digital form. This requires an analog/digital converter. A representative sweep-timing system is shown in block form in Figure 8.8-1a. The input is sampled at a regular rate, the sampled values

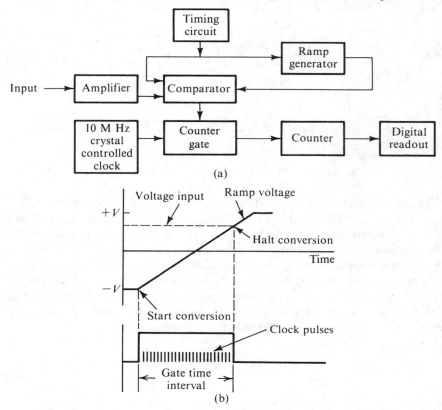

Figure 8.8-1. (a) Block diagram of a sweep-timing A/D converter
(b) Features of operation

being compared with the value achieved by a repetitive linear ramp in a comparator. Two pulses are produced, one at the start of the sampling instant and the other at the point of equality with the ramp. Hence the two pulses specify a time proportional to the input voltage. These pulses open and close a gate, thereby allowing a number of clock pulses to reach an electronic counter, with a subsequent digital readout that is proportional to the input voltage.

A modification of the sweep-timing circuit, one that replaces the linear ramp generator by a staircase voltage waveform generated by a D/A converter at the output of the counter, has some advantages. This so-called feedback method of A/D conversion operates on the same principle as the sweep-timing circuit. It is a preferred method because the staircase voltage can be generated with precision resistors and adjustments are not required. The accuracy depends on the accuracy of the D/A converter and the comparator resolution. A block diagram of the feedback method is given in Figure 8.8-2. It is instructive to compare the form of this figure with Figure 8.8-1.

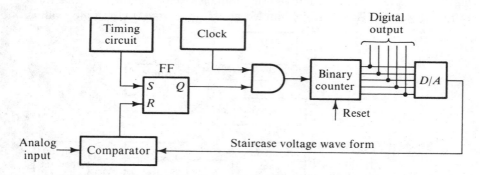

Figure 8.8-2.   Feedback method of A/D conversion

The *digital voltmeter* using a dual slope technique is widely used, and is essentially an A/D converter. The features of this device are shown in Figure 8.8-3. In this device the input voltage V_x is applied to an integrator at time t_1. The capacitor C in this integrator charges for a fixed time T_F. At t_2, established by the number of clock pulses that have been counted, the control logic switches the input to the integrator from V_x to V_F, a fixed reference voltage. The capacitor discharges at a rate that is proportional to V_F, with the counter being reset at t_2 to count until the comparator indicates that the integrator ouput v_P has retuned to zero. The operation establishes that

$$V_X T_F = V_F T_x$$

or

$$V_x = \frac{T_x}{T_F} V_F$$

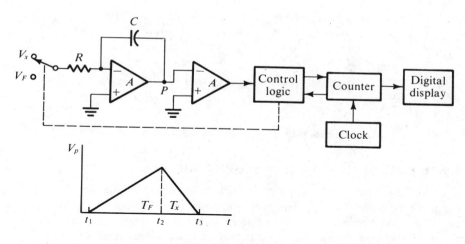

Figure 8.8-3.   A digital voltmeter using dual-slope technique

The count at t_3, which is proportional to the input voltage, is displayed on a digital display.

A requirement in the sweep-timing methods is that the ramps must be extremely linear if high precision is desired. Conversion accuracies using this technique of approximately 1 per cent can be achieved practically. Higher accuracies have been obtained using circuits with special compensation techniques and adjustments. A slope adjustment is usually required for the ramp generator in Figure 8.8-1.

A number of other type A/D converters exist. Commercial A/D converters are standard items that are readily available.

Digital/analog conversion proves to be a less difficult problem than the A/D conversion. A number of different techniques have been developed for accomplishing D/A conversion. One of the simplest is to use a resistive ladder network, as shown in Figure 8.8-4. This ladder network can be extended to n bits, even though the circuit shows only a 5 bit input. The open circuit analog output voltage resulting in this network is ½ the voltage of the most significant bit, $b_4/2$, plus $b_3/4$, plus $b_2/8$, etc. For 5 bits

$$V_a = \frac{b_4}{2} + \frac{b_3}{4} + \frac{b_2}{8} + \frac{b_1}{16} + \frac{b_o}{32}$$

(8.8-1)

which is the properly weighted sum of the input binary digits. Observe that the input bits have been assumed to be of a single reference polarity V and 0 for the binary digits 1 and 0. This will result in a single polarity signal. If the reference ground for the pulses is replaced by a source $-V$ volt, corresponding to the reference V for the pulse heights, then the analog output will be an ac or bipolar signal.

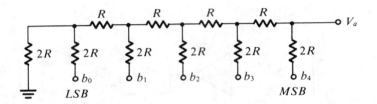

Figure 8.8-4.   Digital/analog ladder network

8.9   CATHODE RAY OSCILLOSCOPE (CRO)

The cathode ray oscilloscope shown schematically in Figure 8.9-1 is one of the most versatile single instruments available. It can be used as a voltmeter, ammeter, and frequency and phase meter, over a wide range of test conditions, from microvolts to hundreds of volts and from dc to hundreds of MHz. The principle of operation of the cathode ray tube (CRT) involves a deflection of a highly focused electron beam as it passes between a pair of deflecting plates.

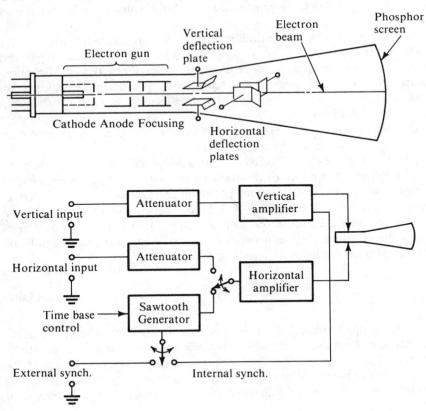

Figure 8.9-1.   Schematic diagram of the cathode ray oscilloscope

The result is that the deflection on the CRT screen is directly proportional to the voltage on the deflecting plates. Hence if the gain of the associated amplifier is set, the peak of any applied voltage waveform can be compared with a calibration voltage. Although such a procedure is often awkward and slow and is of limited precision, it is often a very desirable procedure. Moreover with its set of plates in the X-axis and in the Y-axis, a time base can be applied to one set of plates with the signal applied to the second set. The result, if the time base is linear (which requires a recurring ramp function) is that the signal is presented as a time function, voltage versus time, which is stationary on the face of the tube. This assumes that the time base recurring frequency is integrally related to the period of the applied periodic wave. Moreover, depending on the amplifiers, frequency ranges to 50 MHz are quite common. The pattern on the face of the CRT can be photographed for detailed study.

Among the features that are available in modern CROs are

1. *Differential Inputs.* This permits two signals to be applied simultaneously with the amplifier amplifying the difference. Owing to the high common mode rejection a common signal such as hum is rejected.

2. *Dual Channels.* Two different waveforms can be displayed simultaneously by switching the signals alternately to the vertical deflection system. This time division feature is accomplished at a high rate. Dual beam tubes are available in more expensive CROs, permitting independent displays simultaneously. These tubes are provided with separate electron gun assemblies and deflecting systems.

3. *Delayed and Expanded Sweep.* The sweep speeds can be adjusted, and the signal position can be moved. This permits a study of a magnified portion of a given waveform, if desired.

4. *Storage Phosphors.* For examining nonrepetitive waveforms, the signal can be stored on long persistence phosphors. With the use of a special storage mesh behind the phosphor, the rate at which the charge pattern leaks away can be controlled, thereby yielding a variable persistence screen.

5. *Digital Readout.* Some of the newer CROs are provided with a built-in *microprocessor*, which provides direct digital readout of voltage, frequency, time interval, in addition to the CRO display.

In addition, special probes can be obtained for use in inputing the signal to improve the input characteristics, by increasing the input impedance, or by voltage-current converters.

Of course, as more features are made available, more control knobs and input terminals are provided. Hence care must be exercised in using such CROs to be sure that they are properly connected for the anticipated use.

8.10 INSTRUMENTATION TRANSDUCERS

The discussion in Chapter 12 will be centered on incremental transducers of a variety of types. Generally such transducers become part of more complete systems. A number of these provide end-use application, e.g., telephone

receivers, loud speakers. Others of these provide electrical signals which serve
as inputs to more extensive systems. The type and range of transducers has
become almost as large as the particular needs dictate, since electronic instrumentation finds applications in almost every discipline.

STATISTICAL EVALUATION OF MEASUREMENT DATA
AND ERRORS

8.11 EXPERIMENTATION AND ERRORS

The importance of models has received considerable attention in this text.
Models in experimentation, whether they be physical or mathematical, also
prove to be very helpful, since they provide a basis for organizing information
into clear and possibly exact relationships among the variables. They help to
identify dependent and independent variables, and input-output relationships.
However, to obtain meaningful and accurate data from a model study requires
that both geometric and dynamic *similitude* must exist between the model and
the prototype. This means that in addition to linear scaling, which would
satisfy geometric similitude, certain dimensionless ratios, such as Reynold's
number, temperature ratio, and velocity ratio, must be the same in both the
model and in the prototype. Assuming that all of these requirements are ful-
filled, attention to detail is critical in both the measurement process and in the
data. That is, errors of observation are critical since it must be possible to insure the repeatability of the experiment.

The success or failure of a measurement is dependent on the proper selection
of instruments. Instruments are characterized by: *sensitivity*, the ratio of an
output change to an input change; *drift*, a change in the response of the instrument with time; *time constant*, the time required for the instrument to reach
63.2 per cent of its final value; e.g., the value unity if the input is a step function of magnitude one; and *fidelity*, the accuracy with which the system
reproduces the input. Clearly, the instrument must be appropriate to the
needs.

This discussion should make clear that measurements of significance require
attention to many details. Moreover, experiments should be so planned that a
minimum number of variables are measured, desirably only one in each experiment. Variables may be controlled by the experimenter; often they cannot be
controlled. It is also important to be able to identify variables which are irrele-
vant to a given measurement. If the exact effect of certain variables is known,
they would ordinarily be maintained constant during an experiment. Even with
attention paid to variables, errors may arise.

For a number of reasons errors are introduced into any measurement.
Among these are degradation of the sensitivity of the instruments, and failure
of the observer to read the instruments correctly during the data-taking phase
of the investigation. In addition, errors may occur at many steps in the subsequent handling of the data: during the transfer of data from one form to
another, during calculations, and during the calculations themselves.

By definition *error* is the difference between the indicated value and the true value of the measured value. This is rather different from a *mistake*, which is a misunderstanding or a misconception of the measurements or in the approach of the experiment. *Random errors* are variations due to uncontrolled variables and can be interpreted by means of statistical analysis. *Precision errors* are those that result when successive measurements of an unchanged variable yield different values. When the average of successive readings consistently deviates from the correct known value, independent of the number of observations, this denotes an *accuracy error*.

The Histogram and the Normal Curve

When many causes produce errors in measurements, the laws of probability help us make reasonable predictions of what might be expected to happen. Consider the case of a set of 50 resistors which have been labelled by the manufacturer as being 54 ohm. Suppose that these are measured, with the results shown in Table 8.11-1. The data contained in this table are plotted in Figure 8.11-1. This is known as a *histogram*. Observe from this figure that there is a tendency of the data to group around some *central* point. The figure also reveals the tendency of the values to spread. This type of representation is very important since it enables the determination of the mean value, a measure of deviation from the mean value, and a prediction of the number of resistors from any given group of 54 ohm resistors from the same manufacturer whose values lie in the range from 51 to 55 ohm.

Table 8.11-1. Resistance of 54 Ohm Resistors

Measured Resistance	59	58	57	56	55	54	53	52	51	50	49	48
Number of units within one Ohm difference	1	2	4	6	5	7	11	6	4	1	2	1

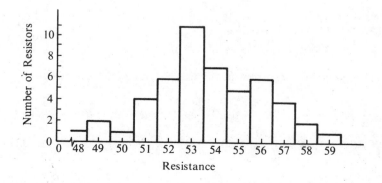

Figure 8.11-1. Histogram of 50 resistors

MEAN VALUE. The mean value of a set of measurements, which is the arithmetic mean, is defined by

$$\bar{x} = \frac{1}{N} \sum_{i=1}^{N} x_i \qquad (8.11\text{-}1)$$

where the x_i-s are the values of each measurement, and N is the number of measurements. The mean value of the 50 resistors included in the histogram of Figure 8.11-1 is

$$\bar{x} = R_m = \frac{1}{50}(1 \times 59 + 2 \times 58 + 4 \times 57 + 6 \times 56 + 5 \times 55 + 7 \times 54 + 11 \times 53$$

$$+ 6 \times 52 + 4 \times 51 + 1 \times 50 + 2 \times 49 + 1 \times 48) = 53.74$$

The mean value is not the true value, but if a large number of observations are included, then x approaches the true value.

STANDARD DEVIATION. Often our interest is in determining quantitatively the scattering of the measurements from the mean value. The *standard deviation* gives this value. It is given by the formula

$$\sigma = \left[\frac{1}{N} \sum_{i=1}^{N} (x_i - \bar{x})^2 \right]^{1/2} \qquad (8.11\text{-}2)$$

The square of the standard deviation, σ^2, is called the *variance*.

Equation (8.11-2) can be expanded as shown

$$\sigma^2 = \frac{1}{N} \sum_{i=1}^{N} (x_i - \bar{x})^2 = \frac{1}{N} \sum_{i=1}^{N} (x_i^2 + \bar{x}^2 - 2x_i\bar{x})$$

$$= \frac{1}{N} \sum_{i=1}^{N} x_i^2 + \frac{\bar{x}^2}{N} - \frac{2\bar{x}}{N} \sum_{i=1}^{N} x_i = \frac{1}{N} \sum_{i=1}^{N} x_i^2 - \bar{x}^2$$

$$\text{(a)} \quad (8.11\text{-}3)$$

or

$$\sigma^2 = \frac{1}{N} \sum_{i=1}^{N} x_i^2 - \left(\frac{1}{N} \sum_{i=1}^{N} x_i \right)^2 \qquad \text{(b)}$$

Using the data for the resistors in the example above, there results

$$\sigma^2 = \frac{1}{50}(1 \times 59^2 + 2 \times 58^2 + 4 \times 57^2 + 6 \times 56^2 + 5 \times 55^2 + 7 \times 54^2 + 11 \times 53^2$$

$$+ 6 \times 52^2 + 4 \times 51^2 + 1 \times 50^2 + 2 \times 49^2 + 1 \times 48^2) - 53.74^2 = 5.8324$$

and

$$\sigma = 2.415 \text{ ohm}$$

STANDARD DEVIATION OF THE MEAN. The specified data from the sample of 50 resistors have been used to find their mean and standard deviation values. It is intuitively anticipated that the selection of another sample of 50 resistors from the same batch will yield different values for the mean and standard deviation. This suggests that the values found are not the mean and the standard deviation values for the resistors in the entire batch, which probably measure in the thousands in any standard manufacturing process. For the case when the histogram has a Gaussian distribution, it can be shown that the standard deviation of the mean is given by

$$\sigma_m^2 = \frac{\sigma^2}{N} \qquad \text{or} \qquad \sigma_m = \frac{\sigma}{\sqrt{N}} \tag{8.11-4}$$

This describes the precision of the mean in a set of measurements. In our problem

$$\sigma_m = \frac{2.415}{\sqrt{50}} = 0.3415 \qquad \text{ohm}$$

8.12   ERRORS AND THEIR PROPAGATION

Very often sets of mathematically related readings are required, which means that the total error due to the errors of the individual measurements must be found. Suppose, for example, that a relation of the form

$$z = cxy \tag{8.12-1}$$

is under investigation, where x and y are measured quantities, and c is a known constant. If x_i and y_i are the deviations from the mean, Equation (8.12-1) becomes

$$\bar{z} + z_i = c(\bar{x} + x_i)(\bar{y} + y_i) = c(\bar{x}\bar{y} + \bar{y}x_i + \bar{x}y_i + x_iy_i)$$
$$\doteq c(\bar{x}\bar{y} + \bar{y}x_i + \bar{x}y_i) = c\bar{x}\bar{y} + c(\bar{y}x_i + \bar{x}y_i) \tag{8.12-2}$$

where x_iy_i was neglected as a second order quantity. From this it follows that

$$z_i = c(x_i\bar{y} + y_i\bar{x}) \tag{8.12-3}$$

But from the definition of the variance

$$\sigma_z^2 = \frac{1}{N}\sum_{i=1}^{N} z_i^2 = \frac{c^2}{N}\left(\bar{y}^2\sum_{i=1}^{N} x_i^2 + \bar{x}^2\sum_{i=1}^{N} y_i^2 + \bar{x}\bar{y}\sum_{i=1}^{N} x_iy_i\right) \tag{8.12-4}$$

$$= c^2\left(\bar{y}^2\frac{1}{N}\sum_{i=1}^{N} x_i^2 + \bar{x}^2\frac{1}{N}\sum_{i=1}^{N} y_i^2\right)$$

$$= c^2(\bar{y}^2\sigma_x^2 + \bar{x}^2\sigma_y^2)$$

where the sum $\Sigma x_i y_i$ was neglected since there is the same likelihood that the product $x_i y_i$ will be positive or negative. Further, since $z = cxy$, then Equation (8.12-4) becomes

$$\frac{\sigma_z^2}{\overline{z}^2} = \frac{\sigma_x^2}{\overline{x}^2} + \frac{\sigma_y^2}{\overline{y}^2} \tag{8.12-5}$$

This shows that the fractional standard deviation of z is equal to the sum of the fractional standard deviations of the observation quantities. Equation (8.12-5) can be extended for cases with more than two measurable quantities that are related by a product form as given in Equation (8.12-1).

Ordinarily our interest is in the variance of the mean rather than in the variance of the individual observations. By combining Equations (8.11-4) and (8.12-5) it follows that

$$\frac{\sigma_{mz}^2}{\overline{z}^2} = \frac{\sigma_{mx}^2}{\overline{x}^2} + \frac{\sigma_{my}^2}{\overline{y}^2} \tag{8.12-6}$$

It can also be shown that when z is related to x and y by a quotient relationship of the form

$$z = c\frac{x}{y} \tag{a} \quad (8.12\text{-}7)$$

then

$$\frac{\sigma_z^2}{\overline{z}^2} = \frac{\sigma_x^2}{\overline{x}^2} + \frac{\sigma_y^2}{\overline{y}^2} \tag{b}$$

Similarly, for a relationship of the form

$$z = c\frac{xy}{w} \tag{a} \quad (8.12\text{-}8)$$

there results

$$\frac{\sigma_z^2}{\overline{z}^2} = \frac{\sigma_x^2}{\overline{x}^2} + \frac{\sigma_y^2}{\overline{y}^2} + \frac{\sigma_w^2}{\overline{w}^2} \tag{b}$$

EXAMPLE 8.12-1. The measurements of a rectangular plot of ground are: $a = 10 \pm 0.5$ m and $b = 100 \pm 1$ m, where $\pm$ in each case refers to the standard deviation. Find the resulting fractional deviation of the area.

SOLUTION. Apply Equation (8.12-5) to find

$$\left(\frac{\sigma_z}{\overline{z}}\right)^2 = \left(\frac{0.5}{100}\right)^2 + \left(\frac{1}{100}\right)^2 = 0.0026 \quad \text{thus} \quad \frac{\sigma_z}{\overline{z}} = 0.05$$

□ □ □

Finally for the case where z is related to x and y by a relationship of the form

$$z = x^m y^n \qquad \text{(a)} \quad (8.12\text{-}9)$$

then it will be found that

$$\frac{\sigma_z^2}{\bar{z}^2} = m^2 \frac{\sigma_x^2}{\bar{x}^2} + n^2 \frac{\sigma_y^2}{\bar{y}^2} \qquad \text{(b)}$$

8.13 THE METHOD OF LEAST SQUARES

The Ohm's law relation

$$V = RI \qquad (8.13\text{-}1)$$

is used to determine experimentally the resistance R in a particular case. Suppose that a plot of the points in the V,I plane looks like that shown in Figure 8.13-1. In this plot each point represents a pair of observations (ammeter, voltmeter) both of which are subject to random errors. It is required to determine the most probable value of the curve and so the value of R.

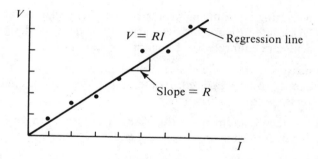

**Figure 8.13-1. Experimental determination of resistance
by the method of least squares**

In general, a first order equation for a straight line is given by

$$y = mx + b \qquad (8.13\text{-}2)$$

where m is the slope and b is the intercept. By proceeding in the manner discussed above, it can be shown that m and b can be found using the equations

$$m = \frac{\displaystyle\sum_{i=1}^{N} x_i y_i - \frac{\displaystyle\sum_{i=1}^{N} x_i \sum_{i=1}^{N} y_i}{N}}{\displaystyle\sum_{i=1}^{N} x_i^2 - \frac{\left(\displaystyle\sum_{i=1}^{N} x_i\right)^2}{N}} \qquad\text{(a)} \quad \text{(8.13-3)}$$

$$b = \frac{\displaystyle\sum_{i=1}^{N} y_i}{N} - m\frac{\displaystyle\sum_{i=1}^{N} x_i}{N} \qquad\text{(b)}$$

Equations (8.13-2) and (8.13-3) are often called *regression equations*, and it is said that we make a regression of *y* on *x*.

SUMMARY

- Most measurements involve a comparison between a standard or known, and a related quantity under consideration.

- Electrical measuring instruments or meters are of two classes: absolute and secondary. Absolute instruments depend on their physical design. Secondary instruments are calibrated in terms of the standards.

- Electrical measuring instruments are classed according to method of operation and quantity to be measured. Examples are voltmeters, ammeters, frequency meters, speed, and frequency.

- Basic to most dc measurements is the d'Arsonval meter movement which is essentially a galvanometer or current dependent device.

- Ammeters usually include a shunt to divert most of the current away from the d'Arsonval movement, allowing a known fraction to pass through the movement.

- Voltmeters involve a d'Arsonval movement with a large series resistance to reduce the current to acceptable levels.

- Portable d'Arsonval movements ordinarily range from 10 microamperes to 100 microamperes for full scale deflection.

- Resistance can be measured using a voltmeter and ammeter and applying Ohm's law. Due account must be taken to loading effects of the instruments on each other.

- The general purpose ohmmeter makes use of the voltmeter method of measuring resistance.

- AC instruments incorporate special movements: electrodynamometer, iron vane. They also might involve thermocouples or bridge rectifiers.

- Passive electrical elements can be compared with known elements in a variety of bridge networks.

- The Wheatstone bridge is basic to most bridge measurements. It is useful for directly comparing resistors, with high precision.

- Similar angle bridges are used for measuring R, L, C in terms of known R, L, C.

- Opposite angle bridges permit measuring C in terms of L, L in terms of C, M in terms of L and C.

- The potentiometer permits measuring dc voltage very accurately.

- Self balancing potentiometers simplify dc voltage measurements.

- A wide variety of electronic indicating instruments exists. Among the different electronic voltmeters are rms reading, average reading, peak reading (diode, slide back), and logarithmic.

- Electronic counters are used extensively for counting events, and as frequency or time interval instruments.

- A/D and D/A converters find widespread use, since they permit digital signal processing of analog signals.

- A/D counters involve the comparison of the sampled analog signal with a point on a ramp generator, in sweep timing circuits. This generates start and stop pulses of a flipflop which opens a circuit for pulse counting during this interval, there being a clock provided to generate pulses.

- The feedback method of D/A conversion is similar to the sweep timing technique except that the ramp is replaced by a staircase voltage circuit.

- A digital voltmeter is essentially an A/D converter, often employing a dual slope technique.

- A simple D/A converter comprises a ladder network which accepts the binary pattern and then properly weights these before combining them into an output reading.

- The CRO is one of the most generally versatile instruments in general use. It provides for a wide variety of uses, but requires care to insure its proper operation.

- Instrument transducers provide electrical signals from the signal source to be measured.

- The mean value of a set of measurements is given by

$$\bar{x} = \frac{1}{N} \sum_{i=1}^{N} x_i$$

- The standard deviation of a set of measurements is given by

$$\sigma = \left[\frac{1}{N} \sum_{i=1}^{N} (x_i - \bar{x})^2 \right]^{1/2}$$

- The standard deviation of the mean is given by

$$\sigma_m = \frac{\sigma}{\sqrt{N}}$$

- The fractional standard deviation of the quantity z, when a relation exists of the form $z = x^m y^n$ is given by

$$\frac{\sigma_z^2}{z^2} = m^2 \frac{\sigma_x^2}{x^2} + n^2 \frac{\sigma_y^2}{y^2}$$

REVIEW QUESTIONS

1. Distinguish between absolute and secondary electrical measuring instruments.
2. How are portable ammeters and voltmeters standardized as secondary instruments?
3. Describe the essential principle of operation of the d'Arsonval movement.
4. Describe the voltmeter-ammeter method of measuring resistance.
5. Describe the voltmeter method of measuring resistance.
6. Design a 150 Volt voltmeter with a sensitivity of 10,000 ohm/volt. Specify the resistance banks if full scale is to be switchable to 10, 50, 150 volt.
7. Discuss the principle of operation of electrodynamometer, iron vane, thermocouple, rectifier instruments. Will they operate on ac, dc, circuits?
8. Describe the Wheatstone bridge for measuring resistance. Why is an ac source plus a headset as a detector used in preference to a dc source plus a dc null detector?
9. Derive the balance equations for the similar angle inductance bridge. Repeat for the capacitance bridge.
10. What measurements are possible using a Maxwell bridge?
11. Discuss the operation of the slidewire potentiometer.
12. What is the reading at the output of the following ac voltmeters (not the scale markings): rms, average reading, peak reading, logarithmic. If these have been calibrated with an ac sinusoidal source, will they read accurately if a periodic nonsinusoidal waveform is applied? Will they read for an applied dc? Is there a turnover effect in each?
13. Discuss the principle of operation of an A/D converter. What is the function of the binary counter?
14. Discuss the principle of operation of the dual slope digital voltmeter.
15. Discuss the features available in an oscilloscope that you have been using in your laboratory work.

16. Discuss the various errors that might exist in carrying out laboratory measurements.

17. Define the following terms: mean value, standard deviation, standard deviation of the mean. Do any of these quantities presuppose a particular distribution of the variables?

18. What is meant by the fractional standard deviation? If a functional relation among variables is $w = cxyz$, what is the form of the fractional standard deviation? What is the meaning of each term in the result?

19. A regression line is the optimum fit in the least squares sense of experimental points to a smooth curve. What does this sentence mean?

REFERENCES

1. Hall, C. W., *Errors in Experimentation*, Matrix Publishers, Inc., Portland, OR, 1977.

2. Schenck, H. and R. J. Hawks, *Theories of Engineering Experimentation*, 3rd ed. McGraw Hill Book Co., New York, NY, 1979.

3. Sifferlen, T. P., and V. Vartanian, *Digital Electronics with Engineering Applications*, Prentice Hall, Inc., Englewood Cliffs, NJ, 1970.

4. Young, H. D., *Statistical Treatment of Experimental Data*, McGraw Hill Book Co., New York, NY, 1962.

PROBLEMS

8.2-1. Interpret Equations (8.2-1) through (8.2-4).

8.2-2. You have available a 50 μA d'Arsonval movement having an internal resistance of 10,000 ohm. Design a multirange milliammeter with ranges of 500 μA, 10 mA, 100 mA.

8.2-3. The d'Arsonval movement of Problem 8.2-2 is to be used as the indicating movement of a dc voltmeter. Design the voltmeter to read 1, 50, 250 volt.

8.3-1. Determine the reading on a rectifier meter and the true rms values of the waves shown in Figure P8.3-1.

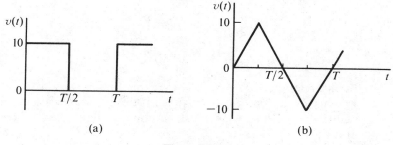

(a)   (b)

Figure P8.3-1

8.4-1. A simple resonance bridge for determining frequency is shown in Figure P8.4-1.

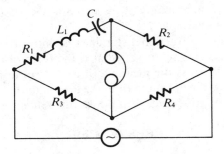

Figure P8.4-1

(a) Determine the conditions at balance.
(b) Discuss whether with fixed L the bridge can be calibrated to read frequency directly.

8.4-2. The Heydweiller MC bridge for comparing mutual inductance and capacitance is shown in Figure P8.4-2.

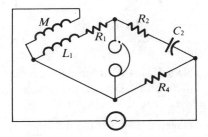

Figure P8.4-2

(a) Determine the balance equations and show that the two relations for M are

$$M = \mp L_1 \frac{R_4}{R_2 + R_4}$$

$$M = \mp R_1 R_4 C_2$$

(b) In the relation involving L_1, does this impose a constraint on whether L_1 must be greater than M. If this is not the case in a particular connection, what must be done to permit the bridge to operate?

8.6-1. A recurring voltage is given in Figure P8.6-1. Calculate the reading on the following instruments for both directions of the applied input:

(a) Single diode average reading;
(b) Bridge diode average reading;
(c) Peak reading diode;
(d) RMS reading.

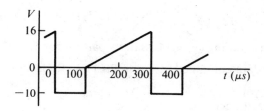

Figure P8.6-1

8.6-2. The waves of Problem 8.3-1 are read on a number of different type voltmeters, all of which were calibrated in terms of rms of a sine wave. What are the readings using the following instruments:

(a) Electrodynamometer;
(b) Positive peak reading;
(c) Negative peak reading.

8.7-1. Devise a suitable arrangement for measuring the speed of a rotating shaft. You are provided with a phototube and an electronic counter, among other miscellaneous items.

8.8-1. Shown in Figure P8.8-1 is a binary staircase generator.

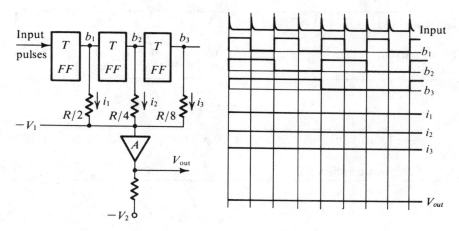

Figure P8.8-1

    (a) Complete the time diagram by sketching the current waves for i_1, i_2, i_3 to proper scale.

    (b) Combine these and show the resulting output.

8.9-1. A voltage $v_x = V_1 \sin(\omega t + \theta_1)$ is applied to the horizontal plates, and a voltage $v_y = V_2 \sin(\omega t + \theta_2)$ is applied to the vertical plates of a CRO. Show that these lead to the equation

$$\frac{v_x^2}{V_1^2} + \frac{v_y^2}{V_2^2} - \frac{2v_x v_y}{V_1 V_2} \cos(\theta_1 - \theta_2) = \sin^2(\theta_1 - \theta_2)$$

Sketch the resulting (v_x, v_y) Lissajous pattern for $\theta_1 - \theta_2 = 0$; $\pi/4$; $\pi/2$.

8.11-1. Using the data contained in Table P8.11-1, find the following:

    (a) Mean value;

    (b) Standard deviation;

    (c) Standard deviation of the mean.

Table P8.11-1.   Values of Capacitors, in microFarad

Capacitance	5	6	7	8	9	10	11	12	13	14	15	16	17	18	19
Number of capacitors	1	2	4	7	12	14	10	8	10	4	2	1	2	1	1

8.12-1. The current through a resistor and its resistance were measured. These data are contained in Tables P8.12-1a and P8.12-1b. Find the fractional variance of the voltage across the resistor.

Table P8.12-1a

Current (mA)	4.6	4.7	4.8	4.9	5.0	5.1	5.2	5.3	5.4	5.5	5.6	5.7	5.8
No of current values	1	2	7	12	15	10	8	9	4	0	2	1	1

Table P8.12-1b

Resistance ($\times 10^{-2}$ Ω)	9.2	9.4	9.6	9.8	10.0	10.2	10.4	10.6	10.8
No. of resistance values	1	7	6	10	15	8	4	2	1

8.13-1. The pair of values of voltage across and current through a resistor were measured and are given in Table P8.13-1. Find the regression line and determine the resistance of the resistor.

Table P8.13-1

Current (mA)	1	2	3	4	5	6	7	8	9	10
Voltage (V)	1	1.8	1.6	2.2	4.5	5	4	5.2	6	5.5

Chapter Nine

Digital Systems

9.1 DIGITAL COMPUTERS

We begin our studies by considering selected features of a digital computer. The computer (a digital system), apart from being one of the great inventions of the century, involves relatively simple mathematics in its understanding. While the basic operations are inherently simple, the number of operations and the speeds involved are spectacular, with times measured in nanoseconds (10^{-9} s) to microseconds (10^{-6} s).

In its basic concept, the digital computer, in carrying out specified orders, performs its many operations by means of transistors or diodes. These operate basically as switches which are in one of two states, ON or OFF. The operations to be performed must be translated into a language that this digital system will understand and to which it can be made to respond. The desired operations or sequence of operations are expressed in terms of statements which are written in binary coded form. The rules of Boolean algebra permit manipulations of the statements to reduce redundancies. A sequence of symbolic statements (the program) will dictate the order of operations of the logic circuits which will perform the steps necessary to fulfill the program orders.

All computers contain the following five basic units: the *input*, the *internal memory*, the *control unit*, the *arithmetic unit*, and the *output*. A typical computer configuration is shown in Figure 9.1-1.

The input section accepts the data which are translated to *machine* language, the language that the computer can understand. It also allows the output from the computer to be displayed. This section has been labeled I/O in Figure 9.1-1.

The arithmetic unit is made up of high speed electronic accumulators (registers), each constructed of electronic two-state devices which carry out the logical and arithmetic operations prescribed by the *central processing unit* (CPU) or control unit.

The central processing unit controls and coordinates the overall operation of the computer. This unit, which is made up of registers and logic circuits, se-

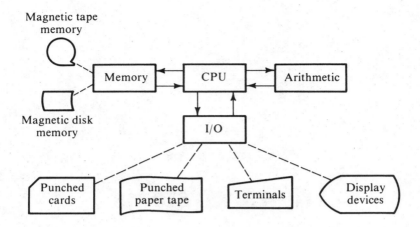

Figure 9.1-1.   Typical configuration of a digital computer

quences the execution of instructions which are obtained from the input or which it generates as steps in the execution process. The CPU communicates with the *memory* unit of the computer where *words* of n-binary digits (bits) are stored. Each of these words has an address associated with it which specifies the location of each storage area or storage bin, and which can be accessed ordinarily in a random order. The *program*, which is a set of instructions to be executed by the computer, is stored in the memory. The CPU calls out each instruction from the memory, interprets it, executes it, and then moves on to the next instruction.

This chapter will discuss how certain specific logic operations are performed; e.g., addition, subtraction, multiplication, certain logic operations, and how such logic devices can be combined to carry out extensive operations. As a specific example, the elements of a very elementary computer are presented, and the complete sequence of operations in carrying out simple arithmetic operations is discussed.

9.2   LOGIC FUNCTIONS

There are three basic logic functions: NOT, AND, and OR. The devices for carrying out these functions are called *logic gates*. There are several basic electronic classes of devices that carry out these prescribed functions. The electronic details are important in device manufacture, but these details are not of special importance to an understanding of the logic functions. Some electronic details were considered in Chapter 7.

To consider the NOT function, think of a simple flashlight. We designate the OFF state when the bulb is out as the converse or complement of the state when the bulb is ON. If we write

$$L = 1 \qquad \text{if the bulb is ON}$$

then we write

$$L = 0 \qquad \text{if the bulb is OFF.}$$

Furthermore, since for the two-state system 0 is the complement of 1, then we can write $\bar{L}$ to denote the complement of L, and now we have

$$\text{if} \qquad L = 0 \qquad \bar{L} = 1.$$

A device which produces a 1 from a 0 or a 0 from a 1 is a NOT gate and it is shown in Figure 9.2-1. The logical combinations involved in this operation are

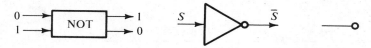

Figure 9.2-1. The NOT operation

given in Table 9.2-1. Other representations of implementation of the NOT operation will be given below, and circuits for achieving this were studied in Chapter 7.

Table 9.2-1. Description of Operation of NOT Circuit

L	$\bar{L}$
0	1
1	0

The AND function relates two or more input events. For example, you might specify that to do your homework will require both paper and pencil. Either by itself is not sufficient. If we denote the paper by A and the pencil by B then the necessary condition for homework W is

$$W = A \cdot B$$

where the dot is read AND. Another example would be a flashlight with two switches in series in the manner shown in Figure 9.2-2. For the bulb to be on,

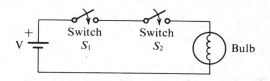

Figure 9.2-2. A two series switch system

both S_1 and S_2 must be closed. This can be written symbolically

$$L = S_1 \cdot S_2$$

The operation of the AND circuit is summarized in Table 9.2-2. This circuit

Table 9.2-2.   Decription of Operation of AND Circuit

Switch S_1	Switch S_2	Light
Open	Open	Off
Open	Closed	Off
Closed	Open	Off
Closed	Closed	On

can also be described by concentrating on the contacts. If we let 0 denote the open state and 1 denote the closed state, then the circuit operation is described by Table 9.2-3 which gives all possible combinations of conditions. Another

Table 9.2-3.   Representation Tables for the AND Gate

Combinations			Truth Table		
Path through contact S_1	Path through contact S_2	Path through both S_1 and S_2	S_1	S_2	$S_1 \cdot S_2$
0	0	0	F	F	F
0	1	0	F	T	F
1	0	0	T	F	F
1	1	1	T	T	T

representation for the circuit operation is the "truth table." Here F (false) denotes open or 0, T (true) denotes closed or 1. In the form shown, with 0 denoting low and 1 denoting high, we are employing what is referred to as "positive logic." We shall consistently choose the output of an AND gate to be 0 when either input is 0. In "negative logic" the output may be specifically elected to be a 1 when either input is 0.

Consider the circuit shown in Figure 9.2-3. This would require, for the bulb to be on, that S_1 is closed and S_2 is open, which is

$$L = S_1 \cdot \overline{S_2}$$

A graphical representation for the simple AND gate is shown in Figure

9.2-4a. Figure 9.2-4b shows a *multiple input* AND gate, Figure 9.2-4c shows a *mixed* AND gate, and Figure 9.2-4d shows the result of AND gating of data.

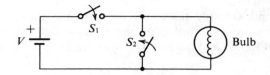

Figure 9.2-3.   A switch circuit

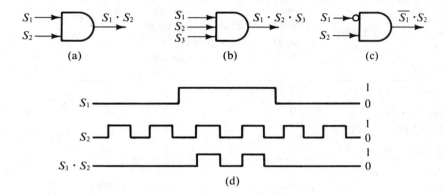

Figure 9.2-4.   (a, b, c) The graphical symbol for the AND gate
(d) AND gating of data

The OR function also relates two or more input events. An illustration of this is the circuit shown in Figure 9.2-5. Clearly, the bulb will be on *if S_1 or S_2*

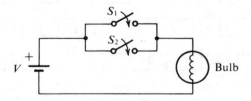

Figure 9.2-5.   Illustrating an OR circuit

or both are closed. This situation in logic form is written

$$L = S_1 + S_2$$

where the + is read OR. This is the *inclusive* OR operation. In the case when the "or both" is eliminated, the operation is the *exclusive* OR (XOR). In this case the notation is changed to $\oplus$, and implies that when $S_1 \equiv T$ and $S_2 \equiv T$ then $S_1 \oplus S_2 = F$, and when $S_1 \equiv F$ and $S_2 \equiv F$, then $S_1 \oplus S_2 = F$. In general, $S_1 \oplus S_2 = \bar{S}_1 \cdot S_2 + S_1 \cdot \bar{S}_2$.

The logical representation tables for the OR and XOR gate are given in Table 9.2-4. The graphical symbols for the inclusive OR and the exclusive OR gates and typical inputs and outputs for each are given by Figure 9.2-6.

Table 9.2-4.   Representation Tables for the OR and XOR Gates

Switch S_1	Switch S_2	Light $S_1 + S_2$	Path through S_1	Path through S_2	Path through contacts in parallel $S_1 + S_2$	S_1	S_2	$S_1 \oplus S_2$
Open	Open	Off	0	0	0	F	F	F
Open	Closed	On	0	1	1	F	T	T
Closed	Open	On	1	0	1	T	F	T
Closed	Closed	On	1	1	1	T	T	F

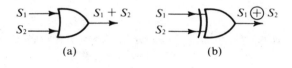

(a)   (b)

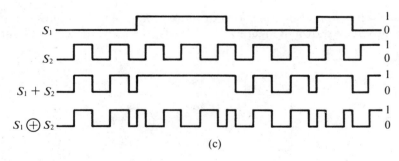

(c)

Figure 9.2-6.   The graphical symbols for the OR gate   (a) Inclusive OR gate (b) Exclusive OR gate   (c) Inclusive and exclusive OR gating data

EXAMPLE 9.2-1. Use AND and OR gates to operate a bubble-gum vending machine. The gum costs 10¢, and the machine accepts pennies, nickels and dimes. Not more than a single input to the machine can be made at any one time. We are not concerned with what happens if too much money is input. The excess money will simply cause the next person to get gum with less money.

SOLUTION. The coins are denoted as follows: D (dimes), N_1 (nickel #1), N_2 (nickel #2), P_1 (5 pennies), and P_2 (5 pennies). One possible implementation is shown in Figure 9.2-7.

Truth Table

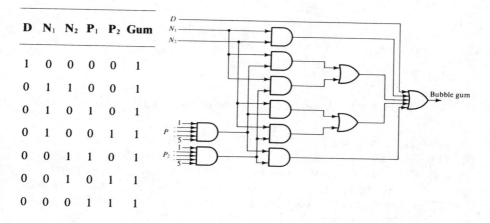

D	N_1	N_2	P_1	P_2	Gum
1	0	0	0	0	1
0	1	1	0	0	1
0	1	0	1	0	1
0	1	0	0	1	1
0	0	1	1	0	1
0	0	1	0	1	1
0	0	0	1	1	1

Figure 9.2-7. Bubble gum vending machine

□ □ □

EXAMPLE 9.2-2. Find the outputs of the XOR gates shown in Figure 9.2-8.

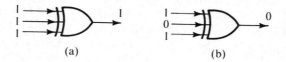

(a)   (b)

Figure 9.2-8. XOR gates with odd and even number of 1 inputs

SOLUTION. From the definition of the XOR operation, the results follow: $1 \oplus 1 \oplus 1 = 1 \oplus 0 = 1$ and $1 \oplus 0 \oplus 1 = 1 \oplus 1 = 0$. Therefore we can use the XOR gates to check the parity of a signal input. In Figure 9.2-8a the input word has an odd number of inputs and is therefore said to have *odd parity*. In Figure 9.2-8b the input word has *even parity*. In general an XOR gate is an *odd parity* device, the output being 1 for odd parity and 0 for even parity inputs.

□ □ □

EXAMPLE 9.2-3. Find the output of the XOR gates shown in Figure 9.2-9 when the input is low or high. By convention, we associate a "low" input with a 0 and a "high" input with a 1.

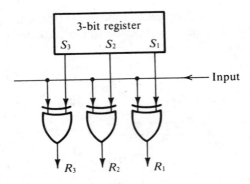

Figure 9.2-9.   A scheme to invert the output of a 3 bit register

SOLUTION. Let $S_1 = 1$, $S_2 = 0$ and $S_3 = 1$. If the input is low, 0, then $R_1 = 1 \oplus 0 = 1$, $R_2 = 0 \oplus 0 = 0$ and $R_3 = 1 \oplus 0 = 1$. However, if input is high, 1, then $R_1 = 1 \oplus 1 = 0$, $R_2 = 0 \oplus 1 = 1$ and $R_3 = 1 \oplus 1 = 0$. Observe that this latter sequence $R_3 R_2 R_1 = 010$ is the inverted form of the word $S_3 S_2 S_1 = 101$. Thus this digital system transmits the contents of the 3-bit register when the input is low and inverts the contents of the register when it is high.

□   □   □

9.3   NAND AND NOR GATES

Two very important switching operations that are useful in developing NOT, OR and AND operations are the NAND and the NOR gates. NAND is equivalent to AND followed by NOT, and similarly, NOR is equivalent to OR followed by NOT. Graphical representations of these essential operations are contained in Figure 9.3-1. The manner in which the NAND and NOR gates can

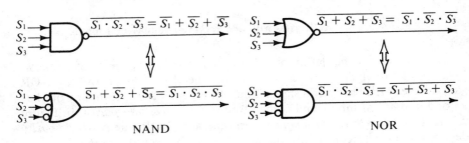

Figure 9.3-1.   NAND and NOR operations

be used to achieve NOT, AND, and OR operations is shown in Table 9.3-1. The reader should use truth tables to show the equivalence of the expressions given as outputs in Figure 9.3-1.

Table 9.3-1. Logic Gates

	Symbol	Circuit Representation	Using NAND and NOR Gates	DeMorgan Implementation
AND	$S = S_1 \cdot S_2$		$S = S_1 \cdot S_2$	$S = \overline{\overline{S_1} + \overline{S_2}} = \overline{\overline{S_1}} \cdot \overline{\overline{S_2}} = S_1 \cdot S_2$
OR	$S = S_1 + S_2$		$S = S_1 + S_2$	$S = \overline{\overline{S_1} \cdot \overline{S_2}} = \overline{\overline{S_1}} + \overline{\overline{S_2}} = S_1 + S_2$
NOT	$S = \overline{S_1}$		$S = \overline{S_1 \cdot S_1} = \overline{S_1}$ $S = \overline{S_1 + S_1} = \overline{S_1}$	

Truth Table

AND:

S_1	S_2	$S_1 \cdot S_2$	$\overline{S_1}$	$\overline{S_2}$	$\overline{S_1} + \overline{S_2}$	$\overline{\overline{S_1} \cdot \overline{S_2}}$
0	0	0	1	1	0	0
0	1	0	1	0	0	0
1	0	0	0	1	0	0
1	1	1	0	0	1	1

OR:

S_1	S_2	$S_1 + S_2$	$\overline{S_1}$	$\overline{S_2}$	$\overline{S_1} \cdot \overline{S_2}$	$\overline{\overline{S_1} \cdot \overline{S_2}}$
0	0	0	1	1	1	0
0	1	1	1	0	0	1
1	0	1	0	1	0	1
1	1	1	0	0	0	1

NOT:

S_1	S
0	1
1	0

Table 9.3-1. Logic Gates

Symbol	Circuit Representation	Using NAND and NOR Gates DeMorgan Implementation	Truth Table

NAND

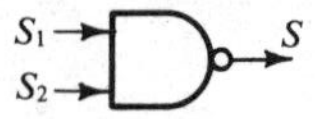

Symbol: $S = \overline{S_1 \cdot S_2} = \overline{S_1} + \overline{S_2}$

DeMorgan Implementation: $S = \overline{S_1} + \overline{S_2}$

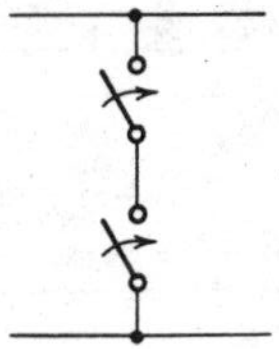

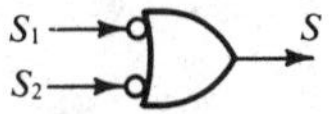

S_1	S_2	$\overline{S_1}+\overline{S_2}$	$\overline{S_1}$	$\overline{S_2}$	$\overline{S_1}+\overline{S_2}$
0	0	1	1	1	1
0	1	1	1	1	1
1	0	1	0	0	1
1	1	0	0	0	0

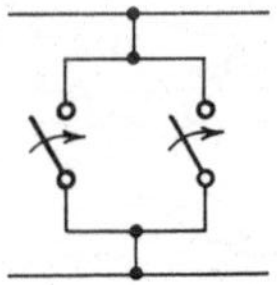

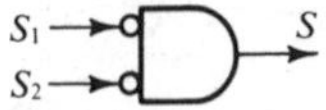

NOR

Symbol: $S = \overline{S_1 + S_2} = \overline{S_1} \cdot \overline{S_2}$

DeMorgan Implementation: $S = \overline{S_1} \cdot \overline{S_2}$

S_1	S_2	$\overline{S_1}\cdot\overline{S_2}$	$\overline{S_1}$	$\overline{S_2}$	$\overline{S_1}\cdot\overline{S_2}$
0	0	1	1	1	1
0	1	0	1	0	0
1	0	0	0	1	0
1	1	0	0	0	0

9.4 BOOLEAN FUNCTION REALIZATION

Certain simplifications are often possible when realizing a Boolean function. The so-called "DeMorgan rules" are particularly useful in simplifying Boolean expressions and in yielding expressions which are realizable with NAND or NOR logic. These two rules are

$$\overline{S_1 + S_2} = \overline{S}_1 \cdot \overline{S}_2 \quad (\text{or } \overline{\overline{S}_1 \cdot \overline{S}_2} = \overline{\overline{S}}_1 + \overline{\overline{S}}_2 = S_1 + S_2; \overline{\overline{S}} = S)$$

$$\overline{S_1 \cdot S_2} = \overline{S}_1 + \overline{S}_2 \quad (\text{or } \overline{\overline{S}_1 + \overline{S}_2} = \overline{\overline{S}}_1 \cdot \overline{\overline{S}}_2 = S_1 \cdot S_2)$$

EXAMPLE 9.4-1. Simplify the expression $S = \overline{\overline{S_1 \cdot \overline{S}_2 \cdot S_3 \cdot (S_1 + S_2)}}$ which is shown by the logic diagram in Figure 9.4-1a.

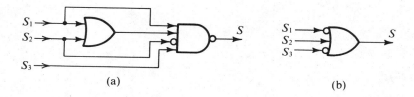

(a)

(b)

Figure 9.4-1. Logic diagrams of Example 9.4-1

SOLUTION. Using the DeMorgan rules we can make the following transformations:

$$\overline{S_1 \cdot \overline{S}_2 \cdot S_3 \cdot (S_1 + S_2)} = \overline{S_1 \cdot \overline{S}_2 \cdot S_3} + \overline{(S_1 + S_2)}$$

$$= \overline{S}_1 + \overline{\overline{S}}_2 + \overline{S}_3 + \overline{S}_1 \cdot \overline{S}_2$$

$$= \overline{S}_1 + S_2 + \overline{S}_3 + \overline{S}_1 \cdot \overline{S}_2 = \overline{S}_1 \cdot (1 + \overline{S}_2) + S_2 + \overline{S}_3$$

$$= \overline{S}_1 + S_2 + \overline{S}_3 = S$$

In this development, we note that the quantity $1 + \overline{S}_2$ is always 1, since it is immaterial whether $\overline{S}_2$ is 0 or 1. The simplified expression is shown by a logic diagram in Figure 9.4-1b.

□ □ □

Some useful rules of Boolean algebra are contained in Table 9.4-1. All entries in this table can be proved by means of truth tables.

A relation of importance in Boolean operations is that relating to *complementary* expressions. Complementary expressions are those which, for every set of values, have the opposite values.

EXAMPLE 9.4-2. Find the complement of the following function

Table 9.4-1   Boolean Algebra Relations

---

1. $S + \bar{S} = 1$

2. $S \cdot \bar{S} = 0$

3. $S + S = S$

4. $S \cdot S = S$

5. $\overline{S_1 \cdot S_2} = \bar{S}_1 + \bar{S}_2$ (DeMorgan's rule)

6. $\overline{S_1 + S_2} = \bar{S}_1 \cdot \bar{S}_2$ (DeMorgan's rule)

7. $S_1 + \bar{S}_1 \cdot S_2 = S_1 + S_2$

8. $S_1 \cdot S_2 + S_1 \cdot S_3 = S_1 \cdot (S_2 + S_3)$

9. $S + 0 = S$

10. $S \cdot 1 = S$

11. $S + 1 = 1$

12. $S \cdot 0 = 0$

13. $S_1 + S_1 \cdot S_2 = S_1 \cdot (1 + S_2) = S_1$

14. $S_1 \cdot (S_1 + S_2) = S_1$

15. $S_1 \cdot (\bar{S}_1 + S_2) = S_1 \cdot \bar{S}_1 + S_1 \cdot S_2 = 0 + S_1 \cdot S_2 = S_1 \cdot S_2$

16. $\left.\begin{array}{l} S_1 + S_2 = S_2 + S_1 \\ S_1 \cdot S_2 = S_2 \cdot S_1 \end{array}\right\}$ Commutative law

17. $\left.\begin{array}{l} S_1 + S_2 + S_3 = (S_1 + S_2) + S_3 = S_1 + (S_2 + S_3) \\ S_1 \cdot S_2 \cdot S_3 = (S_1 \cdot S_2) \cdot S_3 = S_1 \cdot (S_2 \cdot S_3) \end{array}\right\}$ Associative law

18. $\left.\begin{array}{l} S_1 + (S_2 \cdot S_3 \cdot S_4 \ldots) = (S_1 + S_2) \cdot (S_1 + S_3) \cdot (S_1 + S_4) \ldots \\ S_1 \cdot (S_2 + S_3 + S_4 \ldots) = S_1 \cdot S_2 + S_1 \cdot S_3 + S_1 \cdot S_4 \end{array}\right\}$ Distributive law

19. $\bar{\bar{S}} = S$

$$y = A \cdot B + C$$

SOLUTION. We begin with the desired result

$$\bar{y} = \overline{A \cdot B + C}$$

This becomes, using the DeMorgan dot rule

$$\bar{y} = \overline{(A \cdot B)} \cdot \bar{C}$$

By the DeMorgan plus rule, we write

$$\bar{y} = (\bar{A} + \bar{B}) \cdot \bar{C}$$

We observe that a simple procedure for writing complementary functions is contained in this result: to complement a function, complement each element and replace $\cdot$ by $+$ and $+$ by $\cdot$.

□ □ □

EXAMPLE 9.4-3. Determine whether $\bar{A} \cdot \bar{B} + \bar{C}$ is the complement of $(A + B) \cdot C$.

SOLUTION. This result is in accord with the complementation rules established in Example 9.4-2. We give a second proof in terms of the truth table for the two functions. This tabulation shows the validity of the equality of the assumed relations.

A	B	C	$\bar{A} \cdot \bar{B} + \bar{C}$	$(A + B) \cdot C$	Entry of Table 9.4-1 Used in Proof
0	0	0	1	0	Entry 4 and 1
0	0	1	0	1	Entry 4 and 1
0	1	0	1	0	Entry 2 and 1
0	1	1	0	1	Entry 2 and 4
1	0	0	1	0	Entry 2 and 1
1	0	1	0	1	Entry 2 and 9
1	1	0	1	0	Entry 4 and 1
1	1	1	1	0	Entry 4 and 1

□ □ □

EXAMPLE 9.4-4. Simplify the following logical expression

$$y = a \cdot \bar{b} \cdot c + a \cdot b \cdot c + a \cdot b \cdot \bar{c}$$

whose logic representation is shown in Figure 9.4-2a.

SOLUTION. We proceed in the following way:

$$y = a \cdot b \cdot c + a \cdot b \cdot \bar{c} + a \cdot \bar{b} \cdot c \qquad \text{(Commutative law)}$$

$$y = a \cdot b \cdot (c + \bar{c}) + a \cdot \bar{b} \cdot c \qquad \text{(Distributive law)}$$

$$y = a \cdot b \cdot 1 + a \cdot \bar{b} \cdot c \qquad \text{(Entry 1, Table 9.4-1)}$$

$$y = a \cdot b + a \cdot \bar{b} \cdot c \qquad \text{(Entry 10, Table 9.4-1)}$$

$$y = a \cdot (b + \bar{b} \cdot c) \qquad \text{(Distributive law)}$$

$$y = a \cdot (b + c) \qquad \text{(Entry 7, Table 9.4-1)}$$

The next-to-last expression is shown in its logic circuit representation in Figure 9.4-2b. The reader should seek other possible solutions to the same problem.

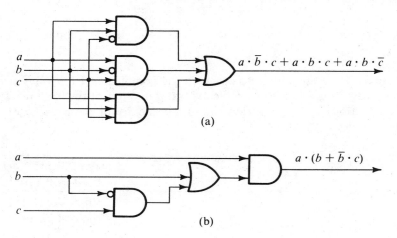

(a)

(b)

Figure 9.4-2.   Logic diagrams of Example 9.4-4

□   □   □

EXAMPLE 9.4-5. Simplify the expression $y = a \cdot \bar{b} \cdot c \cdot d + a \cdot b \cdot d \cdot e + a \cdot \bar{c} \cdot d \cdot e$.

SOLUTION. Write this expression by factoring $a \cdot d$ from all terms

$$y = a \cdot d \cdot [\bar{b} \cdot c + (b + \bar{c}) \cdot e]$$

But

$$\overline{\bar{b} \cdot c} = b + \bar{c}$$

and the factor can be eliminated (by Entry 7, Table 9.4-1). Hence the simplified expression is

$$y = a \cdot d \cdot \bar{b} \cdot c + a \cdot d \cdot e = a \cdot d \cdot [\bar{b} \cdot c + e]$$

□   □   □

EXAMPLE 9.4-6. Simplify the function $y = (a + \bar{b} + c + d) \cdot (a + b + c + d + e)$.

SOLUTION. The variable b is complemented in one factor but not in the other. It can be eliminated from the larger factor, which, except for $\bar{b}$ includes the smaller factor. Then the simplified expression is

$$y = (a + \bar{b} + c + d) \cdot (a + c + d + e)$$

□   □   □

EXAMPLE 9.4-7. Simplify the expression $y = (a + b + c + d) \cdot (a + b + c + d + e)$.

SOLUTION. Since $(a + b + c + d)$ appears in the larger factor, the larger factor can be replaced by 1 without affecting the value for any set of variables (see Entry 14, Table 9.4-1). Then

$$y = (a + b + c + d).$$

□   □   □

9.5   THE KARNAUGH MAP

The Karnaugh map (KM) provides a very convenient graphical method for minimizing Boolean functions in sum of product form. Its limitation is that it ceases to be convenient for use for functions of more than five variables. To understand the use of the map, consider first a 2-variable KM, whose truth table is given in Figure 9.5-1.

Figure 9.5-1.   (a) Truth table   (b) Corresponding Karnaugh map

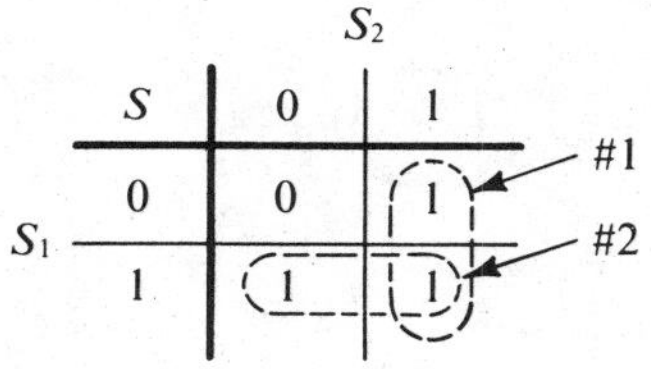

From the truth table we construct the Boolean equation

$$S = \bar{S}_1 \cdot S_2 + S_1 \cdot \bar{S}_2 + S_1 \cdot S_2 \tag{9.5-1}$$

using the following rules:

1. Write a term for each row for which the value of S is 1.
2. Each term contains all the input variables, in either true or inverted form, ANDed together.

3. The input variable is written in inverted form if the value of the input variable in that row is 0, and in true form if the value in that row is 1.

4. All the terms are then ORed together.

5. For three or more variables the entries in the rows and columns of the KM are arranged in such an order that one digit changes at a time.

The map contains squares, one for each row of a corresponding truth table, as shown in Figure 9.5-1. A feature of this map is that two adjacent 1-squares can be combined because these include one of the Boolean variables in both direct and complemented form to yield essentially $(S + \overline{S}) = 1$. The purpose is to seek the largest group of 1-squares for combinations. If no groupings are possible, then each individual 1-square must be included. Specifically in the map shown in Figure 9.5-1 there is a two 1-square group shown as #1, which combines (see Table 9.4-1)

$$\overline{S}_1 \cdot S_2 + S_1 \cdot S_2 = S_2 \cdot (S_1 + \overline{S}_1) = S_2$$

There is a second two 1-square grouping shown as #2 which combines

$$S_1 \cdot \overline{S}_2 + S_1 \cdot S_2 = S_1 \cdot (S_2 + \overline{S}_2) = S_1$$

In this particular example, since all 1-squares have been accounted for, the final result is

$$S = S_1 + S_2 \qquad\qquad (9.5\text{-}2)$$

The Boolean equation, Equation (9.5-1), and its simplified form, Equation (9.5-2), are shown in Figures 9.5-2a and 9.5-2b.

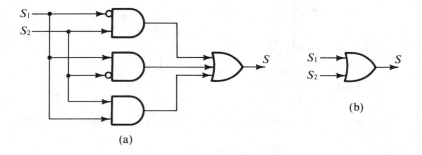

(a)   (b)

Figure 9.5-2.   Logic diagrams for Equations (9.5-1) and (9.5-2)

To illustrate this further, consider a three term truth table and its corresponding Karnaugh map contained in Figure 9.5-3. In this map, by following the same procedure as above, we obtain

S_1	S_2	S_3	S
0	0	0	1
0	0	1	1
0	1	0	0
0	1	1	0
1	0	0	1
1	0	1	1
1	1	0	1
1	1	1	1

Figure 9.5-3. Truth table and corresponding Karnaugh map

four 1-square grouping #1

$$S_1 \cdot S_2 \cdot \bar{S}_3 + S_1 \cdot S_2 \cdot S_3 + S_1 \cdot \bar{S}_2 \cdot \bar{S}_3 + S_1 \cdot \bar{S}_2 \cdot S_3$$

$$= S_1 \cdot S_2 \cdot (S_3 + \bar{S}_3) + S_1 \cdot \bar{S}_2 \cdot (S_3 + \bar{S}_3)$$

$$= S_1 \cdot S_2 + S_1 \cdot \bar{S}_2 = S_1 \cdot (S_2 + \bar{S}_2) = S_1$$

four 1-square grouping #2

$$\bar{S}_1 \cdot \bar{S}_2 \cdot \bar{S}_3 + \bar{S}_1 \cdot \bar{S}_2 \cdot S_3 + S_1 \cdot \bar{S}_2 \cdot \bar{S}_3 + S_1 \cdot \bar{S}_2 \cdot S_3$$

$$= \bar{S}_1 \cdot \bar{S}_2 \cdot (\bar{S}_3 + S_3) + S_1 \cdot \bar{S}_2 \cdot (S_3 + \bar{S}_3)$$

$$= \bar{S}_1 \cdot \bar{S}_2 + S_1 \cdot \bar{S}_2 = (S_1 + \bar{S}_1) \cdot \bar{S}_2 = \bar{S}_2$$

Hence, the final result is

$$S = S_1 + \bar{S}_2$$

A requirement in drawing the Karnaugh map is that every product term must be included. This may require that expansion of the Boolean function be undertaken to show all product terms explicitly. We show this requirement by an example.

EXAMPLE 9.5-1. Can the function $S = \bar{S}_1 \cdot S_2 + \bar{S}_2 \cdot S_3$ be minimized?

SOLUTION. The given function is expanded so that every term includes the three variables S_1, S_2, S_3. This gives

$$S = \bar{S}_1 \cdot S_2 + \bar{S}_2 \cdot S_3 = \bar{S}_1 \cdot S_2 \cdot (S_3 + \bar{S}_3) + (S_1 + \bar{S}_1) \cdot \bar{S}_2 \cdot S_3$$

$$= \bar{S}_1 \cdot S_2 \cdot S_3 + \bar{S}_1 \cdot S_2 \cdot \bar{S}_3 + S_1 \cdot \bar{S}_2 \cdot S_3 + \bar{S}_1 \cdot \bar{S}_2 \cdot S_3$$

For the truth table shown in Figure 9.5-4a, the Karnaugh map is shown in

S_1	S_2	S_3	S
0	0	0	0
0	0	1	1
0	1	0	1
0	1	1	1
1	0	0	0
1	0	1	1
1	1	0	0
1	1	1	0

(a)

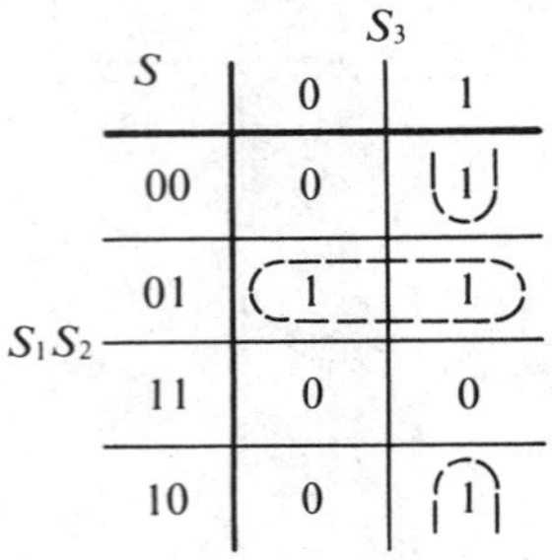

Karnaugh map (b), rows $S_1 S_2$ = 00, 01, 11, 10; columns S_3 = 0, 1:

S	0	1
00	0	1
01	1	1
11	0	0
10	0	1

(b)

Figure 9.5-4. (a) Truth table (b) Corresponding Karnaugh map

Figure 9.5-4b. The adjacent 1-squares that can be combined are shown circled, and the final result is

$$S = \bar{S}_1 \cdot S_2 + \bar{S}_2 \cdot S_3$$

which shows that no reduction of the original function is possible.

□ □ □

In developing certain Boolean functions the values of some of the possible entries are of no special interest. In such a case one has "*don't care*" entries, and these are written x in the truth table. In the Karnaugh map, each x can be used as a 0 or a 1 depending on which is most preferable in the expansions and combinations.

An alternate procedure to construct a Karnaugh map exists and results in a product of sums expression. Here the complementary functions are employed, which requires only that all 0s be replaced by 1s, and all 1s by 0s. The result is the function $\bar{S}$. The resulting Boolean function can be complemented to give a sum of product realization.

EXAMPLE 9.5-2. Carry out the complementation of the function described by the Karnaugh map shown in Figure 9.5-5a. This complement is shown in Figure 9.5-5b.

SOLUTION. The complementary Karnaugh map is shown, and the function specified thereby can be found from the complemented map. From the complemented map we write

$$\bar{S} = \bar{S}_1 \cdot S_2 \cdot \bar{S}_3 + \bar{S}_1 \cdot S_2 \cdot S_3 + \bar{S}_1 \cdot S_2 \cdot S_3 + S_1 \cdot S_2 \cdot S_3 + S_1 \cdot \bar{S}_2 \cdot \bar{S}_3$$

$$= (\bar{S}_1 \cdot S_2) \cdot (\bar{S}_3 + S_3) + (\bar{S}_1 + S_1) \cdot (S_2 \cdot S_3) + S_1 \cdot \bar{S}_2 \cdot \bar{S}_3$$

$$= \bar{S}_1 \cdot S_2 + S_2 \cdot S_3 + S_1 \cdot \bar{S}_2 \cdot \bar{S}_3$$

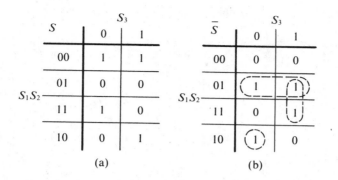

Figure 9.5-5. **Karnaugh maps for Example 9.5-2**

The desired function is then

$$S = \bar{\bar{S}} = \overline{\bar{S}_1 \cdot S_2 + S_2 \cdot S_3 + S_1 \cdot \bar{S}_2 \cdot \bar{S}_3} = \overline{(\bar{S}_1 \cdot S_2)} \cdot \overline{(S_2 \cdot S_3)} \cdot \overline{(S_1 \cdot \bar{S}_2 \cdot \bar{S}_3)}$$

$$= (S_1 + \bar{S}_2) \cdot (\bar{S}_2 + \bar{S}_3) \cdot (\bar{S}_1 + S_2 + S_3)$$

□ □ □

9.6 SYNTHESIS

In the case of *analysis*, a given circuit is examined (e.g., from the truth table) to ascertain whether it satisfies the conditions of the specified problem. In circuit *synthesis*, we are to design a circuit to meet certain logical conditions of a problem and then to check its operation.

EXAMPLE 9.6-1. Synthesize an odd-parity circuit (for example, one which is ON when an odd number of switches is closed) that uses 3 switches, with the circuit closed (ON) when 1 or 3 switches are closed.

SOLUTION. To proceed, a truth table is prepared for the specified problem (see Figure 9.6-1). From this truth table it is seen that odd parity exists when

$$y = \bar{a} \cdot \bar{b} \cdot c + \bar{a} \cdot b \cdot \bar{c} + a \cdot \bar{b} \cdot \bar{c} + a \cdot b \cdot c \tag{9.6-1}$$

The Karnaugh map of this equation is first examined to establish the minimized function. The KM is shown in Figure 9.6-1b, but it is observed that no combination of 1-squares is possible, and so no reduction of Equation (9.6-1) can be effected. A gate realization is shown in Figure 9.6-2.

□ □ □

A question that might be raised is, "can Equation (9.6-1) be written in a form that might favor one realization over another? To answer this question,

Truth Table for Odd Parity Circuit

Switch a	Switch b	Switch c	3-switch odd parity; y
0	0	0	0
0	0	1	1
0	1	0	1
0	1	1	0
1	0	0	1
1	0	1	0
1	1	0	0
1	1	1	1

		c	
	y	0	1
	00	0	1
ab	01	1	0
	11	0	1
	10	1	0

(a)   (b)

Figure 9.6-1.   Truth table and Karnaugh map for odd parity circuit

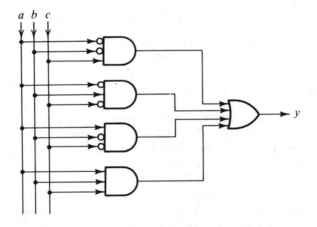

Figure 9.6-2.   An implementation of Equation (9.6-1)

since the basic function has already been shown to be the minimum function, we might proceed by considering the number of soldered connections that must be made. If it is assumed that the available gates provide both complemented and uncomplemented terminals, then the implementation in Figure 9.6-2 involves 12 soldered joints to the abc bus lines: 12 joints to the AND gate inputs, 4 joints from these outputs, 4 joints to the OR gate input, and 1 final output line, for a total of 33 soldered joints.

Suppose that Equation (9.6-2) is rewritten in the following form:

$$y = \bar{a} \cdot (\bar{b} \cdot c + b \cdot \bar{c}) + a \cdot (\bar{b} \cdot \bar{c} + b \cdot c)$$
$$= \bar{a} \cdot \overline{(\bar{b} \cdot \bar{c} + b \cdot c)} + a \cdot (\bar{b} \cdot \bar{c} + b \cdot c) \tag{9.6-2}$$

The implementation of this Boolean function is given in Figure 9.6-3a. A count of the soldered joints required in this implementation is 29, plus the requirement for 6 gates as against 5 in the implementation in Figure 9.6-2.

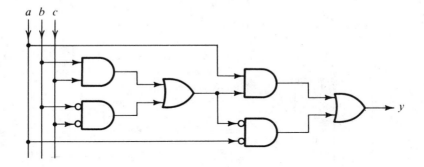

Figure 9.6-3.   Realization of Equation (9.6-2)

9.7   ADDITIONAL CIRCUIT DEVICES IN DIGITAL SYSTEMS

Our prior discussion of logic circuit elements, involving AND, OR, NOT, NAND, NOR gates, allowed the implementation of Boolean functions in a so-called combinational manner. It was implicit in our discussion that the response of the elements was instantaneous. There are a number of other devices which are used as basic building blocks in digital systems. In these, the action may be designed not to be instantaneous, but involves memory.

The Flipflop

The *flipflop* (or bistable device) is a two-state device which can remember (or store) a binary bit of information, and is able to change from one state to the other state by a triggering action. A typical block diagram is shown in Figure 9.7-1a, and for the RS-FF (*Reset-Set-Flipflop*) shown the action is given in the accompanying tables. As shown in the table, the output lines are the complements of each other. In Figure 9.7-1b is shown a possible sequence of input signals. This FF is set by a pulse input to S and is reset by a pulse input to R. The absence of a pulse has no effect on the operation. As shown in the tables in Figure 9.7-1b and 9.7-1c, storing a 1 is called setting; putting in a 0 is called clearing or resetting (often the terminals are denoted S, C).

Some RS-FF's have a third input line CL or CP which is for a clock signal which is used to synchronize the operations in digital systems. Refer to Figure 9.7-2 which shows the block representation and a timing diagram. The small triangle symbol on the clock line indicates that triggering takes place during the positive edge of the clock pulse. The clock is connected in parallel (ANDed) to both inputs. A true input is required to both S and CL to set the

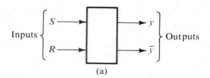

(a)

Ordered	RS-FF Action Table				Comments	RS-FF Action Table (abbreviated form)		
sequence of inputs	S_n	R_n	y_{n+1}	$\bar{y}_{n+1}$	(y is state of FF after S and R applied)	S_n	R_n	y_{n+1}
	1	0	1	0	FF is set	0	0	y_n
	0	0	1	0	FF remains set	0	1	0
	0	1	0	1	FF is reset	1	0	1
	0	0	0	1	FF remains reset	1	1	Ambiguous— this input combination is not supposed to exist.
	1	0	1	0	FF is set			
		(b)					(c)	

Figure 9.7-1.   The RS flipflop and a sequence of system actions

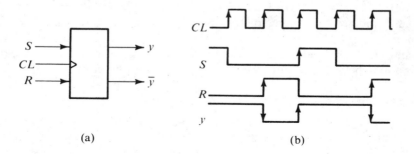

(a)   (b)

Figure 9.7-2.   A clocked RS-FF

FF, and a true input to R and CL is required for reset. This action is made clear in Figure 9.7-2b.

The RS-FF is readily obtained by using NAND or NOR gates which are cross-connected in the manner shown in Figure 9.7-3a and 9.7-3b respectively. These are also referred to as *latch* circuits. The clocked RS-FF is shown in Figure 9.7-3c.

If there is the possibility that a 1 appears on both S and R lines simultaneously, an ambiguity will occur because the SR-FF cannot respond uniquely to these simultaneous inputs. For this reason, the JK-FF is usually preferred. With the JK-FF, the simultaneous application of a 1 to both inputs will cause the state of the FF to reverse. The connections to convert an SR-FF to a JK-FF are shown in Figure 9.7-4b, and the truth tables and timing for a JK-FF are shown in Figure 9.7-4c and d.

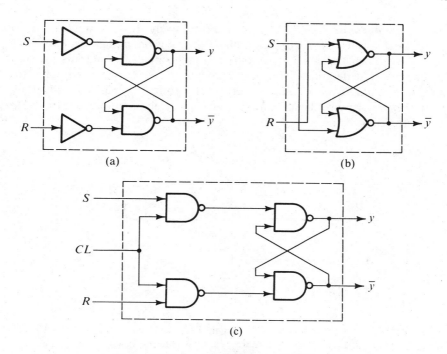

Figure 9.7-3. **(a) RS-FF using NAND gates**
(b) RS-FF using NOR gates **(c) RS-FF with clock**

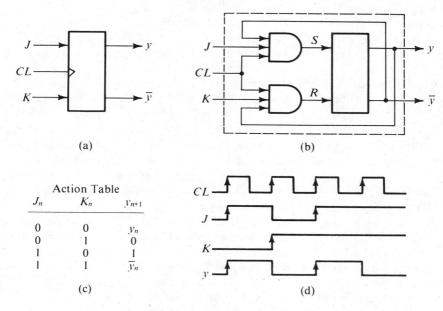

Figure 9.7-4. **(a) The JK-FF** **(b) RS-FF to JK-FF transformation**
(c) Action table **(d) Pulse sequence**

The T or *toggle* FF is one which is used extensively. It has a single input. If the FF is off, a pulse on T will turn it on. If the FF is on, a pulse on T will turn it off. Thus each time that the input T goes positive, the outputs y and $\bar{y}$ change state. The details are shown in Figure 9.7-5. Since two input pulses (or cycles) are required for a complete return of y to its original state, the T-FF acts as a *divide-by-two* device, and is used extensively in counting circuits, as will be discussed below.

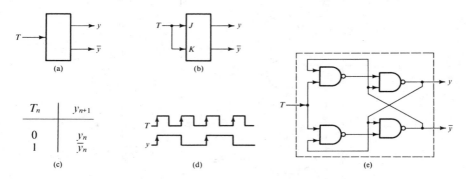

T_n	y_{n+1}
0	y_n
1	$\bar{y}_n$

Figure 9.7-5.   (a) Schematic of the toggle FF   (b) Realization using JK-FF (c) Truth table   (d) Pulse sequence   (e) Construction using NAND gates

The *D-FF* is often used to time delay a digital signal by the duration of one clock cycle. If the D input is on at the time of the clock pulse, the flipflop will turn on or remain on. If the D input is off at the time of the clock pulse, the FF will turn off or remain off. That is, while the clock is low, the FF is latched in its last state; whereas if the clock is high, the FF sets or resets depending on the state of D.

A diagrammatic representation of a D-FF is shown in Figure 9.7-6a. The input and output characteristics of this FF are shown in Figure 9.7-6d where the positive-going transition of the clock is used as the triggering point in time.

To effect triggering of FFs at a precise instant of time, one often includes a so-called differentiating circuit in the clock pulse line. This circuit produces a narrow positive pulse at the leading edge of the clock pulse, and it produces a similar narrow negative pulse at the trailing edge of the clock pulse. An edge-triggered D-FF is shown in Figure 9.7-7. The narrow positive spike enables the AND gates for an intant; the narrow negative spike does nothing.

It is necessary at the start of a computer run to *preset* or to *clear* (set) all of the flipflops. To do this, additional gates are added, as shown in Figure 9.7-8a for a D flipflop. Its schematic representation is shown in Figure 9.7-8b.

If we connect two flipflops as shown in Figure 9.7-9 we create a combination known as the *master-slave* flipflop. The reader can verify (see Problem 9.7-5) that the slave repeats whatever the master does. When the master sets, the

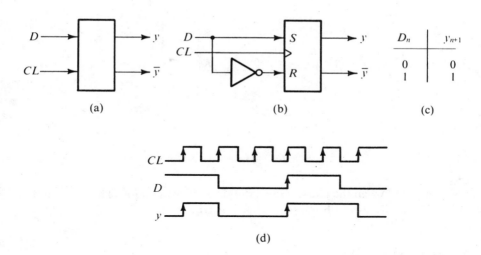

Figure 9.7-6.   (a) The D-FF schematic   (b) Implementation using an RS-FF
(c) Action table   (d) Pulse sequence

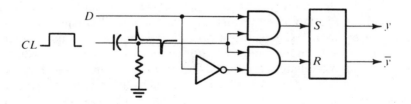

Figure 9.7-7.   Edge-triggered D-flipflop

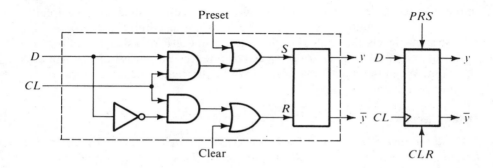

Figure 9.7-8.   (a) D flipflop with clear and preset   (b) Its schematic representation

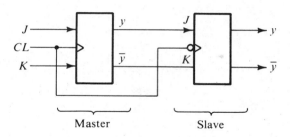

Figure 9.7-9. Master-slave flipflop

slave sets, and when the master resets the slave does the same. The circle in the clock line of the slave FF indicates that it is triggered on the negative edge of the clock pulse.

Multivibrator Circuits

In addition to the bistable flipflops just discussed, a number of related type circuits are very important in electronic and digital circuits. There are three classes of circuits that are often included within this general classification: astable or unstable (the free running multivibrator), one-shot or monostable circuit, and the flipflop already considered and a special circuit known as a Schmitt trigger circuit. The details of operation were discussed in Chapter 7.

The astable or free-running multivibrator circuit is a device which ordinarily produces an almost square waveshape. The one-shot or monostable circuit is often used as an active delay device. It is triggered by an external trigger pulse, and after a time interval determined by the circuit R and C values it will return to its stable state and will remain in this state until again triggered.

The Schmitt trigger circuit is a device which is operated by setting the input level at a value above a given threshold level. If the input does not exceed the threshold level, the circuit does not operate. In essence, therefore, it is an amplitude sensitive switch, with the output level established by the circuit elements. This circuit can be used as a pulse-height discriminator, responding only to signal levels above the threshold. It is also useful as a signal squaring or signal shaping device, since for a triggered state, the output is independent of the input. When the input level falls below the threshold, the circuit returns to its quiescent state.

Delay Circuits

For a number of reasons, it is often necessary to delay a signal by a known amount behind some established time reference. This can be accomplished by using a transmission line of appropriate electrical length, but most delay elements in computers are active ones. These are usually designed around the monostable (one-shot) circuit discussed above. Here the trailing edge of a triggered one-shot is differentiated to produce a sharp triggering pulse. This pulse can be used to trigger a short duration pulse generator, say a Schmitt trigger, or the pulse itself can be shaped to provide an output of proper height and duration. The graphical representation of a delay element is given in Figure 9.7-10.

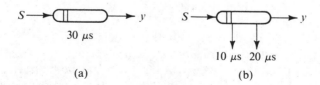

Figure 9.7-10.   Typical active delay elements   (a) Single delay   (b) Tapped delay

9.8   NUMBER SYSTEMS AND BINARY CODES

Of particular importance in this work is the binary number system. We wish to examine relations between and similarities of the decimal and the binary number systems.

The decimal number system is composed of ten different symbols, 0, 1, 2, ..., 9. The number of symbols is the *base* or *radix*. The value of a number depends on the symbols used and their symbol position in the number. Specifically, the number 2613 is a contraction of $2 \times 10^3 + 6 \times 10^2 + 1 \times 10^1 + 3 \times 10^0$, where 10 is the base. The *radix point* (or decimal point in this case) designates the separation between the negative powers of the base from the non-negative powers. Hence, the number 127.418 is a contraction of $1 \times 10^2 + 2 \times 10^1 + 7 \times 10^0 + 4 \times 10^{-1} + 1 \times 10^{-2} + 8 \times 10^{-3}$, where 10 is the base.

The *binary* system, in an entirely parallel way, uses 2 as the base. In the binary number system, the number 81 in the decimal system (often written 81_{10}) is written 1010001, which is a contraction of $1 \times 2^6 + 0 \times 2^5 + 1 \times 2^4 + 0 \times 2^3 + 0 \times 2^2 + 0 \times 2^1 + 1 \times 2^0$. The fractional numbers are also formed in a way that is similar to that in the decimal system. In the binary system the number 32.9375_{10} is found to be

$$32.9375_{10} = 100000.1111 = 1 \times 2^5 + 0 \times 2^4 + 0 \times 2^3 + 0 \times 2^2 + 0 \times 2^1 + 0 \times 2^0$$

$$+ 1 \times 2^{-1} + 1 \times 2^{-2} + 1 \times 2^{-3} + \times 2^{-4}$$

Other radix systems are in use in digital systems. Of special importance are the *octal* (8) and the *hexadecimal* (16) systems.

A simple method for the conversion of decimal numbers to equivalent binary numbers, although this system is rather cumbersome, is repeated division by 2. For example, the decimal number 61 in the binary system becomes

$$61 \div 2 = 30 + \text{remainder 1} \quad \leftarrow \text{least significant digit}$$

$$30 \div 2 = 15 + \text{remainder 0}$$

$$15 \div 2 = 7 + \text{remainder } 1$$

$$7 \div 2 = 3 + \text{remainder } 1$$

$$3 \div 2 = 1 + \text{remainder } 1$$

$$1 \div 2 = 0 + \text{remainder } 1$$

and so $61_{10} = 111101_2$ in the binary number system.

The conversion of decimal fractions to binary fractions is accomplished by subtracting the highest negative power of 2 which may be subtracted from the decimal fraction. This process is continued until there is no remainder or until one achieves the desired precision in the conversion. For example, the binary equivalent of 0.9375_{10} is found as follows:

$$0.9375 - 1 \times 2^{-1} = 0.9375 - 0.5 \quad = 0.4375$$

$$0.4375 - 1 \times 2^{-2} = 0.4375 - 0.25 \quad = 0.1875$$

$$0.1875 - 1 \times 2^{-3} = 0.1875 - 0.125 \quad = 0.0625$$

$$0.0625 - 1 \times 2^{-4} = 0.0625 - 0.0625 = 0$$

Hence $0.9375_{10} = 0.1111_2$.

As already mentioned, the octal and hexadecimal number systems are often used in computers. The change from decimal to any of these two systems and back follows exactly the procedure developed above for the decimal-binary combination. The number 233_{10}, for example, is converted to octal system by repeated division by 8, hence we have

$$8 \underline{233}$$
$$\quad 29 \quad \text{remainder } 1 \quad \leftarrow \text{ least significant digit}$$

$$8 \underline{29}$$
$$\quad 3 \quad \text{remainder } 5$$

$$8 \underline{3}$$
$$\quad 0 \quad \text{remainder } 3 \text{ or } 233_{10} = 351_8.$$

Table 9.8-1 shows four number systems which are most often used.

This table allows us to find the relationship between octal or hexadecimal and binary numbers systems: for the binary to octal transformation, we group the digits into groups of three relative to the binary point; for the binary to hexadecimal we do the same but now we use groups of four. For the inverse problem the steps are reversed. The following conversions show the procedure just described.

**Table 9.8-1.   Decimal-Octal-Hexadecimal-Binary
Equivalent Number Systems**

Decimal	Octal	Hexadecimal	Binary
0	0	0	0000
1	1	1	0001
2	2	2	0010
3	3	3	0011
4	4	4	0100
5	5	5	0101
6	6	6	0110
7	7	7	0111
8	10	8	1000
9	11	9	1001
10	12	A	1010
11	13	B	1011
12	14	C	1100
13	15	D	1101
14	16	E	1110
15	17	F	1111
16	20	10	10000

Decimal   42.53125

Binary   101010.10001

Binary to Octal: 101   010   .   100   010
                     5   2   4   2
                    add extra zeros to complete groups of three
                    $101010.10001 = 52.42_8$

Binary to Hexadecimal: 0010   1010   .   1000   1000
                           2   A   8   8
                          $101010.10001 = 2\Lambda.88_{16}$

9.9   ARITHMETIC OPERATIONS

Computers perform all four basic arithmetic operations: addition, subtraction, multiplication, and division. Since almost all mathematical operations can be accomplished using these four basic operations, computers can solve almost any mathematical problem, such as differentiation, integration, or the solution of ordinary differential equations. The four basic arithmetic operations are easily performed using circuit devices which will be discussed in Section 9.10. We shall examine certain of the details of arithmetic operations in this section; specifically, we shall consider addition, subtraction, and multiplication.

Addition

Binary addition follows the same general rules as decimal addition, with the requirement that the sum of two 1s is equal to zero with a carry of 1 and the sum of three 1s is equal to 1 with a carry of 1. The following are some examples of addition (the values in the parentheses are the corresponding decimal equivalents)

$$
\begin{array}{llll}
100 \quad (4_{10}) & 1011 \quad (11_{10}) & 100.01 \quad (4.25_{10}) \\
\underline{110} \quad (6_{10}) & \underline{1011} \quad (11_{10}) & \underline{101.11} \quad (5.75_{10}) \\
1010 \quad (10_{10}) & 10110 \quad (22_{10}) & 1010.00 \quad (10_{10})
\end{array}
$$

When decimal numbers are to be added by binary arithmetic, round-off errors might be introduced, owing to the fact that the decimal number may not be exactly possible in binary form.

EXAMPLE 9.9-1. Add the numbers 12.29_{10} and 8.17_{10} in binary form. The desired accuracy is the nearest tenth.

SOLUTION. The number 12.29 is written approximately as

$$N_1 = 1100.01001 = 12.28125$$

Also

$$N_2 = 1000.00101 = 8.15625$$

The sum is

$$
\begin{array}{l}
1100.01001 \\
\underline{1000.00101} \\
10100.01110 = 20.4376 = 20.4
\end{array}
$$

rounded to the nearest tenth. The hundredth place is in error. The accuracy can be improved by increasing the number of binary digits to the right of the binary point in expressing the numbers.

□   □   □

Subtraction

Binary subtraction follows roughly the same general rules as for decimal subtraction. This requires that the subtraction of 1 from 0 is equal to 1 with a necessary borrowing of 1 from the next column to the left. The following are several examples of subtraction

$$
\begin{array}{ll}
1000 & (8_{10}) \\
-1 & (1_{10}) \\
\hline
111 & (7_{10})
\end{array}
\qquad
\begin{array}{ll}
10000 & (16_{10}) \\
-11 & (3_{10}) \\
\hline
1101 & (13_{10})
\end{array}
\qquad
\begin{array}{ll}
101.01 & (5.25_{10}) \\
-10.10 & (2.50_{10}) \\
\hline
10.11 & (2.75_{10})
\end{array}
$$

Digital computers seldom are provided with subtractors, but instead, adders are used for accomplishing both addition and subtraction. To accomplish this, negative numbers are introduced into the addition process, with the negative numbers being stored in their *complemented* form. For example, the 10s complement of a decimal number in an n-digit system is 10^n minus the number. The 9s complement is $999\ldots$ minus the number, the number of 9s usually being equal to the number of digits in the number. Similarly, the 2s complement of a binary number is obtained by subtracting the number from 2^n.

EXAMPLE 9.9-2. Write the 10s complement of 693 in a 5 digit system, and also the 9s complement of this number in a 3 digit system.

SOLUTION. From the definition

$$10^5 - 693 = 99307$$

The 9s complement is

$$999 - 693 = 306$$

To carry out subtraction employing the appropriate complemented form is slightly more involved. The details are best discussed through specific examples.

□ □ □

EXAMPLE 9.9-3. Subtract $A = 127$ from $B = 364$ in the decimal system using 10s complements.

SOLUTION. We write the number 127 in a 3-digit system $10^3 - 127 = 873$. Now we combine $364 + 873 = 1237$. We now erase the most significant digit, yielding the result 237. Basically, of course, what we have done is first added 1000 and then subtracted the 1000.

□ □ □

EXAMPLE 9.9-4. Repeat Example 9.9-3 using the 9s complement arithmetic.

SOLUTION. Here the procedure is to take $999 - 127 = 872$. This is added to 364, thus $364 + 872 = 1236$. Now take the most significant bit (1 in this case) and add it to 236 to get $236 + 1 = 237$. This procedure is called an "end around carry."

□ ·□ □

EXAMPLE 9.9-5. Subtract $A = 55$ from $B = 25$ in the decimal system using 10s complements.

SOLUTION. The 10s complement of the subtrahend is $10^2 - 55 = 45$. This is added to the minuend $45 + 25 = 70$. But now there is no digit in the hundreds column. This means that the result is a negative number. If we proceed as in Example 9.9-3 we see that the result is $70 - 100 = -30$.

□ □ □

Clearly, subtraction of decimal numbers by 10s and 9s complements serves no significant purpose, since a subtraction process must be included to carry out the procedure. In the case of a binary system, while a subtraction process is also involved, this proves to be a simple matter. The important 2s and 1s complements are accomplished by the very simple procedure of bit reversing. Otherwise the procedure parallels that above.

EXAMPLE 9.9-6. Subtract the binary number 1001110 from 1110001 by employing 2s complements (bit reversing and adding 1 to the least significant bit).

SOLUTION. The subtraction process requires bit reversing the subtrahend, adding 1 to the least significant bit, and erasing the most significant bit. Thus we have

$$1110001 - 1001110 = 1110001 + 0110001 + 0000001$$

$$= 10100011 \text{ with the first 1 erased}$$

$$= 0100011$$

□ □ □

EXAMPLE 9.9-7. Repeat Example 9.9-6 using 1s complements arithmetic.

SOLUTION. The procedure here parallels that using 9s complements in the decimal system, and requires an end-around carry. Thus

$$1110001 - 1001110 = \quad 1110001$$
$$+0110001$$
$$\overline{10100010}$$

end around carry $\llcorner\!\longrightarrow 1$

$$\overline{0100011}$$

□ □ □

EXAMPLE 9.9-8. Carry out the following operations: (a) $3.25_{10} + 4.50_{10}$; (b) $4.50_{10} - 3.25_{10}$; (c) $3.25_{10} - 4.50_{10}$.

SOLUTION. (a) In binary form $3.25_{10} = 11.01_2$; $4.50_{10} = 100.10_2$. Then

$$\begin{array}{ll} 0011.010 & (3.25_{10}) \\ \underline{0100.100} & (4.50_{10}) \\ 0111.110 & (7.75_{10}) \end{array}$$

(b) $3.25_{10} = 0011.010_2$; 1s complement $= 1100.101$; 2s complement $= 1100.101 + 0000.001 = 1100.110$

$$\begin{array}{ll} 0100.100 & (4.50_{10}) \\ \underline{1100.110} & (-3.25_{10}) \\ 10001.010 & (1.25_{10}) \\ \downarrow \end{array}$$

overflow is eliminated

(c) $4.50_{10} = 0100.100_2$; 2s complement $= 1011.011 + 0000.001 = 1011.100$

$$\begin{array}{ll} 0011.010 & (3.25_{10}) \\ \underline{1011.100} & (-4.50_{10}) \\ 1110.110 & (-1.25_{10}) \\ \downarrow \end{array}$$

indicates a negative number (not more than four digits)

To find the number, take the 2s complement of 1110.110 which is

$$0001.001 + 0000.001 = 0001.010 = 1.25_{10}$$

□ □ □

Multiplication

To understand multiplication in the binary system, we first examine the multiplication of two numbers in the decimal system. Two procedures are shown:

$$
\begin{array}{ll}
237 & \\
\underline{491} & \\
237 & \\
2133 & \\
\underline{948} & \\
116367 &
\end{array}
\qquad
\begin{array}{ll}
237 & \text{multiplicand} \\
\underline{491} & \text{multiplier} \\
237 & \\
2133x & \text{two multiplications} \\
21567 & \text{partial sum} \\
\underline{948xx} & \\
116367 & \text{final sum}
\end{array}
$$

Refer to the second form. Here multiplication is shown to consist of the addition of two numbers at a time to form a running or partial sum. Next involved is to take the first product, effectively shift the multiplicand one unit to the left, and then take the partial sum. Once again the multiplicand is shifted one unit to the left, and the running sum is taken with the previous partial sum. The operation can be considered to involve a shift of the running sum one unit to the right when the addition process is performed.

EXAMPLE 9.9-9. Multiply the two binary numbers 1101 by 1010.

SOLUTION. Proceed directly as follows:

$$
\begin{array}{ll}
1101 & \text{multiplicand} \\
\underline{1010} & \text{multiplier} \\
0000 & \\
\underline{1101x} & \text{two multiplications} \\
11010 & \text{partial sum} \\
\underline{0000xx} & \\
011010 & \text{partial sum} \\
\underline{1101xxx} & \\
10000010 & \text{final sum}
\end{array}
$$

Observe that after obtaining each partial sum, the partial sum is essentially shfited one bit to the right, or equivalently, the multiplicand is shifted one bit to the left in each successive multiplication. Note that the number of bits in the product equals the sum of the number of bits of multiplier and multiplicand.

□   □   □

Division

Division is more difficult and more time consuming than multiplication, although it involves only repeated subtractions. The difficulty arises because a computer cannot look ahead into the dividend and select the proper number of digits for successful subtraction. The ideas behind the method used are illustrated by an example in the decimal system.

EXAMPLE 9.9-10. Divide 12 by 2 using the method of repeated subtractions.

SOLUTION. The steps are shown.

Number of subtractions

```
 12
 -2      1
----
 10
 -2      2
----
  8
 -2      3
----
  6
 -2      4
----
  4
 -2      5
----
  2
 -2      6
----
  0
```

In this example six subtractions were completed in the procedure, with the result $12/2 = 6$. Had the given number been 13, we would have found 6 subtractions plus a remainder of 1. The subtractions would cease when the remainder is less than the divisor. In this particular example, the method yields an answer that is accurate to the nearest integer.

□ □ □

When noninteger numbers must be divided or when the answer is nonintegral, the process of long division is employed.

EXAMPLE 9.9-11. Divide 7 by 2, and give the answer to the nearest tenth.

SOLUTION. The long division will be carried out using binary digits. Hence begin with 7 in binary code = 111, and 2 in binary code = 010. Also, to obtain an answer that is correct to the nearest tenth, the answer must be correct to 4 places to the right of the binary point. The details of the process are shown.

The first step is to divide 10 (neglecting the zero on the left in 010) into 11. The difference is 01, and we bring down a 1. Next divide 10 into 11. The difference is 01, and we bring down a zero. The next step finds 10 greater than 00;

hence we record a 0 on top and bring down another 0. Since 10 is greater than 000, we record a 0 on top and another 0 is brought down. This procedure would be continued to insure the desired accuracy. The process has been the following:

$$
\begin{array}{r}
11.1000 \\
10)\overline{111.0000} \\
\underline{10} \\
11 \\
\underline{10} \\
1\,0 \\
\underline{1\,0} \\
0000
\end{array}
$$

Observe that this procedure requires the computer to perform successive subtractions. If one of these subtractions produces a negative result, the step is not acceptable, and the subtracted divisor must be restored to the dividend and another trial subtraction must be made with the divisor shifted with respect to the dividend. If the subtractor produces a positive result, the quotient bit is 1 and the subtraction was proper. The divisor and dividend are shifted relative to each other and the procedure iterates again.

□   □   □

9.10   COMPLEX LOGICAL CIRCUITS

In this section we shall discuss certain complex circuits, including adders, registers, and counters, that can be considered basic building blocks for digital systems.

The Half Adder

The device that adds two binary digits to yield the sum digit and the carry digit is known as the *half adder*. The two digits to be added have only four possibilities, and these are given in Figure 9.10-1. From this truth table it is evident that

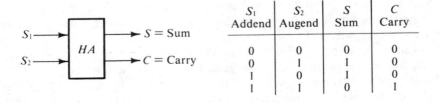

S_1 Addend	S_2 Augend	S Sum	C Carry
0	0	0	0
0	1	1	0
1	0	1	0
1	1	0	1

Figure 9.10-1.   The half adder and its truth table

$$S = \bar{S}_1 \cdot S_2 + S_1 \cdot \bar{S}_2 = \bar{S}_1 \cdot S_2 + S_1 \cdot \bar{S}_2 + S_1 \cdot \bar{S}_1 + S_2 \cdot \bar{S}_2$$

$$= (S_1 + S_2) \cdot (\bar{S}_1 + \bar{S}_2) = S_1 \oplus S_2 \qquad \text{(a)} \quad (9.10\text{-}1)$$

$$C = S_1 \cdot S_2 \qquad \text{(b)}$$

Three logic diagrams to realize these functions are given in Figure 9.10-2.

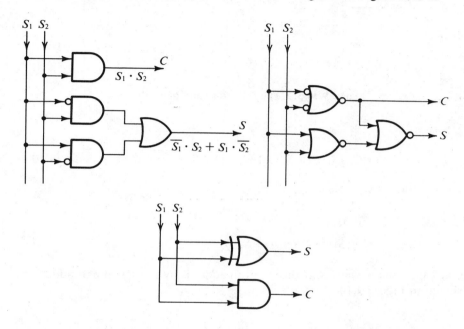

Figure 9.10-2.   Half adder realizations

The Full Adder

The half adder cannot accommodate carry inputs, a necessary feature when it is one of the linear members of an adding chain. This requires the use of a *full adder*, a device which has the characteristics shown in Figure 9.10-3. From this table, the functions performed are

$$S = \bar{S}_1 \cdot \bar{S}_2 \cdot C_i + \bar{S}_1 \cdot S_2 \cdot \bar{C}_i + S_1 \cdot \bar{S}_2 \cdot \bar{C}_i + S_1 \cdot S_2 \cdot C_i$$

$$= \bar{C}_i \cdot (\bar{S}_1 \cdot S_2 + S_1 \cdot \bar{S}_2) + C_i \cdot (\bar{S}_1 \cdot \bar{S}_2 + S_1 \cdot S_2)$$

But

$$\bar{S}_1 \cdot \bar{S}_2 + S_1 \cdot S_2 = (\bar{S}_1 + S_2) \cdot (S_1 + \bar{S}_2) = S_1 \cdot \bar{S}_2 + \bar{S}_1 \cdot S_2$$

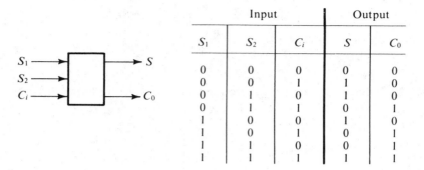

	Input			Output	
S_1	S_2	C_i		S	C_0
0	0	0		0	0
0	0	1		1	0
0	1	0		1	0
0	1	1		0	1
1	0	0		1	0
1	0	1		0	1
1	1	0		0	1
1	1	1		1	1

Figure 9.10-3.   The full adder and its truth table

Hence

$$S = \bar{C_i} \cdot (\bar{S_1} \cdot S_2 + S_1 \cdot \bar{S_2}) + C_i \cdot \overline{(S_1 \cdot \bar{S_2} + \bar{S_1} \cdot S_2)} \tag{9.10-2}$$

Also

$$C_o = \bar{S_1} \cdot S_2 \cdot C_i + S_1 \cdot \bar{S_2} \cdot C_i + S_1 \cdot S_2 \cdot \bar{C_i} + S_1 \cdot S_2 \cdot C_i$$
$$= C_i \cdot (\bar{S_1} \cdot S_2 + S_1 \cdot \bar{S_2}) + S_1 \cdot S_2 \tag{9.10-3}$$

One of the many ways to realize the full adder is by using two half adders, as shown in Figure 9.10-4.

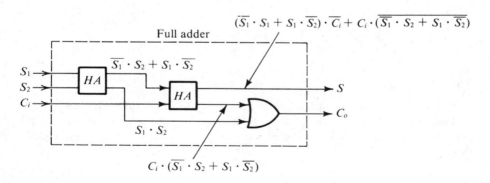

Figure 9.10-4.   A full adder realization

EXAMPLE 9.10-1. Use the full adder to add serially the following two numbers $S_1 = 1101$ and $S_2 = 1011$.

SOLUTION. The timing diagrams of the two numbers are shown in Figure 9.10-5a. Figure 9.10-5b shows the full adder with a delay circuit. Figure

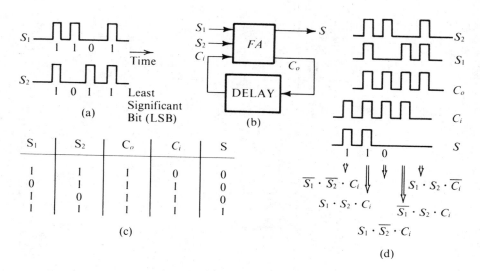

Figure 9.10-5. Serial adder

9.10-5c shows the truth table of the process, and Figure 9.10-5d shows the timing of the complete process. The value of S for the adder is given in Equation (9.10-2).

□ □ □

Parallel Binary Adder

Binary numbers can be added in parallel as well as in serial form. The parallel adder is simpler to implement than the serial adder. A three-bit parallel adder is shown in Figure 9.10-6. It is the purpose of this unit to add two 3-bit integers. If the two numbers $S_2'S_1'S_0'$ and $S_2''S_1''S_0''$ are positive, the adder can add numbers whose sum is less than or equal to 7. Often an extra bit is included at the beginning of the number to designate the sign, using 0 for $+$ and 1 for $-$. Further, if 1s complement arithmetic is used, an end-around carry is required, and HA_o must be replaced by FA_o to receive this end-around carry. If 2s complement arithmetic is used instead of 1s complement, no end-around carry is required and the circuit shown is suitable.

A simple 3-bit 2s complement (reversing the bits of the subtrahend and adding one to the least significant bit) adder/subtractor is shown in Figure 9.10-7. It is noted that the *arithmetic logic unit* (ALU) is that part of a computer which carries out arithmetic and logic operations. Hence the adder/subtractor unit can be used as the ALU of an elementary computer which can only add and subtract.

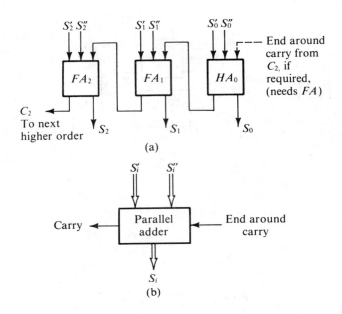

Figure 9.10-6. A parallel adder (a) Schematic for 3-bit parallel adder (b) Symbol for a binary adder

Parity Circuits

A *parity bit* generator/checker is a very useful circuit to check errors in transmission. In an odd-parity system, the total number of 1-bits in any transmitting symbol, including the parity bit, is odd. The opposite is true for even-parity bit systems. Figure 9.10-8 shows an even parity system with its parity checker. Consider the case in which we have coded the word "no" as 001. Since there is only one 1-bit, the parity generator will add one 1-bit to the extreme left place of the coded word. Hence the word 1001 will be transmitted. If an error is introduced and the received message is 011 instead of 001, the parity generator will produce a bit indicating that an error is present. This may be found easily by studying the logic function of the parity checker shown in Figure 9.10-8b which in the particular message becomes

$$S = (S_1 \oplus S_2) \oplus (S_3 \oplus S_4) = (1 \oplus 1) \oplus (0 \oplus 1) = (0) \oplus (1) = 1$$

A parity error bit is present, as was expected. It must be noted that for this type of coded procedure, if two errors are present, the parity checker is not capable of detecting the error. More complicated coded procedures have been devised that can detect multiple errors.

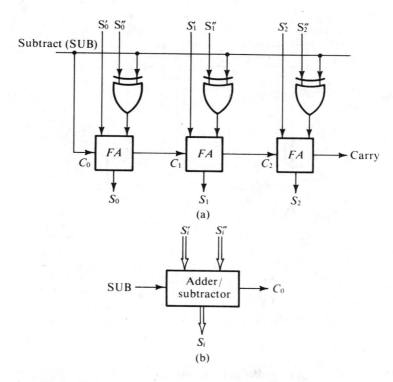

Figure 9.10-7. **(a) A 3-bit 2s complement adder/subtractor**
(b) Symbol for an adder/subtractor of any length

Registers

A register is a collection of flipflops used for storing binary encoded collection of bits, whether these denote numbers or data. Registers supply temporary fast access storage for data and addresses to storage, as well as control information. Two important classes of registers exist: the *storage* or *buffer* register and the *shift* register. The storage register is used to store binary information, such as numbers or instructions. It is often made up of FFs in combination, each of which will store one bit. The shift register is a device for handling data. Figure 9.10-9 shows a four bit shift register. This device operates in such a manner that the state of each flipflop is shifted to the right upon the application of a clock or shift pulse. Shifting can be arranged to be to the left or in either direction. Suppose that the input to this circuit is 1011. The states of the register after each clock pulse are given in the table, assuming that the register is initially cleared. Because the clock pulse is usually long compared with the switching time of the circuits, signals may propagate through the FFs before switching is intended. This is known as a *race* condition. The

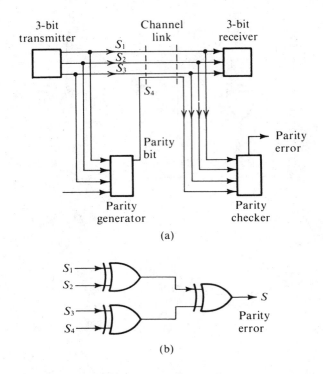

(a)

(b)

Figure 9.10-8. (a) Complete data transmission system (b) Parity checker

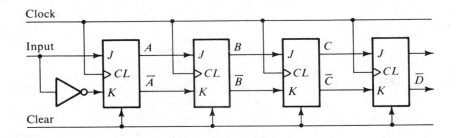

Figure 9.10-9. A 4-bit shift register using JK-FF with serial input and serial output

race problem can be avoided in several ways. One way is to provide delay elements that will delay the signals for switching until after the clock pulse changes. Figure 9.10-10 shows such delay elements. A time diagram showing the action of the shift register of Figure 9.10-10 is given in Figure 9.10-11.

Shift registers are basic to and one of the most fundamental components of a computer. It will perform any or all of the following operations:

1. Permit a serial word with the least significant digit (LSD) first at one

Table 9.10-1.   States of Shift Register with 1011 Input

Time	Input	A	B	C	D
0	0	0	0	0	0
1	1	1	0	0	0
2	1	1	1	0	0
3	0	0	1	1	0
4	1	1	0	1	1

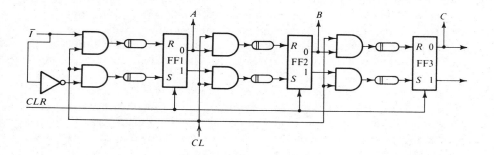

Figure 9.10-10.   A 3-bit shift register

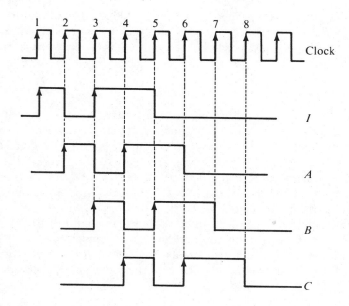

Figure 9.10-11.   A typical waveform diagram of the shift register

clock frequency and deliver the same word out with the LSD first at a different clock frequency.

2. Permit a word to be shifted in serially and shift the same word out in parallel.

3. Permit a parallel in and a parallel out format.

4. Provide a predetermined number of bits to be shifted either to the right or to the left.

Storage registers are rather different in design from the shift register. They are used to accumulate data either by parallel or serial input, and will transfer the stored data either in parallel or in serial form. Rudiments of a simple parallel input, parallel output storage register with common reset and direct entry is illustrated in Figure 9.10-12. A control circuit, perhaps a control counter, pulses lines P_o, P_1, P_2 in sequence. When P_o is pulsed, the old word is cleared; i.e., the word is erased from the register and the register is reset. When P_1 is pulsed, a new word is gated in or registered. When P_2 is pulsed, the registered word is gated out and read; i.e., the contents of the register is transferred.

An important class of three-state registers exist which use three-state switches. These devices have greatly simplified the wiring of computers. Such a *three-state* switch is shown diagrammatically in Figure 9.10-13. When the Enable signal is low, the switch acts in the manner shown in Figure 9.10-13b and S_{out} floats. When Enable is high, the switch acts as shown in Figure 9.10-13c and S_{out} is high or low, and is the same as S_{in}.

A 2-bit storage register using 3-state switches is shown in Figure 9.10-14. When the input, Load, and Enable controls are low, the register is isolated from the input and output lines. When the Load is 1, then at the first positive clock pulse the two-bit word is loaded into the buffer register. When Enable goes high then at the next positive clock pulse the two-bit word is transferred out.

Binary Counters

A *counter* is a device for counting incoming pulses to some prescribed count and then resetting for a new count sequence. It is the equivalent of the binary odometer in an automobile. If the counter is made up of 3 FFs, it can sequence from 000 to 111 (0 through 7, decimal), and it is called a *Modulo-8* counter. If this counter is arranged to count 000, 001, 010, 011, 111, and then recycles to 000 omitting the binary equivalents for 4, 5, 6, it is a Modulo-5 counter. By its operation, a counter is related to the shift register.

A simple ripple Modulo-8 counter is shown in Figure 9.10-15. A timing diagram is also shown. In this counter the FFs are connected in the T or toggle mode, with input pulses, plus or minus, causing the FF state to alternate or toggle with the input excitation. The count sequence of this counter is 000,

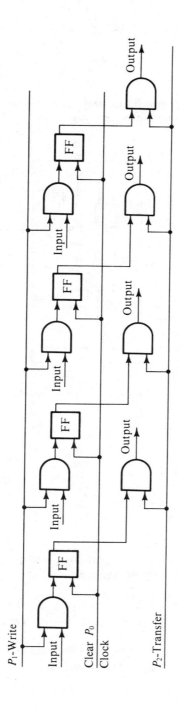

Figure 9.10-12. Parallel input, parallel output storage register

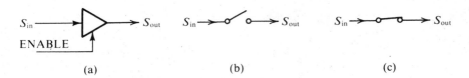

Figure 9.10-13.   (a) Symbol for the three-state switch
(b) Switch state when Enable is zero (low)   (c) Switch state when Enable is one (high)

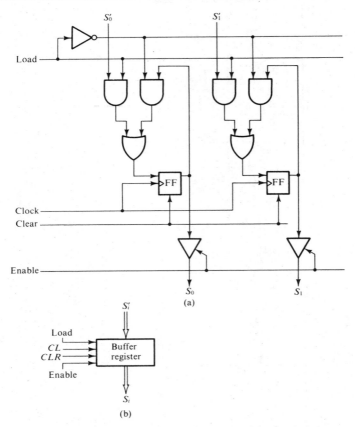

Figure 9.10-14.   (a) A 2-bit storage (buffer) register
(b) Symbol for the storage register

100, 010, 110, 001, 101, 011, 111. If the word order is reversed with FF1 being
S_o, FF2 being S_1 and FF3 being S_2 the counter is a simple ripple counter that
counts successively from 0_{10} to 7_{10}.

In most cases there are advantages in using *synchronous counters* (all FFs
are clocked together) rather than ripple counters. Among the advantages are

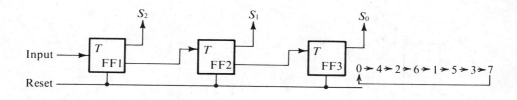

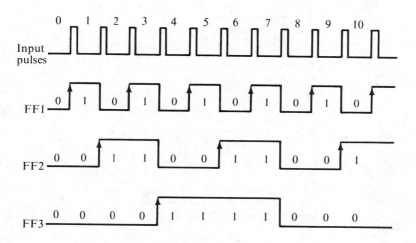

Figure 9.10-15.   Three stage ripple counter

that they are easier to design; they respond on the positive edge of the pulse, which makes them compatible with most medium scale integration (MSI) devices; and they serve more satisfactorily for decoding since they do not generate spikes. However, they are more complex than ripple counters which have the advantage of being less expensive, have less power dissipation, and are usually smaller than the synchronous type. A typical synchronous counter with its time diagram is shown in Figure 9.10-16.

The *ring counter* creates words which have only a single bit 1 with the rest being 0s. Figure 9.10-17 shows such a ring counter, which is composed of D-type FFs. When *CLR* goes high, FF2 and FF3 have low outputs (0) and FF1 is preset. Hence the initial output word is 001. When *CLR* goes low, the ring counter is ready to operate under the influence of the clock pulses. At the first positive clock pulse, the bits shift to the left by one, and the word out is 010. The second pulse creates the word 100, and at the third pulse the counter starts from word 001.

This type of counter is useful when a sequence of operations must be controlled. Because each output ring word has only one high bit, the ring can be used to activate one of several devices.

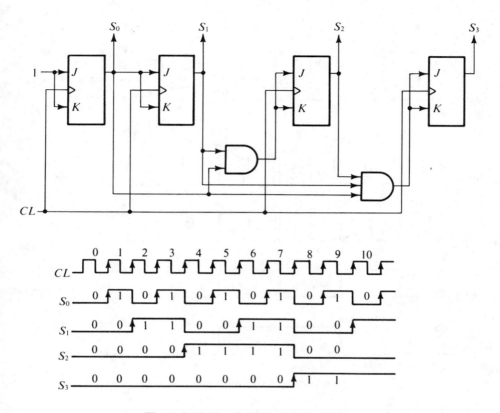

Figure 9.10-16. Synchronous counter

Program Counter

When the features of a storage register and a counter are combined, the logic circuit is called a *program counter* (PC). The program counter can load a word and also count. The program counter is represented symbolically as in Figure 9.10-18. If *CLR* goes high and then low, all the FFs are reset at low, that is, the S_is are zero. When all of the control signals are low, the clock pulses have no effect. When Count is high, each positive clock pulse advances the register content by one. When Load goes high, the next clock pulse stores the word S_i'. When Enable goes high, the contents of the stored register S_i' are delivered to the output S_i.

Accumulator

A right and left shift register which includes three-state switches is called an *accumulator*. The accumulator is capable of temporarily storing algebraic sums. Figure 9.10-19 symbolically shows such a device.

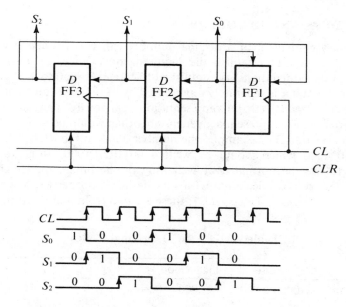

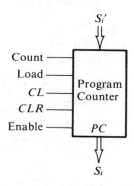

Figure 9.10-17.   (a) Ring counter   (b) Timing diagram

Figure 9.10-18.   Symbol for three-state program counter

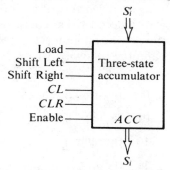

Figure 9.10-19.   Symbolic representation of an accumulator

9.11   CODERS AND DECODERS

The binary equivalent of a decimal number can be extended to whatever length is necessary to establish the required equivalence. In many cases a binary 8421 (weighted digits) is established to extend from 0 to 9. If each digit of a decimal number is separately represented by its binary equivalent, this is a *binary coded decimal* (BCD) representation. Obviously many more binary digits are required to represent a given number than would be required with the simple binary code. For example, the number 368_{10} in the BCD 8421 code is 0011 0110 1000 which would be written 001101101000. It is not always desirable to use the normal 8421 weighting of the binary digits, and other binary codes are possible, often with very desirable properties. We show the 8421 and 4311 codes in Table 9.11-1; these are two from many possible codes.

Table 9.11-1.   BCD-Decimal Codes

Number	8421 Code	4311 Code	
0	0000	0000	
1	0001	0001	
2	0010	0011	
3	0011	0100	
4	0100	1000	9-complementation by bit reversal
5	0101	0111	
6	0110	1011	
7	0111	1100	
8	1000	1110	
9	1001	1111	

In these codes, the weight of each digit of the binary number is that specified by the code. A feature of the 4311 code is that there is a decimal 9-weight with the paired binary digits being complements of each other.

A fairly simple example of a decoder that could be found in an airplane is one that presents information to the pilot on actions to be taken. Suppose that flight information is coded in the following way:

00	fly straight ahead
01	fly left
10	fly right
11	fly up

When such information is received the message in binary coded form will be introduced to a decoder, as illustrated in Figure 9.11-1. Observe, for example,

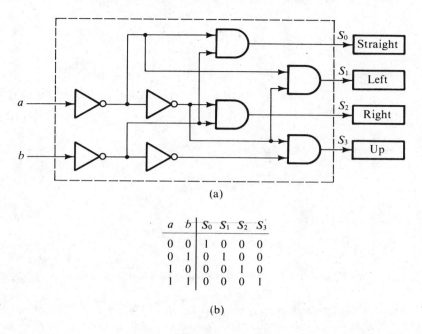

(a)

a	b	S_0	S_1	S_2	S_3
0	0	1	0	0	0
0	1	0	1	0	0
1	0	0	0	1	0
1	1	0	0	0	1

(b)

Figure 9.11-1.   A two-bit binary decoder   (a) Decoder   (b) Truth table

that when $a = 0$, $b = 1$, the input to the second NAND gate is 00 and hence its output is 1. The reader can readily verify the remaining relations of the truth table.

EXAMPLE 9.11-1. Let four light emitting diodes be arranged in the form shown in Figure 9.11-2a, such that when the appropriate binary inputs are

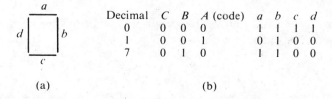

Decimal	C	B	A (code)	a	b	c	d
0	0	0	0	1	1	1	1
1	0	0	1	0	1	0	0
7	0	1	0	1	1	0	0

(a)   (b)

Figure 9.11-2.   Code CBA to decimal conversion

present the numbers 0, 1 and 7 appear. Figure 9.11-2b shows the correspondence among the decimal, code and LEDs. Deduce the Boolean process involved in this decoder.

$$
\begin{array}{c}
\quad\quad CB \\
\begin{array}{c|c|c}
a & 00 & 01 \\
\hline
\end{array} \\
A\ \begin{array}{c|c|c}
0 & 1 & 1 \\
\hline
1 & 0 & x
\end{array}
\end{array}
\qquad \bar{A}\cdot\bar{C}\cdot\bar{B}+\bar{A}\cdot\bar{C}\cdot B=\bar{A}\cdot\bar{C}\cdot(\bar{B}+B)=\bar{A}\cdot\bar{C}
$$

$$
\begin{array}{c}
\quad\quad CB \\
\begin{array}{c|c|c}
b & 00 & 01 \\
\hline
\end{array} \\
A\ \begin{array}{c|c|c}
0 & 1 & 1 \\
\hline
1 & 1 & x
\end{array}
\end{array}
\qquad
\begin{aligned}
&\bar{A}\cdot\bar{C}\cdot\bar{B}+\bar{A}\cdot\bar{C}\cdot B+\bar{A}\cdot\bar{C}\cdot\bar{B}+A\cdot\bar{C}\cdot\bar{B} \\
&=\bar{A}\cdot\bar{C}\cdot(\bar{B}+B)+\bar{C}\cdot\bar{B}\cdot(\bar{A}+A)=\bar{A}\cdot\bar{C}+\bar{C}\cdot\bar{B}
\end{aligned}
$$

$$
\begin{array}{c}
\quad\quad CB \\
\begin{array}{c|c|c}
c & 00 & 01 \\
\hline
\end{array} \\
\begin{array}{c|c|c}
0 & 1 & 0 \\
\hline
1 & 0 & x
\end{array}
\end{array}
\qquad \bar{A}\cdot\bar{C}\cdot\bar{B}
$$

$$
\begin{array}{c}
\quad\quad CB \\
\begin{array}{c|c|c}
d & 00 & 01 \\
\hline
\end{array} \\
\begin{array}{c|c|c}
0 & 1 & 0 \\
\hline
1 & 0 & x
\end{array}
\end{array}
\qquad \bar{A}\cdot\bar{C}\cdot\bar{B}
$$

Figure 9.11-3.   The construction of a simple decoder

SOLUTION. Using the Karnaugh maps shown in Figure 9.11-3 we obtain the binary A, B and C signals which appropriately will light the LEDs. For example, if $C=0$, $B=1$ and $A=0$ enters the decoder, we must have LED a and LED b on (one) and c and d off (zero). From Figure 9.11-3 we obtain

$$a=\bar{A}\cdot\bar{C}\cdot\bar{B}+\bar{A}\cdot\bar{C}\cdot B=1\cdot1\cdot0+1\cdot1\cdot1=0+1=1$$

$$b=\bar{A}\cdot\bar{C}\cdot\bar{B}+\bar{A}\cdot\bar{C}\cdot B+\bar{A}\cdot\bar{C}\cdot\bar{B}+A\cdot\bar{C}\cdot\bar{B}=1\cdot1\cdot0+1\cdot1\cdot1+1\cdot1\cdot0+0\cdot1\cdot0$$

$$=0+1+0+0=1$$

$$c=\bar{A}\cdot\bar{C}\cdot\bar{B}=1\cdot1\cdot0=0$$

$$d=\bar{A}\cdot\bar{C}\cdot\bar{B}=1\cdot1\cdot0=0$$

The reader should show that with appropriate excitations the numbers 0 and 1 are obtained. The encoder is shown in Figure 9.11-4.

□   □   □

We shall consider, as a more complicated BCD converter, the seven segment display that is used extensively in displaying the decimal digits in digital calculators. A normal binary (8421)-to-decimal converter may be used to control the segments of the special digit display tubes for which one of 10 numerals (0 to 9) lights when a corresponding pin receives a signal. A typical arrangement for the segments is shown in Figure 9.11-5a. We wish to devise a code conversion system (a decoder) that changes the logical input signal that

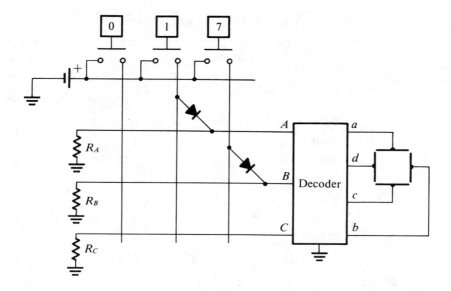

Figure 9.11-4. Encoder for Example 9.11-1

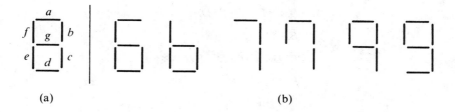

(a)   (b)

Figure 9.11-5. Representation of decimals using lighted segments

describes the decimal value into the seven signals that are needed to cause the appropriate segment array to produce the desired integer display. A conversion table is prepared for specifying the segments that must be used to represent each digit. This tabulation is given in Table 9.11-2. Note the appearance of "don't-care" entries in the output lines for generating 6, 7, 9 because alternate representations are equally acceptable, as shown in Figure 9.11-5b. We observe from the table that a 1 occurs in 7 or 8 instances out of the possible 10 shown, plus don't cares for the remaining 6 cases. If the appropriate functions are written for a through g, for example,

$$a = \bar{A} \cdot \bar{B} \cdot \bar{C} \cdot \bar{D} + \bar{A} \cdot \bar{B} \cdot C \cdot \bar{D} + \bar{A} \cdot \bar{B} \cdot C \cdot D + \ldots$$

and then available reduction techniques are used (e.g., Karnaugh maps) for each segment, one of the possible solutions is found to be

Table 9.11-2.   8421 to Decimal Conversion

Symbol (decimal) in Display	Inputs 8421 Code ABCD	a	b	c	d	e	f	g
					Outputs			
0	0000	1	1	1	1	1	1	0
1	0001	0	1	1	0	0	0	0
2	0010	1	1	0	1	1	0	1
3	0011	1	1	1	1	0	0	1
4	0100	0	1	1	0	0	1	1
5	0101	1	0	1	1	0	1	1
6	0110	x	0	1	1	1	1	1
7	0111	1	1	1	0	0	x	0
8	1000	1	1	1	1	1	1	1
9	1001	1	1	1	x	0	1	1

$$a = A + C + B \cdot D + \bar{B} \cdot \bar{D}$$

$$b = B \cdot \bar{C} \cdot D + B \cdot C \cdot \bar{D}$$

$$c = B + \bar{C} + D$$

$$d = \bar{B} \cdot \bar{D} + B \cdot \bar{C} \cdot D + \bar{B} \cdot C + C \cdot \bar{D}$$

$$e = \bar{B} \cdot \bar{D} + C \cdot \bar{D}$$

$$f = A + B + \bar{C} \cdot \bar{D}$$

$$g = A + C \cdot \bar{D} + B + C$$

Other implementations are possible. The gate implementation using discrete gate assemblies would be extensive, but commercial single package so-called BCD 7-Segment Decoder Drivers are readily available at quite moderate cost.

9.12   MEMORY CIRCUITS

Information and data are stored in the *memory* section of a computer. The two general classes of memory are *external* and *internal*. External storage devices include cards, paper tape, and magnetic tape. Internal storage devices include registers, ferrite cores, semiconductor memories, and sometimes magnetic drums and magnetic discs. Some of these memory devices are non-destructive, e.g., punched cards; and some are erasable, e.g., magnetic cores. The erasable storage memories have the desired quality that they can be used to store different data each time.

A variety of memory types is available. Semiconductor memories are *integrated circuit* (IC) devices in which the diodes, transistors, and resistors are formed on a semiconducting base called a *chip*. Digital integrated circuits are classified as *small scale integration* (SSI), *medium scale integration* (MSI), *large scale integration* (LSI) and *very large scale integration* (VLSI) devices. A semiconductor memory is ordinarily an MSI or LSI structure that is made up of bipolar transistors or of *metal oxide silicon* (MOS) transistors, or of metal oxide silicon field effect transistors (MOSFET). A typical 4K (4096) memory chip consists of 64×64 rows and columns. A typical memory board used in minicomputers consists of 8 rows by 16 columns of LSI memory chips, and this has a capacity of $8 \times 16 \times 64 \times 64 = 524,288$ bits. In addition, other types of memories are also available, such as magnetic bubble memories, charge coupled devices, and optical memories.

One general class of memory known as *read only memory* (ROM) is very important. This memory is equivalent to many registers, each of which stores a binary word and which can be read at will. However, the content of the registers is retained in the process and can be read at any time. The programmable read only memory (PROM) is fabricated with all zeros in all of its cells, and when it is programmed by the customer it becomes a ROM. Erasable PROMs, called EPROMs, have the characteristics of ROM memories, but have the advantage of being reprogrammable.

Figure 9.12-1a shows a primitive ROM made up of switches. This memory can store four words, each of 4 bits. This is called a 4×4 word memory. Figure 9.12-1b shows the same memory but with a decoder. A feature of this memory plus the decoder is that any of the 4 words can be addressed without using any switching. The need for a decoder is essential since only an 8-bit address is needed to cover 256 registers of a 256 word memory.

If, in addition, three state switches are used at the output, then the result is a three-state ROM. This memory is shown schematically in Figure 9.12-1c. Suppose we wish to read the fourth word from the memory. The *address* word 100 is inputed at $S_2' S_1' S_0'$ and the Enable must go high. The output word from the ROM of Figure 9.12-1b is $S_3 S_2 S_1 S_0 = 1001 = 9_{10}$. A look at all stored words shows that these are $0000 = 0_{10}$, $0001 = 1_{10}$, $0100 = 4_{10}$ and $1001 = 9_{10}$. These are the squares of the numbers 0, 1, 2 and 3. In fact, this is the practice followed in most calculators when the x^2 button is pressed.

If we wish to access each bit in a ROM memory, then a configuration such as that shown in Figure 9.12-2 is used. This is a 64×1 memory structure.

Another important class of memories is the *random access memory* (RAM). The word random in this case means that we can access any location (bit) of the memory with equal ease. The RAM memory is also known as a *read and write* memory. As in ROM memories, the capacity of a RAM memory is equal to the number of words times the word length. For example, a RAM unit having a 256 bit capacity may be organized as 32 words of 8 bits each, or as a 256×1 bit. A 32×8 RAM memory is shown in Figure 9.12-3, and a 256×1 memory is shown in Figure 9.12-4.

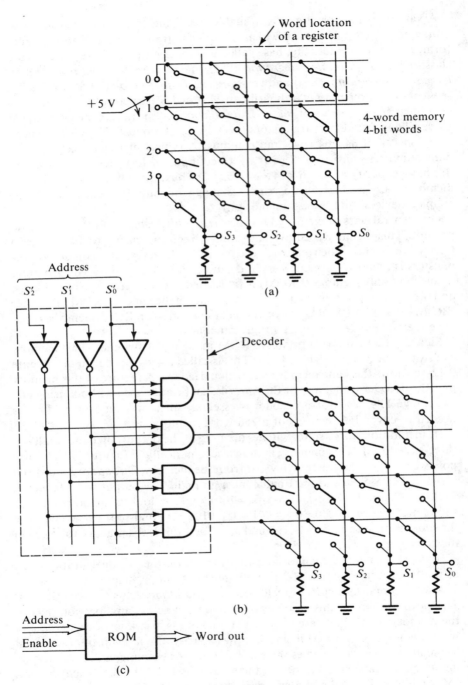

Figure 9.12-1.   Read-only memory   (a) ROM without decoding
(b) ROM with decoding   (c) Schematic representation of ROM

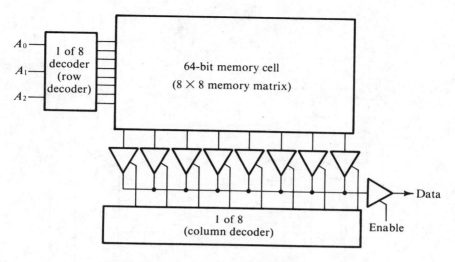

Figure 9.12-2. A 64×1 ROM memory

J or N
Dual-In-Line Package
(Top View)

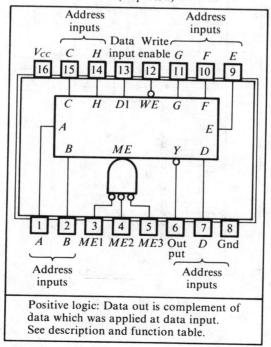

Positive logic: Data out is complement of
data which was applied at data input.
See description and function table.

(a)

Figure 9.12-3. A 256 bit RAM memory configured as 32×8
(a) Chip   (b) Functional block diagram

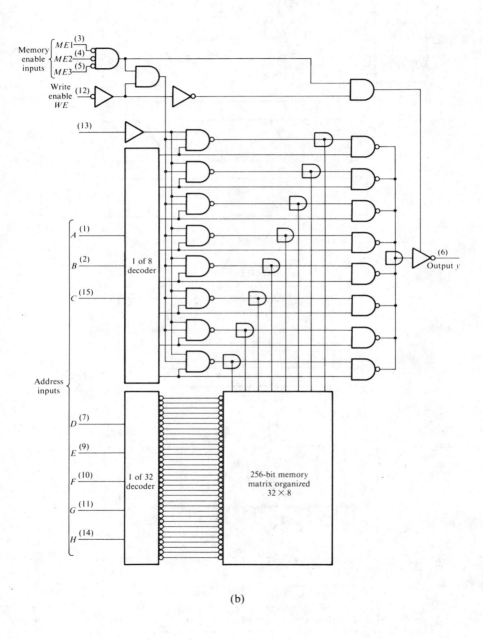

(b)

**Figure 9.12-3.   A 256 bit RAM memory configured as 32 × 8
(a) Chip   (b) Functional block diagram**

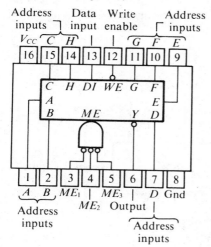

J or N dual-in-line
or W flat package
(top view)

Address   Data Write   Address
inputs ⌐   input enable ⌐   inputs

V_{CC} C H | | G F E

| 16 | 15 | 14 | 13 | 12 | 11 | 10 | 9 |

C   H DI WE G F
A   E
B   ME   Y D

| 1 | 2 | 3 | 4 | 5 | 6 | 7 | 8 |

A B ME_1 | ME_3 | D Gnd

Address ME_2 Output |
inputs   Address
                         inputs

Positive logic: Data out is complement of
data which was applied at data
input. See description and function table.

(a)

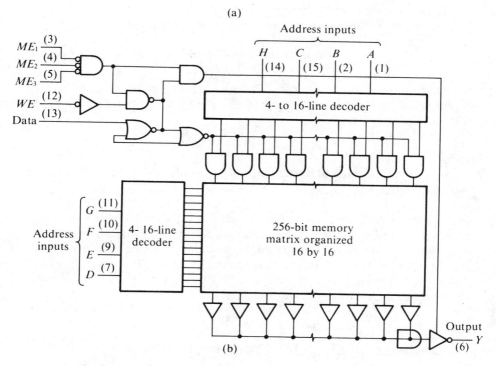

Address inputs

ME_1 (3)
ME_2 (4)
ME_3 (5)

H   C   B   A
(14) (15) (2)   (1)

WE (12)
Data (13)

4- to 16-line decoder

Address
inputs

G (11)
F (10)
E (9)
D (7)

4- 16-line
decoder

256-bit memory
matrix organized
16 by 16

Output
Y
(6)

(b)

Figure 9.12-4.   A 256 bit RAM memory configured as 16×16
(a) Chip   (b) Functional block diagram

EXAMPLE 9.12-1. Available memory chips are arranged in a 16×2 format. Show how to increase the bits per word from two to four.

SOLUTION. The desired result is accomplished by arranging two chips in parallel, as shown in Figure 9.12-5. Observe that both chip-select and write-

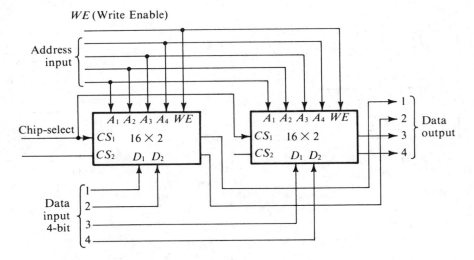

Figure 9.12-5.   Word increase from two to four

enable are common to both chips. Memories can be expanded to any desired capacity, but the expansion is limited by the overall system speed and electrical current requirements.

□   □   □

EXAMPLE 9.12-2. Expand the desired words in a memory from 16 to 32 using two 16×2 chips.

SOLUTION. The desired configuration is shown in Figure 9.12-6. Observe that a 1 to the chip-select line will be a 1 input into the first chip and a 0 into the second. Hence the word will come from the first chip. Conversely, when a 0 appears in the CS line, the word will come from the second chip. Since these particular chips have two select inputs, we can use up to $2^2 = 4$ chips, thus allowing a memory to be built for 128 words.

□   □   □

9.13   DETAILS OF AN ELEMENTARY COMPUTER

We shall examine the important elements of a very simple computer, which we will designate EC (elementary computer). The essential components of EC

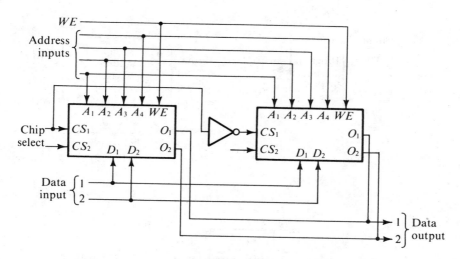

Figure 9.12-6.   Expansion of word memory from 16 to 32

are shown in Figure 9.13-1. This computer has very limited capabilities since it is provided with only a 12 8-bit word PROM. Note that connections to the address/data bus are 3-state connections, and all others are 2-state connections. We shall review the various elements involved in this computer even though some of these might already have been discussed.

Program Counter

As discussed in Section 9.10, the program counter is a buffer register and a counter. The symbolic diagram is shown in Figure 9.13-1a (see also Figure 9.10-19). When count is high, the register contents advance by one at each positive clock edge. When Enable is high, the content of the program counter register is available to the address/data bus.

Bus

The *bus* comprises the set of lines which connect the different parts of the computer. The *control bus* is the set of lines which connect the *control* unit of the computer to the appropriate other units of the computer. The *address/data bus* (A/D bus) is the set of lines which connects units of the computer and through which the appropriate words at specific times move from one specified unit of the computer to another specified unit.

Memory Address Register

The *memory address register* (MAR) for our EC is a 4-bit register which can select any of the 12 words of our computer. This register receives the address of the program counter through the address/data bus and transfers it to the

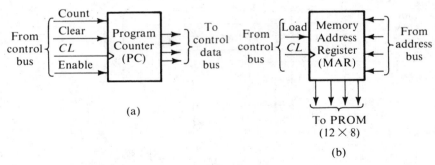

(a)

(b)

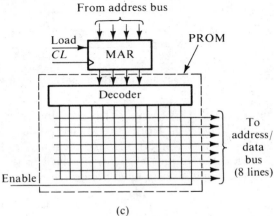

(c)

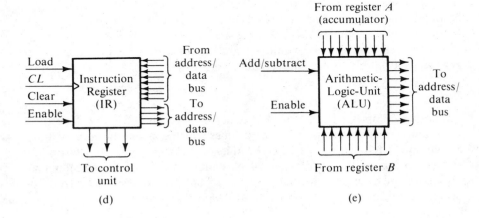

(d)

(e)

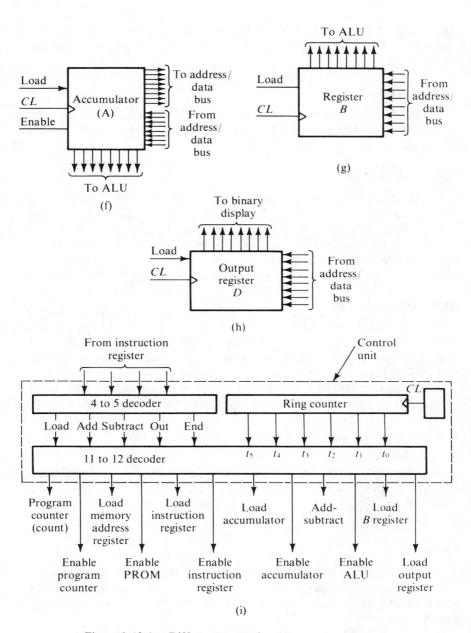

Figure 9.13-1. Different parts of an elementary computer
(a) Program counter   (b) Memory address register
(c) Programmable read-only memory   (d) Instruction register
(e) Arithmetic-logic unit   (f) Accumulator   (g) Regiser B
(h) Output register   (i) Control unit

PROM decoder to identify one of the 12 words stored in the PROM and to make it ready for delivery to the address/data bus. A symbolic diagram is shown in Figure 9.13-1b.

Programmable Read-Only Memory

As already noted, the PROM of EC contains 12 8-bit words. When the write line is high, the word addressed by MAR will be delivered to the address/data bus. A symbolic representation of the PROM is shown in Figure 9.13-1c.

Instruction Register

When the word from PROM is delivered to the address/data bus, it goes to the *instruction register* (IR) when its load line goes high. There the word is split into smaller words of 4-bits each. The four *most significant bits* (MSB) go directly, via a 2-state connection, to the decoder of the control unit. The four *least significant bits* (LSB) are read into the address/data bus when the Enable goes high. A symbolic representation of the IR is shown in Figure 9.13-1d.

Arithmetic Logic Unit

The *arithmetic logic unit* (ALU) is a combinational logic network that can perform binary addition and subtraction almost instantly; that is, it does not require the pulses of the clock for its operation. When the Enable line goes high, its contents are transferred to the address/data bus. When the add/subtract line goes high, addition is performed; when it goes low, subtraction is performed. A symbolic representation of the ALU is shown in Figure 9.13-1e.

Accumulator

As already discussed, the accumulator stores intermediate answers during a computer run. When the Enable line goes high, the accumulator word is transferred to the bus. When the load line goes high, then at the next positive clock pulse the accumulator receives the next word. A symbolic representation is shown in Figure 9.13-1f.

Register B

Suppose that the load line goes high. Then at the next positive clock pulse the word in the bus loads the register. At once it transfers its contents to ALU where an addition or subtraction takes place. The symbolic representation is shown in Figure 9.13-1g.

Output Register

The *output register* is used to take the results from the ALU and transfer them to an output device where they can be observed. With appropriate interfacing circuits, the output register can drive printers, cathode ray tubes, plotting equipment, light-emitting diodes, etc. Its symbolic representation is shown in Figure 9.13-1h.

Control Unit

The *control unit* is the nerve center of the computer. This unit, at the instant that we press the start button, sends a clear signal to all appropriate units and sets the program counter to 0000. The control unit also provides the clock pulses to synchronize the entire process. In addition, it sends the appropriate signals (high or low) through the control lines to all units of the computer, thereby establishing how the registers will react to the next positive clock pulse. However, in order for the control to function, it must be told what to do. These instructions are stored in the PROM. When the start button is pressed, the control starts to execute the first instruction. After the instruction has been executed, the control fetches the next instruction, and so on, until it reaches the instruction STOP. The symbolic representation of the control unit is shown in Figure 9.13-1i.

The sketch in Figure 9.13-2 shows all the parts of EC in an interconnected layout. This sketch specifies the *architecture* (structure) of the device.

A calculator differs from a computer because it does not include a control section. As a result, the operator must enter instructions and data during the prescribed sequence of operations.

9.14 OPERATION OF COMPUTER EC

The sequence of operations of elementary computer EC shown schematically in Figure 9.13-2 will be followed in performing the arithmetic operations $4 + 7 - 2$. To do this, we must first tell the computer in its own *machine language* what steps it must take. This is done by writing the following program, which is given in Table 9.14-1. Since EC does not contain an automatic input mechanism, we must first load the program into PROM by the proper adjustment of the switches, with open (0) and closed (1). The appearance of PROM will be exactly like the Instruction-Address column of Table 9.14-1.

Table 9.14-2 includes all of the steps that EC must complete to execute the program given in Table 9.14-1.

9.15 MICROCOMPUTERS AND MICROPROCESSORS

The study in the previous section was concerned with the operation of a primitive computer. In general computers are very versatile devices. Large scale computers and minicomputers are general purpose instruments, usually with extensive input/output capabilities and with large memory assemblies which will accommodate large problems. Microcomputers are much more limited in both their physical size and their system capabilities. Often, in fact, such a unit might be dedicated to a particular task and is made an integral part of the process it might be designed to control.

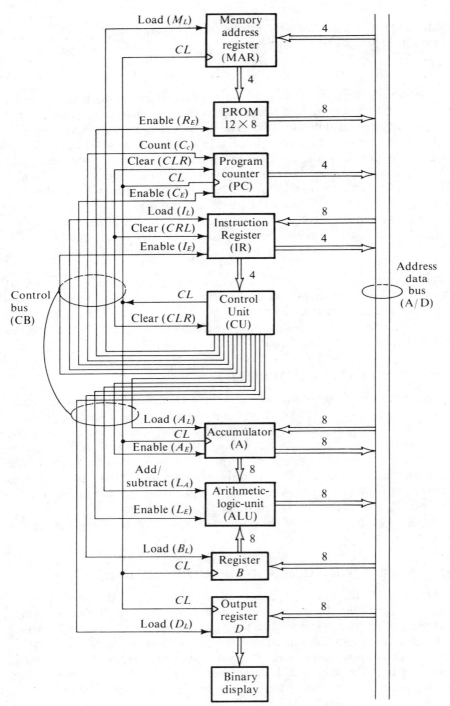

Figure 9.13-2.   The architecture of elementary computer (EC)

Table 9.14-1.   Program for Computer EC

	Mnemonic	Instruction Field	Address Field	Meaning of the Instruction
Instructions	LDA W_6	0000	0110	Load accumulator with the 6th word of PROM
	ADD W_7	0001	0111	Add the 7th word of PROM to accumulator
	SUB W_8	0010	1000	Subtract the 8th word of PROM from accumulator
	END	0011	not used	Load the output register with accumulator word
	STOP	0100	not used	Stop any more calculations
Data	W_6	0000	0100	Word in the 6th location of PROM $= 4_{10}$
	W_7	0000	0111	Word in the 7th location of PROM $= 7_{10}$
	W_8	0000	0010	Word in the 8th location of PROM $= 2_{10}$

We can think of a microcomputer as comprising six parts, as shown in Figure 9.15-1. As illustrated, the essential elements are (1) the clock, for establishing the timing to sequence all operations; (2) the central processing unit, CPU, which coordinates all activities within the microcomputer and coordinates the movement of data from the inputs, through the data manipulation phase, and then to the output; (3) the input ports, which accept inputs as allowed by the CPU; (4) the output ports which open on CPU instructions, to release processed information; (5) the ROMs, read-only memories, which contain the instructions for implementing the algorithms fitting the microcomputer to its application. They also contain the fixed tables and fixed constants which are useful to this application; and (6) the RAMs, random access memories, which provide for the temporary storage of data which are obtained from the input ports or which are generated within the CPU.

In employing a microcomputer in an instrument, the essential stages in the design consist of the following: the hardware necessary to develop the microcomputer structure shown in Figure 9.15-1; the hardware that will be necessary to bring the microcomputer together with the instrument components for the particular application; and the software considerations leading to the sequence of instructions so that the microcomputer executes the appropriate functions to perform the operations desired.

The term *microprocessor* is used to denote the microcomputer, but more

Table 9.14-2. Time Sequence in EC in Performing the Operation 4 + 7 − 2

Clock Period	Ring Counter	Control Lines M_t R_t C_r C_i I_t I_f A_t A_r L_A L_r B_t D_t	Explanation	PC	MAR	IR	A	ALU	Register B	Register D (Output)	
1	000001 T_0 phase = address phase	1 0 0 1 0 0 0 0 0 0 0 0	During this phase C_r and M_t go high and at the positive clock pulse the word in PC which holds the address of the current instruction is loaded in MAR. Observe that the positive clock pulse happens in the middle of each machine phase.	0000	0000	0000 0000	0000	0000	0000	0000	
2	000010 T_1 phase = memory phase	0 1 0 0 1 0 0 0 0 0 0 0	During this phase R_t and I_t go high and at the next positive clock pulse the addressed PROM instruction is transferred from the memory to the instruction register.	0000	0000	0000 0110	0000	0000	0000	0000	
3	000100 T_2 phase = increment phase	0 0 1 0 0 1 0 0 0 0 0 0	During this phase, C_r goes high and at the next positive clock pulse the program counter increases by one.	0001	0000	0000 0110	0000	0000	0000	0000	
4	001000 T_3 phase	1 0 0 0 1 0 0 0 0 0 0 0	During this phase, M_t and I_t go high and at the next positive clock pulse the instruction field goes to CU and the address field goes into MAR.	0001	0110	0000 0110	0100	0000	0000	0000	Fetch and Accumulator Routine
5	010000 T_4 phase	0 1 0 0 0 0 1 0 0 0 0 0	During this phase R_t and A_t go high and at the next positive clock pulse the addressed data word (6th word) of PROM will be loaded into the accumulator.	0001	0110	0000 0110	0100	0000	0000	0000	
6	100000 T_5 phase	0 0 0 0 0 0 0 0 0 0 0 0	During this phase nothing happens.	0001	0110	0000 0110	0100	0000	0000	0000	
7	000001 T_6 phase	1 0 0 1 0 0 0 0 0 0 0 0	Same as clock period one.	0001	0001	0000 0110	0100	0000	0000	0000	
8	000010 T_7 phase	0 1 0 0 1 0 0 0 0 0 0 0	Same as clock period two.	0001	0001	0001 0111	0100	0000	0000	0000	
9	000100 T_7 phase	0 0 1 0 0 1 0 0 0 0 0 0	Same as clock period three.	0002	0001	0001 0111	0100	0000	0000	0000	

Table 9.14-2. Time Sequence in EC in Performing the Operation 4 + 7 − 2

Clock Period	Ring Counter	M_L	R_F	C_C	C_F	I_L	I_L	A_L	A_F	L_A	L_F	B_L	D_L	Explanation	PC	MAR	IR	A	ALU	Register B	Register D (Output)	
10	001000 T_5 phase	1	0	0	0	0	1	0	0	0	0	0	0	During this phase the M_L and I_F go high and at the next positive clock pulse the instruction field goes to CU and the address field goes to MAR.	0002	0111	0001 0111	0100	0000	0000	0000	Add Routine
11	010000 T_6 phase	0	1	0	0	0	0	0	0	0	0	0	1	During this pulse, the R_F and B_L go high and at the next positive clock pulse the addressed word is loaded into the B register. ALU contains the sum of A and B registers.	0002	0111	0001 0111	$0100 = 4_{10}$	$1011 = 11_{10}$	$0111 = 7_{10}$	0000	
12	100000 T_1 phase	0	0	0	0	0	0	1	0	0	1	0	0	During this phase, the A_L and L_F go high and at the next positive clock pulse the sum is loaded from ALU into accumulator.	0002	0111	0001 0111	1011	1011	0111	0000	
13	000001 T_0 phase	1	0	0	1	0	0	0	0	0	0	0	0	Same as clock period one.	0002	0002	0001 0111	1011	1011	0111	0000	
14	000010 T_1 phase	0	1	0	0	1	0	0	0	0	0	0	0	Same as clock period two.	0002	0002	0010 1000	1011	1011	0111	0000	
15	000100 T_2 phase	0	0	1	0	0	0	0	0	0	0	0	0	Same as clock period three.	0003	0002	0010 1000	1011	1011	0111	0000	
16	001000 T_3 phase	1	0	0	0	0	1	0	0	0	0	0	0	Same as clock period ten.	0003	1000	0010 1000	1011	1011	0111	0000	
17	010000 T_4 phase	0	1	0	0	0	0	0	0	0	0	1	0	Same as clock period eleven. However, since the instruction word (0010 = SUB) the result in ALU is the difference between 1011 and 0010 ($11_{10} - 2_{10}$).	0003	1000	0010 1000	1011	1001	0010	0000	Subtract Routine
18	100000 T_5 phase	0	0	0	0	0	0	1	0	0	1	0	0	Same as clock period twelve.	0003	1000	0010 1000	1001	1001	0010	0000	
19	000001 T_0 phase	1	0	0	1	0	0	0	0	0	0	0	0	Same as clock period one.	0003	0003	0010 1000	1001	1001	0010	0000	
20	000010 T_1 phase	0	1	0	0	1	0	0	0	0	0	0	0	Same as clock period two.	0003	0003	0011 xxxx	1001	1001	0010	0000	
21	000100 T_2 phase	0	0	1	0	0	0	0	0	0	0	0	0	Same as clock period three.	0004	0003	0011 xxxx	1001	1001	0010	0000	

Table 9.14-2. Time Sequence in EC in Performing the Operation $4 + 7 - 2$

Clock Period	Ring Counter	Control Lines $M_i\ R_r\ C_c\ C_r\ I_i\ I_r\ A_i\ A_r\ L_i\ L_r\ B_L\ D_i$	Explanation	PC	MAR	IR	A	ALU	Register B	Register D (Output)
22 T_1 phase	001000	0 0 0 0 0 0 1 0 0 0 0 1	Since A_i and D_i are high the content of the accumulator is loaded in register D which drives the display.	0004	0003	0011 xxxx	1001	1001	0010	1001
23 T_2 phase	010000	0 0 0 0 0 0 0 0 0 0 0 0	Since no control pulses are sent nothing happens.	0004	0003	0011 xxxx	1001	1001	0010	1001
24 T_3 phase	100000	0 0 0 0 0 0 0 0 0 0 0 0	Nothing happens.	0004	0003	0011 xxxx	1001	1001	0010	1001
25 T_0 phase	000001	1 0 0 1 0 0 0 0 0 0 0 0	Same as clock period one.	0004	0004	0011 xxxx	1001	1001	0010	1001
26 T_1 phase	000010	0 1 0 0 1 0 0 0 0 0 0 0	Same as clock period two.	0004	0004	0100 xxxx	1001	1001	0010	1001
27 T_2 phase	000100	0 0 1 0 0 1 0 0 0 0 0 0	Same as clock period three.	0005	0004	0100 xxxx	1001	1001	0010	1001
28 T_3 phase	001000	1 0 0 1 0 0 0 0 0 0 0 0	Same as clock period tour. Since during this phase the CU is loaded with the instruction STOP the CU through appropriate circuitry stops the clock and the procesing stops.	0005	0004	0100 xxxx	1001	1001	0010	1001

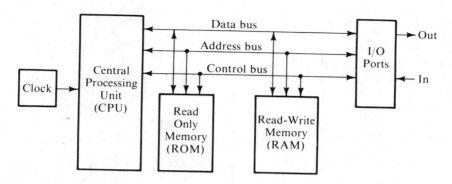

Figure 9.15-1. A simplified diagram of a microcomputer

typically it denotes the large-scale integration chip or integrated circuit which includes the CPU. Some microprocessor chips also include other parts of the microcomputer such as the clock or input/output ports.

The microcomputer will run, if an appropriate program is stored, in binary form, in successive locations in the memory. In binary form, the program is said to be in *machine language.* Because machine language programming is a rather forbidding task, one approach to a less formidable effort is to establish a number of mnemonics of two to four letters, each of which specifies a particular action. The resulting program is known as the *assembly form.* This program is then *assembled* (translated) to machine language and is stored in the memory.

Instruction Set of a Microcomputer

The total instruction set for each type of microcomputer can be very extensive. We shall discuss some important instructions which are found in commercially available microprocessors. These instructions are given only to illustrate the software development of a microprocessor. If the student wants to learn more about programming microprocessors, he must consult special publications provided by the manufacturer, such as the M6800 Programming Reference Manual, from Motorola.

A number of key issues must be provided for in the software and hardware of the microcomputer. Memory organization and *addressing* is of special importance because many components of the microcomputer must call on instructions stored in the memory. Since the number of memory locations which must be addressed for read or write instructions is large, an appropriate address organization must be effected. Suppose, for example, there is a 4K memory (4096 bytes of 4 bits each) as shown in Figure 9.15-2a. To address any position in this memory requires an address of 10 bits, as shown in Figure 9.15-2b, to address any of the possible 1024 combinations within one row. The extra 2 bits in locations 11 and 12 are used, when decoded, to use one of the 4 rows.

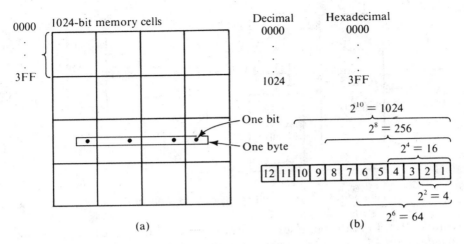

Figure 9.15-2.   (a) A 4096 byte (4K) memory   (b) Memory address organization

The arithmetic unit comprises basically a number of *registers*, usually 0 volt for 0 and +5 volt for 1. These will be 4, 8, or 16 bit assemblies, depending on the length of the basic unit of information that the particular microcomputer is designed to handle. An 8-bit microcomputer to effect multiplication often results in a product which exceeds the length of the register, which is equal to the sum of the number of bits in each number, and two registers are used simultaneously to accommodate the result. *Index registers* may be part of the arithmetic unit; they may be part of the control unit. They are used to act as counters for repetitive operations and to modify the memory address.

The program stored in the memory containing the instructions is read in successive steps, and the instructions are transferred to the control unit which produces signals to carry out the instructions. For any given computer, the designers must decide what instructions the computer will execute. The selection is influenced primarily by the intended use of the microcomputer. For example, the instruction set for a scientific computer will differ from the instruction set for a dedicated computer that is being used to control traffic lights.

Computer instruction sets are grouped into classes, according to their function. Each instruction is given a short name, and this is abbreviated to a 3 or 4 letter symbol, e.g., LDA = Load accumulator.

To access a computer with 4K memory requires an instruction format, as shown in Figure 9.15-3a. The 12 bits for address are needed to accomplish the reading or writing in any one of the 4096 locations of the memory, as discussed above. The *operation code* is a number which instructs the computer what operation is to be performed. With 8 bits of operation code, there will be up to $2^8 = 256$ instructions associated with this computer. Table 9.15-1 gives a number of instructions with their operation code number (shown in octal arithmetic). These instructions are found in most microcomputers.

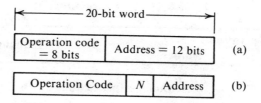

Figure 9.15-3.   Instruction format

Table 9.15-1.   Instruction Set

Code	MNE	Name	Explanation
		Operation	
		Halt Instruction	
000	HLT	Halt	Halt instruction is used to stop the computer processing. It is set at the end of the program, but can be specified at any part of the program.
		Load Instructions	
001	CLA	Clear accumulator	The contents of the accumulator are replaced with zeros.
010	LDA	Load accumulator	The address selects the memory location and its contents are loaded directly into the accumulator.
012	LDS	Load stack pointer	Stack pointer is a register usually used to store an address.
013	LDX	Load index register	The register is loaded from the addressed memory location. The instruction format is that shown in Figure 9.15-3b where a 3-bit number (N) specifies which one of the index registers must be loaded.
014	LIX(N)	Load immediately index register #N	Loads in index register #N the number given in the address position.
015	STA	Store accumulator	Stores the contents of the accumulator in a memory location specified by the address.
016	STX(N)	Store index register	Stores the contents of the index register #N in a memory location specified by the address.

Table 9.15-1.   Instruction Set

	Operation		Explanation
Code	MNE	Name	
Arithmetic Instructions			
020	ADD	Add	Adds the memory contents addressed by the address to the current contents of the accumulator, and the results remain in the accumulator.
021	SUB	Subtract	The contents of the addressed memory location are subtracted from the accumulator, and the difference appears in the accumulator.
022	ADX(N)	Add index register #N	The contents of the index register specified by the number (N) are added to the contents of the accumulator and the sum remains in the accumulator.
023	CMP	Compare	Compares the contents of the accumulator with the contents of the addressed memory location. This determines the condition codes which may be used subsequently for controlling conditional branching. Both operants are unaffected.
024	CPX(N)	Compare index register #N	The contents of the #N index register are compared with the addressed memory location. Special indicators are set; i.e., high, low, zero, depending on whether the contents in the register are higher, lower, or equal to the contents in the memory. These special indicators are called flags or status registers. A status register is shown in Figure 9.15-4a and data paths in Figure 9.15-4b.

Table 9.15-1. Instruction Set

Code	Operation MNE	Name	Explanation
		Logical Instructions	
030	AND	Logical AND	The contents of the memory location chosen by the address are ANDed with the present contents of the accumulator, and the results remain in the accumulator.
031	ORA	Inclusive OR	Perform logical OR between the contents of the accumulator and the addressed location of the memory. The results are placed in the accumulator.
032	EOR	Exclusive OR	Perform logical Exclusive-OR between memory content and accumulator, as for Inclusive-OR.
		Modification of Index Registers	
040	DEX(N)	Decrement index register #N	Subtract one from the index register #N.
041	INX(N)	Increment index register #N	Add one to the index register #N.
		Branch and Jump Instructions	
050	BRE	Branch on equal	Tests the flags set by CMP, CPX, or logic instructions. If they indicate equality, the branch address replaces the current contents of the instruction address and a "branching" or "jumping" to another part of the computer takes place.
051	BPL	Branch on plus (positive)	Checks the sign of the sign flag, and branching is accomplished if the sign is positive.
052	BRU	Branch unconditionally	The instruction places the branch address in the instruction address counter and automatically branching takes place.

Table 9.15-1. Instruction Set

Code	Operation MNE	Name	Explanation
053	BRZ	Branch on zero	Tests contents of the accumulator and if all its bits are zero, branching takes place.

Stack and Exit Instructions

Code	MNE	Name	Explanation
060	SBU	Stack and branch unconditionally	The current contents of the instruction address register are stored on the top of a stack of, for example, 8 registers, forcing down all other stored "branch from" addresses. Then the branch address is placed in the instruction-address register and branching takes place. This stack of special registers is used when many branch operations are needed.
061	EXU	Exit unconditionally	The computer returns from a stack and branch operation.

I/O Instructions

Code	MNE	Name	Explanation
071	RIN	Read in	Takes data from the input port and stores the data in the accumulator.
072	OUT	Read out	Takes data from the accumulator to the output port.

As called for under CPX(N), a status register or flag is a necessary component. The features of the Motorola 6800 microprocessor are shown in Figure 9.15-4. It is noted that the instruction set for the M6800 is considerably more extensive than that contained in Table 9.15-1.

With the available instruction set, we may use them in any order to create a program. Figure 9.15-5a shows how an instruction will look in machine code. This instruction stores the contents of the accumulator into a memory location specified by the address. To include all of the necessary zeros and ones in each instruction as required by the machine proves to be a burden on the programmer. As previously noted, a higher-level language, which is then translated by assemblers and compilers to binary form, greatly alleviates the burden in programming. Figure 9.15-5b shows the mnemonic form of the operation code STA which will be translated by the assembler program into the binary

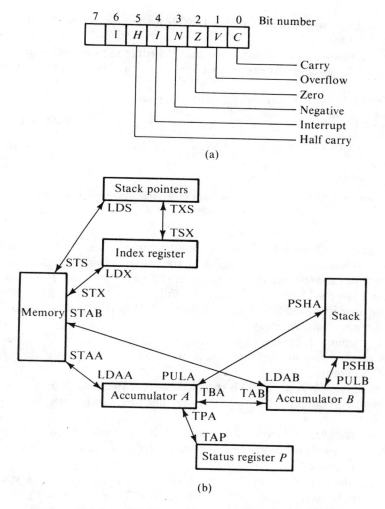

Figure 9.15-4.   (a) Status register of M6800 microprocessor
(b) Data paths of M6800

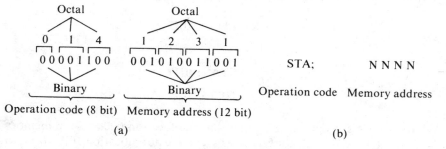

Figure 9.15-5.   The instruction address in binary form

00001100. The semicolon is recognized by the assembler program as the beginning of the address.

A *source statement* is an instruction that is written in assembler language. A typical source statement is shown in Figure 9.15-6a. The assembler program

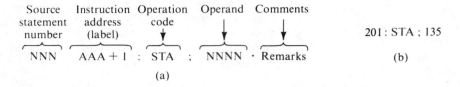

201: STA ; 135

(b)

Figure 9.15-6. The instruction-address field, operation code field, and the operand field

will assign a number to $AAA+1$, or the programmer could set the number, e.g., 200_8. The colon (:) is recognized by the assembler as the termination of the instruction address and the beginning of the operation code. The statement shown in Figure 9.15-6b will produce the following steps in the computer:

1. The instruction-address counter contents (201 in octal) with a ready command are sent to the memory.

2. The memory delivers the contents of the memory location 201 to memory address register and the control unit transfer to the operation code register (part of the control unit).

3. The operation code (STA) is decoded (say 111 in octal). The control unit knows that the contents of the accumulator must be sent to memory location 135.

4. The control unit continues to hold and decode the STA instruction and produces the signals necessary to move the contents of the accumulator to the memory in location 135.

5. When the time allocated for read and execute cycle is over, the control unit increases the instruction-address counter by 1 (202 in the present case) and proceeds to read the next instruction from memory.

EXAMPLE 9.15-1. What is the meaning of the keyboard table shown?

$$STAR : LDA \; ; \; 10D$$

$$AND \; ; \; 00D$$

$$STA \; ; \; 01D$$

$$HLT$$

SOLUTION. This program, assuming that the location 0000 of the memory has all four bits zeros, will convert any byte in memory location $10_{10} = \emptyset A_{16}$ to zeros and the result will be stored in memory location $1_{10} = 1_{16}$. The letter D indicates a decimal number to the assembler.

□ □ □

EXAMPLE 9.15-2. Discuss the meaning of the given program

SOLUTION.

LIX1	; 20D	Loads the index register No. 1 with the starting address of the storage location for the five samples. These are 20, 21, 22, 23, 24.
LIX2	; 5D	Loads index register No. 2 with the number 5. Uses this register as a counter.
RTRN : LDA	; 1002D	Loads the accumulator with data ready signal from port at address 1002.
AND	; 001D	ANDs the number 001 with the data in the accumulator.
BRZ	; RTRN	Returns to point RTRN as long as the accumulator has zero.
RIN	; 1004D	When the data are ready, read in data from port 1004D.
STA	; X1	Use index No. 1 address to store data into memory pointed by the register.
INX1	;	Increment index register No. 1 by 1.
DEX2	;	Decrement index register No. 2 by 1.
CPX2	; 60D	Compare index register No. 2 with the value (5) in location 60.
CLA		Clear accumulator.
BPL	; RTRN	Branch to point RTRN of the program, if the flag points to a positive bit.
HALT		

This program reads five values from a specified input and stores them in the memory. The flow chart diagram of this problem is shown in Figure 9.15-7a. Figure 9.15-7b shows the flow chart symbols.

□ □ □

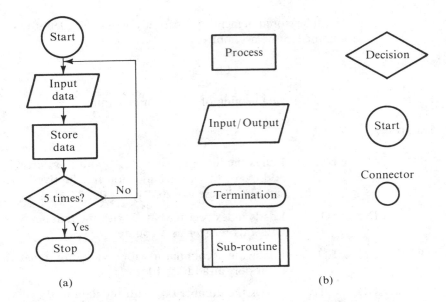

Figure 9.15-7   (a) Flow chart   (b) Flow chart symbols

9.16   INPUT AND OUTPUT DEVICES

The input and output devices of a computer provide the interface for communication with the outside world. In small general-purpose computers, communication with the machine is usually accomplished through a teletypewriter terminal provided with a keyboard, a typing mechanism, and a means for reading and punching paper tape. The initial directions to the computer are often given by a series of front panel control switches.

Large scale computers are provided with a number of input/output devices, often including several of the following:

Input Devices: (1) keyboards and consoles, (2) punched card readers, (3) punched tape readers, (4) optical or magnetic character readers, (5) light pens.

Output Devices: (1) typewriters, (2) line printers, (3) card punches, (4) tape punches, (5) cathode ray tube consoles, (6) plotters.

When a computer is used as a controller for industrial process control, it may be directly connected to signal transducers, with outputs directly to control process actuators. Often the input/output terminals are located at points that are remote from the central CPU and memory, with telephone lines being used for transmitting the input and output signals. A convenience device through which the user can be in contact with the computer is an *acoustical* coupler, or *dataphone*. This device resembles a telephone in many respects. A *touch-tone* remote terminal unit consists of a keyboard and a speaker through which the user can signal numbers and instructions using push buttons. The computer responds by giving the results in a human-like voice.

Program codes that include instructions and data are prepared manually in a form that the computer can recognize. Such programs are prepared in punched cards or as a tape at separate stations, and these are fed into the machine directly from the remote terminal or from the computer center control room.

Computers are often coupled together to allow the direct interchange of information and data automatically. This communication link is extremely fast with the speed limited by the quality of the electrical lines, if they are located remotely from each other. Of course, computers which are physically near each other can be interconnected by cables.

9.17 TYPICAL INTEGRATED CIRCUITS

The following figures are self-explanatory, showing some of the many varieties of integrated circuits.

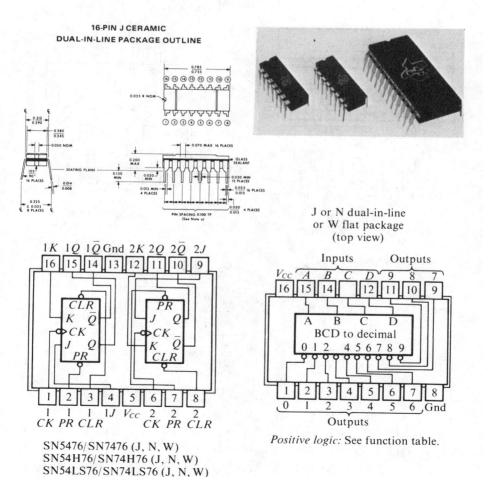

SN5476/SN7476 (J, N, W)
SN54H76/SN74H76 (J, N, W)
SN54LS76/SN74LS76 (J, N, W)

Positive logic: See function table.

AND gates

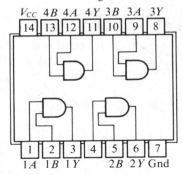

SN5408/SN7408 (J, N, W)
SN54LS08/SN74LS08 (J, N, W)

NAND gates

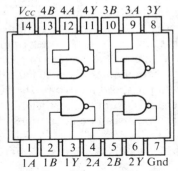

SN5426/SN7426 (J, N)

OR gates

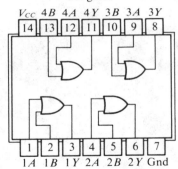

SN5432/SN7432 (J, N, W)
SN54LS32/SN74LS32 (J, N, W)

NOR gates

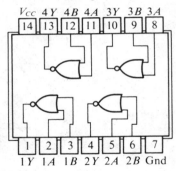

SN5402/SN7402 (J, N)
SN54L02/SN74L02 (J, N)
SN54LS02/SN74LS02 (J, N, W)
SN54S02/SN74502 (J, N, W)

'LS76 Function Table

Inputs					Outputs	
Preset	Clear	Clock	J	K	Q	$\bar{Q}$
L	H	X	X X		H	L
H	L	X	X X		L	H
L	L	X	X X		H*	H*
H	H	↓	L L		Q_0	$\bar{Q}_0$
H	H	↓	H L		H	L
H	H	↓	L H		L	H
H	H	↓	H H		Toggle	
H	H	H	X X		Q_0	$\bar{Q}_0$

'76, 'H76 Function Table

Inputs					Outputs	
Preset	Clear	Clock	J	K	Q	$\bar{Q}$
L	H	X	X X		H	L
H	L	X	X X		L	H
L	L	X	X X		H*	H*
H	H	⊓	L L		Q_0	$\bar{Q}_0$
H	H	⊓	H L		H	L
H	H	⊓	L H		L	H
H	H	⊓	H H		Toggle	

Function Table

No.	Inputs				Outputs									
	D	C	B	A	0	1	2	3	4	5	6	7	8	9
0	L	L	L	L	L	H	H	H	H	H	H	H	H	H
1	L	L	L	H	H	L	H	H	H	H	H	H	H	H
2	L	L	H	L	H	H	L	H	H	H	H	H	H	H
3	L	L	H	H	H	H	H	L	H	H	H	H	H	H
4	L	H	L	L	H	H	H	H	L	H	H	H	H	H
5	L	H	L	H	H	H	H	H	H	L	H	H	H	H
6	L	H	H	L	H	H	H	H	H	H	L	H	H	H
7	L	H	H	H	H	H	H	H	H	H	H	L	H	H
8	H	L	L	L	H	H	H	H	H	H	H	H	L	H
9	H	L	L	H	H	H	H	H	H	H	H	H	H	L
	H	L	H	L	H	H	H	H	H	H	H	H	H	H
	H	L	H	H	H	H	H	H	H	H	H	H	H	H
	H	H	L	L	H	H	H	H	H	H	H	H	H	H
	H	H	L	H	H	H	H	H	H	H	H	H	H	H
	H	H	H	L	H	H	H	H	H	H	H	H	H	H
	H	H	H	H	H	H	H	H	H	H	H	H	H	H

H = high level (off), L = low level (on)

Invalid

These monolithic BCD-to-decimal decoder/drivers consist of eight inverters and ten four-input NAND gates. The inverters are connected in pairs to make BCD input data available for decoding by the NAND gates. Full decoding of valid BCD input logic ensures that all outputs remain off for all invalid binary input conditions. These decoders features high-performance, n-p-n output transistors designed for use as indicator/relay drivers or as open-collector logic-circuit drivers. Each of the high-breakdown output transistors (15 volts) of the SN54145, SN74145, or SN74LS145 will sink up to 80 milliamperes of current. Each input is one Series 54/74 or Series 54LS/74LS standard load, respectively. Inputs and outputs are entirely compatible for use with TTL or DTL logic circuits, and the outputs are compatible for interfacing with most MOS integrated circuits. Power dissipation is typically 215 milliwatts for the '145 and 35 milliwatts for the 'LS145.

Functional Block Diagram

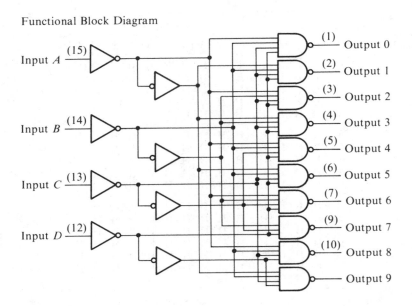

9.18 POSTLUDE

Computer engineering and computer science have had tremendous growth, and digital devices and controllers of diverse nature are used extensively. The extent of these fields is evident by the fact that graduate studies are available in both, with curriculums that lead to advanced degrees and to the doctorate level. Since the body of computer knowledge is large and growing rapidly, this chapter could only introduce some of the principles of logic circuits and logical design, some of the basic structural elements that are used, and some few ideas of how one might structure digital devices. Only simple ideas of data structures, digital architecture, and rudiments of machine language programming have been discussed. With continued reading and with future courses, the interested student can explore the digital world. The opportunities for computer development are extensive, but serious study is essential.

SUMMARY

- The main elements of a computer are the central processing unit, the memory, the arithmetic unit, and the input-output devices.

- The basic logic operations are AND, OR, NOT, NAND and NOR. The symbols for these are shown in the figure.

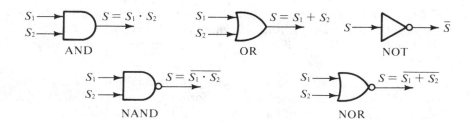

- Boolean algebra relations are summarized in Table 9.4-1. Two important rules are the DeMorgan rules, which are

$$\overline{S_1 \cdot S_2} = \overline{S_1} + \overline{S_2} \qquad\qquad \overline{S_1 + S_2} = \overline{S_1} \cdot \overline{S_2}$$

- The Karnaugh map provides a very convenient graphical method for minimizing Boolean functions. It displays the Boolean function in graphical form which permits a ready view of possible functional combinations.

- Addition, subtraction, multiplication and division of binary numbers are subject to the following rules:

$$
\begin{array}{cccc}
0 & 0 & 1 & 1 \\
+\,0 & +\,1 & +\,0 & +\,1 \\
\hline
0 & 1 & 1 & 0 \text{ plus carry-over of } 1
\end{array}
$$

$$
\begin{array}{c}
1 \\
1 \\
1 \\
\hline
1 \text{ plus carry-over of } 1
\end{array}
$$

$$
\begin{array}{cccc}
0 & 1 & 1 & 0 \\
-\,0 & -\,0 & -\,1 & -\,1 \\
\hline
0 & 1 & 0 & 1 \text{ with a borrow of } 1
\end{array}
$$

$$0 \times 0 = 0 \qquad 1 \times 0 = 0 \qquad 0 \times 1 = 0 \qquad 1 \times 1 = 1 \qquad 0 \div 1 = 0 \qquad 1 \div 1 = 1$$

- The flipflop is a bistable (two state) device which can store (or remember a binary bit of information. The device is able to change from one state to the other state by a triggering action. The basic RS-FF is set by $S = 1$ and is reset by $R = 1$.

- The half adder is a device that adds two binary digits to yield the sum digit and the carry digit. If the adder accommodates an input carry it is called a full adder.

- For arithmetic addition operations, chains of full adders are required. These may be combined as parallel or serial adders.

- Two important classes of registers exist: the storage register and the shift register. The storage register is used for storing binary information, such as numbers of instructions. It is usually made of FFs in combination, each of which will store one bit. The shift register is a device designed to handle data.

- Two important classes of counters exist: ripple and synchronous types. These will accept input pulses, either uniformly or randomly distributed in time, and will keep count of the numbers up to the counter capacity and will then reset and continue with the counting.

- Memories are broadly divided into three categories: random access memories (RAM), read only memories (ROM), and programmable read only memories (PROM).

REVIEW QUESTIONS

1. State the basic unit blocks which comprise a computer and describe their functions.
2. Draw the logic symbols for AND, NOT, OR, NAND, NOR, and develop their truth tables.
3. Convert decimal to binary numbers, and vice versa.
4. State the two logic rules of DeMorgan.
5. Is the Karnaugh map used to minimize or to maximize Boolean functions?
6. Which of the KMs shown below allow functional combinations?

S	S_2 0	1
S_1 0	0	1
1	1	0

S	S_2 0	1
S_1 0	0	0
1	1	0

S	S_2 0	1
S_1 0	1	1
1	1	1

7. What are flipflops used for?
8. What are toggle, master-slave, and D FFs?
9. What is an RS-FF and how can it be changed to a JK-FF and to a D-FF?
10. What is the difference between a half adder and a full adder?
11. What is the difference between a serial and a parallel adder?
12. What is the function of parity circuits?
13. What is the difference between a storage and a shift register?
14. What is a ripple Modulo-8 counter?
15. What is a BCD coder?
16. What is meant by the term *access time*?
17. What do the symbols listed mean: SSI, MSI, LSI, ROM, PROM, MAR?
18. Name some output devices of a computer.

REFERENCES

1. Camp, R. C., T. A. Smay and C. J. Triska, *Microcomputer Systems Principles*, Matrix Publishers, Inc., Portland, OR, 1978.

   A suitable text for courses which emphasize hands-on experience with computers. Discusses KIM-1 and its relation to the microprocessor element MCS 6502. Provides a background that permits ready transfer to other systems.

2. Doty, K. L., *Fundamental Principles of Microcomputer Architecture*, Matrix Publishers, Inc., Portland, OR, 1979.

   Explains the design, analysis, modeling, and evaluation of digital computer instruction sets, machine organization, peripherals, network structures and system software. The emphasis is on the functional, algorithmic behavior of microcomputer components, not their electrical characteristics.

3. Malvino, A. P., *Digital Computer Electronics*, McGraw Hill Book Co., New York, NY, 1977.

   Provides an introduction to computers and microprocessors in a clear and methodical way. The text first develops digital theory and devices and then applies this knowledge to bus-organized computers. Includes significant discussion concerning microprocessors.

4. Peatman, J. B., *The Design of Digital Systems*, McGraw Hill Book Co., New York, NY, 1972.

   Discusses the various digital principles and elements that are important to the digital computer.

PROBLEMS

9.2-1. Develop the truth table for the AND gate and XOR gate with 3 inputs.

9.2-2. Show that the combination of the gates illustrated represents an exclusive OR (XOR) gate.

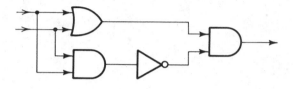

Figure P9.2-2

9.2-3. Develop the truth table for the two input exclusive NOR (XNOR) gate.

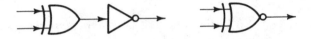

Figure P9.2-3

9.2-4. Establish the logic diagram for the so-called 3-way light which can be operated from two separate switch locations, say at the bottom and at the top of a flight of stairs.

9.2-5. Determine the output logical functions for the logic circuits shown.

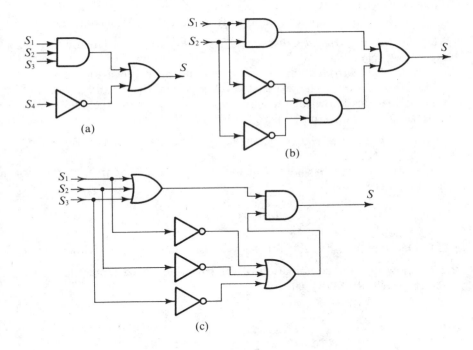

Figure P9.2-5

9.2-6. A *digital comparator* is to compare the magnitude of two *n*-bit binary numbers, e.g., $S_1 = 101001$ and $S_2 = 1101110$; also $S_1 = 1011$ and $S_2 = 1011$.

(a) Determine the outputs from the logic circuit shown in Figure P9.2-6.

(b) What conclusions can be drawn concerning the relative values of S_1 and S_2 at the respective outputs A, B, C?

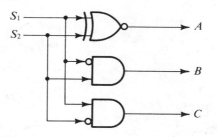

Figure P9.2-6

9.2-7. Find the output of the *word comparator* shown in Figure P9.2-7

(a) if the two 3-bit words are the same;

(b) if the two 3-bit words are different.

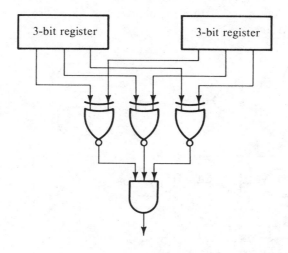

Figure P9.2-7

9.2-8. Find the output functions for the logic circuits shown.

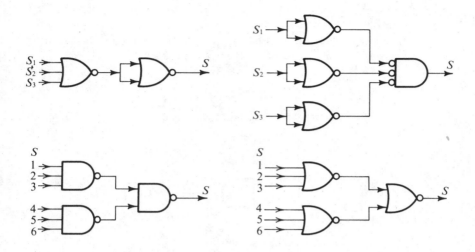

Figure P9.2-8

9.2-9. Show that a NAND gate can be made from an AND gate and a NOT gate.

9.2-10. Find the outputs from the following gate combinations. Identify the equivalent gates of those combinations which are shown enclosed by broken lines.

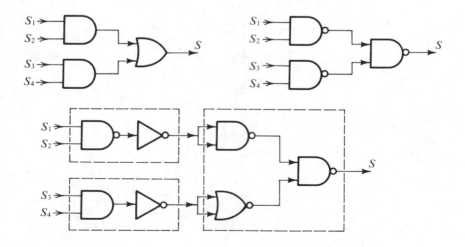

Figure P9.2-10

9.2-11. Find the outputs of the gate combinations shown in Figure P9.2-11.

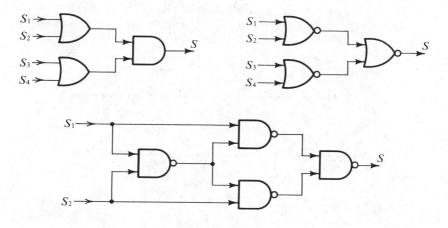

Figure P9.2-11

9.2-12. Suppose that to start a car the following must be implemented: doors closed, seat belt fastened, ignition key on, fuel indicator on. If any one of these is not in order, a warning signal is present. Construct the logic diagram using NAND gates; using NOR gates.

9.2-13. Refer to Example 9.2-1. Develop a logic circuit that will accept quarters, dimes, nickels and pennies and will return the correct change.

9.4-1. Use the properties of Boolean algebra to simplify the logical functions

$$S = \bar{S}_1 \cdot S_2 \cdot \bar{S}_3 + S_1 \cdot \bar{S}_2 \cdot S_3 + \bar{S}_1 \cdot \bar{S}_2 \cdot S_3 + S_1 \cdot S_2 \cdot S_3$$

$$S = \overline{\bar{S}_1 \cdot \bar{S}_2} + \bar{S}_2 \cdot S_3$$

$$S = S_1 \cdot [\overline{\bar{S}_1 + \bar{S}_2 \cdot (S_3 + \bar{S}_1 \cdot \bar{S}_3)}]$$

9.4-2. Represent the results of Examples 9.4-5, 9.4-6, and 9.4-7 by logic gates.

9.5-1. Use Karnaugh map procedures to find the minimized output functions for the following truth tables.

S_1	S_2	S_3	S
0	0	0	0
0	0	1	0
0	1	0	1
0	1	1	1
1	0	0	0
1	0	1	0
1	1	0	1
1	1	1	1

S_1	S_2	S_3	S
0	0	0	0
0	0	1	1
0	1	0	1
0	1	1	0
1	0	0	0
1	0	1	1
1	1	0	1
1	1	1	0

9.7-1. The input waveforms to an RS-FF are shown in Figure P9.7-1. Complete these diagrams by including the waveforms for the outputs y and $\bar{y}$.

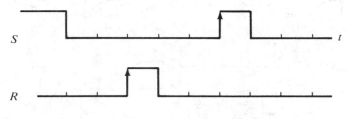

Figure P9.7-1

9.7-2. Find the output y of the clocked RS-FF for signals as shown in Figure P9.7-2.

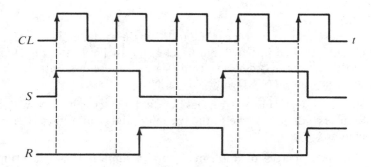

Figure P9.7-2

9.7-3. A 3-bit word is introduced into the set of D-FFs shown in Figure P9.7-3.

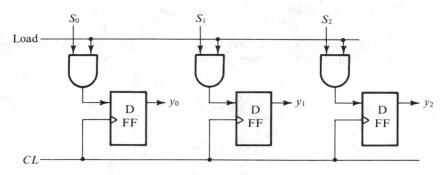

Figure P9.7-3

(a) If Load is low, what is the value of the ys after the positive clock edge?

(b) Repeat for the case when Load is high.

9.7-4. Refer to the chain of JK-FFs which are connected to have both J and K equal to 1 as shown in Figure P9.7-4. If the ys are zero (low) at the beginning of a sequence of clock pulses, find the decimal equivalent of the outputs at the first, second and third clock pulses.

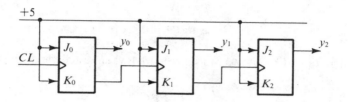

Figure P9.7-4

9.7-5. Verify the behavior of the master-slave flipflop shown in Figure 9.7-9.

9.8-1. Construct a table with decimal numbers from 1 to 30 and their corresponding binary numbers. Also, construct a table of decimal numbers corresponding to 2^n and 2^{-n} with n from 0 through 10.

9.8-2. Convert the following decimal numbers to their equivalent binary, octal and hexadecimal form:

(1) 22   (2) 34   (3) 131   (4) 1125   (5) 64   (6) 888
(7) 971   (8) 0.4425   (9) 0.225   (10) 0.375   (11) 0.4375
(12) 33.375   (13) 125.125   (14) 333.0625.

9.8-3. Convert the following binary numbers to decimal, octal and hexadecimal numbers:

(1) 101   (2) 1000   (3) 1011   (4) 10011   (5) 1111
(6) 11   (7) 10001   (8) 1011.001101   (9) 100.111011.

9.9-1. Carry out the following additions and subtractions in binary form:

$$\begin{array}{ccccc} 14 & 15 & 21 & 31 & 32 \\ +\,12 & +\,9 & -\,9 & -\,21 & -\,16 \end{array}$$

9.9-2. Perform the following additions and subtractions and check your answers by converting the binary numbers to decimal form:

(1) $10100 - 10011$ (2) $10000 - 1101$ (3) $1010 + 10010$
(4) $1001 + 1001 + 110$ (5) $10010 - 111$ (6) $111.11 - 111.1$
(7) $111.11 + 111.01$ (8) $1011 - 111.1$ (9) $1101.001 + 1101.001$
(10) $0.011 + 0.111$.

9.10-1. Prove that the diagram shown in Figure P9.10-1 is that of a half adder, and identify the sum and carry lines.

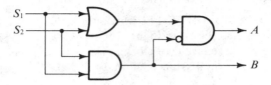

Figure P9.10-1

9.10-2. The full adder shown in Figure 9.10-4 when tested yields the following truth table:

S_1	S_2	C_i	S	C_o
0	0	0	0	0
0	0	1	1	0
0	1	0	1	0
0	1	1	0	1
1	0	0	1	0
1	0	1	0	1
1	1	0	0	
1	1	1	1	

If one of the half adders is faulty, determine which one is at fault.

9.10-3. A 4-bit storage register is shown in Figure P9.10-3. If the input and output words before point 1 of the clock signal are different describe what happens as the clock runs ($S'_i = 1101$ and $S_i = 0110$).

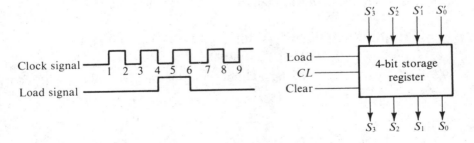

Figure P9.10-3

9.10-4. Show that when the SUB line of Figure 9.10-7 goes low the arithmetic unit is an adder, and when it goes high, it is a subtractor.

9.10-5. A three bit 2s complement adder/subtractor is shown in Figure P9.10-5. If $S'_i = 011$ and $S''_i = 010$ find the y_is when SUB is low and when it is high after the positive clock edge.

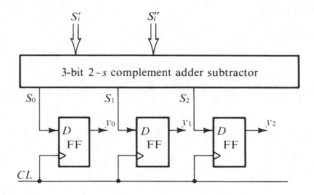

Figure P9.10-5

9.10-6. *Shift-left* and *shift-right* registers are shown in Figure P9.10-6. If the input I is one, what are the output words at the first, second, and third positive pulse?

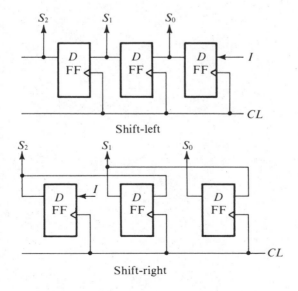

Figure P9.10-6

9.11-1. Use logic gates to build the decoder for Example 9.11-1.

9.12-1. Use chips with features as described in Example 9.12-1 and build a memory of 128 2-bit words. Also design a decoder for selecting one of the four chips.

Chapter Ten

Waves and Radiation

Our studies to this point have dealt largely with problems which are essentially one-dimensional, in the sense that currents were confined to wires and branches making up the system. Our discussion of mechanical problems was limited to one-dimensional motion. Of tremendous importance to our further studies, especially for communications—radio, television, fiber optics, satellite control, etc.—are "fields" which may exist in space, as in the case of radio waves. A discussion of the origin and the propagation of electrical waves in space and in confined regions involves aspects of electricity and magnetism and electrodynamics, phenomena which are multidimensional and which require two or three dimensions in their description. In fact, the fundamental equations that describe electric, magnetic and electrodynamic phenomena are each three-dimensional space quantities, often involving time. These equations when written together are known as the Maxwell equations and are the starting point for all electromagnetic field problems.

The phenomenon of wave motion is described mathematically by a second order differential equation which contains both space and time derivatives. Depending on the types of waves, the fields may be scalars or vectors. Such a mathematical equation is called a *partial differential equation* and its solution provides a description of the wave phenomenon. Many types of waves exist, and often their mathematical representations are rather complex. Electromagnetic waves require vector relations in their description, and are complicated even for simple cases. As a result, we shall restrict our discussion to *plane waves* whose spatial and time variations are sinusoidal functions.

10.1 THE WAVE EQUATION

To describe the movement of a wave, consider the sinusoidal curve shown in Figure 10.1-1 at two instants of time. The expression

$$y = A \sin kz \qquad (10.1\text{-}1)$$

will describe the sine curve at $t=0$. It is readily observed that when $z=2\pi/k$ the distance denotes one full cycle or one wavelength λ. The quantity k

$$k = \frac{2\pi}{\lambda} \tag{10.1-2}$$

is called the *wave number* of the wave.

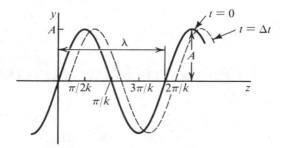

Figure 10.1-1.   Sinusoidally varying waves

To take into consideration the periodic time variation of such a wave, Equation (10.1-1) must be modified to read

$$y = A \sin\left(kz - \frac{2\pi}{T}t\right) = A \sin\left(kz - \omega t\right) \tag{10.1-3}$$

where $\omega = 2\pi f = 2\pi/T$, with f denoting the frequency and T the period of the wave. For an elapsed time $t=T$, the phase $(2\pi/T)t$ of the curve will change by 2π, and the sine wave will progress one wavelength. The velocity of the wave, called the *phase velocity*, is

$$v_{ph} = \frac{\lambda}{T} = f\lambda = \frac{2\pi f\lambda}{2\pi} = \frac{\omega}{2\pi/\lambda} = \frac{\omega}{k} \tag{10.1-4}$$

Suppose that Equation (10.1-3) is differentiated twice with respect to the spatial variable z, and twice with respect to the time. The resulting equations are

$$\frac{\partial^2 y}{\partial z^2} = -k^2 A \sin\left(kz - \omega t\right) \qquad \text{(a)} \quad (10.1\text{-}5)$$

$$\frac{\partial^2 y}{\partial t^2} = -\omega^2 A \sin\left(kz - \omega t\right) \qquad \text{(b)}$$

where the symbol ∂ is used to denote partial differentiation. By substituting the value $A \sin\left(kz - \omega t\right)$ from Equation (10.1-5b) into Equation (10.1-5a) we find that

$$\frac{\partial^2 y}{\partial z^2} = \frac{1}{v_{ph}^2} \frac{\partial^2 y}{\partial t^2} \qquad (10.1\text{-}6)$$

This is known as the *wave equation*.

The following examples will provide an understanding of how, from basic principles, the wave equation is developed. They will also show the relation between the phase velocity and physical quantities which characterizes the medium in which the wave propagates.

EXAMPLE 10.1-1. Find the equation which specifies the voltage at any point along a lossless parallel wire transmission line, shown in Figure 10.1-2a.

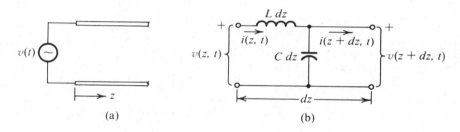

(a)   (b)

**Figure 10.1-2. (a) Schematic representation of an electrical transmission line
(b) Infinitesimal portion of the line**

SOLUTION. Assume that the parallel wires which constitute the line have a series inductance L per unit length, and a shunt capacitance C per unit length. It is always possible to represent an infinitesimal portion of the line in lumped parameter form, as shown in Figure 10.1-2b. By an application of the Kirchhoff voltage and current law to the infinitesimal section, we write.

$$v(z+dz,t) - v(z,t) = -Ldz\frac{\partial i(z,t)}{\partial t} \qquad \text{(a)} \quad (10.1\text{-}7)$$

$$i(z+dz,t) - i(z,t) = -Cdz\frac{\partial v(z+dz,t)}{\partial t} \qquad \text{(b)}$$

For this to represent the continuous line, the limit is taken as $dz \to 0$. Then

$$\frac{\partial v(z,t)}{\partial z} = \lim_{dz \to 0} \frac{v(z+dz,t) - v(z,t)}{dz} = -L\frac{\partial i(z,t)}{\partial t} \qquad \text{(a)} \quad (10.1\text{-}8)$$

$$\frac{\partial i(z,t)}{\partial z} = \lim_{dz \to 0} \frac{i(z+dz,t) - i(z,t)}{dz} = -C\frac{\partial v(z,t)}{\partial t} \qquad \text{(b)}$$

By differentiating Equation (10.1-8a) with respect to z and Equation (10.1-8b) with respect to t and then combining the results, the wave equation that results is

$$\frac{\partial^2 v(z,t)}{\partial z^2} = LC \frac{\partial^2 v(z,t)}{\partial t^2} = \frac{1}{v_{ph}^2} \frac{\partial^2 v(z,t)}{\partial t^2} \qquad \text{(a)} \quad (10.1\text{-}9)$$

where

$$v_{ph} = \frac{1}{\sqrt{LC}} \qquad \text{(b)}$$

From the relation $\omega/k = v_{ph}$, it follows that

$$k = \frac{\omega}{v_{ph}} = \omega\sqrt{LC} \qquad\qquad \lambda = \frac{1}{f\sqrt{LC}} \qquad (10.1\text{-}10)$$

$\square \quad \square \quad \square$

EXAMPLE 10.1-2. Find the equation that describes the vibrations of a stretched flexible string (see Figure 10.1-3).

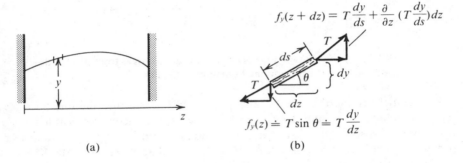

$$f_y(z + dz) = T\frac{dy}{ds} + \frac{\partial}{\partial z}(T\frac{dy}{ds})dz$$

$$f_y(z) \doteq T\sin\theta \doteq T\frac{dy}{dz}$$

(a)   (b)

Figure 10.1-3.   A flexible string under tension

SOLUTION. Assume that the string is initially distorted by a small amount. This creates a force or tension in the string, and this is a continuous function since no discontinuities in the shape of the string are assumed. Also, it is supposed that the motion occurs in the Y-Z plane. From Figure 10.1-3b it is noted that for small displacements

$$ds = \left[1 + \left(\frac{dy}{dz}\right)^2\right]^{1/2} dz \doteq dz$$

from which, therefore

$$\frac{dy}{ds} \doteq \frac{dy}{dz} \qquad (10.1\text{-}11)$$

The mass of the element ds of the string is written

$$\varrho_L ds \doteq \varrho_L dz \qquad (10.1\text{-}12)$$

where ϱ_L is the linear density of the string in kg/m. The perpendicular force acting on the element dz is obtained by taking the algebraic sum of the forces. At the ends of the sample element, the forces are

$$-f_y(z) = -T \sin \theta \doteq -T \frac{dy}{ds} \doteq -T \frac{dy}{dz} = -T \frac{\partial y}{\partial z} \qquad (a) \quad (10.1\text{-}13)$$

$$f_y(z+dz) = T \frac{\partial y}{\partial z} + T \frac{\partial}{\partial z}\left(\frac{\partial y}{\partial z}\right) dz \qquad (b)$$

It is the unbalanced force that causes the motion of the string, and this is related to the inertial force through Newton's law. That is

$$f_y(z+dz) - f_y(z) = \frac{\partial}{\partial t}(mv_y) = \varrho_L dz \frac{\partial v_y}{\partial t} \qquad (10.1\text{-}14)$$

By combining Equations (10.1-12) through (10.1-14) we find that

$$\frac{\partial^2 y}{\partial z^2} = \frac{1}{v_s^2} \frac{\partial^2 y}{\partial t^2} \qquad (a) \quad (10.1\text{-}15)$$

where

$$v_s = \sqrt{\frac{T}{\varrho_L}} \qquad (b)$$

The wave number and the wavelength of the disturbance are

$$k = \frac{\omega}{v_s} = \omega \sqrt{\frac{\varrho_L}{T}} \qquad \lambda = \frac{2\pi}{\omega \sqrt{\varrho_L/T}} = \frac{1}{f \sqrt{\varrho_L/T}} \qquad (10.1\text{-}16)$$

It is noted without proof that a pressure disturbance in water or air proves to be described by the wave equation in the form

$$\frac{\partial^2 p}{\partial z^2} = \frac{1}{c_a^2} \frac{\partial^2 p}{\partial t^2} \qquad (a) \quad (10.1\text{-}17)$$

where

$$c_a = \sqrt{\frac{\gamma p_o}{\varrho_o}} \qquad (b)$$

with p_o and ϱ_o the ambient pressure and density of the fluid and where γ is the ratio of specific heats at constant pressure to that at constant volume. p is the small pressure perturbation ($p \ll p_o$); i.e., the extra pressure or pressure differential above the ambient pressure. Similar wave equations describe such diverse phenomena as water waves, compressional waves in solids, torsional waves in a wire, and elastic waves in a homogeneous medium.

Another very important wave which touches the lives of all of us is the electromagnetic wave. In this connection, we accept the Maxwell equations as postulates and from these we can derive all of the properties of natural and man-made electromagnetic phenomena. The Maxwell equations describe the sources and the field vectors in the broad fields of electrostatics, magnetostatics, and electromagnetic induction, subjects which it is assumed the reader has previously studied in a formal course in electricity and magnetism. These include such topics as Coulomb's law and Gauss' law in electrostatics, the work of Ampère and others in magnetism and magnetic phenomena, and the laws of electromagnetic induction formulated by Faraday. The resulting fields so involved are vector fields since they have magnitude and direction at every point in space. In consequence, electromagnetic waves in their generality can be described only by vector equations, which are difficult to solve and interpret. We shall limit our discussion to simple plane waves since it can proceed in terms of scalar quantities. A schematic representation of a simple plane electromagnetic wave is shown in Figure 10.1-4.

Maxwell's equations which characterize a *plane wave* propagating in a homogeneous dielectric medium such as air, devoid of free charges and currents, involve both electric and magnetic fields $\bar{E} = \bar{a}_x E_x$ and $\bar{H} = \bar{a}_y H_y$. These are vectors in the planes, as shown in Figure 10.1-4a. The equations which describe these fields are

$$\frac{\partial E_x(z,t)}{\partial z} = -\mu \frac{\partial H_y(z,t)}{\partial t} \qquad \text{(a)} \quad (10.1\text{-}18)$$

$$\frac{\partial H_y(z,t)}{\partial z} = -\epsilon \frac{\partial E_x(z,t)}{\partial t} \qquad \text{(b)}$$

where μ is the permeability (Hm^{-1}) and ϵ is the permittivity (Fm^{-1}) of the medium. By differentiating Equation (10.1-18a) with respect to z and Equation (10.1-18b) with respect to t, and by combining the resulting equations, we obtain the wave equation

$$\frac{\partial^2 E_x(z,t)}{\partial z^2} = \mu\epsilon \frac{\partial^2 E_x(z,t)}{\partial t^2} = \frac{1}{c^2} \frac{\partial^2 E_x(z,t)}{\partial t^2} \qquad \text{(a)} \quad (10.1\text{-}19)$$

where

$$c = \frac{1}{\sqrt{\mu\epsilon}} \qquad \text{(b)}$$

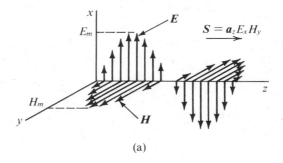

(a)

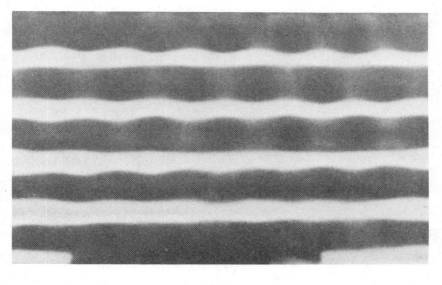

(b)

**Figure 10.1-4. (a) Schematic representation of a periodic plane electromagnetic wave
(b) Periodic straight water waves**

One of the fundamental properties of any wave is its ability to transfer energy from one point in space to another. It is this remarkable ability that provides the basis for modern communication. For the electromagnetic wave in particular, a propagation vector $\bar{S}$, called the *Poynting vector*, gives the rate of energy flow across a unit area perpendicular to the direction of flow. The dimensions of $\bar{S}$ are W/m², and its mathematical representaion is given by the vector product

$$\bar{S} = \bar{E} \times \bar{H} \qquad \text{W/m}^2 \qquad\qquad (10.1\text{-}20)$$

For the plane wave shown in Figure 10.1-4, the Poynting vector is

$$\bar{S} = E_x H_y \bar{a}_x \times \bar{a}_y = E_x H_y \bar{a}_z$$

To deduce other aspects of electromagnetic energy and power flow, multiply Equation (10.1-18a) by $H_y(z,t)$ and Equation (10.1-18b) by $E_x(z,t)$. The resulting equations are

$$H_y(z,t)\frac{\partial E_x(z,t)}{\partial z} = -\mu H_y(z,t)\frac{\partial H_y(z,t)}{\partial t} = -\frac{1}{2}\mu\frac{\partial H_y^2(z,t)}{\partial t} \qquad \text{(a)} \quad (10.1\text{-}21)$$

$$E_x(z,t)\frac{\partial H_y(z,t)}{\partial z} = -\epsilon E_x(z,t)\frac{\partial E_x(z,t)}{\partial t} = -\frac{\epsilon}{2}\frac{\partial E_x^2(z,t)}{\partial t} \qquad \text{(b)}$$

Add the last two equations to obtain

$$\frac{\partial}{\partial z}[E_x(z,t)H_y(z,t)] = -\frac{\partial}{\partial t}\left[\frac{\epsilon}{2}E_x^2(z,t) + \frac{\mu}{2}H_y^2(z,t)\right] \qquad (10.1\text{-}22)$$

The individual quantities in this expression are identified as follows:

$$S_z = E_x(z,t)H_y(z,t) = \text{power (propagating) per unit area} \qquad \text{(a)} \quad (10.1\text{-}23)$$

$$U_E = \frac{\epsilon}{2}E_x^2(z,t) = \frac{\text{electric energy stored in space per unit}}{\text{volume}} \qquad \text{(b)}$$

$$U_M = \frac{\mu}{2}H_y^2(z,t) = \frac{\text{magnetic energy stored in space per unit}}{\text{volume}} \qquad \text{(c)}$$

There results

$$\frac{\partial S_z(z,t)}{\partial z} = -\left(\frac{\partial U_E}{\partial t} + \frac{\partial U_M}{\partial t}\right) = -\frac{\partial}{\partial t}(U_E + U_M) \qquad (10.1\text{-}24)$$

EXAMPLE 10.1-3. Find the values of U_E, U_M and $\bar{S}$ for a plane electromagnetic wave, and verify Equation (10.1-22) in the volume specified by $-1 \leqslant x \leqslant 1$, $-1 \leqslant y \leqslant 1$, $-1 \leqslant z \leqslant 1$.

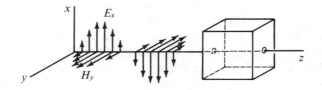

Figure 10.1-5.   Energy in space due to an electromagnetic wave

SOLUTION. The solution of the wave equation for plane waves has been found to be [see Equation (10.1-3)]

$$E_x = E_m \sin (kz - \omega t) \qquad\qquad \text{(a)} \quad (10.1\text{-}25)$$

$$H_y = H_m \sin (kz - \omega t) \qquad\qquad \text{(b)}$$

The inclusion of a similar form for the H-field is allowed because the wave equation for H is identical to Equation (10.1-18) (see Problem 10.1-6). Combining Equations (10.1-25) with Equations (10.1-23) yields

$$U_E = \frac{1}{2} \epsilon E^2{}_m \sin^2 (kz - \omega t) \qquad\qquad \text{(a)} \quad (10.1\text{-}26)$$

$$U_M = \frac{1}{2} \mu H^2_m \sin^2 (kz - \omega t) \qquad\qquad \text{(b)}$$

$$S_z = E_m H_m \sin^2 (kz - \omega t) \qquad\qquad \text{(c)}$$

Next introduce Equation (10.1-25) into Equation (10.1-22) and integrate over the required volume. There results

$$\int_{-1}^{1} \int_{-1}^{1} \int_{-1}^{1} \frac{\partial}{\partial z} [E_m H_m \sin^2 (kz - \omega t)] \, dx \, dy \, dz =$$

$$\int \int \int_{-1}^{1} \frac{\partial}{\partial t} \left[\left(\frac{\epsilon E^2_m}{2} + \frac{\mu H^2_m}{2} \right) \sin^2 (kz - \omega t) \, dx \, dy \, dz \right]$$

From this

$$4 E_m H_m k \int_{-1}^{1} \sin 2(kz - \omega t) \, dz =$$

$$\frac{4 \epsilon E^2_m \omega}{2} \int_{-1}^{1} \sin 2(kz - \omega t) \, dz + \frac{4 \mu \omega}{2} H^2_m \int_{-1}^{1} \sin 2(kz - \omega t) \, dz$$

or

$$2 E_m H_m [\cos 2(-k - \omega t) - \cos 2(k - \omega t)] =$$
$$\left(\epsilon E^2_m \frac{\omega}{k} + \mu H^2_m \frac{\omega}{k} \right) [\cos 2(-k - \omega t) - \cos 2(k - \omega t)] \qquad (10.1\text{-}27)$$

Observe therefore that

$$2 E_m H_m = \epsilon E^2_m \frac{\omega}{k} + \mu H^2_m \frac{\omega}{k} \qquad\qquad (10.1\text{-}28)$$

We note specifically that the electric and magnetic fields are related in a way dictated by Maxwell's equations. Therefore upon introducing the fields given by Equations (10.1-25) into Equation (10.1-18a) there results

$$H_m = \frac{k}{\mu\omega} E_m = \sqrt{\frac{\epsilon}{\mu}} \, E_m \qquad\qquad (10.1\text{-}29)$$

so that

$$\frac{E_m}{H_m} = Z = \sqrt{\frac{\mu}{\epsilon}} \qquad \text{ohm} \qquad\qquad (10.1\text{-}30)$$

Z is known as the *characteristic impedance* of the medium.

By substituting Equation (10.1-29) into Equation (10.1-28) and remembering that $k = \omega/c = \omega\sqrt{\mu\epsilon}$, it is easily shown that Equation (10.1-28) is an identity (see Problem 10.1-7).

□   □   □

10.2   PLANE WAVES IMPINGING ON A PLANE SEPARATING TWO MEDIUMS

When waves are incident on a plane surface dividing two mediums, for example air and matter, both reflection and transmission occurs. For the case of an electromagnetic wave, the sense of the wave polarization must also be defined. We shall assume that the $\bar{E}$-field is perpendicular to the *plane of incidence*, as shown in Figure 10.2-1. First consider the relationship between the angle of incidence θ_i and the angle of reflection θ_r. It is noted that for all three waves to be in step, their apparent phase velocities parallel to the boundary of the two mediums must be equal. This requires that

$$\frac{v_i}{\sin\theta_i} = \frac{v_r}{\sin\theta_r} = \frac{v_t}{\sin\theta_t} \qquad\qquad (10.2\text{-}1)$$

where $v_i = 1/\sqrt{\mu\epsilon_1}$, $v_r = 1/\sqrt{\mu\epsilon_1}$ and $v_t = 1/\sqrt{\mu\epsilon_2}$ are the speeds along the directions of propagation. Since the incident and the reflected waves are both in the same medium $v_i = v_r$, it follows from the first equality of Equation (10.2-1) that $\sin\theta_i = \sin\theta_r$, or

$$\theta_i = \theta_r \qquad\qquad (10.2\text{-}2)$$

By the last equality of Equation (10.2-1) we obtain Snell's law of refraction

$$\frac{\sin\theta_i}{\sin\theta_t} = \frac{v_i}{v_t} = \frac{\sqrt{\mu\epsilon_2}}{\sqrt{\mu\epsilon_1}} = \sqrt{\frac{\epsilon_2}{\epsilon_1}} = \frac{\sqrt{\epsilon_{2r}}}{\sqrt{\epsilon_{1r}}} = \frac{\eta_2}{\eta_1} \qquad\qquad (10.2\text{-}3)$$

where η is the *index of refraction* and ϵ_{2r}, ϵ_{1r} are the relative permittivities (dielectric constants) of the two mediums.

To develop the reflection and transmission coefficients, the relationship of the $\bar{E}$ and $\bar{H}$ fields at the boundaries must be known. The boundary conditions

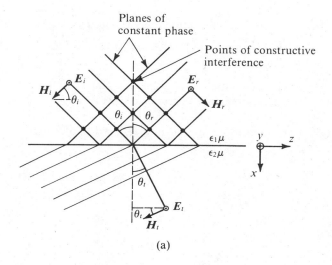

(a)

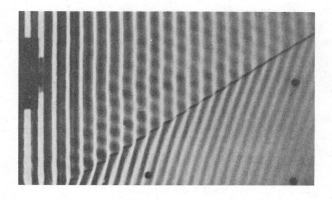

(b)

Figure 10.2-1. **(a) Schematic representation of electromagnetic waves impinging on an interface between two different mediums**
(b) Reflection and refraction of water waves at the boundary between regions of different wave speed. Observe the difference of wavelengths in the two mediums.

are developed from Maxwell's equations. However, they are here stated in simplified form without proof. They are

$\epsilon_1 E_{1n} = \epsilon_2 E_{2n}$: The normal components of the vectors $\bar{D}_{1n}$, $\epsilon_1 E_{1n} = D_{1n}$, and $\bar{D}_{2n}$, $\epsilon_2 E_{2n} = D_{2n}$, are continuous when no charges are located on the surface between the two mediums.

$E_{1t} = E_{2t}$: The tangential components of the $\bar{E}$ fields are continuous.

$\mu_1 H_{1n} = \mu_2 H_{2n}$: The normal components of the vectors $\bar{B}_{1n}$ and $\bar{B}_{2n}$ are continuous.

$H_{t1} = H_{t2}$: The tangential components of the $\bar{H}$ fields are continuous when no surface currents are present.

Using the boundary conditions at the interface $x = 0$ of Figure 10.2-1a, we obtain

$$E_i + E_r = E_t \qquad \text{(a)} \quad (10.2\text{-}4)$$

$$H_{zi} + H_{zr} = H_{zt} \qquad \text{(b)}$$

or equivalently

$$E_i + E_r = E_t \qquad \text{(a)} \quad (10.2\text{-}5)$$

$$-H_i \cos\theta_i + H_r \cos\theta_r = -H_t \cos\theta_t \qquad \text{(b)}$$

The fields are also related as follows [see Equation (10.1-29)]

$$\frac{E_i}{H_i} = \frac{E_r}{H_r} = Z_1 = \sqrt{\frac{\mu}{\epsilon_1}} \qquad\qquad \frac{E_t}{H_t} = Z_2 = \sqrt{\frac{\mu}{\epsilon_2}} \qquad (10.2\text{-}6)$$

Upon substituting Equation (10.2-6) into Equation (10.2-5b) there results

$$E_i - E_r = E_t \frac{Z_1}{Z_2} \frac{\cos\theta_t}{\cos\theta_i} \qquad (10.2\text{-}7)$$

When this equation is combined with Equation (10.2-5a) we have

$$E_i = \frac{E_t}{2}\left(1 + \frac{Z_1}{Z_2}\frac{\cos\theta_t}{\cos\theta_i}\right) \qquad \text{(a)} \quad (10.2\text{-}8)$$

$$E_r = \frac{E_t}{2}\left(1 - \frac{Z_1}{Z_2}\frac{\cos\theta_t}{\cos\theta_i}\right) \qquad \text{(b)}$$

Now define the *reflection coefficient* Γ_r and the *transmission coefficient* Γ_t in the following way

$$\Gamma_r = \frac{E_r}{E_i} = \frac{Z_2\cos\theta_i - Z_1\cos\theta_t}{Z_2\cos\theta_i + Z_1\cos\theta_t} \qquad \text{(a)} \quad (10.2\text{-}9)$$

$$\Gamma_t = \frac{E_t}{E_i} = \frac{2Z_2\cos\theta_i}{Z_2\cos\theta_i + Z_1\cos\theta_t} \qquad \text{(b)}$$

For acoustic waves, the reflection and the transmission coefficients are identical in form to Equations (10.2-9), with the difference in the definition of the *acoustic impedance*, which is

$$Z = \frac{1}{\varrho_o c_a} \qquad (10.2\text{-}10)$$

where ϱ_o is the density of the medium and c_a is the speed of sound; for air at 20°C and sea level pressure $c_a = 340$ m/s.

10.3   RESONANCE

To understand the phenomenon of resonance, we must investigate the general solution of the wave equation in a medium terminated by boundaries. Consider, for example, a plane wave field that is launched between two parallel planes with infinite conductivity as shown in Figure 10.3-1a. The plane wave will be reflected back and forth, with a field distribution of the form shown in Figure 10.3-1b.

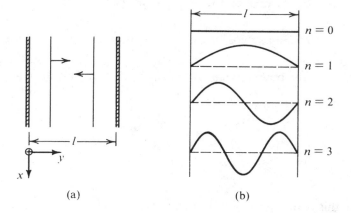

(a)   (b)

Figure 10.3-1.   (a) Plane electromagnetic wave between two parallel, infinite conducting planes   (b) Normal modes of the wave

Assume that the two waves have equal amplitudes but different initial phases. The solution to the wave equation can be written as follows:

$$E_z = E_r + E_l = E_m[\sin(kz - \omega t) + \sin(kz + \omega t + \varphi)] \qquad (10.3\text{-}1)$$

where E_r is the wave propagating to the right and E_l is the wave propagating to the left. The acceptability of these two solutions is dictated by the fact that the wave equation is of second order, thereby indicating the presence of two solutions. Expand Equation (10.3-1) to the form

$$E_t = E_m[\sin kz \cos \omega t - \sin \omega t \cos kz + \sin kz \cos (\omega t + \varphi)$$

$$+ \cos kz \sin (\omega t + \varphi)] \tag{10.3-2}$$

Because the planes have infinite conductivity, $E_t = 0$ at $z = 0$ and $z = l$. To satisfy the boundary condition $E_t = 0$ at $z = 0$ demands of Equation (10.3-2) that

$$\sin \omega t = \sin (\omega t + \varphi) \tag{10.3-3}$$

This requires that $\varphi = 2m\pi$ for $m = 0, 1, 2, \ldots$. Introduce this condition into Equation (10.3-2) to obtain

$$E_t = E_m \sin kz[\cos \omega t + \cos (\omega t + \varphi)]$$

or

$$E_t = E_m \sin kz \left[\cos \left(\omega t - \frac{\varphi}{2} \right) + \cos \left(\omega t + \frac{\varphi}{2} \right) \right]$$

$$= 2E_m \sin kz \cos \omega t \cos \frac{\varphi}{2} = A \sin kz \cos \omega t \tag{10.3-4}$$

Now introduce the boundary condition $E_t = 0$ at $z = l$. This demands that

$$kl = n\pi \qquad\qquad n = 0, 1, 2, \ldots \tag{10.3-5}$$

so that

$$k = \frac{n\pi}{l} \qquad\qquad \frac{\omega}{k} = c = \frac{\omega l}{n\pi} \qquad\qquad \omega = \frac{cn\pi}{l} \tag{10.3-6}$$

Combine this relationship with Equation (10.3-4) to obtain the final form of the field configuration

$$E_t = A \sin \frac{n\pi}{l} z \cos \frac{cn\pi}{l} t \tag{10.3-7}$$

This is known as a *standing wave* because its configuration in space is specified and varies only in time; that is, it does not propagate.

Figure 10.3-1b shows the form of the total field $\bar{E}_t$ between the two planes for several values of n. These wave configurations are called the *normal modes* and the points of zero amplitude are called *nodes*. The quantity $\omega = cn\pi/l$ is called the characteristic value of the system, and this indicates that only discrete frequencies can exist in such a configuration. Each mode, i.e., each allowable value of n, specifies a particular frequency, known as the *eigenvalue* (characteristic value). To each eigenvalue there corresponds a function $\sin (n\pi z/l)$ which is an *eigenfunction* of the system.

10.4 DIFFRACTION AND INTERFERENCE

Another important property of waves is their ability to diffract and interfere. There is no significant physical distinction between these two phenomena although often only one of these phenomena is discussed. Figures 10.4-1a and 10.4-1b show two examples of diffraction and interference.

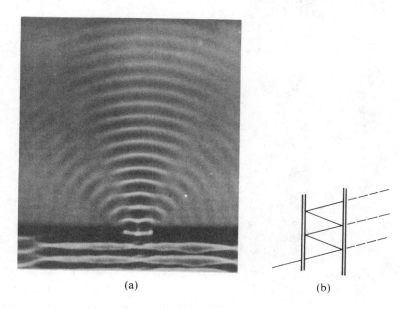

(a)   (b)

**Figure 10.4-1.   (a) Diffraction of water waves through a slit
(b) Multiple beam interference: Fabry-Perot etalon**

When two or more waves of the same frequency reach the same region of space, the amplitude at a point is the sum of the amplitudes of the contributing waves, taking into account their phase relationships. The pattern thus produced will show regions of higher intensity and regions of lower intensity, and regions of no intensity. This phenomenon is called *interference*. We have, in fact, already met such phenomena in Section 10.2 where we developed an understanding of reflection, transmission, and resonance (see Figures 10.2-1 and 10.3-1).

It is apparent that the phenomenon of interference will occur only when a constant relationship exists between the phases of the interfering waves. This means that the waves must be *coherent*. It is the noncoherent character of ordinary light sources, e.g., lamps, fires, etc., that makes interference from such sources difficult to achieve. However, light from a laser beam which is emitted with a constant phase relationship readily lends itself to interference. Experimentally we can easily demonstrate interference with a laser source by conducting Young's experiment. In this experiment a plane wave of laser light falls on two small holes, as shown in Figure 10.4-2a. The wavefronts at the two

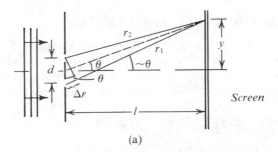

(a)

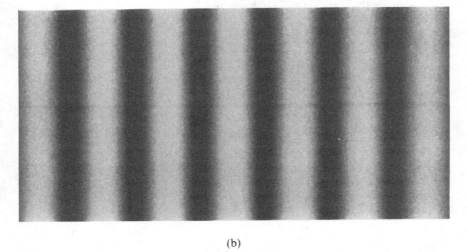

(b)

Figure 10.4-2.   (a) Young's experiment   (b) The corresponding interference fringes

pinholes are in phase. At point y on the screen the waves from the two pinholes traverse slight path differences; the difference in path length between the rays r_2 and r_1 is given by

$$\Delta r = r_1 - r_2 = d \sin \theta \doteq \theta d$$

since $\sin \theta \doteq \theta$ for small angles. But $\theta = y/l$ so that the path difference is

$$\Delta r = r_1 - r_2 = \frac{yd}{l} \tag{10.4-1}$$

Constructive interference will take place when Δr is a multiple of the wavelength, or when

$$\Delta r = m\lambda \qquad\qquad m = 0, 1, 2, \ldots \tag{10.4-2}$$

Combine this with Equation (10.4-1) which yields

$$y_{max} = \frac{l}{d}m\lambda \qquad (10.4\text{-}3)$$

This gives the position of the m-th bright fringe.

Another extremely useful interferometer for measuring changes in length less than a quarter of a wavelength, for measuring changes in index of refraction, etc., is the *Michelson interferometer*. This is shown schematically in Figure 10.4-3. Any change of the position of one of the mirrors will make the interference fringes become displaced. If the movable mirror moves by $\lambda/2$, each fringe will move to the position previously occupied by an adjacent fringe. Any change of index of refraction creates an apparent change of path length since it takes longer for the wave to transverse the same physical distance. Therefore if it is arranged that one arm of the interferometer includes an experimental setup, e.g., a shock tube, a plasma, etc., any change in the index of refraction due to a shock front, or due to a change in the properties of the plasma, can be detected by the fringe displacement.

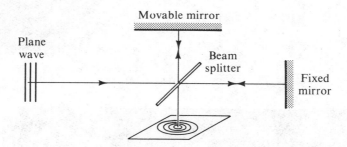

Figure 10.4-3. The essentials of the Michelson interferometer

Consider a circular aperture that is illuminated by a plane wave, as shown in Figure 10.4-4a. The intensity and phase of the radiation at point P on the screen from any point S in the aperture will vary depending on the path of the wave from S to P. By adding (integrating) the contributions at point P from all the points S in the aperture, the total field can be evaluated. This process can be repeated for all points on the screen, the result being the intensity pattern (the field squared, E^2) shown in Figure 10.4-4b. A diffraction pattern from an aperture depicting the number 3 is shown in Figure 10.4-4c.

Because the diffraction pattern will be different for different shaped apertures, considerable effort is presently directed toward manipulating and detecting such patterns in order to be able to identify the shape from which the pattern was obtained. It was with the invention of the laser that a new engineering discipline has been created to take advantage of the interference

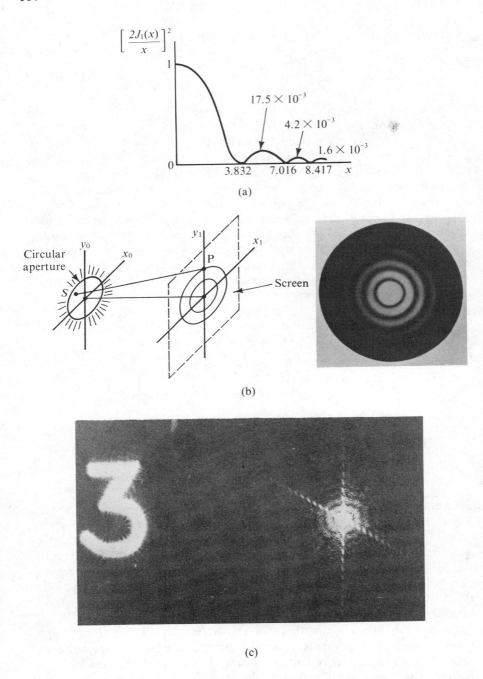

Figure 10.4-4. (a) Schematic representation of diffraction from a circular aperture
(b) Intensity distribution of the field at a screen diffracted from a circular aperture
(c) Pattern from number 3

patterns to study and analyze signals, reduce noise in images, produce images from radar signals, etc.

10.5   GUIDED WAVES

We are most familiar with guided electromagnetic waves which are used for communication purposes. However, there are many other types of waves, such as elastic waves traveling along rods, acoustic waves within musical instruments, and low frequency electromagnetic waves guided by the earth and the ionosphere.

Parallel Transmission Lines

One of the simplest electromagnetic wave guiding systems is the two-wire transmission line. The equations governing the propagation of waves on such a guiding structure were developed in Example 10.1-1. When such a line is excited by a sinusoidal source, the voltage at any instant of time and at any point along the line assumes the form

$$v = V_m \cos (kz - \omega t + \varphi) \qquad (10.5\text{-}1)$$

where φ is an arbitrary phase which can be taken to equal zero, for simplicity. Observe that Equation (10.5-1) is a solution to the wave equation, Equation (10.1-9). Upon introducing Equation (10.5-1) with $\varphi = 0$ into Equation (10.1-8a) and integrating with respect to time, it is found that

$$i = \frac{k V_m}{L} \int \sin (kz - \omega t) \, dt = \frac{k V_m}{\omega L} \cos (kz - \omega t) = \frac{v}{\sqrt{L/C}} = Y_o v \qquad (10.5\text{-}2)$$

where

$$Z_o = \frac{1}{Y_o} = \sqrt{\frac{L}{C}} \qquad \text{ohm} \qquad (10.5\text{-}3)$$

is the *characteristic impedance* of the transmission line.

Suppose that the transmission line, shown in Figure 10.5-1, is terminated by a load, say an antenna, whose input impedance is different from the character-

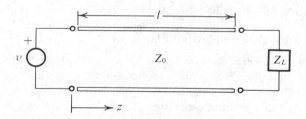

Figure 10.5-1.   Transmission line terminated by a load Z_L

istic impedance of the transmission line Z_o. This impedance mismatch results in a reduction in the power to the antenna. To study this, note that the impedance discontinuity results in a reflected wave, the total voltage and current in such a line being the sum of the oppositely moving incident and reflected waves. The expressions for the moving waves are

$$v_1 = V_{m1} \cos{(kz - \omega t)} \tag{a} \quad (10.5\text{-}4)$$

Forward wave

$$i_1 = \frac{V_{m1}}{Z_o} \cos{(kz - \omega t)} \tag{b}$$

$$v_2 = V_{m2} \cos{(kz + \omega t)} \tag{c}$$

Backward wave

$$i_2 = -\frac{V_{m2}}{Z_o} \cos{(kz + \omega t)} \tag{d}$$

The minus sign in i_2 indicates a 180° phase reversal between i_2 and v_2. The total voltage and current at each point on the line are:

$$v = v_1 + v_2 = V_{m1} \cos{(kz - \omega t)} + V_{m2} \cos{(kz + \omega t)} \tag{a} \quad (10.5\text{-}5)$$

$$i = i_1 + i_2 = \frac{1}{Z_o}[V_{m1} \cos{(kz - \omega t)} - V_{m2} \cos{(kz + \omega t)}] \tag{b}$$

The impedance at any point on the line is v/i at that point; at point $z = l$ the impedance is Z_L. By taking the ratio of these two equations, rearranging and setting $z = l$, we find that

$$\frac{V_{m2} \cos{(kl + \omega t)}}{V_{m1} \cos{(kl - \omega t)}} = \frac{Z_L - Z_o}{Z_L + Z_o} \tag{10.5-6}$$

The time average values of the squares of the numerator and the denominator yields, when one examines the square root of the result, the rms values of the voltages

$$\frac{V_2}{V_1} = \frac{Z_L - Z_o}{Z_L + Z_o} \tag{10.5-7}$$

This is called the *voltage reflection coefficient.*

Waves Between Parallel Conducting Planes

Now consider two parallel perfectly conducting planes, as shown in Figure 10.5-2. This is the guiding structure for electromagnetic waves having wavelengths comparable with the separation of the planes. If the electric field $\bar{E}$ is arranged to be parallel to the X-axis, then the magnetic field vector $\bar{H}$ will have a component parallel to the Z-direction. This type of guided wave is called

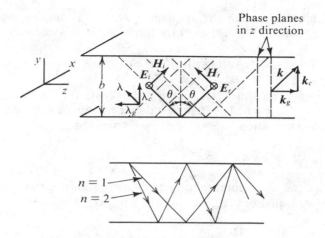

Figure 10.5-2.   Field description for propagation between parallel planes

transverse electric (TE). Similarly, when $\bar{H}$ is parallel to the X-axis, the resulting wave is called *transverse magnetic* (TM). It turns out that only TE and TM waves will propagate in waveguides.

The electric vector of the incident wave is represented by the relation

$$\bar{E}_i = \bar{a}_x E_o \cos \left[k(-y\cos\theta + Z\sin\theta) - \omega t\right] \tag{10.5-8}$$

This describes the field of the wave propagating at an angle θ with respect to the Y-axis. To check the validity of this expression, we first set $\theta = 0$. The field in this case is $\bar{E}_i = \bar{a}_x E_o \cos(-ky - \omega t)$ which describes a wave that is propagating in the negative Y-direction as it should. If the angle θ is set to $90°$, $\bar{E}_i = \bar{a}_x E_o \cos(kz - \omega t)$, which denotes a wave that is propagating in the positive Z-direction, as expected.

At the interface of the conductor the total electric field must be zero, $\bar{E}_i + \bar{E}_r = 0$ and so $\bar{E}_r = -\bar{E}_i$. Since this relation is valid at any z, including $z = 0$, the relation $|\bar{E}_r| = |\bar{E}_i| = E_o$ is true. Hence the reflected wave is specified by the equation

$$\bar{E}_r = -\bar{a}_x E_o \cos \left[k(y\cos\theta + z\sin\theta) - \omega t\right] \tag{10.5-9}$$

Make use of the known relations: $\cos\theta = \text{Re}[e^{j\theta}]$ and $\text{Re}(a + jb) + \text{Re}(c + jd) = \text{Re}[(a + c) + j(b + d)]$ to write Equations (10.5-8) and (10.5-9) in the form

$$\text{Re}[\underline{\bar{E}_t}] = \text{Re}[\underline{\bar{E}_i} + \underline{\bar{E}_r}] = \text{Re}[\bar{a}_x E_o e^{jk(-y\cos\theta + z\sin\theta) - j\omega t} - e^{jk(y\cos\theta + z\sin\theta) - j\omega t}]$$

$$= \text{Re}[\bar{a}_x E_o e^{jkz\sin\theta} e^{-j\omega t}(e^{-jky\cos\theta} - e^{jky\cos\theta})] \tag{10.5-10}$$

$$= \text{Re}[\bar{a}_x E_o e^{jkz\sin\theta} e^{-j\omega t} 2j\sin(ky\cos\theta)]$$

where the symbol $\sim$ beneath a field quantity denotes a complex quantity. The real part of Equation (10.5-10) gives the total field in the waveguide, namely

$$\bar{E}_t = -2\bar{a}_x E_o \sin(kz \sin\theta - \omega t) \sin(ky \cos\theta) \qquad (10.5\text{-}11)$$

The $\bar{E}$ field is entirely transverse, and it must satisfy the boundary condition $\bar{E} = 0$ at $y = 0$ and at $y = b$. The first boundary condition is automatically satisfied; the second condition imposes the requirement that

$$kb \cos\theta = n\pi \qquad\qquad n = 0, 1, 2, \ldots \qquad (10.5\text{-}12)$$

Further, since the wave number (propagation constant) in the Y direction is $k_c = k \cos\theta$ [see Equations (10.5-8) and (10.5-9)], then

$$\lambda_c = \frac{\lambda}{\cos\theta} = \frac{2b}{n} \qquad\qquad k_c = k \cos\theta = \frac{n\pi}{b} \qquad (10.5\text{-}13)$$

This is a characteristic wavelength (effective wavelength) in the Y direction which is specified by the *node number* n and width b. In addition, Equation (10.5-12) shows that for a particular angle of incidence θ only discrete frequencies

$$\omega_n = \frac{n\pi c}{b \cos\theta} \qquad\qquad \left(k = \frac{\omega}{c}\right) \qquad (10.5\text{-}14)$$

are permitted. For each n there corresponds a particular field configuration called the *wave mode*.

The planes of constant phase for the wave propagating along the guiding structure are, from Equation (10.5-11),

$$kz \sin\theta - \omega t = \text{constant} \qquad (10.5\text{-}15)$$

Therefore, they advance with velocity

$$c_{ph} = \frac{dz}{dt} = \frac{\omega}{k \sin\theta} = \frac{c}{\sin\theta} = \frac{f\lambda}{\sin\theta} = f\lambda_g \qquad (10.5\text{-}16)$$

It follows from this that

$$\lambda_g = \frac{\lambda}{\sin\theta} \qquad (10.5\text{-}17)$$

If we square and add the inverse of Equation (10.5-17) and Equation (10.5-13), it is found that

$$\frac{1}{\lambda_c^2} + \frac{1}{\lambda_g^2} = \frac{1}{\lambda^2} \qquad \text{(a)} \qquad (10.5\text{-}18)$$

or

$$k^2 = k_c^2 + k_g^2 \qquad \text{(b)}$$

This means that

$$k_g = \frac{2\pi}{\lambda_g} = \sqrt{k^2 - k_c^2} = \sqrt{\left(\frac{2\pi}{\lambda}\right)^2 - \left(\frac{n\pi}{b}\right)^2} \qquad (10.5\text{-}19)$$

If $(\pi n/b) < 2\pi/\lambda$, then k_g is real, and there is propagation without attenuation; this mode is called the *propagating mode*. When $(\pi n/b) > 2\pi/\lambda$ there is heavy attenuation of the mode and no propagation exists. When $\pi n/b = 2\pi/\lambda$ then

$$\frac{2\pi f}{\lambda f} = \frac{\omega}{c} = \frac{n\pi}{b} \qquad \text{or} \qquad \omega = \frac{c\pi n}{b} \qquad (10.5\text{-}20)$$

which is known as the *cutoff frequency*.

Rectangular Wave Guides

The *rectangular waveguide* shown in Figure 10.5-3a is used extensively for transmitting electromagnetic energy. This is the simplest waveguide configura-

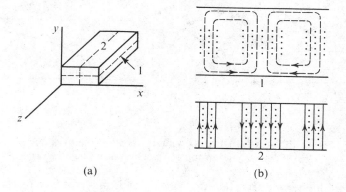

(a)   (b)

Figure 10.5-3. (a) Rectangular waveguide (b) TE_{10} mode field configuration, where solid lines indicate the electric field and broken lines indicate the magnetic field

tion in regular use. The TE_{10} mode field configuration is illustrated in Figure 10.5-3b. The equations that characterize this mode are

$$E_x = E_z = H_y = 0 \qquad\qquad \text{(a)} \quad (10.5\text{-}21)$$

$$E_y = E_o \frac{\omega\mu\pi}{k_x^2 a} \sin \frac{\pi}{a}x \sin (k_z z - \omega t) \qquad\qquad \text{(b)}$$

$$H_x = -E_o \frac{k_z \pi}{k_x^2 a} \sin \frac{\pi}{a}x \sin (k_z z - \omega t) \qquad\qquad \text{(c)}$$

$$H_z = E_o \cos \frac{\pi}{a}x \sin (k_z z - \omega t) \qquad\qquad \text{(d)}$$

and the propagation constants are related through the expression

$$k_z^2 = k^2 - k_x^2 \qquad\qquad (10.5\text{-}22)$$

For this mode, $k_x = \pi/a$, which is a special case of the mode having $k_x = n\pi/a$, with n set equal to unity. Therefore it follows that

$$k_z^2 = \frac{\omega^2}{c^2} - \left(\frac{\pi}{a}\right)^2 \qquad\qquad (10.5\text{-}23)$$

which is plotted in Figure 10.5-4. This figure shows the behavior of the phase constant versus frequency for the TE_{10} mode. The same shaped curves are ob-

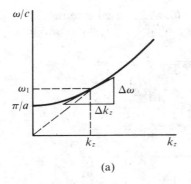

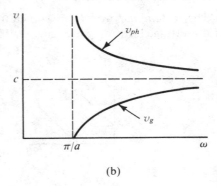

(a)   (b)

**Figure 10.5-4.   (a) Dispersion characteristics of waveguides
(b) Phase v_{ph} and group v_g velocities in waveguide**

tained for all higher modes when the waveguide is made of a uniform hollow tube. From the figure the phase and group velocities of the waveguide are defined as follows:

$$v_{ph} = \frac{\omega}{k_z} \qquad\qquad \text{(a)} \quad (10.5\text{-}24)$$

$$v_g = \frac{\Delta\omega}{\Delta k_z} \qquad\qquad \text{(b)}$$

These are graphically shown for a particular frequency ω_1 in Figure 10.5-4a. Figure 10.5-4b shows the variation of these two velocities versus frequency. These curves show that in a waveguide the phase velocity is always greater than the speed of light, and this indicates that no energy can be transmitted with this velocity. However, the group velocity is always less than the speed of light, and energy is transmitted along the tube with this velocity. At the cutoff frequency for the TE_{10} mode, $\omega_c = \pi c / a$, $v_{ph} = \infty$ and $v_g = 0$, and transmission ceases to exist.

Fiber Optics

Propagation of laser light in thin films is an interesting and important application of electromagnetic waves in dielectric slabs. The introduction of integrated optics and the development of special optical coupling devices has contributed to the development of optical modulators, frequency converters, and parametric oscillators in planar thin film form. More will be said about this matter in Chapter 11 in its relation to communications.

A simple guiding structure is shown in Figure 10.5-5. The existence of a guided mode is easily explained in simple terms, thereby avoiding the complicated formalism necessary for a detailed discussion. Essentially, a plane wave is bouncing back and forth between the dielectric interfaces in medium 1; it is propagating at an angle that is greater than the critical angle. Outside in medium 2 a wave exists which decays away from the interface and propagates along the Z-axis. This type of wave is called an *evanescent* wave.

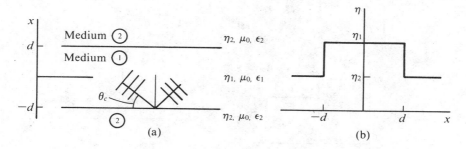

Figure 10.5-5.   (a) A dielectric slab   (b) Index of refraction versus x

The use of materials with different though nearly equal index of refraction from that of the film produces what is known as *cladding*. This configuration is important since it provides a way to control the number of modes in the film. In general, an overmoded fiber with an index of refraction difference from the cladding of 1% can have a time spread of 50 ns/km which limits the bandwidth of a 1 kilometer fiber to about 10 MHz. On the other hand, a single mode fiber will not limit the bandwidth below 50 GHz, since a typical 8 ps pulse does not spread more than 4 picoseconds.

A problem of importance in practice is how to couple the light beam of a laser into a propagating mode inside a thin dielectric film or fiber, such as on the order of 1 μm. Methods have been used employing prisms, gratings, or tapered sections as couplers. To understand that it is not possible to couple energy into the film by merely illuminating the film by a laser light source, consider that a wave is traveling towards the film in a direction that makes an angle θ_2 with the normal to the film surface. The Z-component of the propagation vector in medium 2 is $k_o \eta_2 \sin \theta_2$. For this wave to produce the mth mode in the film with $k_z^{(m)}$ requires that

$$k_z^{(m)} = k_o \eta_1 \sin \theta_m = k_o \eta_2 \sin \theta_2 \tag{10.5-25}$$

where θ_m is the angle shown in Figure 10.5-6. Since θ_m is larger than the critical angle $\eta_1 \sin \theta_m > \eta_2$, Equation (10.5-25) cannot be satisfied and no energy can be coupled into the film.

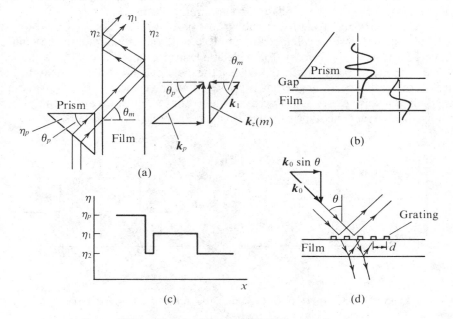

Figure 10.5-6. **Prism and grating couplers**

Now consider the situation when a prism is present, with $\eta_p > \eta_1$, as shown in Figure 10.5-6. If the prism is brought very close to the film surface (~ 1 μm or less) and the condition

$$k_o \eta_p \sin \theta_p = k_z^{(m)} \tag{10.5-26}$$

is satisfied, energy will leak into the film creating the mth mode. By changing θ_p we can produce any mode desired in the film. The input coupler serves equally well as an output coupler. It has been found that prism couplers are about 80 percent efficient. The field distribution in a prism coupler is shown in Figure 10.5-6b. It is noted that the evanescent fields (non-propagating fields) of the prism and the film overlap in the gap region.

A phase grating coupler as shown in Figure 10.5-6d can be fabricated on a thin film by means of a photoresist technique like that used in the semiconductor device preparation. A laser beam incident on the grating at an angle θ has a phase variation in the Z-direction equal to $k_o/\sin\theta$, as illustrated. As the beam passes through the grating, it acquires an additional spatial phase modulation $\Delta E \sin(2\pi z/d)$ where ΔE is the amplitude variation due to the phase grating. Since a periodic variation can be analyzed into Fourier components, the light reaching the film will be of the form

$$e^{j[k_o \sin\theta + m(2\pi/d)]z}$$

where m is an integer. Clearly, the grating makes it possible to feed the mth mode in the film provided that

$$k_o \sin\theta + \frac{2\pi}{d}m = k_z^{(m)} \tag{10.5-27}$$

If θ is varied, energy can be coupled into all modes in the film. As in the case of a prism, the grating acts as an output coupler also, and its efficiency is about the same as that for the prism.

The tapered film coupler consists of a film of slowly varying thickness. When light reaches the tapered section, it undergoes successive reflections with progressively smaller angles θ_m. When this angle becomes less than the critical angle, the light refracts into the substrate.

In broad outline, the foregoing discussion applies equally well to cylindrical fibers. However, the mathematics of cylindrical fibers is rather more involved, and we shall not discuss the matter in detail. We shall discuss some of the important features in a qualitative manner.

Optical fibers are fabricated by using multicomponent glasses which contain a number of oxides and high-silica glasses which are made of fused silica. The fiber core is contained within a cladding material, and this must have a smaller index of refraction than the core, which is made of boron-doped silica.

The optical characteristics of fibers are affected by absorption, scattering, and mode conversion. To achieve low loss, extremely pure and defect-free glasses are required. Absorption and scattering account for approximately equal parts of the total attenuation in the spectral region of about 0.85 μm. The absorption losses are due mainly to impurities, such as Cr, Mn, Fe, water, as well as the intrinsic material absorption. Scattering losses in glasses are caused by microheterogeneities, boundary roughness, and intrinsic material scattering.

The radius of the fibers must be constant to reduce waveguide losses, and to facilitate cabling and connector techniques. In addition, it is important to be able to control precisely the radial distribution of the refractive index in order to minimize mode dispersion. An index profile that is approximately parabolic will eliminate mode dispersion. Also, care must be exercised in fiber bending since, in extreme cases, radiation away from the core will take place.

Bandwidth is limited by pulse broadening, which can result in pulse overlapping. Pulse broadening is caused by dispersion that results from normal waveguide dispersion and the dispersion due to the glasses. A broadening of only 5 picoseconds/km for single mode fibers has been achieved, and this will allow a large capacity transmission system.

Typical fiber waveguide structures are shown in Figure 10.5-7. The basic guiding structure is the core, which is surrounded by a cladding layer with a slightly lower refractive index than the core. Each mode is reflected at the core-cladding interface.

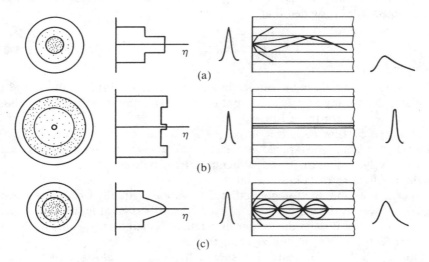

Figure 10.5-7.   (a) Multimode fiber, stepped index profile
(b) Single mode stepped index profile   (c) Multimode fiber, graded index profile

Multimode fibers have considerably larger diameters (on the order of 100 μm) than single mode fibers, which have diameters on the order of a wavelength. The disadvantage of multimode fibers results from the large dispersion which is present because each mode is reflected at a different incident angle. To avoid the large dispersion of multimode fibers, single mode fibers are often used, or fibers with a graded index profile, as shown in Figure 10.5-7c. In these, a mode (ray) traveling at a large angle with respect to the axis, is propagating in the medium with progressively lower index of refraction. Because of the gradient in the refractive index, the ray is bent back toward the center. Thus the ray spends most of the time in the material with the lower index of refraction, which corresponds to higher velocities, than the ray that travels along the axis of the fiber. The near parabolic profile forces the rays to be in phase along the fiber axis, and this reduces the dispersions.

10.6 RADIATION AND RADIATING ELEMENTS

In our discussion of phenomena involving electromagnetic fields, it has been assumed that these fields are available. We wish now to examine the basic ideas of radiation that is produced by localized sources. That part of a system that radiates energy is called an *antenna*. It will be assumed that radiation occurs only from the radiator, and that leakage is negligible.

A study of radiating systems is important because it permits evaluating a number of important properties of radiators: the field strength at a specified distance from the source; the load represented by the radiator on the driving source; the efficiency of the radiating element; and the power radiated in different directions, that is, the so-called radiation pattern.

The simplest form of radiator is the *infinitesimal dipole*, sometimes called the Hertzian dipole. The geometry of the problem is given in Figure 10.6-1.

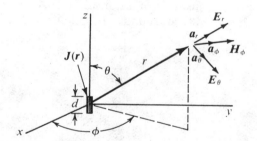

Figure 10.6-1. The infinitesimal dipole radiator

The electric and magnetic fields for such a dipole are found to be given by

$$\bar{H} = \frac{C}{\mu_o}\left[\frac{1}{kr^2}\cos(kr-\omega t) + \frac{1}{r}\sin(kr-\omega t)\right]\sin\theta\,\bar{a}_\varphi \qquad \text{(a)} \quad (10.6\text{-}1)$$

$$\bar{E} = \omega C\left[\left(\frac{2\cos(kr-\omega t)}{k^2 r^2} - \frac{2\sin(kr-\omega t)}{k^3 r^3}\right)\cos\theta\,\bar{a}_r + \right.$$

$$\left.\left(-\frac{\sin(kr-\omega t)}{k^3 r^3} + \frac{\cos(kr-\omega t)}{k^2 r^2} + \frac{\sin(kr-\omega t)}{kr}\right)\sin\theta\,\bar{a}_\theta\right] \qquad \text{(b)}$$

where

$$C = \frac{\mu_o k}{4\pi} \int_V \bar{J}(\bar{r}^1)\, dV^1 \tag{c}$$

These formulas indicate the following features for the $\bar{E}$ and $\bar{H}$ fields:

1. The magnetic field lines are concentric circles about the dipole, and are strong near the equator but weak near the poles.

2. Two terms are involved in the equation for $\bar{E}$; one is the *radiation field*, which varies as $1/r$; the second is the *induction field*, which varies as $1/r^2$.

3. At large distances from the dipole when $kr \to \infty$, Equations (10.6-1a) and (10.6-1b) become approximately

$$\bar{H}_\varphi \doteq \frac{C}{\mu_o} \frac{\sin\,(kr - \omega t)}{r} \sin\theta\, \bar{a}_\varphi \qquad\qquad \text{(a)} \quad (10.6\text{-}2)$$

$$E_\theta \doteq \omega C \frac{\sin\,(kr - \omega t)}{kr} \sin\theta\, \bar{a}_\theta \qquad\qquad \text{(b)}$$

At these large distances the $\bar{H}$ and $\bar{E}$ lines are orthogonal circles having their maximum amplitudes at the equator and zero amplitudes at the poles. Furthermore, each amplitude decreases as $1/r$. The ratio E_θ/H_φ [units are $(V/m) \times (m/At) =$ ohm] becomes $E_\theta/H_\varphi = \omega\mu_o/k = Z_o = 377.6$ ohm, where Z_o denotes the characteristic impedance of free space.

Figure 10.6-2 shows the electric field near a dipole for four different instants of time. At $t = 0$ the field is just that of a static dipole. As time progresses the field lines are pinched off, and these bundles of field lines propagate outward.

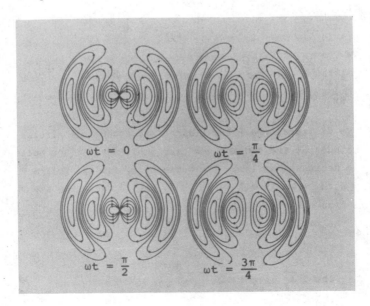

Figure 10.6-2. Electric field lines from a radiating dipole

Three important characteristics of the infinitesimal dipole will be found, and similar characteristics are of importance for any antenna system.

Radiated Power

To find the power radiated requires the evaluation of the Poynting vector (see Section 10.1) which specifies the energy flow per unit area, which is then integrated over all space. That is, begin with

$$\bar{S} = \bar{E} \times \bar{H} = \bar{E}_\theta \times \bar{H}_\varphi = S\bar{a}_r = \frac{C^2\omega}{\mu_o} \frac{1}{kr^2} \sin^2\theta \sin^2(kr - \omega t)\,\bar{a}_r \qquad (10.6\text{-}3)$$

The time average value is given by

$$<\bar{S}> = \frac{C^2\omega}{\mu_o} \frac{1}{kr^2} \bar{a}_r \sin^2\theta \frac{1}{2\pi} \int_0^{2\pi} \sin^2(kr - \omega t)\,d(\omega t)$$

$$= \frac{1}{2} \frac{C^2\omega}{\mu_o} \frac{1}{kr^2} \sin^2\theta\,\bar{a}_r \qquad (10.6\text{-}4)$$

The time average total power passing through a spherical surface of radius r_o is

$$<P_{rad}> = \oint_S <\bar{S}> \cdot d\bar{A} = \frac{1}{2} \frac{C^2\omega}{\mu_o} \frac{1}{kr^2} \int_0^{2\pi} d\varphi \int_0^{\pi} \sin^2\theta\, r_o^2 \sin\theta\, d\theta$$

$$= \frac{4\pi}{3} \frac{C^2\omega}{\mu_o} \frac{1}{k} \qquad (10.6\text{-}5)$$

Observe that this real power is independent of the radius of the surface enclosing the dipole. If losses in the antenna are negligible, the power radiated P_{rad} by the antenna is equal to the average power delivered to the antenna terminals by the source. This power is equal to $I_{rms}^2 R$ for I_{rms} in rms ampere so that

$$R_{rad} = \frac{<P_{rad}>}{I_{rms}^2} = \frac{4\pi\omega C^2}{3\mu_o k I_{rms}^2} \qquad (10.6\text{-}6)$$

which is called the *radiation resistance*. For the short dipole the current in the antenna is uniform and Equation (10.6-1c) is readily evaluated for the constant C, to yield

$$C = \frac{\mu_o k I}{4\pi} \qquad (10.6\text{-}7)$$

EXAMPLE 10.6-1. A short dipole is vertically oriented and transmits power with a peak current of 2 A. Find the electric field intensity at a distance of 50 km on an airplane flying at an altitude of 20 km (very high). The transmitter broadcasts at 10 MHz.

SOLUTION. From Equation (10.6-2) we obtain

$$|E_\theta| = \frac{\mu_o}{4\pi} I\omega \frac{\sin\theta}{r} = \frac{4\pi \times 10^{-7} \times 2 \times 2\pi \times 10^7}{4\pi} \quad \frac{\sin\left(\tan^{-1}\frac{20}{50}\right)}{[(20 \times 10^3)^2 + (50 \times 10^3)^2]^{1/2}}$$

$$= 88.05 \times 10^{-6} \text{ V/m.}$$

□   □   □

Power Directivity Pattern

The radiation characteristics of a radiator are usually depicted by means of a radiation pattern. This is a plot of Equation (10.6-3) in magnitude. For the infinitesimal dipole, it has the general properties shown in Figure 10.6-3. The angular width to the *half power points* is called the *beam width*, and is 78 deg. in this case.

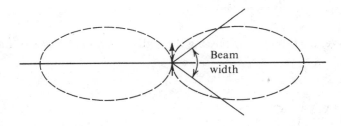

Figure 10.6-3.   The directional characteristics of the infinitesimal dipole

Antenna Gain

The gain of an antenna is defined as the ratio of the maximum radiated power measured with respect to the maximum radiation from a reference antenna with the same total power. For a reference isotropic radiator (one that radiates equally in all directions) the gain of the dipole is 3/2.

A very important practical radiator is the half-wave dipole, which is quite like the infinitesimal dipole except that its length is equal to half the wavelength of the radiated energy. The directional pattern for this radiator is very similar to that for the infinitesimal dipole. The radiation resistance is found to be 73 ohm.

In addition to the simple dipole antenna, and the length may be chosen at other than $\lambda/2$, one can construct a collection of antennas fixed in position with respect to each other. These would be excited simultaneously, the magnitude and the phase of the current in each element of this *array* being chosen to give a desired directional pattern, usually one with a sharp main lobe and with small sidelobes.

Instead of an array of discrete radiators, a paraboloid of revolution or a section of a paraboloid is often used in microwave antenna applications. Refer to Figure 10.6-4 which is presumed to be a parabolic reflector with a dipole at the focal point. A feature of the parabola is that the distance from the focal point to the reflector surface and back to a plane through the focal point is a constant. Hence all of the rays from the reflector are in phase on this surface, and relative to a distance point, the illuminated plane is an equiphase surface. Often the focal point is in the face plane, but it may be either forward or behind this position.

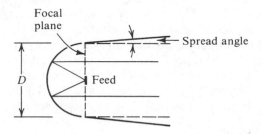

Figure 10.6-4.   A parabolic reflector

The rays that emanate from the parabola are almost parallel to the axis of revolution of the paraboloid. Because of the finite dimensions of the feed at the focal point, and the fact that the discontinuity at the edge of the parabola is illuminated, there is both a spread in angle and side lobes are present. A calculation of the average power distribution is rather complicated, and is beyond the scope of this book. The conclusions from these field calculations for $\pi D/\lambda \gg 1$, where D is the diameter of the face plane, are

$$\text{spread angle} \qquad \theta_s = 1.2\frac{\lambda}{D} \qquad\qquad \text{(a)} \quad (10.6\text{-}8)$$

$$G = f\left(\frac{\pi D}{\lambda}\right)^2 \qquad\qquad \text{(b)}$$

where f is a factor that depends on the properties of the feed at the focus. The factor f will normally range from about 0.6 to 0.8 for practical feed systems. The feeds that may be used assume a wide variety of sizes and shapes. The open end of a waveguide may be used, but for an improved exciting pattern shape, a sectoral horn, that is, a horn flared in one dimension, is preferred.

In some applications a *horn* radiator may be used. Such a device at microwave frequencies yields patterns somewhat reminiscent of dipole arrays. The shape of the horn can vary from the open waveguide, to an *H*-plane sector, an *E*-plane sector, or a pyramidal horn. For a circular waveguide or a coaxial feed line, a conical horn may be used. A horn produces a radiation pattern with a beamwidth that is inversely proportional to the aperture opening. The beam is narrowest in the plane of the widest aperture, a result that is expected from earlier results on arrays.

10.7 LASERS

The laser may be considered to be the most directive "antenna" presently available. A laser beam is so directional that it can be reflected and observed from the moon. The laser is used in many applications, such as material processing, communications systems, optical data processing, holographic technology, geodesy, and biomedical applications. New applications of laser technology indicate a promising future. It is expected that lasers with shorter wavelengths will be developed; possibly an x-ray laser will be invented. A particularly important possible application is its use in nuclear fusion processing.

The success of the laser results from its unique properties of *directionality*, *brightness*, *monochromaticity*, and *polarization*. These properties are present in the laser to a far greater degree than in any other light or radiowave source of radiation.

Actually there exists no light source which is capable of producing nearly completely monochromatic light. The spreading in frequency of a radiation line, or equivalently, the spread in wavelength of the line is the essential *linewidth* of the source. For example, white light has a linewidth of $\Delta\lambda \doteq 350 \times 10^{-9}$ m $= 350$ nm, whereas a small power gas laser has a linewidth of $\Delta\lambda \doteq 0.1$ nm.

Directionality is one of the most pronounced properties of laser light. For a typically small laser, the *beam divergence* is on the order of 10^{-3} rad. In other words, the beam increases 1 mm for every meter of beam travel. The laser beam diameter is generally determined by its beam diameter inside of the laser cavity, as shown in Figure 10.7-1. The *beam waist* W_o is minimum inside of the

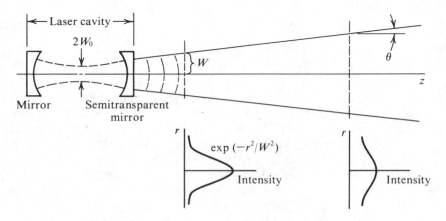

Figure 10.7-1. Laser cavity and beam divergence

cavity. At a large distance from the cavity, the full angle of divergence is given by

$$\theta = \frac{2\lambda}{\pi W_o} \tag{10.7-1}$$

A small laser of 1 milliwatt power and 1 mm beam diameter is about 100 times brighter than the sun. This indicates that laser light should not be allowed to enter the eyes directly or by reflection. In fact, protective goggles should always be worn when working with lasers.

When a laser beam is viewed on a screen, small intensity variations are observed. This phenomenon is called the *speckle pattern*, and it is the result of interference. However, interference is the result of coherence. When the amplitude and phase of a wave is known at a point and at an instant of time, this is a completely coherent wave. When these features are not known, the wave is *incoherent*. Obviously between these two extreme cases there exists *partial coherence*. A diagrammatic representation of the two extreme cases is shown in Figure 10.7-2. The degree of coherence is measured using interferom-

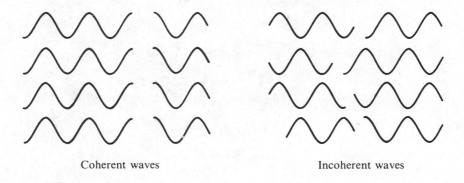

Coherent waves   Incoherent waves

Figure 10.7-2.   Coherent and incoherent states of light waves

eters. Young's experiment, for example, is capable of measuring the coherence between two points of the same source. The *fringe visibility* is taken as a direct measure of the degree of coherence, where we write

$$V = \frac{\text{maximum fringe irradiance} - \text{minimum fringe irradiance}}{\text{maximum fringe irradiance} + \text{minimum fringe irradiance}} \tag{10.7-2}$$

This expression shows that complete incoherence is specified when $V = 0$, and that $V = 1$ denotes complete coherence. Since the two points of the Young experiment belong to two different points on the same source, this type of coherence is called *spatial coherence* and characterizes the spatial variation in coherence across the wavefronts in the direction transverse to the propagation. In addition to spatial coherence, *longitudinal coherence* (*temporal coherence*) can also exist. This form of coherence characterizes the correlation of the wavefronts at two points along the beam, or at the same point at two different times. Different degrees of coherence are illustrated in Figure 10.7-3.

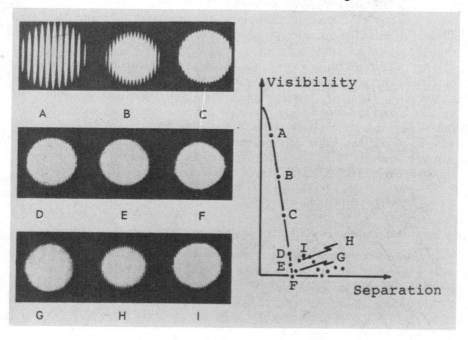

Figure 10.7-3.   Visibility versus separation of pinholes

Laser Fundamentals

For a laser to be activated and to emit radiation, it must possess the following properties: *active medium, population inversion,* and *feedback.* The active medium consists of a collection of atoms, molecules or ions; the population inversion takes place under a strong excitation process known as *pumping*; feedback is accomplished by the end mirrors of the laser cavity.

When an atom can change from an arbitrary energy state E_j to another lower energy state E_i, it emits a photon of frequency $\nu_{ij} = (E_j - E_i)/h$, where $h = 6.626 \times 10^{-34}$ joule Hz^{-1} is Planck's constant. The reverse action can also happen with the atom jumping from a lower energy state E_i to a higher energy state E_j when it absorbs a photon of the same frequency. These changes are called *atomic transitions.* If some of the transitions have a high probability that they will occur, they are called *allowable transitions.* The highly improbable ones are called *forbidden transitions.* The quantum mechanical rules that govern these transitions are called *selection rules*. The time that an atomic system will remain in a particular excited state is called the *transition time τ*. The transition time is on the order of a microsecond or less for allowed transitions and a millisecond or more for forbidden transitions.

Let us assume that light of a particular frequency ν passes through a gas cell which contains atoms capable of being in only two states E_1 and E_0 ($E_1 > E_0$). If the incident frequency $\nu = (E_1 - E_0)/h$, then part of the light beam will be absorbed since photons from the beam will dissipate their energy by raising the state of the atoms of the gas from E_0 to E_1. This type of absorption is called *stimulated absorption*. In addition to stimulated absorption, there are two types of emission. When emission occurs without stimulation, it is called *spontaneous emission*, otherwise it is called *stimulated emission*. Emission and absorption are shown graphically in Figure 10.7-4. Stimulated emission is essential for the laser amplification process.

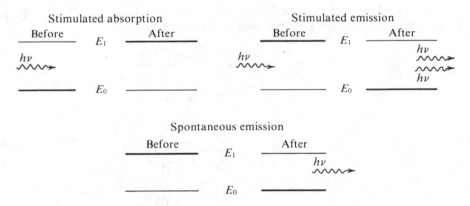

**Figure 10.7-4.   Energy state transition diagrammatic representation.
The heavy lines indicate the state of the atom**

In thermal equilibrium the population of atoms in higher energy states is never greater than the population of atoms in lower energy states. To create an "abnormal" situation when there are more atoms in higher level states than in lower energy states, the medium must be excited by pumping it, i.e., by stimulated absorption from an outside source, such as a light source. When a *population inversion* is achieved then *l*ight *a*mplification by *s*timulated *e*mission of *r*adiation (LASER) can take place. A three and a four level scheme for lasing are shown in Figure 10.7-5.

Finally, the resonator must be of such a shape that the light that is generated inside the cavity will continue to exist for some time, during which time the light will make many round trips between the mirrors. It is the confined radiation which contributes to the stimulated emission. The unconfined radiation constitutes a loss. Additional losses are produced by the impurities of the medium, edge diffraction effects, absorption, etc. If the losses are less than the

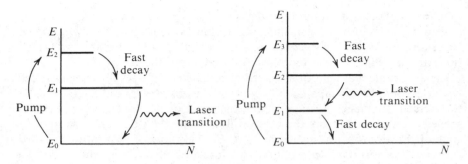

Figure 10.7-5.   Population of energy levels   (a) Three-level system
(b) Four-level system

generation, then amplification takes place. It has been found that some geometries lend themselves to stable resonators and some do not. Figure 10.7-6 shows some typical resonators and their stability criteria.

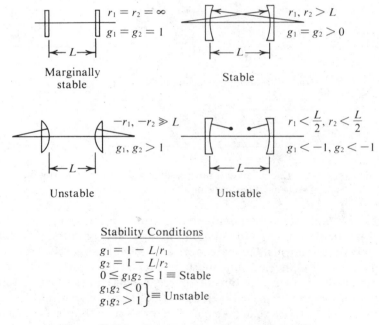

Figure 10.7-6.   Laser cavity mirror configurations

The wave patterns in laser resonators consist of a large number of waves that are propagating along the axis or in directions only slightly off axis. The total field in a cavity is replicated after a round trip in the cavity. However, since the cavity is a three dimensional structure, both *longitudinal* and *transverse* modes exist. The laser mode is thus characterized by three mode numbers, one corresponding to the longitudinal character of the mode, and two for specifying the transverse mode. It has been found that the wavelength is related to the wave numbers of the radiation and to the dimensional characteristic lengths of the cavity by the equation

$$\lambda_{mnq} = \left[q + (m+n+1)\frac{\cos^{-1}\sqrt{g_1 g_2}}{\pi} \right]\frac{1}{2L} \qquad (10.7\text{-}3)$$

where the integers m and n characterize the transverse mode and q characterizes the longitudinal mode. The different modes are designated by the symbol TEM$_{mnq}$ where *TEM* denotes *t*ransverse *e*lectro*m*agnetic. The values of q are quite large for regular laser dimensions, and are of little value. The values of m and n are small, and these can easily be detected and recorded in films, as shown in Figure 10.7-7. When there are many modes present in the output of the laser, it is called a *multimode* laser. By placing devices in the laser cavity to create losses for certain transverse modes, a single transverse mode laser can be created. It is also possible in a multimode laser to introduce an outside perturbation to force the mode oscillations of different frequency to have a definite phase relationship. The output of such a laser is a train of extremely short pulses separated by $2L/c$, and each pulse has a width of $2L/Nc$, where N is the number of oscillating modes. This phenomenon is called *mode locking*, an extremely useful technique for communication purposes.

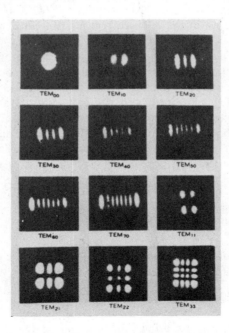

Figure 10.7-7.   Transverse modes of a laser cavity

Types of Lasers

A. L. Schawlow and C. H. Townes in 1958 proposed that lasing at optical wavelengths is possible. T. H. Maiman in 1960 developed the first laser whose active medium was a crystal of pink ruby. In the same year A. Javan built the first CW (continuous wave), not pulsed laser, using an active medium of a He and Ne mixture. A tremendous research effort has been devoted to create different types of lasers since that time. The following discusses some of them.

GAS LASERS. Gas lasers have as active mediums different gases and different mixtures of gases. Most of them are excited (pumped) by means of gas discharges. As the electrons collide with atoms in the gas during their traversal to the electrodes, they transfer part of their energy to induce transitions to higher energy level states. When the pumping is strong, population inversion takes place, and lasing appears. Gas lasers are broadly separated into atomic, molecular and ionic classes. A typical HeNe laser operates at about 1500 volts and consumes on the order of 10 watts. Its output is only 1.5 to 2 milliwatts indicating an efficiency in the range 0.015 to 0.02 percent.

INSULATOR LASERS. Doped insulator lasers are often used since they are simple to build, they are rugged, they are easy to maintain, and they generate high peak power. Their active mediums are crystals (insulators) which have been doped with impurity ions. The pumping energy is provided by a xenon flash lamp. A typical and often used laser is Nd:YAG (YAG—Ytrium Aluminum Garnet) with its output in the infrared region, 1.06 μm.

SEMICONDUCTOR LASERS. Semiconductor lasers are among the smallest and the most easily constructed types. They are used as light sources in fiber optics communications and as light indicator LED (light emitting diodes). When the semiconductor diode is forward biased, optical radiation can take place. When a recombination takes place between an electron in the conduction band and a hole in the valence band, a quantum of light is emitted. This is called *recombination radiation*. If we can succeed in creating more electrons through the junction, the phenomenon of population inversion is present. It requires only stimulation for light emission.

DYE LASERS. Liquid lasers are unique in some respects because a high concentration of active atoms can be supplied, and the concentration is easily varied. Moreover, such a laser medium is inexpensive, is relatively damage-free, and is easily handled. By using a mixture of dyes, the entire visible range can be included. All dye lasers are optically pumped.

SUMMARY

- The amplitude of a propagating sinusoidal plane wave is specified by

$$y = A \sin (kz - \omega t)$$

where $k = 2\pi/\lambda =$ wave number, $v_{ph} = \omega/k =$ phase velocity and $v_g = d\omega/dk =$ group velocity. This amplitude function satisfies the second order partial differential wave equation

$$\frac{\partial y^2}{\partial z^2} = \frac{1}{v_{ph}^2}\frac{\partial y^2}{\partial t^2}$$

- The wave number of an LC transmission line is $k = \omega/v_{ph} = \omega\sqrt{LC}$.

- A plane electromagnetic wave propagating in the Z-direction with its $\bar{E}$-field in the X-direction satisfies the following two Maxwell equations

$$\frac{\partial E_x(z,t)}{\partial z} = -\mu\frac{\partial H_y(z,t)}{\partial t}$$

$$\frac{\partial H_y(z,t)}{\partial z} = -\epsilon\frac{\partial E_x(z,t)}{\partial t}$$

- The rate of flow of energy per unit area in the electromagnetic field is given by the Poynting vector, $\bar{S} = \bar{E}\times\bar{H}$.

- The characteristic impedance of the medium is given by

$$\frac{E}{H} = Z = \sqrt{\frac{\mu}{\epsilon}} \qquad \text{ohm}$$

- Snell's law of refraction is

$$\frac{\sin\theta_i}{\sin\theta_t} = \frac{v_i}{v_t} = \frac{\sqrt{\mu\epsilon_2}}{\sqrt{\mu\epsilon_1}} = \sqrt{\frac{\epsilon_2}{\epsilon_1}} = \sqrt{\frac{\epsilon_{2r}}{\epsilon_{1r}}} = \frac{\eta_2}{\eta_1}$$

- When the phenomenon of resonance occurs, there exist unique wave configurations called modes.

- One of the most pronounced characteristics of a wave is its ability to create interference patterns.

- Electromagnetic waves in waveguides are propagated in transverse electric (TE) and transverse magnetic (TM) modes only.

- Appropriate to each mode number n, there corresponds a particular field configuration called a wave mode.

- The wave number of a two parallel plane guide is given by

$$k_g = \frac{2\pi}{\lambda_g} = \sqrt{\left(\frac{2\pi}{\lambda}\right)^2 - \left(\frac{n\pi}{b}\right)^2}$$

where b is the distance between the two planes.

- The phase velocity of the wave in a rectangular waveguide is always greater than the speed of light, and its group velocity is always less than the speed of light.

- The infinitesimal dipole is shown to have an induction field and a radiation field. The radiation field allows the calculation of the radiated power, the radiation resistance, and the power directivity pattern.

- Lasers can be considered as ideal antennas because of their high directionality, brightness (intensity), monochromaticity, and polarization abilities.

- For laser action there must be an active medium, population inversion, and feedback.

- A number of laser types exist, including gas, insulator, semiconductor, dye, and possibly x-ray lasers.

REVIEW QUESTIONS

1. Does the equation $E = E_m \sin \omega t$ characterize a propagating wave?
2. How is the phase velocity of a wave defined?
3. Name some physical waves.
4. What equations does the electromagnetic field satisfy?
5. What is meant by the term plane electromagnetic wave?
6. What characterizes the characteristic impedance of a medium?
7. What phenomena are observed if a wave falls on an interface between two mediums with different indexes of refraction?
8. Define Snell's law.
9. What are the boundary conditions on an electromagnetic field?
10. What is resonance?
11. When do standing waves appear?
12. Is diffraction a wave phenomenon? Is the rainbow a diffraction phenomenon?
13. What is a Michelson interferometer, and what is it used for?
14. Are guided waves inside waveguides *transverse electromagnetic* (TEM)?
15. What is the difference between a mode number and a wave mode of a guided wave?
16. What is meant by cutoff frequency in a waveguide?
17. Is the group velocity or the phase velocity of the wave larger in a waveguide? Why cannot energy be transported faster than the speed of light?
18. What is the difference between the radiation field and the induction field of an infinitesimal dipole?
19. What is the usefulness of the power directivity pattern?
20. What conditions must be met to create lasing action?
21. Are lasers monochromatic?
22. What is meant by the word coherence?
23. What is stimulated absorption; spontaneous emission; stimulated emission?
24. Do lasers have transverse modes?
25. Name different type lasers.

REFERENCES

1. Hayt, W. H., Jr., *Engineering Electromagnetics*, 3rd ed., McGraw Hill Book Co., New York, NY, 1974.
   An elementary introductory text.

2. Plonsey, R., and R. E. Collin, *Principles and Applications of Electromagnetic Fields*, McGraw Hill Book Co., New York, NY, 1961.
   This text serves as a general introduction to electromagnetic theory with many applications.

3. Seely, S., and A. D. Poularikas, *Electromagnetics, Classical and Modern Theory and Applications*, Marcel Dekker, Inc., New York, NY, 1979.
   Includes a great deal of introductory material as well as advanced topics. Addresses the topics discussed in this chapter.

PROBLEMS

10.1-1. Plot $y = A \sin (kz - \omega t)$ versus z for the following values of t: $10°/\omega$, $20°/\omega$, $60°/\omega$, $90°/\omega$.

10.1-2. Verify the development of Equation (10.1-6) and show that $y = A \sin (kz - \omega t)$ and $y = A \cos (kz - \omega t)$ are solutions of the wave equation.

10.1-3. What is the wavelength of the voltage wave on a transmission line if the oscillator has an angular frequency of 10^6 rad/s, $L = 3$ mH, $C = 5$ μF? What is the speed of the voltage wave?

10.1-4. Verify Equation (10.1-5).

10.1-5. (a) Verify Equation (10.1-19).
   (b) Find the wave number and the wavelength for an electromagnetic field.
   (c) What is the speed of a wave in lake water ($\epsilon = 80 \times 8.85 \times 10^{-12}$ F/m; $\mu = 4\pi \times 10^{-7}$ H/m)?

10.1-6. Show that H_y satisfies the partial differentiation equation

$$\frac{\partial^2 H_y(z,t)}{\partial t^2} = \epsilon\mu \frac{\partial^2 H_y(z,t)}{\partial t^2} = \frac{1}{c^2} \frac{\partial^2 H_y(z,t)}{\partial t^2}$$

10.1-7. Using Equation (10.1-29) show that Equation (10.1-28) is an identity.

10.2-1. Using Snell's law, find θ_t if

(a) $\theta_i = 50°$, $\eta_2 = 4$, $\eta_1 = 2$;
(b) $\theta_i = 50°$, $\eta_2 = 2$, $\eta_1 = 4$.

Also, find the speeds of the waves in a medium with index of refraction $\eta = 4$; with $\eta = 2$.

10.2-2. Find the reflection and transmission coefficients for normal incidence of a uniform plane wave.

10.2-3. Write the reflection and transmission coefficients as a function of the incident angle, characteristic impedances of the two mediums, and their indexes of refraction, using Snell's law. Plot Γ_r and Γ_t versus θ_i for a wave propagating from water $\epsilon_r = 80$ to air $\epsilon_r = 1$.

10.3-1. Assume that the two solutions of the wave equation for the region between two infinite parallel conducting planes are $E_r = E_m \cos (kz - \omega t)$ and $E_l = E_m \cos (kz - \omega t + \varphi)$. Find the eigenvalues and eigenfunctions, and plot several modes for the system.

10.4-1. Find the angular spread of the fringes in Young's experiment. Find the spacing Δy between two consecutive fringes.

10.5-1. Verify Equations (10.5-6) and (10.5-7).

10.5-2. Determine the voltage reflection coefficient for values of Z_L equal to 0, Z_o, ∞, and explain what happens, in physical terms.

10.5-3. Show that Equation (10.5-9) is valid by checking the limited cases $\theta = 0°$ and $\theta = 90°$.

10.5-4. Plot the E_t field of Equation (10.5-11) versus y for the modes $n = 0, 1, 2, 3$. Assume that $\sin (kz \sin \theta - \omega t) = 1$, which is equivalent to saying that you plot E_t at $t = 0$ and at the point $z = \pi/2k \sin \theta$.

10.5-5. Determine the cutoff frequency of a parallel plate waveguide when $b = 3$ cm, $n = 5$, and the frequency of the generator is 10 GHz (10×10^9 Hz).

10.5-6. Using the field equations for the TE_{10} mode, verify Figure 10.5-3b field sketches.

10.5-7. For a rectangular waveguide with dimensions $a = 2.8$ cm, $b = 1.9$ cm, find the phase and group velocities of the TE_{10} mode, if the frequency of the source is 10.5 GHz.

10.5-8. Ascertain the power that is propagating down a waveguide carrying a TE_{10} mode wave. Given: $E_o = 2$ mV/m, $f = 10$ GHz, $a = 3$ cm, $b = 2.5$ cm.

10.6-1. Verify Equation (10.6-5).

10.6-2. A satellite at 100 km above the earth's surface has its short dipole antenna, $d = 0.7$ m, excited with a current $5 \sin (200 \times 10^6 \, t)$.

    (a) Find the time average power hitting the earth.
    (b) Determine the radiation resistance of the antenna.
    (c) Plot the radiating resistance versus excitation frequency.

10.6-3. Find the electric field pattern of a small dipole and compare it with its power pattern.

10.7-1. For a HeNe laser $\lambda = 632.8$ nm, find the full angle of divergence if its minimum beam waist is 0.2 mm. Find the diameter of its beam at the surface of the moon.

Chapter Eleven

Introduction to Communication Systems

Communication systems are concerned with the transmission and reception of intelligence. The form and features of the systems depend upon the type of intelligence being communicated. For example, telegraph transmission requires a frequency band of only several Hz, whereas the frequency band required for transmitting television intelligence is several MHz. Not unexpectedly, the details of the systems will differ markedly. However, despite the different waveforms and frequencies that the intelligence may demand for its transmission, all communication systems may be crudely represented by essentially the same blocks in their schematic representation. These are illustrated graphically in Figure 11.0.

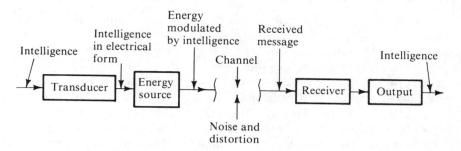

Figure 11.0.   The elements required in a complete communication system

In such a system, it is the function of the transducer to convert the intelligence — whether it is voice or music as in radio, dots and dashes for a telegraph system, voice for a telephone system, or both sounds and pictures as in television — into a form suitable for modulating an energy source. The modulated energy source is in a form which will allow the energy to pass through the transmitting medium. The modulated energy reaches a second transducer, the receiver, which extracts the intelligence and puts it in a suitable form for actuating the output device.

In the specific case of radiobroadcast transmission, the transducer is the microphone which converts the sound energy impinging on it into an appropriate electrical form at low power level. The energy source is a complicated device which includes amplifiers for raising the power level of the audio signal at the microphone to a sufficient level to modulate a high power high-frequency signal which is generated in an oscillator. This modulated h-f "carrier" is fed to an antenna for radiation of the energy into free space.

At the receiver some of the radiated energy is absorbed by an antenna. This energy is at very low power level and is amplified before the intelligence is extracted from the modulated signal. The extracted signal is then applied to a loud speaker which reproduces the original signal.

As stated in the foregoing discussion, the essentials of a communication system are the following:

1. A means or medium for transferring energy from a transmitter to a receiver.

2. A means for modulating the energy which will carry the intelligence from the transmitter to the receiver.

3. A means for preparing the intelligence in a form suitable for performing the function under (2).

4. A means for extracting the intelligence from the transmitted energy.

5. A means for presenting the intelligence in its proper form.

Certain aspects of these processes will be considered in this chapter.

11.1   MEASURE OF INFORMATION AND CHANNEL CAPACITY

An important aspect of the study of information is that information is quantifiable. The study known as "information theory" addresses itself to two basic questions: (a) How can we measure the information content of a message? and (b) How much information per unit time is a given communication system capable of transmitting? We can approach the first question by calling on our individual experiences. For example, if we are hearing or reading a known story, we say that there is little new information. However, if the information that we are receiving is all new and mostly unpredictable, we acknowledge that we have received new knowledge or information. This suggests that new information requires signals, e.g., sound, light, symbols, or words, which change unpredictability into predictability with time.

Consider a typical signal as shown in Figure 11.1-1, which shows a voltage that has been discretized to three levels. We shall assess the *system capacity*. To do this, we observe that there are four different possible amplitude levels in the interval (0, 1, 2, 3). The first time interval will be one of the four levels. For the second interval there are an additional four possibilities, so that there are $4^2 = 16$ possibilities in the two intervals. For the five intervals shown in Figure 11.1-1, there would be 4^5 combinations of signal amplitudes. In the general

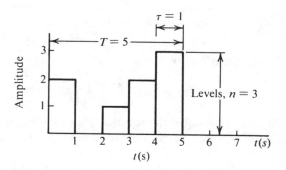

Figure 11.1-1. Typical voltage-time signal to be transmitted

case of a time T with a possible n equally probable levels per time interval τ, the number of combinations is

$$\text{Number of combinations} = n^{T/\tau} \qquad (11.1\text{-}1)$$

We would expect intuitively that the amount of information would be proportional to the amount of time T, which leads to

$$\text{Information in } T \text{ sec.} \propto \frac{T}{\tau} \log n$$

where the log can be taken with any base. The base commonly used is base 2, and we thus write

$$H = \frac{T}{\tau} \log_2 n = m \log_2 n \qquad \text{bits} \qquad (11.1\text{-}2)$$

To further justify Equation (11.1-2) let us assume that we have one interval ($m = 1$) and only one level ($n = 1$). These values when introduced into Equation (11.1-2) give

$$H = 1. \; \log_2 1 = 0$$

This shows that if a sure (predictable) event occurs, it carries zero information, as it should. The system capacity is defined by the relation

$$C = \frac{H}{T} = \frac{1}{\tau} \log_2 n \qquad \text{bits/sec} \qquad (11.1\text{-}3)$$

If we assume that any level (event) is equally likely to appear within an interval, its probability is $P = 1/n$. An equivalent situation is found, for example, in throwing dice. On each throw the probability of any of the six numbers to appear is $P_i = 1/6$. Thus the information over one interval is

$$H_1 = \log_2 n = \log_2 \frac{1}{P} = -\log_2 P$$

and for m intervals the information is

$$H = -m \log_2 P \qquad\qquad (11.1\text{-}4)$$

The probability of an event is equal to the ratio of the number of times that the event occurs during N repeated trials to the total number of trials N.

EXAMPLE 11.1-1. Find the information content of a signal having 10 levels per unit time interval and 5 time units long.

SOLUTION. Since all the levels are equally likely, we have

$$H = -m \log_2 P = -5 \log_2 \frac{1}{10} = 5 \log_2 10 = 16.609 \qquad \text{bits}$$

The average information is

$$H_{av} = \frac{H}{m} = -\log_2 \frac{1}{10} = 3.3218 \qquad \text{bits/interval}$$

□   □   □

We now consider the case involving a sequence of three symbols (a, b, c) which are transmitted, each with a probability of occurrence $P(a)$, $P(b)$, $P(c)$. The information associated with a, for example, is $-\log_2 P(a)$ which occurs $P(a)$ of the time, with similar considerations for the information associated with b and c. The average information content is defined as:

$$H_{av} = -P(a)\log_2 P(a) - P(b)\log_2 P(b) - P(c)\log_2 P(c) \text{ bits/symbol} \quad (11.1\text{-}5)$$

For k symbols this result is generalized to

$$H_{av} = -\sum_{i=1}^{k} P_i \log_2 P_i \qquad \text{bits/symbol} \qquad\qquad (11.1\text{-}6)$$

EXAMPLE 11.1-2. Find the average information per interval if a signal has two levels (e.g., 5 volts and 10 volts) and with corresponding probabilities $P(5) = 0.75$ and $P(10) = 0.25$.

SOLUTION. From Equation (11.1-6) we obtain

$$H_{av} = -0.75 \log_2 0.75 - 0.25 \log_2 0.25 = 0.3113 + 0.4999 = 0.8112 \text{ bits/interval}$$

The average capacity of the system is

$$\frac{H_{av}}{\tau} = \frac{0.8112}{\tau} \quad \text{bits/sec}$$

□ □ □

EXAMPLE 11.1-3. Find the month of the year using a yes-no response.

SOLUTION. Since there are 12 months in the year, and since each is equally likely to be chosen, then $P_i = 1/12$ and the information content is

$$H_{av} = -\sum_{i=1}^{12} P_i \log_2 P_i = -\frac{1}{12} \log_2 \frac{1}{12} \ldots -\frac{1}{12} \log_2 \frac{1}{12} = -\log_2 \frac{1}{12} = 3.585 \text{ bits}$$

Suppose, for example, that we have selected December (12). We can proceed as follows:

Query	Answer
Is it before June (6)	No
Is it after September (9)	Yes
Is it after November (11)	Yes
Is it December	Yes

□ □ □

To transmit information in the most efficient way, i.e., at the highest rate, we must condition the source in a specific way. For example, if we plot H_{av} versus $P(a)$ [$P(b) = 1 - P(a)$] for a two-letter source, we obtain the curve shown in Figure 11.1-2. We observe that H_{av} is a maximum when $P(a) = 1/2$, or equivalently, when the symbols are equally likely to occur. This suggests that the signal be so conditioned that each output is equally likely.

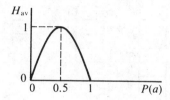

Figure 11.1-2. A graph of H_{av} vs. $P(a)$ for a two-letter source

Another important factor which must be considered is the rate of information transmission. Consider binary data (yes-no) to be used in the transmission of information. These data are in the form of pulses of finite duration T which contain frequencies which occupy a specific bandwidth range. To increase the rate, we must decrease T, which will require that the channel (circuit) must be capable of handling the extra frequencies produced by decreasing the duration of the pulses. But it is not always possible to do this. To send more data per unit time, a somewhat more sophisticated signal processing is required. Such a processing is *coding*.

A deterministic device which converts a message of one form to a message in another form is called an *encoder*. The device which performs the reverse process at the receiving end is called a *decoder*. Consider a continuous signal which is quantized to eight levels (0, 1, 2,..., 7) as shown in Figures 11.1-3a and 11.1-3b. If we select the level 5, we can proceed to locate it by a yes-no sequence, as already discussed. From Figure 11.1-3c, d and e, we observe that $5 \triangleq 101$ in binary form. If we employ a normal binary code for the 8 levels (0 through 7 (see Chapter 9) then we can establish the voltage level using three 0,1 pulses. Each 1,0 label is one bit. Hence, for each voltage level, we need 3 bits of information. If the code contained 16 levels, each level would require 4 bits for its specification. For n levels, we would require $\log_2 n$ bits. It is apparent therefore that for T/τ intervals and n levels, we require $(T/\tau)\log_2 n$ bits of information.

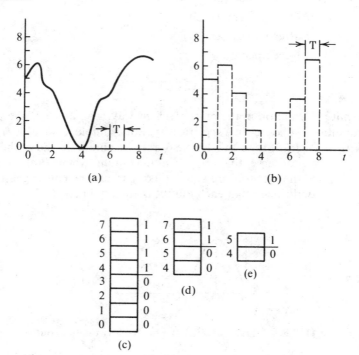

Figure 11.1-3. (a) Continuous signal   (b) The same signal quantized
(c, d, e) Procedure for binary representation

The importance of coding becomes evident if we consider the case of transmitting a string of two letters A and B using a 0,1 voltage representation. Let the letter A be produced with probability ¾ and the letter B with a probability of ¼. The average information per letter is

$$H_{av} = -\frac{3}{4}\log_2\frac{3}{4} - \frac{1}{4}\log_2\frac{1}{4} = 0.811$$

Suppose that the source produces 70 letters per minute. The source transmits

$$H = 0.811 \times \frac{70}{60} = 0.946 \qquad \text{bits/sec}$$

If this information is passing through a channel which will accept only 60 letters per minute, or one bit per second, it will not be possible to transmit the 70 letters in one minute for a coding $A = 0$ and $B = 1$.

Consider next an encoder which bunches together 2 letters, and we encode them together, as indicated in Table 11.1-1. Column 3 indicates the relative probabilities of the various 2 letter groups. Notice that the total probability is one. The fourth column is the probability of a given digit group multiplied by the number of digits in the group. The total of the last column is the average information for two letters (1.6875 bits), or $1.6875/2 = 0.84375$ bits/letter. Clearly, if the source sends 70 letters per minute encoded as shown in Table 11.1-1, the channel will transmit $70 \times 0.84375 = 59.0625$ digits/min, which indicates that transmission of the desired number of letters is possible.

Table 11.1-1. A two-letter coding scheme

Letter	Code	Probability	Weighted number of digits
AA	0	$\frac{3}{4}\cdot\frac{3}{4}=\frac{9}{16}$	$1\cdot\frac{9}{16}=\frac{9}{16}$
AB	10	$\frac{3}{4}\cdot\frac{1}{4}=\frac{3}{16}$	$2\cdot\frac{3}{16}=\frac{6}{16}$
BA	110	$\frac{1}{4}\cdot\frac{3}{4}=\frac{3}{16}$	$3\cdot\frac{3}{16}=\frac{9}{16}$
BB	111	$\frac{1}{4}\cdot\frac{1}{4}=\frac{1}{16}$	$3\cdot\frac{1}{16}=\frac{3}{16}$
		$\frac{16}{16}=1$	$\frac{27}{16}=1.6875$ bits/2 letters

Observe, of course, that we have assumed the transmission path to be entirely noise-free. In a real physical system, the effects of noise should be studied. For the situation being discussed, a typical string of letters and their coding for a noise-free system might look like

string	A B	A A	A A	A B	B A	B A	A B	A B	B A	A A	B B	A B	A A
coded	10	0	0	10	110	110	10	10	110	0	111	10	0

It must be obvious that some sort of storaging is required since the letters are appearing at a faster rate than the digits are generated and transmitted. Because of this some errors will be introduced. However, if the source produces letters at a rate that is less than the channel transmission rate, it will always be possible to devise an encoder that will allow the message to be transmitted through the channel with practically no error.

11.2 COMMUNICATIONS WITH CONTINUOUS SIGNALS

A study of particular methods for transmitting information from one point to another can proceed either in the time domain or in the frequency domain. In particular, every signal has two equivalent representations. For example, consider the periodic signal

$$v(t) = 1 + 2 \sin 2\pi 10t + \sin 2\pi 20t \qquad (11.2\text{-}1)$$

The time domain and the frequency domain representations are shown in Figures 11.2-1a and 11.2-1b. We observe that the heights of the lines in the frequency domain (the frequency spectrum) represent the peak values of the sine waves which constitute the signal and which are located at their respective frequencies. The d-c term is located at the origin or at zero frequency. Since the lines are distinct, this denotes a *discrete* spectrum, and this is characteristic of periodic signals, as already discussed in Chapter 1. The total spread of frequencies from zero to the highest value belonging to the signal is called the

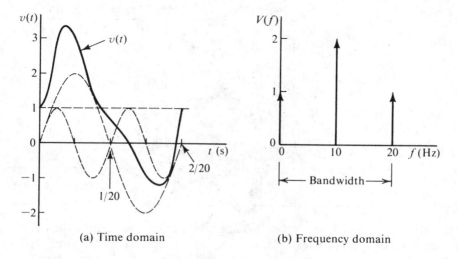

(a) Time domain   (b) Frequency domain

Figure 11.2-1.   Time and frequency representation of a periodic signal

bandwidth. For example, the bandwidth required for a simple telephone channel is 3000 Hz (from 300-3500 Hz). A knowledge of the bandwidth is important since a match must be made between the transmitting system and the requisite bandwidth of the signals to be transmitted.

It is evident from Figure 11.2-1 that the signal $v(t)$ can be constructed either by combining the signals given by the dotted lines as in Figure 11.2-1a, or by using the information contained in the frequency domain representation of Figure 11.2-1b. These two representations are equivalent.

Suppose that the signal given by Equation (11.2-1) and illustrated in Figure 11.2-1 is transmitted through a channel that has a 15 Hz bandwidth. The higher frequency term will not appear at the output of the channel, and what remains is the signal

$$v(t) = 1 + 2 \cos 2\pi 10t$$

which is not the original signal. This indicates, of course, that the bandwidth of the channel has a great deal to do with the quality of a received signal as compared with the transmitted signal. To understand this situation, we note that the human voice requires only about 500 Hz for reasonable understanding. However, if pitch and tonal qualities of the voice are also desired, a bandwidth of about 1500 Hz is required. This indicates that bandwidth limitations introduce *distortion.*

A number of effects can cause degradation of the transmitted signal. The faithful transmission of a signal requires that the amplitudes and phases of the frequency components must be maintained through the channel. Phase delays introduce what is called envelope delay, phase delay distortion or simply *phase distortion.* The reader can readily verify this by redrawing Figure 11.2-1a when one or the other of the two sine waves has been shifted by a small amount in phase. To remedy this situation, special networks known as *delay equalizers* are often introduced into the channel. The human ear is relatively insensitive to phase distortion and simple telephone channels do not require elaborate correction. However, the phase and amplitude of the harmonics and components making up a musical tone from a musical instrument are critical to the tone and timber of the output.

Other types of distraction may also occur in transmission. We have all experienced an outside conversation on the line when we are calling long distance. This type of distraction is known as *cross-talk.* The cause of this phenomenon is mainly due to the inductive coupling (magnetic field linking) of the transmission lines constituting the two circuits. Another type of distraction is called *echo,* which is the return of your own voice; this often occurs during a telephone conversation.

Communication channels are not immune from noise, which are random electrical unwanted signals. *Impulse noise* is produced by the operation of machinery, the closing of switches, and by electrical storms. Impulse noise is of short duration but large amplitude in the audio frequency range, and usually appears as clicks or bursts of static. *White noise* comprises random signals that are spread over a very broad frequency range. It manifests itself in the audio frequency range as a hissing sound, as snow on a television tube.

In addition to the distortion that occurs in the transmitting channel, the power level also falls with distance from the source. There are many reasons for this, e.g., spreading, as in a radio or television broadcast; absorption; or scattering. The attenuation of the channel is generally determined by measuring the input (transmitted) power and the output (received) power. The unit of loss is usually expressed in decibels (dB), which is defined by the relation

$$dB = 10 \log_{10}(P_{out}/P_{in}) \qquad (11.2\text{-}2)$$

From this definition it is evident that the dB alone does not give any measure of the original strength of the signal, since it gives the relationship only between two degrees of power.

Signals which are finite in time and bounded have a *continuous* frequency spectrum rather than the discrete spectrum of the periodic signals. To determine the frequency spectrum of a finite signal requires the use of the Fourier transform

$$\mathcal{F}\{f(t)\} = F(\omega) = \int_{-\infty}^{\infty} f(t)e^{-j\omega t}\, dt \qquad (11.2\text{-}3)$$

Figure 11.2-2 shows some typical time functions and their frequency domain representations.

The equivalence between time and frequency representations of signals is of great engineering significance, and the following observations can be made:

1. Signals have both a time and a frequency representation, and with the proper mathematical manipulation one can be determined from the other.

2. Periodic functions have discrete spectral representations.

3. Finite duration signals have continuous frequency representations.

4. Although the time and the frequency representations are essentially equivalent, each provides useful, but different, information to the engineer; e.g., the peak value of the time signal is not easily determined from its frequency representation.

5. Unending periodic signals carry no information since they are absolutely predictable without any uncertainty.

6. While the bandwidth of finite duration signals extends to infinity, most of the energy contained in the signal is associated with frequencies that extend to some finite value of ω. In practice, we associate the bandwidth with this finite ω. For example, the bandwidth of the pulse in Figure 11.2-2a is often taken as $B = \pi/a$ Hz.

7. The effect of time duration on the bandwidth is indicated in Figure 11.2-2a for the pulse. It shows that pulses of shorter time duration have broader frequency bandwidths. This means that to increase the data rate

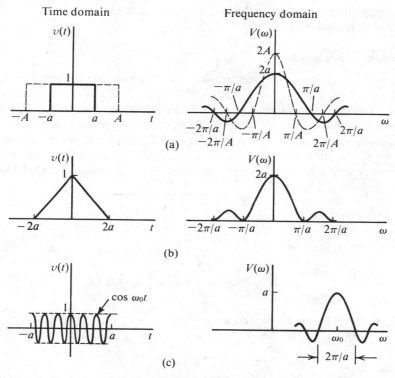

**Figure 11.2-2. Time and frequency domain representations
for signals of finite duration**

(pulses/sec) the system must be capable of passing the extra frequencies which
are created by the shorter pulses. This indicates that the rate of transmission of
information and bandwidth are linearly related.

11.3 SYSTEMS OF MODULATION

We have already noted that an important method of preparing intelligence
for transmission involves the modulation of an energy source by the intelligence. The process of modulation is of significant importance also because it
allows the signals to be relocated to less congested frequency bands, so less interference occurs. In addition, the frequency shifting inherent in modulation
permits the more efficient radiation of energy through the use of high frequencies, particularly when the channel between the transmitter and the receiver is
free space. Specifically, a radio antenna is most efficient if its physical length is
about one-half of the wavelength of the mean radiated frequency. To transmit
a voice signal (say to 10^4 Hz) efficiently (electrical wavelength 3×10^4 m)
directly would require an antenna approximately 18 miles long, a totally im-
practical matter. The modulation process permits the translation of the low

voice frequencies to much higher frequencies, such as 10^6 Hz, with its more practical radiation possibility.

Amplitude Modulation

We wish to examine the essential features of amplitude modulation. Consider, therefore, that a signal $v_m(t) = V_m \cos \omega_m t$, which is the *modulating signal*, must be transmitted. To produce an amplitude modulated signal requires that we must also provide a second signal source of very high frequency. This signal, known as the *carrier*, is easily produced by a stable oscillator and is of the form $v_c(t) = V_c \cos \omega_c t$. These two signals are now multiplied, requiring some type of nonlinear device to accomplish this multiplication. The result is the modulated wave

$$v(t) = V_c V_m \cos \omega_m t \cos \omega_c t \qquad\qquad \omega_m \ll \omega_c \qquad\qquad (11.3\text{-}1)$$

By using the trigonometric identity

$$\cos \theta_1 \cos \theta_2 = \frac{1}{2} \cos (\theta_2 + \theta_1) + \frac{1}{2} \cos (\theta_2 - \theta_1)$$

Equation (11.3-4) can be written in the form

$$v(t) = \frac{V_m V_c}{2} \cos (\omega_c + \omega_m)t + \frac{V_m V_c}{2} \cos (\omega_c - \omega_m)t \qquad\qquad (11.3\text{-}2)$$

These signals in their time and frequency domain representations are shown in Figure 11.3-1. Observe that the carrier frequency does not appear in the spectrum. Because of this, the modulation process is known as *AM double-side band, suppressed carrier*, AM-DSB/SC.

AM-DSB/SC is seldom used because the demodulation process proves to be very difficult. Moreover, the information or intelligence is actually contained in each side band, and if suppressed carrier transmission is to be effected, it is better to suppress one of the side bands as well. In this case of AM-SSB/SC, *single side band, suppressed carrier*, the advantage is considerable because the power contained in the carrier and in one side band can both be used to raise the power level of the side band that is being transmitted. The demodulation process for SSB/SC is such that this technique does not lend itself well for the transmission of music or other signals that are phase sensitive. However, it is entirely satisfactory for voice communication, and it is used extensively commercially for radio-telephone service as well as for radio-ham communication.

Now consider the amplitude modulation process that is specified by the equation

$$v(t) = A[1 + mv_m(t)] \cos \omega_c t \qquad\qquad (11.3\text{-}3)$$

where $v_m(t)$ is the modulating signal. The maximum value of mV_m must be less than one if distortion of the envelope is to be avoided. For $v_m(t) = \cos \omega_m t$ Equation (11.3-6) takes the form

$$v(t) = A \cos \omega_c t + Am \cos \omega_c t \cos \omega_m t$$

$$= A \cos \omega_c t + \frac{1}{2} Am[\cos (\omega_c - \omega_m)t + \cos (\omega_c + \omega_m)t] \tag{11.3-4}$$

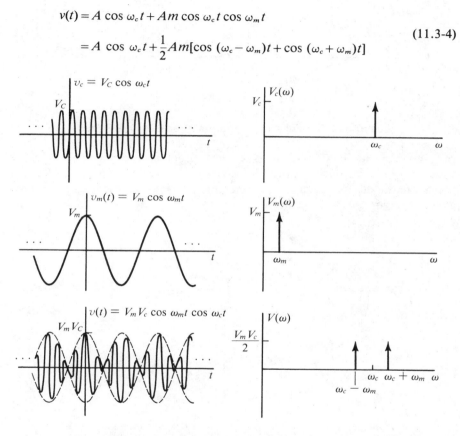

Figure 11.3-1. Time and frequency domains of AM signals

The frequency domain portrayal of this signal is shown in Figure 11.3-2a. We know, of course, that the modulating signal, e.g., the voice, has a finite frequency spectrum, as shown in Figure 11.3-2b, and the modulated signal $v(t)$ becomes that in Figure 11.3-2c instead of that in Figure 11.3-2a. Observe that in this case the modulated signal is AM-DSB with the carrier being included. This is the modulation scheme used in commercial radio broadcasting.

The demodulation process, that is the process of recovering the signal after it has been received as an AM-DSB signal, involves a frequency translation process again, only this time from signals centered about the carrier ω_c to signals given with respect to zero reference level. As for the modulation pro-

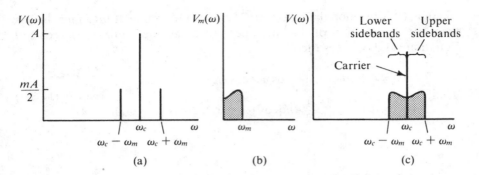

Figure 11.3-2.   Frequency spectrum of an AM-DSB signal

cess, now the modulated signal is multiplied with the carrier frequency ω_c which has been included with the transmitted signal. The resulting lower side bands are the desired signals. A simple diode detector (demodulator) is illustrated in Figure 11.3-3 together with the waveshapes at various points in the circuit.

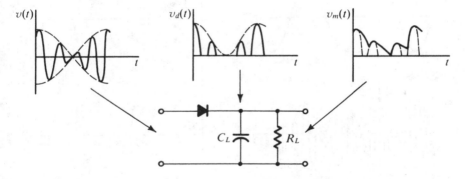

Figure 11.3-3.   Amplitude-modulation detector (demodulator)

A typical transmitting and receiving system for AM-DSB broadcasting are given in Figure 11.3-4. If we assume that the transmitted signal is that given by Equation (11.3-4) then the output of the mixer in the receiver will be the following signal

$$v(t) = A \cos \omega_c t \cos \omega_c t + Am \cos \omega_c t \cos \omega_c t \cos \omega_m t$$

or

$$v(t) = A(1 + m \cos \omega_m t) \left(\frac{\cos (\omega_c - \omega_c)t}{2} + \frac{\cos (\omega_c + \omega_c)t}{2} \right)$$

$$= \frac{A}{2}(1 + m \cos \omega_m t) + \frac{A}{2}(1 + m \cos \omega_m t) \cos 2\omega_c t$$

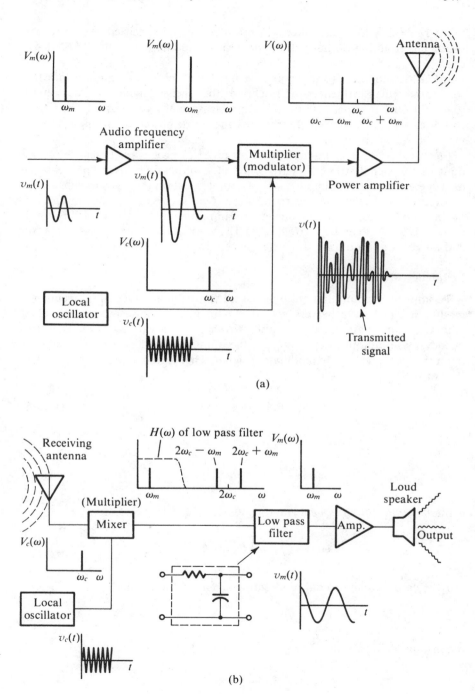

Figure 11.3-4.   AM-DSB transmitter and superheterodyne receiver

Since $2\omega_c \gg \omega_m$ a low pass filter will reject the signal specified by the second term. The resulting output will be the desired modulating signal. $(A/2)(1 + m \cos \omega_m t)$.

In our development to this point, we have not mentioned an important factor, *noise*, which influences the fidelity of the received signal. It is customary to use the output *signal-to-noise ratio* as a measure of signal purity. The signal-to-noise ratio is defined as the ratio of the mean power of the signal to the mean power of the noise.

Electrical noise is characteristic of all physical processes. It sets the lower limit of the signal strength below which it is impossible to comprehend the message. One of the main purposes of communication theory is to study ways to suppress and eliminate electrical noise. One success is the use of the frequency modulation technique instead of amplitude modulation. This is a well known result that can be verified if we listen simultaneously to an AM station and an FM station during the progress of a local thunderstorm.

Frequency Modulation

To improve the immunity to noise of transmission and reception, frequency modulation proves to be very effective. This is so because modulated signal amplitudes are maintained constant, with the signal varying the carrier frequency by an amount depending on the amplitude and at a rate depending upon the frequency of the modulating signal. That is, the modulated signal has the form

$$v(t) = A \cos \theta(t) \tag{11.3-5}$$

where

$$\omega_i = \frac{d\theta(t)}{dt} = \omega_c + m v_m(t) \tag{11.3-6}$$

is the *instantaneous frequency* and $\theta(t)$ is given by the expression

$$\theta(t) = \omega_c t + m \int v_m(t)\, dt \tag{11.3-7}$$

For the case of a sinusoidal modulating signal of the form

$$v_m(t) = \cos \omega_m t \tag{11.3-8}$$

the instantaneous frequency is

$$\omega_i = \omega_c + m \cos \omega_m t \tag{11.3-9}$$

and the maximum frequency deviation is then given by

$$\Delta\omega = \omega_i - \omega_c = m \tag{11.3-10}$$

Introduce the signal given by Equation (11.3-8) into Equation (11.3-5) and use Equation (11.3-7) to obtain

$$v(t) = \cos\left(\omega_c t + \frac{m}{\omega_m}\sin\omega_m t\right) = \cos\left(\omega_c t + \frac{\Delta\omega}{\omega_m}\sin\omega_m t\right)$$

$$= \cos(\omega_c t + \beta\sin\omega_m t) \tag{11.3-11}$$

where

$$\beta = \frac{\Delta\omega}{\omega_m} = \frac{\Delta f}{f_m} \tag{11.3-12}$$

is the *modulation index* and $A = 1$. By definition, β is the ratio of the frequency deviation to the bandwidth of the modulating signal. Expand Equation (11.3-11) as

$$v(t) = \cos\omega_c t \cos(\beta\sin\omega_m t) - \sin\omega_c t \sin(\beta\sin\omega_m t)$$

Equation (11.3-11) becomes, for $\beta \ll 1$ and making the approximations

$$\cos(\beta\sin\omega_m t) \doteq 1 \qquad\qquad \sin(\beta\sin\omega_m t) \doteq \beta\sin\omega_m t$$

$$v(t) \doteq \cos\omega_c t - \beta\sin\omega_m t \sin\omega_c t \tag{11.3-13}$$

If we compare this equation with that in Equation (11.3-4), we see that under the assumption of very small modulation index that AM and FM are similar, except for the shifted side bands in the FM case. It is obvious from Equation (11.3-13) that we may produce a narrow-band FM by an electronic systems whose components are shown in a block-diagram form in Figure 11.3-5. In fact, the Armstrong method of generating FM signals makes use of precisely this idea.

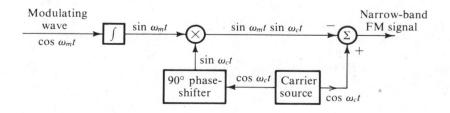

Figure 11.3-5.   Methods generating narrow-band FM signal

Consider next the case of a somewhat larger value for β. To do this, we shall use the approximations

$$\cos\,\theta = 1 - \frac{\theta^2}{2!} + \frac{\theta^4}{4!} - \frac{\theta^6}{6!} + \ldots \doteq 1 - \frac{\theta^2}{2!} = 1 - \frac{\beta^2}{2}\,\sin^2\,\omega_m t$$

$$\sin\,\theta = \theta - \frac{\theta^3}{3!} + \frac{\theta^5}{5!} + \frac{\theta^7}{7!} + \ldots \doteq \theta = \beta\,\sin\,\omega_m t$$

and now we find that

$$v(t) = \cos\,\omega_c t\,\left(1 - \frac{\beta^2}{2}\,\sin^2\,\omega_m t\right) - \beta\,\sin\,\omega_c t\,\sin\,\omega_m t \qquad (11.3\text{-}14)$$

$$= \cos\,\omega_c t - \frac{\beta^2}{4}\,\cos\,\omega_c t(1 - \cos\,2\omega_m t) - \beta\,\sin\,\omega_c t\,\sin\,\omega_m t$$

$$= \left(1 - \frac{\beta^2}{4}\right)\,\cos\,\omega_c t - \frac{\beta}{2}[\cos\,(\omega_c - \omega_m)t - \cos\,(\omega_c + \omega_m)t]$$

$$+ \frac{\beta^2}{8}[\cos\,(\omega_c + 2\omega_m)t + \cos\,(\omega_c - 2\omega_m)t]$$

The closed form expression for $v(t)$ can be written in terms of Bessel functions. A comparison of this expression with Equation (11.3-13) shows that with increasing β more side bands appear in the expansions. The time representation of the signals shown in Figure 11.3-6 shows the effect of the frequency

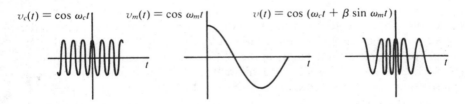

$v_c(t) = \cos\,\omega_c t \qquad\qquad v_m(t) = \cos\,\omega_m t \qquad\qquad v(t) = \cos\,(\omega_c t + \beta\,\sin\,\omega_m t)$

Figure 11.3-6.   Time representation of signals in FM modulation

modulation but these figures do not show what is happening. The effect of a changing modulation index becomes more apparent when the frequency spectrum is drawn, as in Figure 11.3-7. Note that the maximum frequency deviation Δf for FM stations has been set by the Federal Communications Commission (FCC) at 75 kHz. For the highest audio frequency 15 kHz, the modulation index will assume the value [see Equation (11.3-12)]

$$\beta = \frac{75}{15} = 5$$

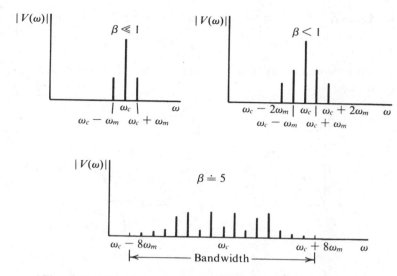

Figure 11.3-7. **Frequency spectrum of FM signal by** $\cos \omega_m t$

From Figure 11.3-7 we observe that for $\beta \doteq 5$ the bandwidth is given by

$$B = 2 \times 8 \times 15 = 240 \qquad \text{kHz}$$

which is considerably larger than the 15 kHz bandwidth required for an AM station.

A receiver for FM signals is rather like that illustrated in Figure 11.3-4b except that the detector or demodulator is one which must convert frequency modulated signals into amplitude modulated signals, after which amplitude modulated detection occurs. There are a number of circuits that effect the desired action, including *discriminators*, *ratio detectors*, and *phase-locked loops*.

11.4 DIGITAL COMMUNICATION SYSTEMS

In digital communications systems the normally continuous intelligence is sampled and digitized. A basic question is, how accurately can one determine the shape of a signal from its sampled values? Actually, a signal can be accurately reproduced from its sample values if a sufficiently large number of samples have been taken, appropriate to the bandwidth of the signal. To understand this, consider the representation of a signal somewhat like that illustrated in Figure 11.4-1. It is assumed that this signal can be described by a finite number of terms in its Fourier series representation; hence this signal is said to be *band limited*. Specifically, suppose that the signal can be expressed explicitly by the expansion

$$v(t) = A_1 \cos \alpha + A_2 \cos 2\alpha + \ldots + A_N \cos N\alpha + B_1 \sin \alpha + B_2 \sin 2\alpha$$
$$+ \ldots + B_N \sin N\alpha \qquad\qquad \alpha = \omega t \qquad\qquad (11.4\text{-}1)$$

This expansion contains $2N$ terms and the highest frequency in the expansion is $N\omega/2\pi$.

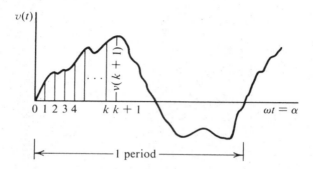

**Figure 11.4-1.   A signal that contains a finite number of terms
in its Fourier representation**

Suppose that we wish to sample the curve in order to obtain a sufficient number of separate equations to permit all of the coefficients, A's and B's, in Equation (11.4-1) to be determined. We shall assume that these sampled values are uniformly spaced. At each position k we will obtain an expression of the form

$$v(k) = A_1 \cos \frac{\omega k}{2N} + A_2 \cos \frac{2\omega k}{2N} + \ldots + A_N \cos N\frac{\omega k}{2N}$$
$$+ B_1 \sin \frac{\omega k}{2N} + \ldots + B_N \sin N\frac{\omega k}{2N} \qquad\qquad (11.4\text{-}2)$$

and for the $2N$ positions shown, we will be able to write the corresponding $2N$ equations. Therefore, we have $2N$ unknowns, A_k and B_k for $1 \leqslant k \leqslant N$, and $2N$ available equations. These equations can be solved and the coefficients are thereby deduced. The foregoing considerations are usually expressed as a theorem, which is known as the *sampling theorem*. In its more formal statement, the sampling theorem is

Let $v(t)$ be a signal with a maximum frequency component f_N, i.e., the signal is band-limited to f_N. Let the values of $v(t)$ be determined at uniform intervals which are separated by the time $T_s \leqslant \frac{1}{2} f_N$, i.e., the signal is sampled at each value T_s. Then these samples $v(NT_s)$ will allow the unique determination of the coefficients A_k and B_k, which therefore defines the signal without error.

The time T_s is called the *sampling time* and the *sampling rate* is defined as $f_s = 1/T_s$. Observe that the theorem states that $f_s = 2f_N$, and so at least two samples are taken during the period corresponding to the highest component of $v(t)$. The minimum sample frequency $f_s = 2f_N$ is called the *Nyquist rate*.

EXAMPLE 11.4-1. A signal $v(t)$ (in this case actually known to be sin ωt) is sampled at twice the Nyquist frequency, in the manner illustrated in Figure 11.4-2. Carry out the calculations to find the wave description.

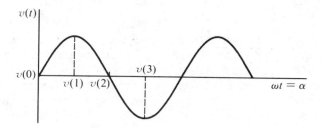

Figure 11.4-2.   A sine signal sampled at the Nyquist rate

SOLUTION. We begin with the oscillogram or with some other diagram of the unspecified waveform. We are to measure the ordinates of the wave at certain appropriate values of angle ($\alpha = \omega t$). In this case the Fourier series representation of the wave is assumed known and of the form

$$v(\alpha) = a_1 \cos \alpha + a_2 \cos 2\alpha + b_1 \sin \alpha + b_2 \sin 2\alpha$$

We are to determine the unknown coefficients appearing in this expansion, which is clearly assumed to be band limited to 2α.

Select the four sampling points and write the equations corresponding to these four sampled values. This gives

$$0 = a_1 \cos 0 + a_2 \cos 0 + b_1 \sin 0 + b_2 \sin 0$$

$$1 = a_1 \cos \frac{\pi}{2} + a_2 \cos 2\frac{\pi}{2} + b_1 \sin \frac{\pi}{2} + b_2 \sin 2\frac{\pi}{2}$$

$$0 = a_1 \cos \pi + a_2 \cos 2\pi + b_1 \sin \pi + b_2 \sin 2\pi$$

$$-1 = a_1 \cos \frac{3\pi}{2} + a_2 \cos 2\frac{3\pi}{2} + b_1 \sin \frac{3\pi}{2} + b_2 \sin 2\frac{3\pi}{2}$$

These expansions lead to the following equations

$$0 = a_1 + a_2 \tag{a}$$

$$1 = -a_1 + b_1 \tag{b}$$

$$0 = -a_1 + a_2 \qquad\qquad\qquad \text{(c)}$$

$$-1 = -a_2 - b_1 \qquad\qquad\qquad \text{(d)}$$

From Equations (a) and (c): $a_1 = a_2 = 0$. From Equations (b) and (d): $b_1 = 1$. Since b_2 does not appear, it must be set to zero. The result is, therefore

$$v(t) = \sin \omega t$$

□   □   □

The sampling theorem states that original function $v(t)$ can be determined given only the sampled values. In the form given, this determination involves the solution of a set of simultaneous algebraic equations, as shown in the example. For the case where $v(t)$ is a complicated function, this can involve considerable algebraic manipulation. There is an alternate form for generating the original function $v(t)$ from the sampled values $v(nT)$. The formula which affects this generation may be shown to be given by

$$v(t) = \sum_{n=-\infty}^{\infty} v(nT) \frac{\sin W(t-nT)}{W(t-nT)} \qquad W = \frac{\pi}{T} \qquad (11.4\text{-}3)$$

The quantity

$$\frac{\sin W(t-nT)}{W(t-nT)}$$

is called the *weighting function*. As can readily be appreciated from this expression, the details also represent a complicated undertaking, and this equation is reserved mainly for theoretical use.

Pulse Amplitude Modulation

A number of pulse modulations methods of transmission have been developed. Such methods depend on the fact, expressed by the sampling theorem, that it is possible to reconstruct a given signal by sampling the wave at periodic intervals.

In the *pulse amplitude modulation* (PAM) method short pulses of rf power are transmitted at regular intervals. The amplitude of each pulse is proportional to the instantaneous amplitude of the signal, as illustrated in Figure 11.4-3. For speech confined to a frequency spread of 5 kHz, the sampling frequency must be not less than 10 kHz. Suppose that the pulse duration at each sampling point is 5 microseconds. This means that the duty cycle is only 5 per cent, permitting a theoretical 20 simultaneous messages at a given carrier frequency without overlap or interference. An adequate commutating means must be provided for switching both transmitter and receiver to the different

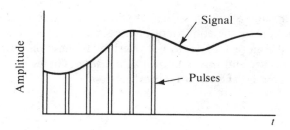

Figure 11.4-3. Pulse-amplitude modulation

channels. If the number of messages is small, then for a given average power the peak power during transmission can be quite high.

One way to accomplish the sampling process is to multiply the function $v(t)$ (voltage) which is to be sampled with a sampling function $s(t)$ (voltage), in the manner shown in Figure 11.4-4a, b, c. Consider first the function $v(t)$ which is assumed band-limited with a bandwidth ω_o, as shown in Figure 11.4-4d. The

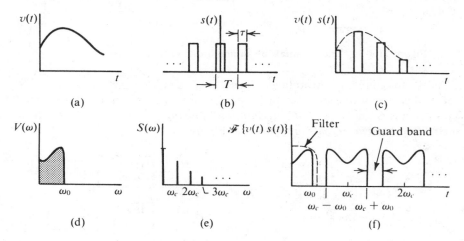

Figure 11.4-4. Sampled functions and their frequency characteristics

periodic sampling function $s(t)$ can be expanded into a Fourier series (see Section 1.2) of the form

$$s(t) = \frac{\tau}{T}\left[1 + 2\sum_{n=1}^{\infty}\frac{\sin n\pi\tau/T}{(n\pi\tau/T)}\cos\left(\frac{2\pi}{T}nt\right)\right] \qquad \omega_c = \frac{2\pi}{T} = 2\pi f_c \quad (11.4\text{-}4)$$

From our discussion of frequency translation (the modulation process) in the previous section, we can conclude that each sinusoid contained in Equation (11.4-4) will cause a frequency translation of the signal $v(t)$ as shown in Figure 11.4-4f. Obviously, we can recover the original signal by passing the sampled signal $v(t)s(t)$ through a low-pass filter of width ω_o. The recovery is unique as long as $\omega_o \geqslant 2\omega_c$; this is the equivalent of the statement that the repeated frequency bands of Figure 11.4-4f do not overlap. If these bands do overlap, a distortion will occur, and this is known as *aliasing*. The essentials of a pulse modulation system are shown in Figure 11.4-5.

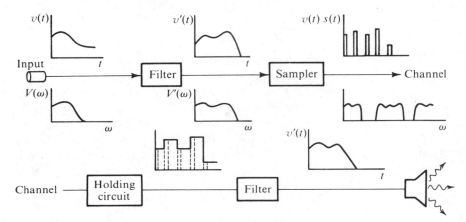

Figure 11.4-5.   The essentials of an amplitude pulse-modulating system

As already noted, an advantage of using PAM signals is that the "dead" time between pulses of one signal can be used for the transmission of other signals. This process is known as *time division multiplexing* (TDM). The essentials of such TDM for two signals are shown in Figure 11.4-6.

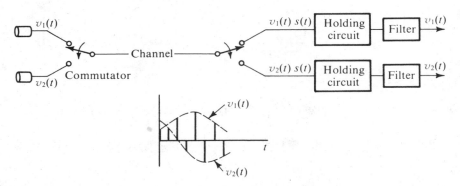

Figure 11.4-6.   Sampling and interlacing of two pulse trains

A variety of other pulse modulation schemes are available. Two such methods are illustrated in Figure 11.4-7. In pulse width modulation (PWM) the pulses which are generated have equal amplitudes but the widths depend on the signal amplitude $v(t)$. For zero signal amplitude (at the cross-over) the

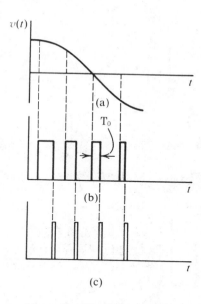

Figure 11.4-7.   (a) Pulse modulation   (b) PWM   (c) PPM

pulse width is T_o with departures from this reference width being dependent on the instantaneous amplitude. This type of modulation is also known as *pulse duration modulation* (PDM) and *pulse length modulation* (PLM). The second modulation scheme shown in Figure 11.4-7c is *pulse-position modulation* (PPM) which generates pulses of constant width but with a distance from the uniform sampling which depends on the signal amplitude.

Pulse Code Modulation

There are a number of reasons for favoring the transmission of signals by a pulse-code modulation method. These include such important factors as: noise reduction by coding, easy reproducibility and reshaping of the signal at repeater stations along the path, digital circuitry used to a large extent in the units, and digital processing of signals.

When only a finite number of discrete levels are used for the transmission of PAM signals, a *quantization* process is employed, and the resulting signal is known as a *quantized* signal. When such signals are to be transmitted over large distances, repeater stations are often placed at intermediate points along the path. At these repeater stations the signals can be amplified and re-quantized, as shown in Figure 11.4-8. It is evident from this figure that the reduction of noise can be significant. Also shown is the occasional error that can be present in such processing.

To see an indication of the processing involved, refer to Figure 11.4-9. As indicated in Figure 11.4-9a, the signals to be quantized are first sampled to create PAM signals. The quantization reduces the effect of noise, and the

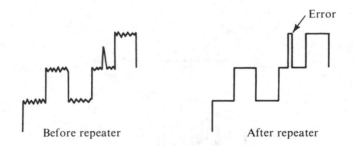

Figure 11.4-8.   The effect of quantization on noise

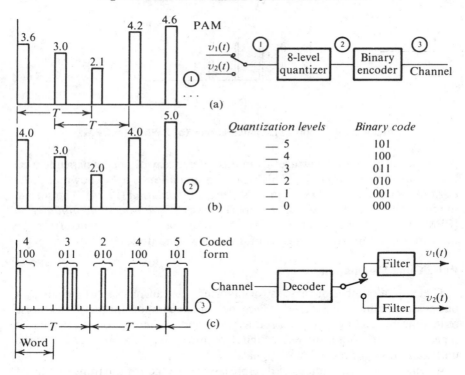

Figure 11.4-9.   Quantization and coding of signals

sampling allows time division multiplexing. Two multiplexed signals are shown in Figure 11.4-9a, and their quantized forms are shown in Figure 11.4-9b. Next the quantized pulses are coded. In our case, we have chosen a 3-bit 8-level binary code. Each 3-bit group, which denotes a specified level, is called a *word*. At the receiving end, all that is required is to determine whether or not within a given time slot a pulse is present or absent, and to separate the words belonging to different signals in case multiplexing is being used.

As illustrated, the sampled signal is applied to an encoder which generates a unique pulse train for a particular signal level. The combination of quantizer and encoder is called an *analog-to-digital converter* (ADC). ADCs are available commercially with 16-bit codes that operate at a recurrence frequency of 10 MHz. The instrument which generates an analog signal from the coded one is known as the *digital-to-analog converter* (DAC).

Suppose that we wish to transmit 100 voice signals, each having a 4 kHz bandwidth. From our previous considerations, the Nyquist rate, which gives the smallest sampling rate, is $2f_{max} = 2 \times 4$ kHz $= 8$ kHz, which specifies the sampling time as $(1/8) \times 10^{-3}$ sec. If an 8-level, 3-bit, quantizer is used, the channel commutator must make 3 revolutions in $(1/8) \times 10^{-3}$ sec, or must rotate at a rate of $(1/24) \times 10^{-3}$ sec. Since there are 100 voice signals to be transmitted, the time between bits is $(1/24) \times 10^{-5}$ sec. If we wish to provide a spacing of $(1/2 \times 24) \times 10^{-5}$ sec between bits, the bit duration must not exceed $(1/48) \times 10^{-5}$ sec or roughly 0.2 microsecond.

The essentials of an optical single channel PCM system are shown in Figure 11.4-10. This system uses a phase-locked laser as the optical source and an electrically controled optical gate. The PCM optical modulator codes the train of optical pulses by transmitting or blocking the individual optical pulses under the control of an electrical PCM encoder. The system shown operates at a rate of 224 Mbits/s (megabits per second). The laser is phase-locked into the cavity by a phase modulator made from deuterated KDP (dihydrogen phosphate type crystal) and which is driven by a clock to produce 224 Mbits/s. The optical pulses from the laser are synchronous with the timing signal, and therefore, with the information output of the word generator.

The important element of the PCM optical modulator, which serves as a gate for the pulses from the laser, is the ferroelectric single crystal of $LiTaO_3$ having dimensions $0.025 \times 0.025 \times 1.0$ cm. When an electric field is applied across the crystal, the polarization of the wave changes by 90 degrees and is reflected towards the detector. If there is no electric field present when the optical pulse traverses the crystal, the polarization of the light does not change and remains the same after its reflection from the end of the crystal. Because the returned optical pulse has the same polarization, no reflection will occur at the separator and so no electrical pulse will appear on the detector. The energy of the reflected pulse is generally very small and does not disturb the stability of the laser as the light reenters into the cavity. The one-channel optical PCM system shown in Figure 11.4-10 can be extended easily to eight or sixteen channels.

On-Off Keying, Frequency Shift Keying (FSK), Phase Shift Keying (PSK)

In the previous sections we studied the transmission of continuous signals that were modulated in frequency or in amplitude. It is also possible to transmit digital (binary) signals on a high frequency carrier. One such system for binary transmission is known as *on-off keying* (OOK). The signal and its

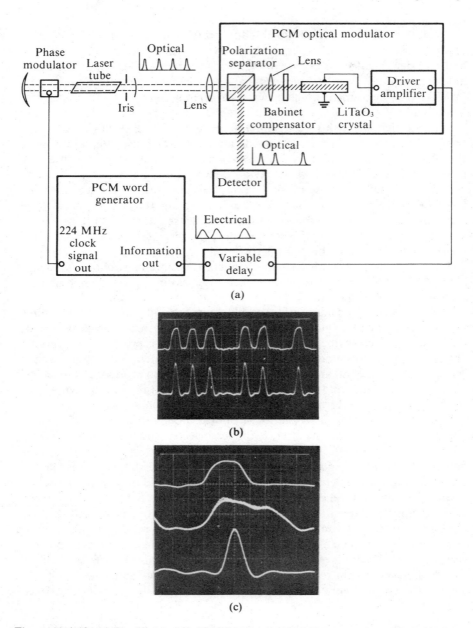

Figure 11.4-10. (a) Single channel, 224-M bit/s optical PCM system. (b) Upper trace:
electrical output of PCM word generator producing pattern 111011010; lower trace:
corresponding output of optical PCM system (c) Top trace: electrical output of
PCM word generator producing one pulse; middle trace: output of PCM optical
moudlator when driven by one electrical pulse and the input light is CW (laser in FM
mode); bottom trace: output of PCM optical modulator when driven by one
electrical pulse and a properly timed optical pulse is incident

modulated form are shown in Figure 11.4-11a. If the frequency of the transmitter is changed to correspond to the two signal levels, the result is *frequency shift keying* (FSK). The features of the signals are shown in Figure 11.4-11b. If the phase of the carrier is shifted to correspond to the two signal levels, the result is *phase shift keying* (PSK). The features of the radiated wave are shown in Figure 11.4-11c.

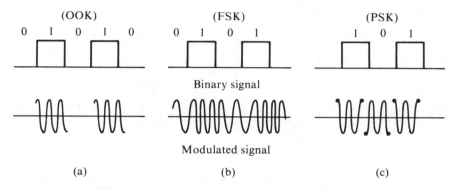

Figure 11.4-11. Binary communication schemes

11.5 DETECTION OF MODULATED SIGNALS

The foregoing two sections have addressed the modulation process, with a clear indication that frequency shifting of the intelligence to a high frequency carrier level permits the efficient launching of such signals from antennas having small dimensions. A critical element in the communication process is the means for extracting the intelligence from the transmitted signal. This process is known as *demodulation* or *detection* of the modulated signals. Just as modulation was frequency shifting to high frequency levels, demodulation is frequency shifting from the carrier levels to the basic signal frequency levels.

The different modulated signals require demodulators which are appropriate to the type of modulation that has been used.

Detection of AM Signals

SYNCHRONOUS DETECTION. This is the simplest type of AM-detection from a conceptual point of view, although it is seldom used. Figure 11.5-1a shows diagrammatically the basic elements for synchronous detection. The signal $v_{in}(t)$ before being filtered is the received modulated carrier [see Equation (11.3-3)] which is multiplied by the local oscillator signal which has been tuned to the carrier frequency. Therefore

$$v_{in}(t) = A[1 + mv_m(t)] \cos^2 \omega_c t$$

$$= \frac{1}{2}A[1 + mv_m(t)] \cos 2\omega_c t + \frac{1}{2}A + \frac{1}{2}Amv_m(t) \tag{11.5-1}$$

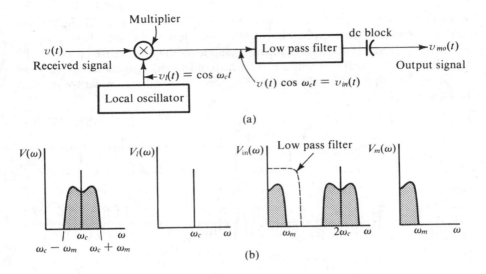

Figure 11.5-1.   The time and frequency domain features of synchronous detection

This shows that the signal that enters the low pass filter comprises the modulating signal on a carrier that is twice the original carrier level, a dc signal, plus the modulating signal $v_m(t)$ that has had its amplitude changed by a constant $Am/2$. The output from the filter plus the blocking capacitor is a signal proportional to $v_m(t)$. The spectra of the various signals are shown in Figure 11.5-1b, and are self-explanatory.

EXAMPLE 11.5-1. Consider a modulating signal $v_m(t) = \cos \omega_o t$, where $\omega_o \ll \omega_c$. Graph the frequency spectra of the signals at the different stages of a synchronous detector.

SOLUTION. Upon introducing $v_m(t) = \cos \omega_o t$ into Equation (11.5-1) we obtain the relation

$$v_{in}(t) = \frac{1}{2}A \cos 2\omega_c t + \frac{1}{2}Am \cos \omega_o t \cos 2\omega_c t + \frac{1}{2}A + \frac{1}{2}Am \cos \omega_o t$$

$$= \frac{1}{2}A \cos 2\omega_c t + \frac{1}{4}Am \cos (2\omega_c + \omega_o)t + \frac{1}{4}Am \cos (2\omega_c - \omega_o)t$$

$$+ \frac{1}{2}A + \frac{1}{2}Am \cos \omega_o t$$

$$(11.5\text{-}2)$$

The spectra of the several functions: $v_m(t) \cos \omega_o t$; $v_l(t) = \cos \omega_c t$; $v_s(t) = A[1 + m \cos \omega_o t] \cos \omega_c t$ and $v_{in}(t)$ are shown in Figure 11.5-2.

□   □   □

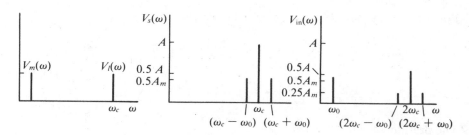

Figure 11.5-2. Amplitude spectra of AM signals and AM detection signals

When the frequency of the local oscillator is the same as that of the carrier, the detection technique is called *homodyne*; when they are different it is called *heterodyne*. Heterodyning creates new frequencies and is used extensively in AM receivers. It is also the technique used in optical receivers about which we shall say more later.

DETECTION BY RECTIFICATION. Another detection technique involves full-wave rectification of the AM signal. Except for amplitude changes, if the modulated wave of Equation (11.3-3) is applied to the input of the circuit shown in Figure 11.5-3 the input to the low pass filter is

$$v_o(t) = A[1 + mv_m(t)]|\cos \omega_c t| \tag{11.5-3}$$

Also shown in Figure 11.5-3 are the waveforms at key points in the circuit. We may express the full-wave rectified cosine wave in terms of its equivalent

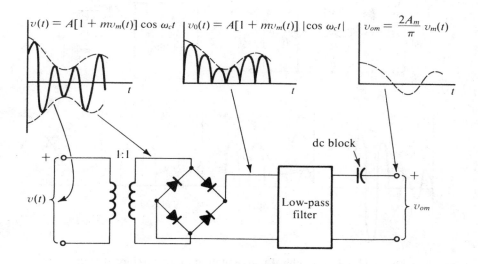

Figure 11.5-3. AM detection by rectification

Fourier series expansion (see Chapter 1), which is

$$|\cos \omega_c t| = \frac{2}{\pi} - \frac{4}{\pi} \left(-\frac{1}{3} \cos 2\omega_c t + \frac{1}{15} \cos 4\omega_c t - \ldots \right)$$

$$= \frac{2}{\pi} - \frac{4}{\pi} \sum_{n=1}^{\infty} \frac{(-1)^n}{4n^2 - 1} \cos 2n\omega_c t \qquad (11.5\text{-}4)$$

The prefiltered signal is then

$$v_o(t) = \frac{2A}{\pi} [1 + mv_m(t)] \left[1 - 2 \sum_{n=1}^{\infty} \frac{(-1)^n}{4n^2 - 1} \cos 2n\omega_c t \right] \qquad (11.5\text{-}5)$$

The low pass filter will eliminate all signal components with frequencies above ω_m, the maximum frequency contained in the modulating signal $v_m(t)$. Hence all terms except the first in Equation (11.5-5) will disappear when $v_o(t)$ passes through the filter. Also, the dc blocking capacitor will eliminate the dc signal $2A/\pi$, the final output being the desired signal, altered by a constant $2Am/\pi$.

$$v_{om} = \frac{2Am}{\pi} v_m(t) \qquad (11.5\text{-}6)$$

ENVELOPE DETECTOR. The essential elements of the envelope detector are shown in Figure 11.5-4. Essentially the system consists of a parallel RC circuit that is fed through a diode. The operation depends essentially on the fact that energy is stored in the capacitor during part of the cycle and when the diode ceases to conduct, the energy on the capacitor drains through the resistor ac-

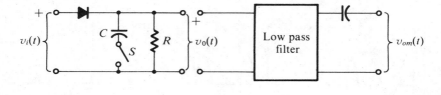

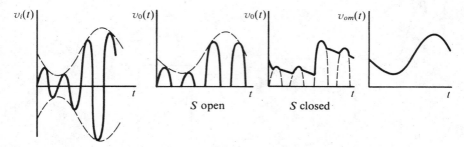

Figure 11.5-4.   Graphical representation of an envelope detector

cording to the simple RC circuit decay. A low pass filter following the detector will eliminate the sharp edges of the output wave thereby providing the signal. The curves of Figure 11.5-4 clearly show the essentials of the operation.

A simple envelope detector is ordinarily used in *superheterodyne* type AM receivers, as shown schematically in Figure 11.5-5. A feature of this receiver is that tuning is accomplished by adjusting the frequency of the local oscillator. The local oscillator frequency is adjusted so that the desired incoming signal is downconverted from its normal RF (radio frequency) level to a new *intermediate* frequency IF level (normally chosen at 455 kHz in broadcast receivers). The IF signal is then amplified in a carefully adjusted fixed-tuned high gain amplifier to raise the modulated signal level, which is then detected using the envelope detector. Since all incoming signals are downconverted to the same IF frequency the selectivity of the circuits can be optimized through the use of double-tuned circuits. While the selectivity (the sharpness of the frequency response characteristics) would improve with more elaborate circuits (e.g., triple tuned circuits), these prove to be too difficult to adjust. Stagger tuning comprising three isolated stages tuned to slightly different frequencies with proper amplitude adjustment has been used in effecting triple-tuned performance; such amplifiers are employed in special applications only.

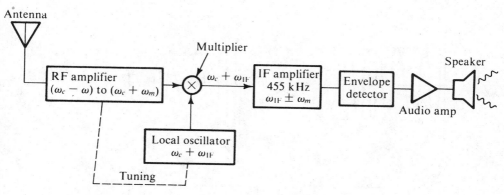

Figure 11.5-5. Schematic representation of a superheterodyne receiver

Detection of FM Signals

A variety of FM demodulators exist, including phase-locked loop, phase-shift discriminator, and ratio detector. We shall present only the method of differentiation. The student will consider other schemes in his later studies.

Recall that the FM signal was specified in Section 11.3 in the form

$$v(t) = A \cos \left[\omega_c t + m \int v_m(t)\, dt \right] \qquad (11.5\text{-}7)$$

with $v_m(t)$ being the modulating signal. By differentiating this equation, we find that

$$\frac{dv(t)}{dt} = -A[\omega_c + mv_m(t)] \sin\left[\omega_c t + m\int v_m(t)\,dt\right]$$

$$= -A\omega_c\left[1 + \frac{mv_m(t)}{\omega_c}\right]\sin\,\theta(t) \qquad\qquad\text{(a)} \quad (11.5\text{-}8)$$

where

$$\theta(t) = \omega_c t + m\int v_m(t)\,dt \qquad\qquad\text{(b)}$$

This resulting equation is that of an AM signal whose envelope is

$$A\omega_c\left[1 + \frac{mv_m(t)}{\omega_c}\right]$$

But since $mv_m(t) \ll \omega_c$, the envelope never crosses the time axis. Thus only an envelope detector is needed to accomplish the *frequency discrimination*, and this is equivalently a frequency-to-amplitude conversion. Typical FM signals and the schematic representation of an FM detector are shown in Figure 11.5-6.

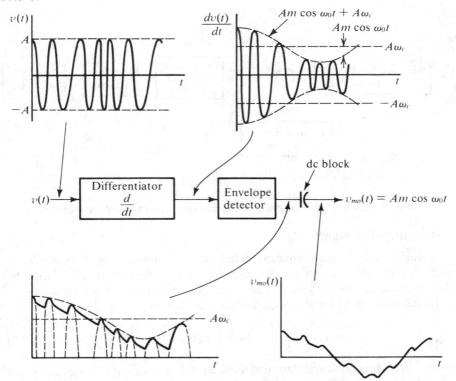

Figure 11.5-6.   FM detector and the corresponding signals

Detection of Pulse Amplitude Modulated (PAM) Signals

The recovery of a PAM signal is easily accomplished by using a simple *sample-and-hold* circuit, as shown in Figure 11.5-7. Since in most cases the input signal is time division multiplexed, the circuit incorporates a switch which closes (is activated) at the appropriate times which are synchronized with the information to be transferred to a particular channel.

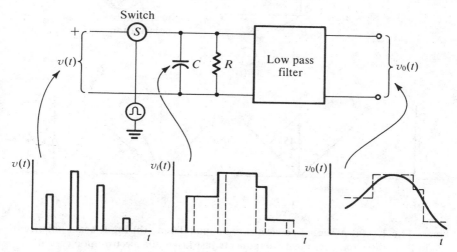

Figure 11.5-7. PAM demodulation scheme

At the instant when the switch closes, the appropriate pulse appears and charges the capacitor to a voltage equal to the height of the pulse. The load resistor R is selected so that the capacitor retains the voltage until the next pulse appears. If in addition a low-pass filter is used, the sharp edges of the sample-and-hold circuit output will be smoothed and a continuous signal which will closely resemble the input signal will be created.

11.6 FIBER OPTICS COMMUNICATIONS

Fiber optics communication is a rapidly growing technology owing to the very large channel capacity possible through small fibers. The details of this technology are involved, but we shall give a qualitative discussion of many of the problems and the solutions currently in use.

Modulation of Light

We shall first consider optical modulation, the process in which some property of light waves is altered, such as amplitude (or intensity), phase, polarization, and wavelength (or frequency).

AMPLITUDE MODULATION. A typical simplified amplitude modulating scheme involving an electro-optical crystal is shown in Figure 11.6-1a. As

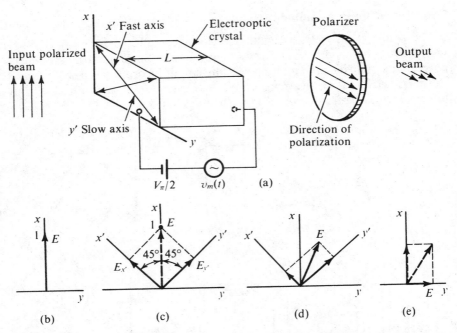

Figure 11.6-1. (a) A simplified electro-optic modulator (b) Input beam polarized in the x-direction (c) Field components just inside the electro-optic crystal (d) Field components and their resultant as they leave the crystal (e) Amplitude of the field permitted to pass through the polarizer

shown in the figure, the polarized incoming optical beam, when passing through the electro-optic crystal, is split into two components along the two optical axes. As a result, the field at the exit is elliptically polarized. By varying the voltage across the electro-optic crystal the changing polarization results in intensity variations by incorporating an analyzer (polarizer) at the output.

It can be shown that the ratio of the output irradiance I_o to the input irradiance I_i varies as follows:

$$\frac{I_o}{I_{in}} = \sin^2 \left[\frac{1}{2} \pi \frac{v_m(t)}{V_\pi} \right] \qquad (11.6\text{-}1)$$

where V_π is the voltage needed to produce total transmission at the modulator. If we set

$$\varphi = \frac{v_m(t)\pi}{V_\pi} = \frac{\pi}{2} + m \sin \omega_m t = \text{phase retardation} \qquad (11.6\text{-}2)$$

where $\pi/2$ is the bias retardation, and $v_m(t) = V_m \sin \omega_m t$, then Equation (11.6-1) becomes

$$\frac{I_o}{I_{in}} = \sin^2 \left(\frac{\pi}{4} + \frac{m}{2} \sin \omega_m t \right) = \frac{1}{2}[1 + \sin (m \sin \omega_m t)]$$

$$\doteq \frac{1}{2}(1 + m \sin \omega_m t) \tag{11.6-2}$$

for $m \ll 1$. This equation shows that the output intensity is identical with the input but with the signal now being modulated. Figure 11.6-2a shows the modulating process, and Figure 11.6-2b shows a typical optical communication system.

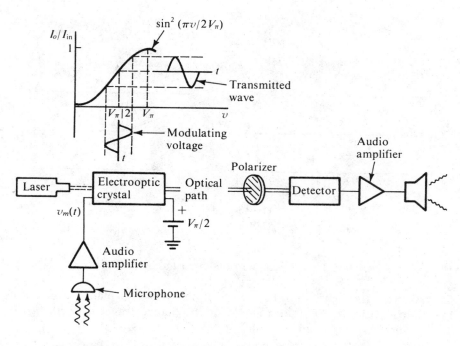

Figure 11.6-2. (a) **Biasing characteristics of an electro-optic system**
(b) **Typical optical communication system**

PHASE MODULATION. To accomplish phase modulation we must set the polarized field vector along one of the two optical axes of the crystal. This will not affect the status of polarization but will change the output phase of the wave proportionally to the input modulating signal. Equations (11.6-3a) and (11.6-3b) describe the output optical field when the electric field is not applied and when it is applied, respectively,

$$E = E_m \sin (\omega t - kz) \qquad \text{(a)} \quad (11.6\text{-}3)$$

$$E = E_m \sin [\omega t - kz + \Delta\varphi(t)] \qquad \text{(b)}$$

Simple optical phase modulators have not found any widespread techno-
logical use.

FREQUENCY MODULATION. Optical frequency modulators have not been
found useful because frequency shifts are small, and complicated heterodyne
systems are needed for demodulation.

MODULATION (SWITCHING) BY ACOUSTO-OPTIC EFFECT. When light interacts
with sound waves, the light beam is deflected, as shown in Figure 11.6-3a.

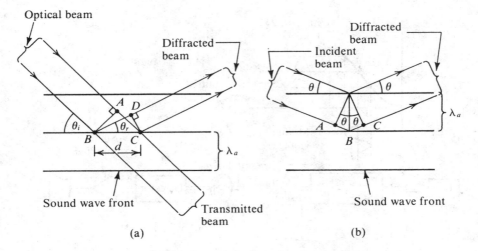

Figure 11.6-3.   Diffraction of optical beams by sound waves

Observe from the figure that the beam will not change its plane wavefront if
the optical path AC-BD is a multiple of the optical wavelength $n\lambda$, $n = 1$,
$2,\ldots$. The following relation results

$$d(\cos \theta_i - \cos \theta_r) = m(n\lambda) \qquad m = 0, +1, +2,\ldots \qquad (11.6\text{-}4)$$

This equation is satisfied for all points along BC (the values of d will differ).
Since $d \neq 0$, Equation (11.6-4) becomes an identity if $\cos \theta_i = \cos \theta_r$, or $\theta_i = \theta_r$.
For $\theta_i = \theta_r$ together with Figure 11.6-3b we obtain

$$ABC = \lambda_a \sin \theta + \lambda_a \sin \theta = n\lambda$$

or

$$2\lambda_a \sin \theta = n\lambda \qquad (11.6\text{-}4)$$

which is the condition for Bragg diffraction.

One of the most important applications of beam diffraction is in switching and in addressing spatial points. When the acoustic-optic interaction causes the operation to be close to the Bragg diffraction condition, any small variation of the acoustic frequency will change the direction of the beam by an angle

$$\Delta\theta = \frac{n\lambda}{v_a}\Delta f_a \qquad (11.6\text{-}5)$$

where v_a is the speed of sound, and Δf_a is the deviation of acoustic frequency.

Of special interest in electro-optic deflection is the number of resolvable spots. Equivalently, we are interested in the factor by which $\Delta\theta$ exceeds the beam divergence angle. The approximate value of the diffraction angle is $\theta_d = 4\lambda/\pi D$, and for $n = 1$ the number of resolvable spots is

$$N = \frac{\Delta\theta}{\theta_d} = \left(\frac{\pi D}{4v_a}\right)\Delta f_a \doteq \frac{D}{v_a}\Delta f_a = \frac{\Delta f_a}{v_a/D} = \frac{\Delta f_a}{\Delta f_r} \qquad (11.6\text{-}6)$$

where $D/v_a = \tau$ is the time that it takes for the sound to cross the optical beam diameter. An experimental arrangement of an acousto-optic light beam scanner is shown in Figure 11.6-4. Suppose, for example, that the deflection bandwidth has the value $\Delta f_a = 500$ MHz, and let $\tau = D/v_a = 10^{-6}$ s. This yields for N the value 500, and $R = v_a/D = 10^6$ spots/s. Suppose that beam diameter is decreased by a factor of 10, then $N = 50$, and $R = 10^7$ spots/s for the same bandwidth. This shows that for a given deflector bandwidth the number of resolvable ports and the scan rate impose conflicting requirements on the light beam aperture in an acousto-optic deflector. This type of deflector has the unique capability of high-resolution, medium speed random access deflection and switching. One of many applications involves a fiber optic system with a large number of fan-out ports.

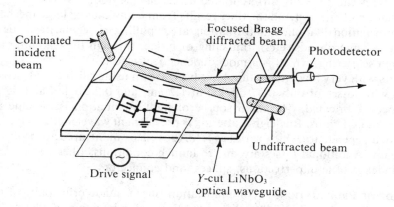

Figure 11.6-4. Experimental arrangement of an acousto-optic light beam scanner

Optical Transmission

Because of fog, rain, atmospheric turbulence and scattering, line-of-sight optical transmission is not an effective channel of information transmission. However, for short distances and for atmospheric channels above the normal disturbances, optical transmission is possible. For reliable channels communications involving optical fibers will dominate the optical information transmission needs for the foreseeable future. Fiber optic links are very important because they require less space than conventional channels to convey the same number of telephone conversations and with the same reliability. It is anticipated that the fiber optics industry during the 1990s will spend upwards of tens of billions of dollars.

Fibers for fiber optic use are made of glasses which have low optical losses (see Chapter 10). The most common glasses are silica (SiO_2); sodium calcium silicates, as used for plate and window glass; sodium borosilicates, often used for chemical apparatus; and lead silicates, which have high refractive indexes and appear shiny. The trend in fiber optics for low loss glass has resulted in a special industry to produce such glasses. These glasses are high in silica content and are produced by the reaction of oxygen and silane (SiH_4) or silicon tetrachloride ($SiCl_4$). Small amounts of dopants are added to modify the index of refraction, as desired.

MEASUREMENT OF LOSSES IN FIBERS. Optical losses in fibers are due mostly to radiation away from the fiber and to absorption. Measurement of losses in fibers requires considerable caution since radiative losses are difficult to measure, and losses along the long lengths of fibers are not uniform. Further, in multimode fibers, the effects are usually mode dependent and the integrated effect over all modes is nonlinear with length.

The measurement of absorption loss in fibers is best done using a calorimetric technique. The scattered energy from the fiber and the energy absorbed by the fiber can be easily differentiated using this method.

Radiation of energy from the fiber results from many causes: large mechanical deformations; applied deformation after pulling (irregularities due to packaging, microbends, etc.); tunneling of modes through the cladding; and Rayleigh scattering, which is a mode-independent effect.

Fibers with very low attenuation have been drawn using silica-based glasses. Fibers with losses of only 0.47 db/km at 1.2 μm, and 0.2 db/km at 1.55 μm have been fabricated. The main source of light attenuation is metallic impurities and OH ions. Rayleigh scattering is prevalent at wavelengths below 1.5 μm with a dependence which varies as λ^{-4}. Above 1.6 μm infrared absorption is dominant. Additional losses are due to launch conditions, fiber-width variation, index-profile imperfections, splices, and connectors.

MODE OF PROPAGATION. A communication fiber is made principally of two parts: a core region of radius r, and a cladding region having a smaller refractive index than the core. The cladding is useful in keeping the energy within the core, and at the same time, it gives good mechanical strength. Figure 11.6-5 shows three of the most used fiber configurations together with their index of refraction profiles.

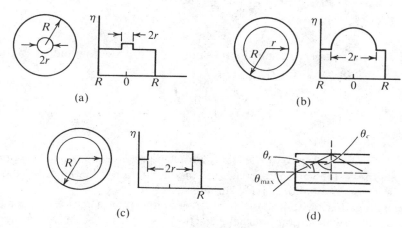

Figure 11.6-5. (a) Single mode step index, $r \doteq 1.5\text{-}10 \ \mu\text{m}$
(b) Graded index multimode, $r \doteq 20\text{-}150 \ \mu\text{m}$ (c) Step index multimode, $r \doteq 20\text{-}150 \ \mu\text{m}$
(d) Numerical aperture (NA) determination

For step-index fibers, the index of refraction of the core is written

$$\eta_i = \eta_c(1 + \Delta) \tag{11.6-7}$$

where η_i is the core refractive index, η_c is the cladding refractive index, and $\Delta \ll 1$. The parameter which describes the number of modes in a fiber is given by

$$P = \left(\frac{2\pi r}{\lambda}\right)\sqrt{\eta_i^2 - \eta_c^2} = \left(\frac{2\pi r}{\lambda}\right)\eta_i\sqrt{2\Delta} \tag{11.6-8}$$

where λ is the wavelength of the light in vacuum. It can be shown that when $P < 2.4$, the fiber supports only one mode. Thus a single-mode fiber can be built by decreasing the diameter of the core, by decreasing the index of refraction, or both.

EXAMPLE 11.6-1. Find the radius of the core for a single-mode step index fiber if $\eta_i = 1.4$ and $\Delta = 0.01$. The light is obtained from a HeNe laser, $\lambda = 0.6328 \times 10^{-6}$ m.

SOLUTION. From Equation (11.6-8) we obtain

$$r = \frac{P\lambda}{2\pi\eta_i\sqrt{2\Delta}} = \frac{2.4 \times 0.6328 \times 10^{-6}}{2\pi \cdot 1.4\sqrt{0.02}} = 1.22 \quad \mu m$$

□ □ □

For step index fibers the maximum number of propagating modes is given by

$$N \doteq \left(\frac{2\pi r}{\lambda}\right)^2 \eta_i^2 \Delta \tag{11.6-9}$$

when $P \gg 2.4$.

Graded index fibers have the desirable property of equalizing the optical path lengths of the various propagating modes. As a result, the pulse distortion due to intermodal dispersion diminishes.

The light gathering ability of a fiber is very important. The sine of the maximum angle at which total internal reflection takes place, as shown in Figure 11.6-5d, is called the *numerical aperture* (NA). From Figure 11.6-5d and Snell's law applied to fibers with step index, we find that

$$NA = \sin\theta_{max} = \eta_i \sin\theta_r = \eta_i \sin(90 - \theta_c) = \eta_i \cos\theta_c$$
$$= \eta_i\sqrt{1 - \sin^2\theta_c} = \eta_i\sqrt{1 - \frac{\eta_c^2}{\eta_i^2}} = \sqrt{\eta_i^2 - \eta_c^2} \tag{11.6-10}$$

For example, a fiber with NA = 0.2 will accept rays at off-axis angle values up to 11.5 deg. However, the NA is a function of radial distance for graded-index profiles, and the situation is more complicated than that for the step-index profile fiber. In fact, they accept less light than the step-index fibers, if both have the same value of Δ.

Pulse Dispersion of Fibers

For communication uses, it is important to know accurately the dispersion and distortion of pulses. This follows because the quantity of information to be transmitted is limited by such irregularities. The three main causes of pulse spreading in fibers are waveguide dispersion, mode dispersion in multimode fibers, and material dispersion. Multimode fibers are dominated by mode dispersion, the result of different group velocities for each mode. The other two effects, waveguide and material dispersion, are negligible in multimode fibers. Waveguide dispersion is important in the single mode fibers.

A ray analysis in multiple mode fibers reveals that the time spread Δt between the fastest and the slowest mode is given by

$$\frac{\Delta t}{L} \doteq \eta_i \frac{\Delta}{c} = \frac{(NA)^2}{2\eta_i c} \qquad (11.6\text{-}11)$$

where L is the length of the fiber and c is the speed of light. For example, with $NA = 0.2$ and $\eta_i = 1.4$, a pulse dispersion is 47.6 ns/km, which is a large dispersion value. Equation (11.6-11) is not completely accurate since it does not take into consideration mode mixing, an effect which causes the actual number of modes to be different from the theoretical one.

Graded index multimode fibers show smaller pulse spreading than for step index fibers. The pulse dispersion is given by

$$\frac{\Delta t}{L} \doteq \frac{(NA)^4}{8\eta_i^3 c} \qquad (11.6\text{-}12)$$

Using the same values as those in conjunction with Equation (11.6-11), namely, $NA = 0.2$ and $n_i = 1.4$, the dispersion is found to be 0.24 ns/km, which is a substantial improvement (about a factor of 200) over that for the step-index fiber. This indicates that a data rate per kilometer on the order of 1 to 5 Gbit/s can be achieved with graded multimode fibers.

That 5 Gbit/s is a large rate of transmission of information is made evident by assuming the need for 5 bits/letter. Then it follows, considering the number of letters per page of a book to be 10^4, that the transmission rate is

$$\frac{5 \times 10^9 \text{ (bits/s)}}{5 \text{ (bits/letter)} \times 10^4 \text{ (letters/page)} \times 500 \text{ (pages/book)}} = 200 \text{ books/s}$$

An experimental arrangement for measuring the pulse dispersion in fibers is shown in Figure 11.6-6. Figure 11.6-7a shows a shuttle pulse train in a 106 m length fiber, and Figure 11.6-7b shows the dispersion of pulses when traveling different lengths.

The dispersion in single-mode fibers is primarily due to material and waveguide dispersion. Note, however, that a finite line width exists, even for the most monochromatic laser, and it is the effect of chromatic dispersion that is the main cause of dispersion in single mode fibers. But the dispersion is rather smaller than in the other types of fibers. Figure 11.6-7 clearly shows these differences.

Optical Sources

The light sources of interest in optical communication are the solid state *light emitting diodes* (LEDs) and lasers. These devices can be divided into two groups: AlGaAs devices that cover the wavelength region from 0.8-0.9 μm, and InGaAsP devices that cover the longer wavelength region from 1.1-1.7 μm. In selecting a source for any particular application, the important con-

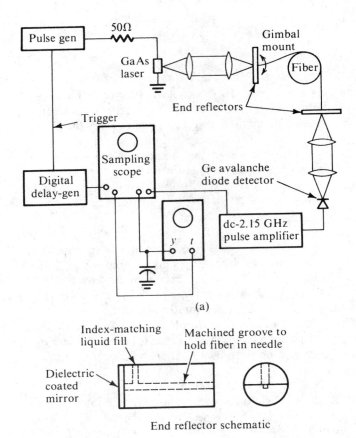

(a)

Index-matching liquid fill   Machined groove to hold fiber in needle

Dielectric coated mirror

End reflector schematic

Figure 11.6-6. **(a) Experimental arrangement for making shuttle pulse measurements with a pulsed GaAs injection laser ($\lambda = 0.9$ μm). It includes the most sensitive detection arrangement, which is a germanium avalanche diode followed by a wideband pulse amplifier**
(b) Schematic of the holder that is used to press a fiber against a reflecting mirror. The holder mates with a gimbal mount that can be tilted at an angle relative to the injected laser beam in order to emphasize the launching of high order modes

siderations include data rate; light coupling abilities; modulation character-istics, that is, frequency response, harmonic distortion, etc.; and dynamic laser properties, such as relaxation oscillations, noise, etc.

LEDs have wide spectrums and poor coupling efficiencies to fibers with small NA. As a result they are less attractive than the laser diodes. On the other hand, for low data rate and small distances, LEDs are suitable since they have a number of advantages over lasers, such as better linearity, less sensitiv-ity to gradual degradation, and smaller temperature dependence of the emitted power.

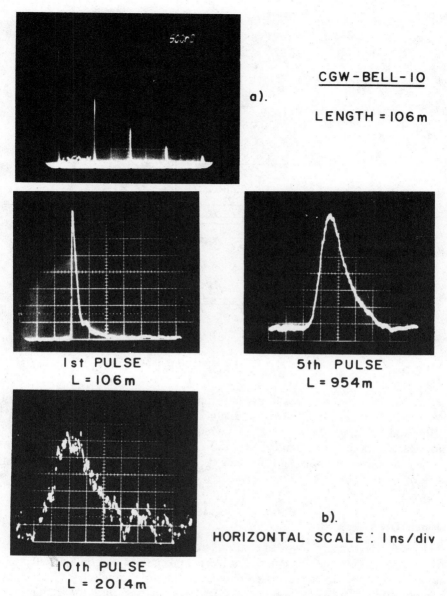

Figure 11.6-7. (a) Shuttle pulse train in a 106-m length of CGW-Bell-10 fiber with nominally 90% reflecting mirrors against each end. Pulse spreading effects were made negligible by injecting 30-nsec wide laser pulses that were broad compared to the fiber dispersion

(b) Pulse spreading is observed when narrow impulses are injected into the fiber. The photographs are sampling scope displays of the first pulse received after $L = 106$ m, the fifth pulse after $L = 954$ m, and the tenth pulse after $L = 2014$ m

To improve their coupling coefficient to fibers, lenses and special diode configurations are incorporated. Typical surface and edge-emitting diodes are shown in Figure 11.6-8.

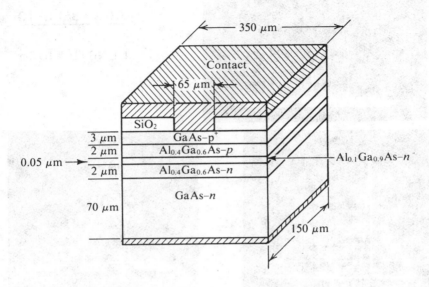

Figure 11.6-8.   Light emitting diodes

Solid state lasers are very desirable for communication purposes since they have narrower emission spectra (<2 nm compared with 30 nm of AlGaAs LEDs and 100 nm of InGaAsP LEDs) which translate to smaller pulse dispersion, larger modulation bandwidths (>2 GHz compared with 100 MHz for LEDs), and greater coupling efficiency to fibers with NA<0.2. The simplest type of diode laser is the *stripe-geometry double heterostructure* (DH) laser shown in Figure 11.6-9.

Optical Detectors

Optical detectors are a type of transducer which converts the incident optical energy to electrical energy. The basic physical mechanisms of optical detectors involved in conversion are release of electrons due to photoelectric effect, i.e., photomultiplier tubes; changing electrical properties due to changes in temperature due to the incident optical energy, i.e., thermocouples; and generation of charge carriers in semiconductors, i.e., photodiodes.

PHOTOMULTIPLIER. The photomultiplier is an extremely sensitive optical detector. It has been reported that levels as low as 10^{-19} watt were detected. The detector comprises a photocathode and a series of dynodes which are kept at progressively higher potential with respect to the cathode. The entire

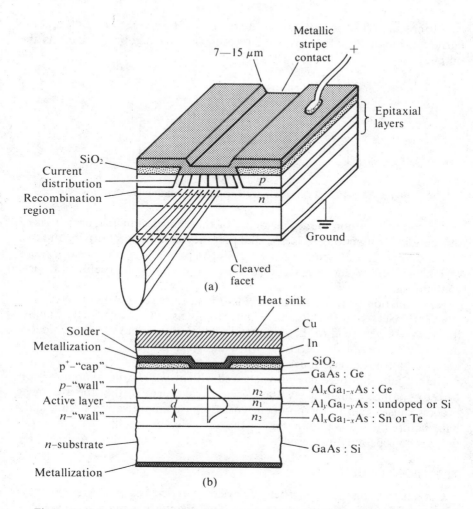

Figure 11.6-9.   Schematic of the strip-geometry double heterostructure laser

assembly is contained in vacuum. When light hits the photocathode electrons are emitted. These are directed and accelerated to the first dynode which is coated with a low surface work function material, e.g., SbCs, where electron multiplication occurs. The electrons emitted from this dynode are then accelerated to the second dynode, where more electrons are emitted. This multiplication process continues until the electrons reach the collecting anode. If the average secondary emission multiplication is 5, the gain of a typical photomultiplier with 9 dynodes is $G = 5^9 = 1.95 \times 10^6$.

PHOTOCONDUCTIVE DETECTORS.   A photoconductor is a semiconductor crystal which, when optical energy falls on it, excites electrons into the conduction band. Refer to Figure 11.6-10 which shows a photoconductive crystal in a simple circuit. When the crystal is radiated by light, its resistance falls and the current through the load resistor increases. This change is detected as the output.

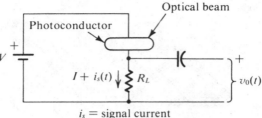

Figure 11.6-10.   Typical circuit for a photoconductive detector

PHOTODIODES. Photodiodes make use of the photoconductive properties of semiconductor junctions. It is essential that they have high sensitivity and fast response time. In the region 0.8-0.9 μm, silicon photodiodes do meet the needs of high sensitivity and fast response times necessary to be useful in optical communications.

A *pn* junction provides the appropriate field to sweep out the free carriers which are released by the absorbed light. High sensitivity is provided by applying a reverse bias field to the *pn* junction which thus behaves as a photoconductive detector. Such detectors, when designed properly with small diode area, can have response times as short as 10^{-9} s.

Higher gain and speed has been achieved with *avalanche photodiodes*. These detectors utilize a high bias voltage (near breakdown) so that the avalanche process causes gain in the photocurrent. Because amplification occurs internally before the signal is amplified by the input electronic amplifiers, the sensitivity is considerably increased.

11.7   POSTLUDE

Communication theory has helped develop a varied and widespread number of systems for transmitting intelligence. This chapter has introduced some of the basic features of the various systems currently in use. Extended studies are necessary for the student to understand fully such matters as information content, noise qualities, bandwidth use, multiplexing capabilities, and their relation to carrier levels and transmission and receiving requirements. Further study is also needed for the student to know the important details of the hardware essential for accomplishing the different methods of communication.

SUMMARY

- Communication systems are concerned with the transmission and reception of intelligence.

- The form and features of communication systems depend on the type of intelligence being communicated.

- Communication systems include a means for modulating the energy that will carry the intelligence; a means for preparing the intelligence in suitable form; a medium for transferring the modulated energy from transmitter to receiver; a means for extracting the intelligence from the transmitted energy; a means for presenting the intelligence in its proper form.

- Information is quantifiable: there is a measurable information content to a message, and a channel has limited information handling capacity.

- The system capacity is defined by the relation

$$C = \frac{1}{\tau} \log_2 n \qquad \text{bits/sec}$$

- The average information content is defined as

$$H_{av} = -\sum_{i=1}^{k} P_i \log_2 P_i \qquad \text{bits/symbol}$$

- For improved information transmission, coding is employed.

- An encoder converts a message from one form to another, the reverse process involves decoding.

- Continuous time signals are discussed in both time-domain and frequency-domain representations.

- The total spread of frequencies from zero to the highest value belonging to the signal is called the bandwidth.

- The faithful transmission of a signal requires that the amplitudes and phases of the frequency components must be maintained through the channel.

- Communication channels are impacted by unwanted signals, including impulse noise and white noise.

- A number of systems of modulation exist and include amplitude modulation, frequency modulation, phase modulation, and a variety of pulse modulation schemes.

- Amplitude modulation methods include AM-DSB/SC and AM-SSB/SC as special forms of simple AM.

- Frequency modulation improves the immunity to noise of transmission and reception. Because of the required wide bandwidth for commercial broadcasting, the carrier frequencies assigned to FM are substantially above the frequency band for AM.

- In digital communication systems the normally continuous intelligence is sampled and digitized.

- The sampling theorem indicates the number of sampled values needed to define completely a given band limited signal.

- Pulse amplitude modulation involves periodic sampling of a signal with amplification prior to modulation and transmission.

- Because of the narrow pulses and the time between them, additional messages can be processed simultaneously over the same channel without interference. This process is known as time division multiplexing.

- Among the important pulse modulation schemes are pulse width, pulse position, pulse code.

- Additional modulation systems exist, including on-off keying, frequency shift keying, and phase shift keying.

- Detection or demodulation is the process of extracting the information-carrying signal from the carrier.

- The detection of AM signals is accomplished by numerous methods: (a) synchronous, (b) rectification, (c) envelope detection.

- Methods for FM detection include (a) differentiation, (b) phase-locked loop, (c) phase shift discriminators, (d) ratio detector.

- Fiber optic communication is accomplished by altering some property of the light waves, such as amplitude, phase, polarization, wavelength (or frequency).

- The NA (numerical aperture) of a fiber defines the light gathering ability of a fiber, and is given by

$$NA = \sqrt{\eta_i^2 - \eta_c^2}$$

where η_i is the index of refraction of the core and η_c is the index of refraction of the cladding material.

- Graded index and single mode fibers are less dispersive than step-index fibers.

REVIEW QUESTIONS

1. Describe the basic elements of a complete communication system. Give three examples of communication channels.
2. Which of the following messages has the highest information content? (a) Mrs. Smith has a boy. (b) School will begin on September 5. (c) man landed on Mars.
3. What is the use of an encoder and a decoder?
4. How much information is contained in a solid state picture TV which comprises 1024×1024 points, with each point having one of 256 levels?
5. What type of signals have discrete spectra, and what type have continuous spectra?
6. What type of networks are used to correct phase distortions?
7. Hearing additional voices in our telephone conversation is called what?
8. What is the difference between impulse and white noise?

9. If the power of a signal through a communication channel falls by 20 dB, what is the original strength of the signal?
10. Are the carrier and modulating signals added or multiplied in an amplitude modulation system?
11. What is meant by AMDS/SC?
12. Identify the modulating schemes illustrated.

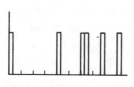 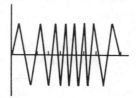 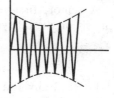

13. When is a frequency modulated signal similar to an amplitude modulated signal? How do they differ?
14. What is the maximum allowable frequency deviation permitted in FM stations?
15. What is the appearance in the frequency domain of a pulse modulated signal?
16. What is a guard band?
17. What is significant about time division multiplexing?
18. What is a "word" in a pulse code modulation scheme?
19. What is the usefulness of a holding circuit?
20. What is the difference between homodyne and heterodyne detection for AM signals?
21. Explain envelope detection of AM signals.
22. Explain how a PAM signal is detected.
23. What changes must be imposed on light in order that the light is modulated?
24. How is the acousto-optic effect utilized?
25. Describe different types of optical fibers.
26. What is the numerical aperture (NA)?
27. What type of fiber has the smallest dispersion?
28. Describe different types of light emitters.
29. Which of the several optical detectors discussed is the most sensitive?
30. What is an avalanche diode?

REFERENCES

1. Roden, M. S., *Analog and Digital Communication Systems*, Prentice-Hall, Inc., Englewood Cliffs, NJ, 1979.

This text provides a mathematical approach to the essential aspects of the subject matter. The mathematics used is as elementary as possible, but has been carefully chosen not to contradict any more sophisticated approach which may eventually be required.

2. Stark, H., and F. B. Tuteur, *Modern Electrical Communications — Theory and Systems*, Prentice-Hall, Inc., Englewood Cliffs, NJ, 1979.

  A senior, first-year gradute level text which undertakes a broad and integrated study of the entire field of electrical communication engineering.

3. Taub, H., and D. L. Schilling, *Principles of Communication Systems*, McGraw Hill Book Co., New York, NY, 1971.

  A senior, first-year graduate level text which places considerable emphasis on digital systems.

PROBLEMS

11.1-1. Read any four lines of this chapter and calculate the probability of finding the letters a, e, i, p. Compare your results if you use eight lines.

  (Ans.: $a = 0.0642$; $e = 0.1031$; $i = 0.0575$; $p = 0.0152$)

11.1-2. Find the average information if the four letters a, e, i, p are sent with equal probability.

11.1-3. How many bits of information are needed to find a number from 0 to 15 which is randomly selected by another person?

11.1-4. Consider a coder which bunches three letters together: *a* with probability 0.3, *b* with probability 0.45 and *c* with probability 0.25. Find the information content for each encoded letter (bits/letter).

11.2-1. Refer to Figure 11.2-1. Phase shift the signal $2 \sin 2\pi 10t$ by $+30$ deg. and the signal $\sin 2\pi 20t$ by -30 deg. and reconstruct the voltage wave.

11.3-1. If the carrier signal is $v_c = V_{c1} \sin \omega_c t + V_{c2} \cos \omega_c t$ and the modulating signal is $v_m = V_m \cos \omega_m t$, find the modulated signal and represent its components in the time and frequency domains.

11.3-2. Find the type of filter that must be used to recover the received signal from $V(t) = A(1 + m \cos \omega_m t) \cos (\omega_c t + \varphi_1)$ if the local oscillator produces the signal $\cos (\omega_c + \varphi_2)$, where φ_1 and φ_2 are constant phase angles.

11.3-3. The energy of a signal is given by the expression

$$U = \int_{-\infty}^{\infty} v^2(t) \, dt$$

Find the energy content of the signals shown in Figure P11.3-3. If the energy contents are divided by the duration of the signal, what is the resulting quantity?

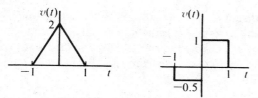 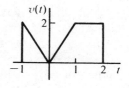

Figure P11.3-3

11.3-4. Verify Equation (11.3-14).

11.3-5. The modulating signal of an FM signal is $v_m(t) = 2 \sin \omega_m t$. Find the FM signal and its frequency components for small β. Repeat for somewhat larger value of β.

11.4-1. Show that you can recover the cosine function using the sampling technique discussed in Example 11.4-1.

11.4-2. Assume that the square wave shown in Figure P11.4-2 is band-limited to the 7th harmonic. Determine, using sampling techniques, the amplitudes of the harmonic terms that result. Compare these with the theoretical values

$$v(\alpha) = \frac{4}{\pi} \left[\sin \alpha + \frac{1}{3} \sin 3\alpha + \frac{1}{5} \sin 5\alpha + \frac{1}{7} \sin 7\alpha \right]$$

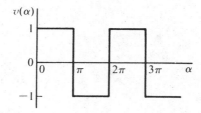

Figure P11.4-2

11.4-3. Refer to the signals shown in Figure P11.4-3. Give the coding signals for a PCM wave.

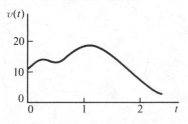 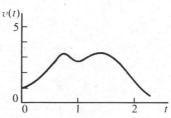

Figure P11.4-3

11.5-1. An amplitude modulated signal $v(t) = A v_m(t) \cos \omega_{c1} t$ is synchronously detected. The local oscillator provides a signal having the form $v_l(t) = \cos \omega_{c2} t$, with $\omega_{c1} \neq \omega_{c2}$. Graph the spectral characteristics of the modulated signal when $v_m(t) = \cos \omega_o t$ for the signals at the different stages of the synchronous detector.

11.5-2. Graph the amplitude spectra of the first three terms of Equation (11.5-5) if $v_m(t) = \cos \omega_o t$, $\omega_o \ll \omega_c$, and indicate the bandwidth of the low-pass filter to recover the signal.

11.5-3. Assume a frequency modulation process with modulating signal $v_m(t) = 2t$. Sketch the signals at the different stages of an FM detector that uses the property of differentiation.

11.6-1. Find the optical wavelength such that only one mode propagates in an optical fiber. Given: $r = 2.5$ μm, $\eta_i = 1.4$, and $\eta_c = 1.402$.

11.6-2. A graded index fiber has $\eta_i = 1.4$ and $\eta_c = 1.39$. Find the distance that two square pulses of width 1 ns spaced 3 ns apart must travel before they merge.

Chapter Twelve

Electromechanics*

There are a number of devices that incorporate electromagnetic fields to couple a moving mechanical member to a stationary electric member, and vice versa. Included are classes of vibration devices, accelerometers, microphones, and rotating machinery. In general, the extent of the mechanical motion in transducers is small, and they are usually classifed as *incremental* transducers. Rotating machinery would be classed as gross motion energy converters.

12.1 ENERGY CONVERSION

In electromechanical devices, electric or magnetic structures are used. A very important class of practical devices allows for the motion of one winding relative to a stationary magnetic structure. If the motion is small about some position of equilibrium, these are incremental transducers. This class of device includes the loudspeaker and the microphone. Gross motion devices, such as rotating machines, are those in which the motion of a portion of the device is so large that special methods are employed in their analyses.

In the limited scope discussed here, energy conversion devices will be those in which electrical energy is converted into mechanical, acoustical, or thermal energy. The inverse process of converting mechanical, acoustical, or thermal energy into electrical energy is equally important.

Many more magnetic field (current operated) devices exist in practical applications than electric field (voltage operated) devices. This fact results not from the inability to create more electric field devices but principally from the limitations of the electrical materials available. It is simply true that electric field materials that will support the same stored energy densities possible with magnetic field materials do not exist. Part of the reason is readily understood by comparing the expressions for the energy densities in the electric and magnetic fields, $\frac{1}{2}\epsilon E^2$ and $\frac{1}{2}\mu H^2$, with ϵ of the order of 10^{-11} F/m and μ of the order of 10^{-6} H/m.

---

* In this chapter we shall use e and E for voltages and v and V for velocities.

To study incremental motion devices, we shall employ the basic circuit and force considerations already introduced, often with the special application of the principle of conservation of energy. When considered from the point of view of conservation of energy, any energy conversion process must be expressible in terms of an energy balance of the form

$$\text{Energy input} = \text{energy output} + \text{energy stored} + \text{energy lost} \qquad (12.1)$$

Consider the electric motor, for example. In this device the input energy is electrical; the output energy is mechanical; the stored energy is both electrical and mechanical; and the energy lost is thermal, resulting from electrical losses in the conductors and in the iron members, and frictional losses in the bearings and in the windage caused by the rotating assembly. Such a representative device has a graphical representation as in Figure 12.1-1. However, considerations of energy alone will not, in general, provide all of the information that is necessary for a description of the operation of the device. Such factors as the features of the coupling field between the electrical and the mechanical variables, and the impedance levels of the device (e.g., voltage and current relationships, or torque and speed relationships) are fundamental to the description of the performance and operation of the device.

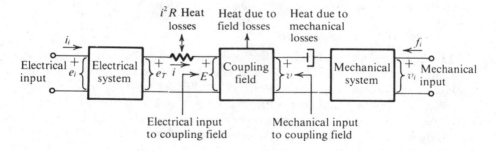

Figure 12.1-1.   General representation of electromechanical energy conversion devices

We first direct our attention to certain results from electricity and magnetism that are basic to an understanding of the devices to be studied. This will be followed by a discussion of incremental motion transducers, and then by a study of rotating machinery.

PRINCIPLES OF ELECTROMECHANICAL ENERGY CONVERSION

12.2   POTENTIAL ENERGY IN A SYSTEM OF RIGID CURRENTS

Let a single circuit carrying a constant current I be placed in a magnetic field of fixed external sources. Let a small virtual displacement be denoted by δr.

The work done by the circuit against the force in the virtual displacement must be supplied by the current source, and is given by the expression

$$d(\delta U) = \delta r\, df \qquad (12.2\text{-}1)$$

where we have assumed that the displacement takes place along the force df. But Ampère's law for the force on a current in a magnetic field is

$$df = I\, dl\, B \qquad (12.2\text{-}2)$$

where the direction of df is on the plane perpendicular to dl and B, as shown in Figure 12.2-1a. Therefore

$$d(\delta U) = I\, \delta r\, dl\, B \qquad (12.2\text{-}3)$$

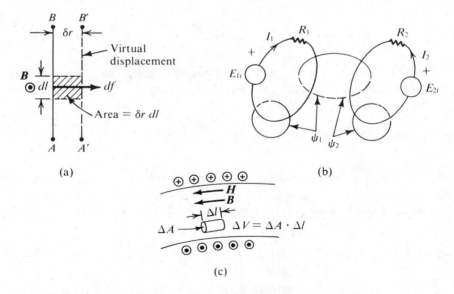

(a)

(b)

(c)

**Figure 12.2-1.   (a) Virtual displacement of rigid currents   (b) Flux linkages
(c) Magnetic energy density distribution**

However, $\delta r\, dl$ is the area swept by dl during its displacement, and the quantity $B\, \delta r\, dl$ is an element of magnetic flux linkages swept out by dl in its motion. For the entire circuit the increment of flux linkages $\delta\psi$ due to the displacement is

$$\int_{AB} B\, \delta r\, dl = \delta\psi \qquad (12.2\text{-}4)$$

Therefore from Equation (12.2-3) we obtain

$$\delta U = I \int_{AB} B \, \delta r \, dl = I \, \delta \psi \tag{12.2-5}$$

Note that although we have used a simplified case, as shown in Figure 12.2-1a, to develop Equation (12.2-5), this result is the same regardless of the geometric shape of the circuit AB, the direction and magnitude of B, and the direction of the virtual displacement.

If the current I and the external sources are maintained constant during the virtual displacement, the work done by the mechanical forces is compensated by a decrease in a potential energy function W, and we may write

$$\delta W = -\delta U = -I \, \delta \psi \tag{12.2-6}$$

This implies that the potential energy of the rigid current in the magnetic field is

$$U = -I\psi \tag{12.2-7}$$

If dr is a real variable rather than a virtual displacement, then work must be done to maintain the current constant. Now, because of the change in flux linkages, an emf will be induced

$$e = -\frac{d\psi}{dt} \tag{12.2-8}$$

where dt is the time that it takes for the displacement to occur. But this induced emf must be counterbalanced by an equal and opposite applied voltage e_i. The work done by the applied voltage on the circuit during this time interval is

$$e_i I \, dt = I \, d\psi \tag{12.2-9}$$

This expression may be interpreted to show that the work done by the mechanical forces in a small displacement of a linear circuit is exactly compensated by the energy supplied by the source to maintain the current constant. The total work of the circuit is zero.

Let us now evaluate the energy that is being supplied during the process of building up the currents in the system of two rigid currents and the current sources i as shown in Figure 12.2-1b. (The results can easily be expanded to n such circuits.) This can be done by considering the energy that is supplied to both currents as they are increased from zero to their final values, or equivalently, as the flux linking each current increases from zero to its final value.

From Figure 12.2-1b we observe that if E_k $(k=1,2)$ is the emf induced by a variation in ψ_k $(k=1,2)$, then

$$E_k + E_{ki} = R_k i_k \qquad\qquad k=1,2 \qquad\qquad \text{(a)} \quad (12.2\text{-}10)$$

or [see Equation (12.2-8)]

$$E_{ki} = R_k i_k + \frac{d\psi_k}{dt} \qquad\qquad k=1,2 \qquad\qquad \text{(b)}$$

The power expended by the input source E_{ki} is $E_{ki} i_k$, and the work done on the k-th circuit is

$$dU_k = R_k i_k^2\, dt + i_k\, d\psi_k \qquad\qquad k=1,2 \qquad\qquad (12.2\text{-}11)$$

Of this work, the amount $R_k i_k^2$ is dissipated as heat, while $i_k d\psi_k$ is stored as magnetic energy. Thus a variation in the magnetic energy of the two current filaments is related to the increments in fluxes by

$$U = \sum_{k=1}^{2} \int_0^{\psi_k} i_k\, d\psi_k = \int_0^{\psi_1} i_1\, d\psi_1 + \int_0^{\psi_2} i_2\, d\psi_2 \qquad (12.2\text{-}12)$$

For a linear system this expression may be conveniently expressed in terms of the self and mutual inductances of the circuits. To find this relation, first recall that the flux linking the k-th circuit is a linear function of the currents in all the circuits, namely,

$$\Psi_k = \sum_{s=1}^{2} M_{ks} I_s \qquad\qquad (12.2\text{-}13)$$

where M_{ks} is the mutal inductance between conductor k and conductor s, and where $M_{kk} = L_k$ is the self-inductance of circuit k. This expression can be written

$$\Psi_k = L_k I_k + \sum_{s=1}^{2}{}' M_{ks} I_s \qquad\qquad (s \neq k) \qquad (12.2\text{-}14)$$

where the summation denoted by Σ' does not include the term for which $s = k$, since this has been written explicitly. It follows from this expression that

$$\delta\Psi_k = L_k\, \delta I_k + \sum_{s=1}^{2}{}' M_{ks}\, \delta I_s \qquad\qquad (12.2\text{-}15)$$

Equation (12.2-6) thus becomes

$$\delta U = \sum_{k=1}^{2} I_k (L_k \delta I_k + \sum_{s=1}^{2}{}' M_{ks} \delta I_s)$$

$$= \sum_{k=1}^{2} I_k (L_k \delta I_k + M_{k1} \delta I_1 + M_{k2} \delta I_2)$$

$$= I_1 (L_1 \delta I_1 + M_{12} \delta I_2) + I_2 (L_2 \delta I_2 + M_{21} \delta I_1)$$

$$= I_1 L_1 \delta I_1 + M_{12} \delta I_2 + L_2 I_2 \delta I_2 + M_{21} I_2 \delta I_1$$

Since $M_{12} = M_{21}$, this expression can be written in the form

$$\delta U = \delta \left(\frac{1}{2} L_1 I_1^2 \right) + \delta \left(\frac{1}{2} L_2 I_2^2 \right) + \delta (M_{12} I_1 I_2)$$

Hence the total magnetic energy takes the form

$$U_m = \frac{1}{2} L_1 I_1^2 + \frac{1}{2} L_2 I_2^2 + M_{12} I_1 I_2 \tag{12.2-16}$$

This expression can be extended to the case of n conductors, and proves to be

$$U_m = \frac{1}{2} \sum_{k=1}^{n} L_k I_k^2 + \frac{1}{2} \sum_{k=1}^{n} \sum_{s=1}^{n}{}' M_{ks} I_k I_s$$

$$= \frac{1}{2} \sum_{k=1}^{n} I_k (L_k I_k + \sum_{s=1}^{n}{}' M_{ks} I_s) \tag{12.2-17}$$

By combining this equation with an extension of Equation (12.2-14) the result is

$$U_m = \frac{1}{2} \sum_{k=1}^{n} I_k \Psi_k \tag{12.2-18}$$

But this is just the result specified by Equation (12.2-12). Hence finally for a linear system

$$U_m = \sum_{k=1}^{n} \int_0^{\Psi_k} i_k \, d\psi_k = \frac{1}{2} \sum_{k=1}^{n} I_k \Psi_k \tag{12.2-19}$$

This expression specifies the total energy supplied during the entire process of building up the currents in the system. It is, therefore, the total amount of energy that is stored in the magnetic field of the system of currents. Note that in this development it is implicitly assumed that no magnetic fields produced outside the system are linking the currents.

Equation (12.2-19) can be written in a form that explicitly shows its relation to the magnetic field. Refer to Figure 12.2-1c which shows the region of the field due to one current. The total magnetic flux linking the current is seen to be

$$\Psi = \sum_{\Delta A} B \, \Delta A \tag{12.2-20}$$

Also, an application of the Ampère line integral around any path yields

$$I = \sum_{\Delta l} H \, \Delta l \tag{12.2-21}$$

Thus the energy stored in the field due to each current is

$$U_{mp} = \frac{1}{2} I \Psi = \frac{1}{2} \sum_{\Delta A} \sum_{\Delta l} B H \, \Delta A \, \Delta l = \frac{1}{2} \sum_{\Delta V} BH \tag{12.2-22}$$

In the limit as $\Delta A \to 0$ and $\Delta l \to 0$, the magnetic energy per unit volume is

$$\frac{\Delta U_{mp}}{\Delta V} = \frac{1}{2} BH$$

But for a linear medium $B = \mu H$, and so

$$\frac{\Delta U_{mp}}{\Delta V} = \frac{B^2}{2\mu} = \frac{1}{2} \mu H^2 \tag{12.2-23}$$

This expression may be interpreted to show that the total energy in the magnetic field of any system of electric currents is distributed throughout the entire field with a density at any point equal to

$$u_m = \frac{\Delta U_m}{\Delta V} = \sum_p \frac{\Delta U_{mp}}{\Delta V} = \frac{1}{2} \mu H^2 \qquad \text{J/m}^2 \tag{12.2-24}$$

12.3   FORCES IN TERMS OF ENERGY CHANGES

The energy expressions discussed above can be used to find expressions for the forces between the currents and certain geometric parameters of the circuit. If we write

U_{mech} = energy associated with the mechanical part of the system

U_m = energy stored in the magnetic field

U_{elec} = energy associated with the electric part of the system then the system energy balance requires that we write

$$dU_{mech} + dU_m = dU_{elec} \tag{12.3-1}$$

where

dU_{mech} = energy of the system that is converted into mechanical energy

$= f_k v_k \Delta t$, where f_k is the force exerted by the electrical system on the mechanical system, and where v_k is the velocity

dU_m = change in stored magnetic energy

dU_{elec} = net electrical energy input after resistive losses have been taken into account

$$= \sum_k E_{ki} I_k \, \Delta t - \sum_k I_k^2 R_k \, \Delta t$$

In terms of power, Equation (12.3-1) can be written

$$f_k v_k + \frac{dU_m}{dt} + \sum_k I_k^2 R_k - \sum_k E_{ki} I_k = 0 \tag{12.3-2}$$

Note that there is no energy storage in electric fields for the systems under consideration. Also, the equation is written in such a form that the electrical and mechanical energy terms (the first and last terms) have positive values for electrical to mechanical conversion (motor action).

Suppose we consider the special constant current process in which the external voltage sources are so controlled that the currents within the system remain constant during any virtual displacement. Neglecting losses and introducing Equations (12.2-10) and (12.2-18), we find

$$f_k v_k + \frac{1}{2} \sum_k I_k \frac{d\Psi_k}{dt} - \sum_k I_k \frac{d\Psi_k}{dt} = 0 \tag{12.3-3}$$

This expression shows the interesting fact that in order to maintain a constant current in the circuit as the geometry changes the batteries must do exactly twice the amount of work that is done by the external sources, in addition to supplying the heat losses. Physically this means that in this process, when the field does work in the k-th conductor, the battery must supply not only this work but must also supply a like additional amount of energy to the energy stored in the field. This is the 50-50 rule for magnetic problems. A similar result applies for electric field situations.

The converse of the foregoing relates to the case when work is done on the circuits by changing their form against the action of electromagnetic forces or by pulling them apart. In this case, the energy returned to the sources (essentially by charging the batteries) is twice the amount of the mechanical work done, the second half being restored to the sources by a reduction in the stored magnetic energy.

Observe that Equation (12.3-3) can be written as

$$f_k v_k = \frac{1}{2} \sum I_k \frac{d\Psi_k}{dt}$$

Making use of Equation (12.2-19), this becomes

$$f_k v_k = \frac{\partial U_m}{\partial t} = \frac{\partial U_m}{\partial x_p} \frac{\partial x_p}{\partial t} \Bigg|_{\substack{I = \text{const.} \\ x_p = \text{const.},\ p \neq k}}$$

and therefore

$$f_k = \frac{\partial U_m}{\partial x_k} \Bigg|_{I = \text{const.}} \tag{12.3-4}$$

Observe from Equation (12.3-3) that the induced emf terms can be ignored in the force calculation, if the flux linkages are held constant. Under these circumstances, it follows directly, as above, that

$$f_k = -\frac{\partial U_m}{\partial x_k} \Bigg|_{\Psi = \text{const.}} \tag{12.3-5}$$

EXAMPLE 12.3-1. Show the validity of the force expressions for the singly excited electromechanical system shown in Figure 12.3-1.

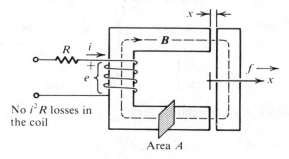

Figure 12.3-1.   A singly excited electromechanical system

SOLUTION. Write Equation (12.3-2) in the form

$$f \frac{dx}{dt} + \frac{dU_m}{dt} = ei$$

where

$$e = L\frac{di}{dt} = \frac{d\psi}{dt}$$

But since

$$U_m = \frac{1}{2}Li^2 = \frac{1}{2}\psi i$$

then clearly

$$\frac{dU_m}{dt} = \frac{1}{2}\left(\psi\frac{di}{dt} + i\frac{d\psi}{dt}\right)$$

Combine with the first equation to find

$$f\frac{dx}{dt} + \frac{1}{2}\left(\psi\frac{di}{dt} + i\frac{d\psi}{dt}\right) = i\frac{d\psi}{dt}$$

(a) For the condition of constant current, this expression reduces to

$$f\frac{dx}{dt} + \frac{1}{2}I\frac{d\psi}{dt} = I\frac{d\psi}{dt}$$

It follows from this that

$$f\frac{dx}{dt} = \frac{1}{2}I\frac{d\psi}{dt}\bigg|_{I=\text{const.}}$$

so that

$$f = \frac{1}{2}I\frac{d\psi}{dx}\bigg|_{I=\text{const.}} = \frac{\partial U_m}{\partial x}\bigg|_{I=\text{const.}}$$

(b) For the case when $\Psi = \text{const.}$, then

$$f\frac{dx}{dt} + \frac{1}{2}\Psi\frac{di}{dt} = 0$$

from which

$$f = -\frac{1}{2}\Psi\frac{di}{dx}\bigg|_{\Psi=\text{const.}} = -\frac{\partial U_m}{\partial x}\bigg|_{\Psi=\text{const.}}$$

The total field energy consists of two components

$$U_m = \int_{\substack{\text{air} \\ \text{gap}}} \frac{1}{2} BH \, dV + \int_{\text{core}} \frac{1}{2} BH \, dV = \frac{B^2 Ax}{\mu_o} + \int_{\text{core}} \frac{1}{2} BH \, dV$$

But for constant Ψ, B will be constant, and the energy stored in the core will be constant. Under these conditions

$$f = -\frac{\partial U_m}{\partial x}\bigg|_{\Psi = \text{const.}} = -\frac{B^2 A}{\mu_o} \qquad \text{newton}$$

□　□　□

12.4 FORCES AND TORQUES BETWEEN CIRCUITS IN TERMS OF CHANGES OF MUTUAL INDUCTANCE

An application of Equation (12.3-4) that is of considerable practical importance involves two circuits which have self-inductance L_1 and L_2 with a mutual inductance M between them. Such doubly-excited circuits are represented by the doubly-excited magnetic transducers to be studied. These might be of the forms illustrated in Figures 12.4-1. If the currents in the windings are I_1 and I_2, then energy stored in the magnetic field is that specified by Equation (12.2-16). Refer to Figure 12.4-1a and suppose that circuit 1 is subjected to a virtual displacement dr. If f_1 is the magnetic force on this circuit in the direction of r, the work done by the circuit against the force in displacing the circuit is, by Equation (12.3-4),

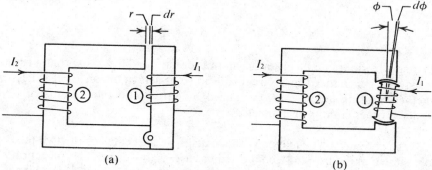

Figure 12.4-1.　Two types of double excited magnetic transducers

$$f_{1r} = \frac{1}{2} I_1^2 \frac{\partial L_1}{\partial r} + \frac{1}{2} I_2^2 \frac{\partial L_2}{\partial r} + I_1 I_2 \frac{\partial M}{\partial r} \qquad (12.4\text{-}1)$$

This expression gives the component of the total magnetic force in any direction r on circuit 1 due to circuit 2 in terms of the currents and the space rate of change of inductances in that direction.

An entirely similar procedure can be employed in conjunction with the device of Figure 12.4-1b to find an expression for the component of torque on circuit 1 due to circuit 2 tending to cause the circuit to move through an angular displacement φ. The result is

$$\mathcal{T}_{1\varphi} = \frac{1}{2} I_1^2 \frac{\partial L_1}{\partial \varphi} + \frac{1}{2} I_2^2 \frac{\partial L_2}{\partial \varphi} + I_1 I_2 \frac{\partial M}{\partial \varphi} \qquad (12.4\text{-}2)$$

In many cases the self inductances are constant with displacement, and the foregoing results are dependent only on changes in the mutual inductance. In these cases the resulting expressions are

$$f_{1r} = I_1 I_2 \frac{\partial M}{\partial r} \qquad \text{(a)} \quad (12.4\text{-}3)$$

$$\mathcal{T}_{1\varphi} = I_1 I_2 \frac{\partial M}{\partial \varphi} \qquad \text{(b)}$$

But from the fact that the flux linkages in the circuits are

$$\psi_1 = L_1 I_1 + M I_2 \qquad \text{(a)} \quad (12.4\text{-}4)$$

$$\psi_2 = L_2 I_2 + M I_1 \qquad \text{(b)}$$

then Equations (12.4-3) become

$$f_{1r} = I_1 \frac{\partial \psi_1}{\partial r} \qquad \text{(a)} \quad (12.4\text{-}5)$$

$$\mathcal{T}_{1\varphi} = I_1 \frac{\partial \psi_1}{\partial \varphi} \qquad \text{(b)}$$

These expressions can be given broad interpretation. They show that a torque or a force is produced in a circuit of constant self-inductance regardless of whether the flux linkages are produced by currents in two circuits or by a group of other circuits or magnets.

EXAMPLE 12.4-1. The magnetic flux density at the center of the two parallel coils shown in Figure 12.4-2 connected in series is uniform. This configuration is known as Helmholtz coils. The magnetic flux density is $B = C N_1 i_1 / r$ where C is a constant. Find the torque on coil 2 which carries current i_2.

SOLUTION. The flux linking coil 2 is

$$\psi_{21} = N_2 A B \cos \varphi \qquad \text{weber}$$

and the mutual inductance between the fixed and the moving coils is

$$M = \frac{\psi_{21}}{i_1} = \frac{N_2 A B}{i_1} \cos \varphi = C \frac{N_1 N_2 A}{r} \cos \varphi$$

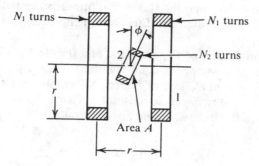

Figure 12.4-2.   An electrodynamic wattmeter

But the self-inductances are independent of angle φ and the torque experienced by coil 2 is [see Equation (12.4-3b)]

$$\mathscr{T}_{2\varphi} = i_1 i_2 \frac{\partial M}{\partial \varphi} = -C \frac{N_1 N_2 A}{r} i_1 i_2 \sin \varphi$$

□   □   □

12.5   MAGNETIC CIRCUITS

Frequent reference has been made to the Ampère line integral and the magnetic flux produced by current carrying conductors. A practical problem of considerable importance is the determination of the magnetic flux produced in a closed iron core by the electric current in a winding about the core. A problem of this sort occurs in almost every electromagnetic field operated device, including the transformer, the rotating dc machine, the rotating ac machine, electromagnetic relays, loud speakers, and solenoid operated devices. Owing to the high permeability of the iron core, the magnetic flux within the core will ordinarily greatly exceed that outside. Also, the magnetic flux that passes through the walls of the core will ordinarily be small compared with the flux through the core itself. Under these conditions the air space is a virtual insulator of magnetic flux and the core is a conductor of the magnetic flux. In this light, the magnetic circuit is analogous to an electric circuit in the steady state, although magnetic conductors and magnetic insulators are concepts that are not nearly so accurate as an electric conductor and insulator.

A second common feature of the magnetic and the electric circuit is that both the flux and the current are continuous around their respective loops. This means that there is a Kirchhoff type flux law corresponding to the Kirchhoff current law. Thus if the core is composed of a number of paths, then the fluxes in the paths which meet in a common point must be zero, or

$$\sum_{\text{Point}} \Phi = 0 \tag{12.5-1}$$

As for the KCL and currents, the fluxes that appear in Equation (12.5-1) are algebraic quantities and a reference direction for flux must be prescribed to insure consistent results.

A third common feature of the magnetic and the electric circuit is that the region within the core comprises equipotential surfaces, that is, surfaces of constant magnetic potential, just as the region within the electric conductor comprises equipotential surfaces of constant electric potential. The difference of magnetic potential is related to the line integral of the vector $\bar{H}$ and is

$$V_{H_b} - V_{H_a} = -\int \bar{H} \cdot \overline{dl} \tag{12.5-2}$$

When taken once around the core, the line integral of $\bar{H}$ is called the *magnetomotive force* (mmf). That is,

$$\oint \bar{H} \cdot \overline{dl} = \text{mmf} = I_c = \sum_{\text{Loop}} \Delta V_H \tag{12.5-3}$$

Of course, if I_c is carried by a winding of N turns, then

$$\oint \bar{H} \cdot \overline{dl} = NI_c \tag{12.5-4}$$

We point out that the name magnetomotive force is misleading because mmf is not a force (it is a current), just as the name electromotive force is misleading since emf is work per unit charge and not force. Thus the term *magnetomotance* is often used, and parallels the term electromotance.

Consider Figure 12.5-1a which shows an iron core that is magnetized by a current-carrying coil. By an application of Equation (12.5-4) along path *ABCDA*, we write

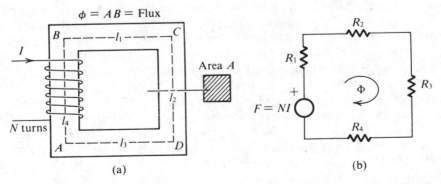

(a)   (b)

Figure 12.5-1. (a) Magnetic iron core   (b) Equivalent circuit representation

$$NI = \oint \bar{H} \cdot d\bar{l} = \int_A^B H \, dl + \int_B^C H \, dl + \int_C^D H \, dl + \int_D^A H \, dl \qquad (12.5\text{-}5)$$

where $NI = F$ is the magnetomotive force (mmf) with units of At.
Assume that the mean length of section BC is l_1, then

$$\int_B^C H \, dl = H l_1 = \frac{B l_1}{\mu} = \frac{B A l_1}{\mu A} = \Phi \frac{l_1}{\mu A} = \Phi \mathscr{R}_1 \qquad (12.5\text{-}6)$$

where $\mathscr{R}_1$ is the reluctance of this portion of the magnetic circuit. If the reluctances of the several sections shown in Figure 12.5-1 are $\mathscr{R}_1, \mathscr{R}_2, \mathscr{R}_3, \mathscr{R}_4$, then Equation (12.5-5) assumes the form

$$F = NI = \Phi(\mathscr{R}_1 + \mathscr{R}_2 + \mathscr{R}_3 + \mathscr{R}_4) \qquad (12.5\text{-}7)$$

The equivalent circuit representation for this is shown in Figure 12.5-1b.

EXAMPLE 12.5-1. The coil shown in Figure 12.5-2 carries 2 A. Find the number of turns necessary to produce a flux density of 2.5 Wb/m² (= tesla). Assume that the relative permeability for the iron core is $\mu_r = 3000$, with a core cross-sectional area = 0.025 m².

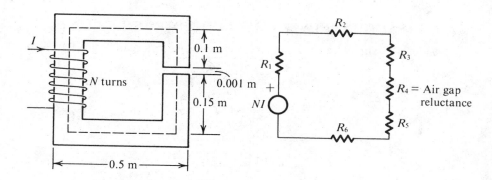

Figure 12.5-2. An iron core with an air gap

SOLUTION. The flux in the core is

$$\Phi = BA = 2.5 \times 0.025 = 0.0625 \qquad \text{Wb}$$

Further for the magnetic circuit

$$NI = F = \Phi(\mathscr{R}_1 + \mathscr{R}_2 + \mathscr{R}_3 + \mathscr{R}_4 + \mathscr{R}_5 + \mathscr{R}_6)$$

where

$$\mathcal{R}_1 = \frac{0.16}{3000 \times 4\pi \times 10^{-7} \times 0.025} = 1.70 \times 10^3$$

$$\mathcal{R}_2 = \mathcal{R}_6 = \frac{0.5}{3000 \times 4\pi \times 10^{-7} \times 0.025} = 5.31 \times 10^3$$

$$\mathcal{R}_3 = \frac{0.1}{3000 \times 4\pi \times 10^{-7} \times 0.025} = 1.05 \times 10^3$$

$$\mathcal{R}_4 = \frac{0.001}{1 \times 4\pi \times 10^{-7} \times 0.025} = 31.83 \times 10^3$$

$$\mathcal{R}_5 = \frac{0.15}{3000 \times 4\pi \times 10^{-7} \times 0.025} = 1.59 \times 10^3$$

Then

$$N = \frac{0.0625 \times 46.79 \times 10^3}{2} = 1462 \qquad \text{turns}$$

□   □   □

12.6   ATTRACTION BETWEEN MAGNETIZED IRON SURFACES

Consider the singly excited magnetic circuit illustrated in Figure 12.6-1.

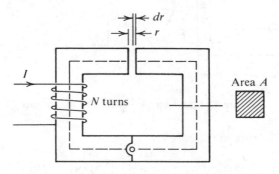

Figure 12.6-1.   A typical singly excited magnetic transducer

When the magnetic flux and the mmf are directly proportional to each other (for linear magnetic circuits), the energy stored in the field is

$$U_m = \frac{1}{2} I \Psi = \frac{1}{2} INAB = \frac{1}{2} F\Phi \qquad (12.6\text{-}1)$$

where $F = NI$ denotes the mmf. This expression can be written in terms of the reluctance of the magnetic path which, by Equation (12.5-6) is

$$\mathscr{R} = \frac{F}{\Phi} \qquad (12.6\text{-}2)$$

The *permeance* P which is the inverse of the reluctance is

$$P = \frac{1}{\mathscr{R}} = \frac{\Phi}{F} \qquad (12.6\text{-}3)$$

Hence for the linear system, the stored energy is

$$U_m = \frac{1}{2} I \Psi = \frac{1}{2} F\Phi = \frac{1}{2} F^2 P = \frac{1}{2} \Phi^2 \mathscr{R} \qquad \text{J} \qquad (12.6\text{-}4)$$

For a small displacement both R and Φ are variables, and for differential changes

$$dU_m = \frac{1}{2} \Phi^2 \, d\mathscr{R} + \mathscr{R} \Phi \, d\Phi \qquad (12.6\text{-}5)$$

from which it follows that

$$f = -\frac{\partial U_m}{\partial x}\bigg|_{\Psi} = -\frac{1}{2} \Phi^2 \frac{d\mathscr{R}}{dx}\bigg|_{\Psi} = -\frac{1}{2} \Phi^2 \frac{dP}{dx}\bigg|_{\Psi} \qquad \text{N} \qquad (12.6\text{-}6)$$

Observe from this expression that a change in reluctance involves an interchange of energy between the field and the mechanical system.

Other useful forms of the force equation can be derived. Both F and P are variables, and for differential changes

$$dU_m = \frac{1}{2} F^2 \, dP + PF \, dF \qquad (12.6\text{-}7)$$

It follows from this, since $F = NI$, that

$$f = \frac{\partial U_m}{\partial x}\bigg|_I = \frac{1}{2}F^2\frac{dP}{dx}\bigg|_I = -\frac{1}{2}F^2\frac{d\mathcal{R}}{dx}\bigg|_I \qquad N \qquad (12.6\text{-}8)$$

This expression shows that a change in permeance or reluctance involves an interchange of energy between the field and the mechanical system. Other equivalent expressions readily follow, namely,

$$f = -\frac{1}{2}\Phi\frac{dF}{dx}\bigg|_\Psi \qquad N \qquad (a) \quad (12.6\text{-}9)$$

$$f = \frac{1}{2}F\frac{d\Phi}{dx}\bigg|_I \qquad N \qquad (b)$$

Further, since $L = N^2/\mathcal{R} = N^2P$, Equation (12.6-8) can be written in terms of current and inductance

$$f = \frac{1}{2}I^2\frac{dL}{dx}\bigg|_I \qquad N \qquad (12.6\text{-}10)$$

For the device illustrated in Figure 12.6-1 the total reluctance of the magnetic path is made up of the reluctance of the iron path and that of the airgap. This is given by

$$\mathcal{R} = \mathcal{R}_{iron} + \frac{x}{\mu_o A}$$

For a positive incremental change in the airgap length

$$\frac{d\mathcal{R}}{dx} = \frac{1}{\mu_o A}$$

and Equation (12.6-6) yields

$$f = -\frac{1}{2}\Phi^2\frac{1}{\mu_o A} = -\frac{1}{2}\frac{B^2 A}{\mu_o} \qquad N \qquad (12.6\text{-}11)$$

This shows that the force is in such a direction as to decrease the airgap length.

EXAMPLE 12.6-1. A simple form of a so-called reluctance motor is illustrated in Figure 12.6-2. (a) Express the inductance as measurable at the electrical terminals in analytic form, assuming that the iron is of such a high permeability that only the airgap reluctance is significant in the magnetic equation. (b) Write expressions for the stored energy. (c) Write the expression for the torque developed. (d) If an ac excitation current is applied, find expressions for the instantaneous torque for rotational speed of the rotor $\omega_m = 0$, $\neq$ applied ω, $=$ applied ω.

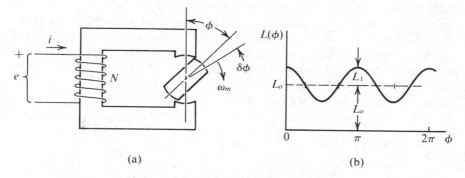

(a)   (b)

Figure 12.6-2. A simple reluctance motor

SOLUTION. (a) In this device, as shown, only an exciting winding is provided. This is on the stator, but the rotor is assumed to be mounted on bearings so that it may rotate freely. We shall assume that the shape of the rotor is such that the inductance varies sinusoidally. The space variation of inductance is of double frequency since for $\varphi = 0$ and π, the inductance is a maximum. Then

$$L(\varphi) = L_o + L_1 \cos 2\varphi$$

(b) The system is linear and the energy is then given by

$$U_m = \frac{1}{2} i^2 L = \frac{1}{2} i^2 (L_o + L_1 \cos 2\varphi)$$

(c) If a torque $\mathcal{T}$ is applied in the direction $\delta\varphi$, there will be a change in flux linkages by an amount $\delta\psi$. Also, a change will occur in the energy stored in the field. The energy supplied in the virtual displacement is partly stored and partly converted into external work. By the principle of conservation of energy, it is required that

$$i\delta\psi = \mathcal{T}_\varphi\, \delta\varphi + \delta U_m$$

For the limiting condition when $\delta\varphi \to 0$, this expression becomes

$$\mathcal{T}_\varphi = i\frac{\partial\psi}{\partial\varphi} - \frac{\partial U_m}{\partial\varphi} \tag{12.6-12}$$

Note that if all or part of the coil were attached to the rotor, the same results would apply; but the formula now gives the torque on the whole core + coil configuration with no clue as to how the torque is shared between the coil and the iron. The torque equation displays two tendencies. The system tends to move so that the flux linkages with the coil increase, and also so that the stored energy in the field diminishes.

Make use of the fact that $\psi = Li$, and so

$$\mathcal{T}_\varphi = i^2\frac{\partial L(\varphi)}{\partial\varphi} - \frac{\partial}{\partial\varphi}\left[\frac{1}{2}L(\varphi)i^2\right]$$

$$= \frac{1}{2}i^2\frac{\partial L(\varphi)}{\partial\varphi} = \frac{1}{2}i^2\frac{\partial(L_o + L_1\cos 2\varphi)}{\partial\varphi} = -i^2 L_1\cos 2\varphi$$

(d) Suppose that the current i is of the form $i = I_m\cos\omega t$. For $\omega_m = 0$ the torque expression becomes

$$\mathcal{T}_\varphi = -I_m^2 L_1\sin 2\varphi\cos^2\omega t$$

The time average torque is

$$\langle\mathcal{T}_\varphi\rangle = -\frac{2}{\pi}I_m^2 L_1\sin 2\varphi$$

Suppose that the rotor is given an initial rotational speed so that $\varphi = \omega_m t$ where $\omega_m \neq \omega$. In this case the torque is

$$\mathcal{T}_\varphi = -I_m^2 L_1\sin 2\omega_m t\cos^2\omega t$$

The time average will be zero (see Problem 12.6-2).

Suppose that the rotor is given an initial rotational speed ω_m so that $\varphi = \omega_m t$ where $\omega_m = \omega$. The time average torque becomes

$$\langle\mathcal{T}_\varphi\rangle = -\frac{1}{\pi}\int_0^\pi I_m^2 L_1\sin 2\omega t\cos^2\omega t\, d\omega t = \frac{I_m^2 L_1}{2\pi} = \text{constant}$$

Since the torque remains constant independent of time, the core will continue to rotate at the frequency dictated by the line frequency ω.

□ □ □

INCREMENTAL MOTION TRANSDUCERS

12.7 BASIC CONSIDERATIONS

The incremental motion transducer can be represented by the general form illustrated graphically in Figure 12.7-1. Illustrated in this diagram are the total variables $e + E$, $i + I$, $f + F$, $x + X$, etc., where the capital letters denote the no-signal quiescent or equilibrium values of the variables and the small letters denote the incremental variations measured with respect to the quiescent or bias levels. Such a variable representation is not possible for gross-motion energy converters. The incremental variables in the figure have the following meanings:

$e =$ instantaneous incremental voltage at the electrical terminals of the transducer

$i =$ instantaneous incremental current into the electrical terminals of the transducer

$(e + E)(i + I) =$ total instantaneous power flow into the transducer (the incremental power flow is measured with respect to the reference EI).

$x =$ instantaneous incremental displacement of the mechanical elements

$v =$ velocity of mechanical elements

$f =$ incremental force applied to the mechanical element

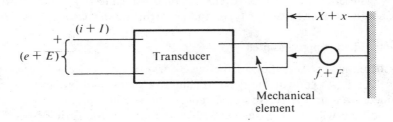

Figure 12.7-1.   The general features of transducers

In the incremental motion transducers here under survey, the signal information is contained either in the amplitude of the displacement or in the velocity. This means that a moving element exists in the input or output, this moving element and the associated stationary element defining the airgap in which the electromagnetic coupling field energy is stored.

Consider two representative transducers — the microphone and the loudspeaker. In both devices, energy is transferred through the coupling field. In the microphone, a mechanical motion that is caused by the acoustic wave power contained in the impinging sound is converted into an electrical signal. In the case of the loudspeaker, an electrical signal is converted into mechanical motion of a cone or diaphragm, and this in turn is converted into acoustic power. In both cases electromagnetic field energy is stored in an air gap and the energy conversion between the electrical and mechanical variables occurs in this region of the transducer. The energy transfer is ordinarily small compared with the energy storage. Usually the mechanical displacement from the equilibrium position is small, although in high-power loudspeakers this may not actually be so.

If the microphone is of the capacitor type, the storage of the energy in the coupling field is electrical energy, and the device is classified as an electric field transducer. If the loudspeaker is of the magnetic type, the stored energy is principally in the magnetic field, and the device is classified as a magnetic field transducer.

Microphones and loudspeakers are information transmitting devices (this is also generally true of transducers). As such they must possess a frequency bandwidth that is sufficient for the signals or information that they process, otherwise distortion results and some of the information is lost. Further, they must be capable of meeting the energy requirements of the load and the sensitivity requirements of the source. Hence careful design is involved in achieving the desired characteristics.

12.8 TYPES OF TRANSDUCERS

There are four important classes of magnetic field transducers, namely, singly excited, multiply excited, permanent magnet, and magnetostriction devices. There are two classes of electric field transducers of special importance: singly excited capacitor type, and piezoelectric devices.

Magnetic Field, Singly Excited

A schematic representation of the basic form of the device is illustrated in Figure 12.8-1. As shown, the device includes a single winding and a spring-restrained armature. A reference current in the winding produces a constant magnetic field which establishes a force that balances the spring force. This establishes a reference or neutral position. A signal current is superimposed on the reference current which causes the armature to move in either direction from this quiescent position in accordance with the signal current. The microphone and loudspeaker are representative of this class of transducer, and a variety of other important transducers of this type are available.

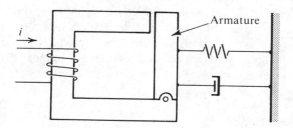

Figure 12.8-1.   Singly excited magnetic field transducer

Multiply Excited

The multiply excited transducer, as the name implies, consists of more than one winding for providing excitation. The transducer shown in Figure 12.8-1 would be converted into a multiply excited unit (two windings) by adding a second winding. Often a reference current is introduced in one winding which maintains the armature in a quiescent position, and the signal current is introduced in the second winding. A sketch of an elementary multiply excited magnetic unit is given in Figure 12.8-2.

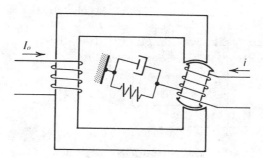

Figure 12.8-2.   The elements of a multiply excited magnetic transducer

Many of the electromechanical transducers of the magnetic type are of the multiply excited class, with one group of windings mounted on the stationary member and another group of windings on the movable member. The operation depends upon the fact that mechanical forces result when the magnetic field energy changes due to the motion of one group of windings with respect to the other group. Devices for denoting translational and rotational motion are often of this general type.

Permanent Magnet

The features of these transducers are not too different from those in the multiply excited types except that now the reference field in the airgap is produced by a permanent magnet rather than by the presence of a reference winding. A second type of device is one in which the signal winding is mounted permanently but the reluctance of the magnetic circuit is varied by an armature of magnetic material. Typical of these transducers in which the airgap changes are permanent magnet loudspeakers and permanent magnet displacement or velocity devices. The varying reluctance units include earphones and certain loudspeakers.

Magnetostrictive

This device, which finds its greatest use at sonic and ultrasonic frequencies, depends for its action on the magnetostrictive properties of certain magnetic materials, such as nickel and nickel alloys. Rods of these materials change their physical length when magnetized along the length of the rod. In the device illustrated in Figure 12.8-3 the signal winding produces a longitudinal magnetic field, and changes in current. The magnetic field also changes, and the result is the movement of the faces of the rod. The permanent magnet, or a reference winding on an iron core, will produce a magnetic bias in the rod in order to permit motion in accordance with the magnitude and sense of the signal current.

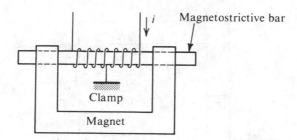

Figure 12.8-3.   A magnetostrictive magnetic field transducer

Electric Field Transducers

A variety of electric field transducers are of considerable importance.

CAPACITOR. The electromechanical system of this class is shown in schematic form, with a signal source, in Figure 12.8-4. The principal shortcoming of such devices is that the force possible in a unit of reasonable size is small unless high voltages are employed. The capacitor microphone is representative of this class of device.

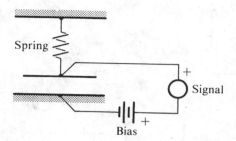

Figure 12.8-4.   The elements of a capacitor type electric field transducer

PIEZOELECTRIC. These devices depend for their action on the property of piezoelectric materials. A change in the applied electric field results in a mechanical deformation of the crystal, and conversely, a change in the mechanical deformation of the crystal results in a changed surface charge. Piezoelectric transducers include microphones, phonograph cartridges, earphones, accelerometers. Often different crystals are cemented together to improve the mechanical deformation characteristics.

12.9   MAGNETIC FIELD TRANSDUCERS

We will now examine several typical magnetic field transducers. Representative of this class are the moving-coil microphone and also the telephone receiver. The essential features of these devices are illustrated in Figure 12.9-1. Note that while these two examples differ somewhat in detail, they are substantially equivalent systems.

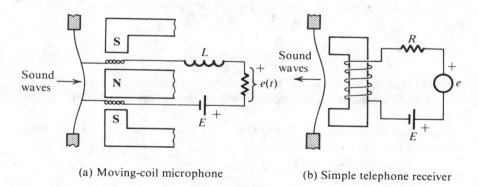

     (a) Moving-coil microphone   (b) Simple telephone receiver

Figure 12.9-1.   Two practical magnetic transducers

As a preliminary to this investigation, we shall study the simple magnetic configuration shown in Figure 12.9-2a. According to results in electricity and magnetism, a configuration such as that in Figure 12.9-2a yields two equa-

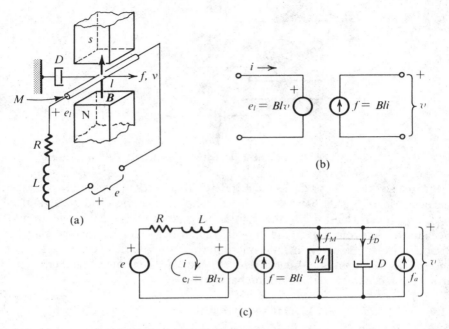

**Figure 12.9-2.   (a) Electromechanical transducer (translational)
(b) Circuit model for the ideal system   (c) Circuit model for the physical system**

tions, depending on how the system is excited. If we apply a force f, thereby causing the rod to move with a velocity v within the magnetic field, an induced voltage, by the Faraday law of induction, appears across the terminals which is equal to

$$e_l = Blv \qquad (12.9\text{-}1)$$

assuming that $\bar{B}$, $\bar{v}$ and $\bar{a}_l$ are all perpendicular to each other. $\bar{a}_l$ is the unit vector along l. The polarity of the voltage e will depend on the direction of motion of the rod.

If, on the other hand, a voltage source is applied across the terminals then because of the resulting current, a force given by the Ampère force law exists on the rod, of amount

$$f = Bli \qquad (12.9\text{-}2)$$

The direction of the force depends on the direction of the current.

To find the power delivered by the electrical and the mechanical ports, we observe that

$$p_e = e_l i = (Blv)i$$

$$p_m = fv = (Bli)v$$

These equations show that any power delivered to the electromechanical system in electrical form will be completely converted into mechanical form, and vice versa. This is true, of course, only if no dissipative elements exist in both the mechanical and electrical portions of the transducer.

Observe from Equations (12.9-1) and (12.9-2) that the induced voltage e depends on the mechanical variable v and the induced force f depends on the electrical variable i. This interdependence suggests controlled source representations as shown in Figure 12.9-2b. However, any practical system will include resistance and inductance in the electrical system, and some mass and damping forces in the mechanical system. When these additional elements are included in the system, the equivalent circuit is that shown in Figure 12.9-2c. Now, by an application of the Kirchhoff voltage law to the electrical circuit and D'Alembert's principle to the mechanical circuit, the equilibrium equations are

$$e - Ri - L\frac{di}{dt} - Blv = 0 \qquad \text{(a)} \quad \text{(12.9-3)}$$

$$-Bli + M\frac{dv}{dt} + Dv - f_a = 0 \qquad \text{(b)}$$

EXAMPLE 12.9-1. Find the transfer function $H(s) = V(s)/E(s)$ of the transducer shown in Figure 12.9-2. The transducer is excited by a voltage source, but no mechanical force is applied.

SOLUTION. Laplace transform Equations (12.9-3a) and (12.9-3b) which gives

$$E(s) - RI(s) - LsI(s) - BlV(s) = 0 \qquad \text{(a)} \quad \text{(12.9-4)}$$

$$-BlI(s) + MsV(s) + DV(s) = 0 \qquad \text{(b)}$$

Eliminate $I(s)$ from these equations to obtain the transfer function

$$H(s) = \frac{\dfrac{Bl}{LM}}{\left(s + \dfrac{R}{L}\right)\left(s + \dfrac{D}{M}\right) + B^2l^2} \qquad \text{(12.9-5)}$$

□   □   □

Now let us return to the moving coil microphone shown in Figure 12.9-1. The figure is redrawn as Figure 12.9-3a. The coil of N turns is assumed to be wound on a nonmagnetic thimble of radius r. It is assumed to have an inductance L. The coil moves perpendicular to the assumed uniform magnetic field under the influence of the applied force $f_a(t)$ caused by the acoustic pressure of the impinging speech waves. The stiffness of the diaphragm is represented by the spring element K and the damping element D represents the loss due to air resistance. The electrical induced voltage and the mechanical force are, respectively,

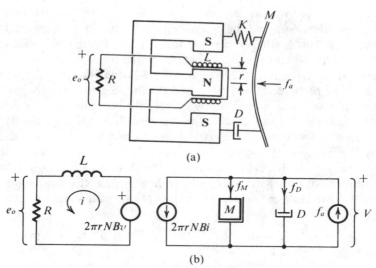

Figure 12.9-3. (a) Schematic representation of the microphone
(b) Equivalent electromechanical circuit

$$e = 2\pi rNB \, v \qquad\qquad\qquad \text{(a)} \quad (12.9\text{-}6)$$

$$f = 2\pi rNB \, i \qquad\qquad\qquad \text{(b)}$$

where $2\pi rN$ specifies the total length of the conductor.

The equivalent circuit is that shown in Figure 12.9-3b, with the appropriate equations for the electrical and the mechanical sections

$$L\frac{di}{dt} + Ri = (2\pi rNB)v \qquad\qquad \text{(a)} \quad (12.9\text{-}7)$$

$$M\frac{dv}{dt} + Dv = -(2\pi rNB)i + f_a \qquad\qquad \text{(b)}$$

Observe that since there is no input electrical source, the current direction is opposite to that shown in Figure 12.9-2c; the induced mechanical force is also opposite to that shown.

EXAMPLE 12.9-2. Find the transfer function $H(s) = E_o(s)/F_a(s)$ for the transducer shown in Figure 12.9-3.

SOLUTION. Rewrite Equations (12.9-7a) and (12.9-7b) in the form

$$\frac{L}{R}\frac{de_o}{dt} + e_o = (2\pi rNB)v$$

$$M\frac{dv}{dt} + Dv = -\frac{(2\pi rNB)}{R}e_o + f_a$$

where $e_o = Ri$. The Laplace transforms of these equations are

$$\left(\frac{L}{R}s + 1\right)E_o(s) = (2\pi rNB)V(s)$$

$$(Ms + D)V(s) = -\frac{(2\pi rNB)}{R}E_o(s) + F_a(s)$$

Eliminate $V(s)$ from these two equations and solve for the ratio

$$\frac{E_o(s)}{F_a(s)} = H(s) = \frac{2\pi rNB}{(Ms + D)\left(\frac{L}{R}s + 1\right) + \frac{(2\pi rNB)^2}{R}}$$

□ □ □

12.10 MAGNETIC TRANSDUCERS – ANGULAR MOTION

In addition to the translational motion of transducers, the motion can be rotational. One of the most widely used instruments, the galvanometer, falls within our definition of a transducer. The essential features of the galvanometer are shown in Figure 12.10-1a. The coil, which is connected to an external source, is mounted on a frame which is on bearings so that it can turn freely. Mechanical and air friction damping is taken into consideration by the damping constant D. The movement of the cylinder-pointer combination is restrained by a spring, with spring constant K_s. The moment of inertia of the coil assembly is J.

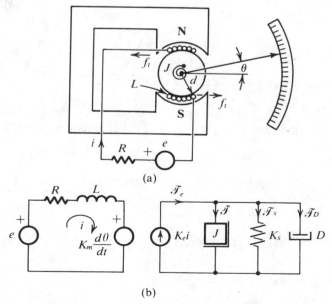

(a)

(b)

Figure 12.10-1. (a) Rotational electromechanical transducer (b) Circuit model

The permanent magnet structure provides a uniform magnetic field in the airgap in which the coil can rotate. Since there are N turns on the coil, there are $2N$ conductors of length l perpendicular to the magnetic field and at a distance a from the center of rotation. A current i in the electrical circuit results in a torque $\mathcal{T}$ being developed, where

$$\mathcal{T}_e = f_t a = (2NBli)a = (2NBla)i = K_e i \qquad (12.10\text{-}1)$$

To counter this torque, the spring will develop an equal and opposite torque. This mechanical torque is proportional to the angle of deflection

$$\mathcal{T}_s = K_s \theta \qquad \left(K_s = \frac{\text{newton-meter}}{\text{degree}} \right) \qquad (12.10\text{-}2)$$

When the coil is moving there will be an induced voltage in the coil which is proportional to the velocity of the coil sides in the magnetic field. This is

$$e_m = 2NBlv = 2NBla\frac{d\theta}{dt} = K_m \frac{d\theta}{dt} = K_m \omega \qquad (12.10\text{-}3)$$

Observe that $K_m = K_e$.

The equivalent circuit for this transducer is given in Figure 12.10-1b. An application of the Kirchhoff voltage law to the electrical circuit and the modified D'Alembert principle to the mechanical circuit, yields the equations

$$L\frac{di}{dt} + Ri + K_m \omega = e \qquad \text{(a)} \quad (12.10\text{-}4)$$

$$J\frac{d\omega}{dt} + D\omega + K_s \int \omega \, dt = K_e i \qquad \text{(b)}$$

These equations completely describe the system.

EXAMPLE 12.10-1. Find the transfer function of the rotational electro-mechanical transducer shown in Figure 12.10-1, assuming that the inductance $L = 0$.

SOLUTION. The Laplace transforms of Equations (12.10-4) are

$$RI(s) + K_m \Omega(s) = E(s) \qquad \text{(a)} \quad (12.10\text{-}5)$$

$$\left(Js + D + \frac{K_s}{s} \right) \Omega(s) = K_e I(s) \qquad \text{(b)}$$

Eliminate $I(s)$ from these two equations to obtain

$$H(s) = \frac{\Omega(s)}{E(s)} = \frac{K_e}{R} \frac{s}{Js^2 + \left(D + \dfrac{K_e K_m}{R}\right)s + K_s} \qquad (12.10\text{-}6)$$

□ □ □

Equations (12.10-4) when expressed in terms of the deflection angle θ become

$$L\frac{di}{dt} + Ri + K_m\frac{d\theta}{dt} = e \qquad \text{(a)} \quad (12.10\text{-}7)$$

$$J\frac{d^2\theta}{dt^2} + D\frac{d\theta}{dt} + K_s\theta = K_e i \qquad \text{(b)}$$

If we set $L = 0$ and eliminate i from these equations, we shall find the second order diferential equation

$$\frac{d^2\theta}{dt^2} + \left(\frac{D}{J} + \frac{K_e K_m}{JR}\right)\frac{d\theta}{dt} + \frac{K_s}{J}\theta = \frac{K_e}{RJ}e \qquad (12.10\text{-}8)$$

The corresponding transfer function is

$$H(s) = \frac{\Theta(s)}{E(s)} = \frac{K_e}{RJ} \frac{1}{s^2 + \left(\dfrac{D}{J} + \dfrac{K_e K_m}{JR}\right)s + \dfrac{K_s}{J}} \qquad (12.10\text{-}9)$$

It is interesting to compare this equation with Equations (4.5-12) and (4.5-14). This permits us to specify the natural undamped frequency of the galvanometer ω_n and the damping ratio ζ. These are

$$\omega_n = \sqrt{\frac{K_s}{J}} \qquad \text{(a)} \quad (12.10\text{-}10)$$

$$\zeta = \frac{1}{2}\frac{1}{\sqrt{K_s J}}\left(D + \frac{K_e K_m}{R}\right) \qquad \text{(b)}$$

These show that ω_n depends only on the mechanical constants whereas ζ depends on both mechanical and electrical constants and the coupling coefficient $K_e = K_m$.

12.11   RESISTOR COUPLING TRANSDUCERS

A simple though important device is the resistor coupled transducer. This makes use of the ability to vary the position of a potentiometer slider by mechanical means. However, since resistors do not store energy, there is no electromechanical coupling. A simple variable resistive transducer is shown in Figure 12.11-1a. Its equivalent circuit representation is shown in Figure 12.11-1b. An application of the Kirchhoff voltage law to the circuit, and knowing that $e_o = R(x)i$, yields

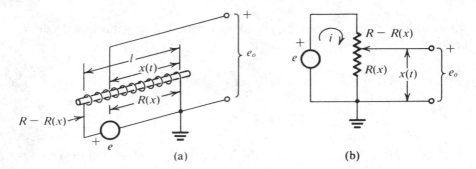

Figure 12.11-1. (a) Potentiometer with linear motion   (b) Equivalent circuit

$$e_o = \left[\frac{R(x)}{R} \right] e = \frac{x(t)}{l} e \qquad (12.11\text{-}1)$$

This shows that the output voltage is related to the input voltage by a gain factor (less than 1) $x(t)/l$, a quantity that is dependent on the mechanical variable $x(t)$.

12.2 ELECTROSTATIC TRANSDUCERS

The capacitor microphone is an electrostatic transducer, a device we wish to examine in some detail. A diagrammatic representation of the essential elements of this device is given in Figure 12.12-1a. The equivalent representation is given in Figure 12.12-1b. In this device the diaphragm translates the impinging waves into mechanical displacements, as for the magnetic field transducers. Owing to the manner of mounting the diaphragm, a displacement caused by the impinging sound pressure wave is translated into a mechanical displacement of the diaphragm, equivalent to the motion of the mass M, with an elastic restoring force that is represented by the spring K. The damping of the motion of the diaphragm by the air cushion between it and the back plate is represented by the damping constant D.

In so far as the electrical circuit is concerned, it consists of the dc polarizing source E which supplies charge to the capacitor that is formed by the diaphragm and the backing plate through a resistor and inductor, as illustrated. As the diaphragm vibrates, the capacitance of the microphone varies instantaneously, causing a current variation in the electrical circuit. The resulting output voltage $e_o(t)$ is assumed to be an electrical reproduction of the sound waves. As a first approximation, the capacitance is given by the expression (see Section 1.3)

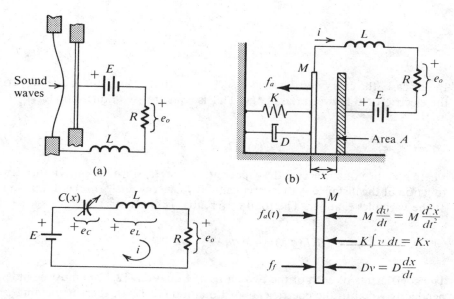

Figure 12.12-1. **(a) Schematic of a capacitor microphone**
(b) Its physical representation   (c, d) Its electrical and mechanical configurations

$$C = \frac{\epsilon_o A}{x} \qquad (12.12\text{-}1)$$

where x denotes the variable distance between the plates, where A is the effective cross-sectional area of the capacitor, and where ϵ_o is the permittivity of the air in the space between the capacitor plates.

From Equation (1.7-3b), the incremental electric energy in a device is given by

$$dU_e = ei\,dt = e\frac{dq}{dt}\,dt = e\,dq \qquad (12.12\text{-}2)$$

where dq is the incremental charge. Moreover, from elementary physics, mechanical energy is related to work by the expression

$$dU_m = f\,dx \qquad (12.12\text{-}3)$$

The electric input energy to the device is used to set up a field (electric or magnetic) and to produce some mechanical movement or deformation. That is, the energy balance in an electromechanical lossless system is

$$dU_e = dU_f + dU_m \qquad \text{(a)} \quad (12.12\text{-}4)$$

or

$$e\, dq = dU_f + f_m\, dx \qquad\qquad \text{(b)}$$

In our case, the energy of the field associated with the capacitor is due only to the electric field between the plates. This is equal to [see Equation (1.7-4)]

$$U_f = \frac{1}{2}\frac{q^2}{C(x)} = \frac{1}{2}e_c^2 C(x) \qquad\qquad (12.12\text{-}5)$$

where e_c is the voltage across the capacitor. However, since the capacitance is a function of the distance x, the incremental field energy is $dU_f(q,x)$ is a function of the variables q and x. The total differential is given by

$$dU_f(q,x) = \frac{\partial U_f}{\partial q}\, dq + \frac{\partial U_f}{\partial x}\, dx \qquad\qquad (12.12\text{-}6)$$

The coefficients of each of the two terms of Equation (12.12-6) must be independently equal to the coefficients of Equation (12.12-4), thereby yielding

$$e = \frac{\partial U_f}{\partial q} \qquad\qquad \text{(a)} \quad (12.12\text{-}7)$$

$$f_m = f_f = -\frac{\partial U_f}{\partial x} \qquad\qquad \text{(b)}$$

From Equations (12.12-5) and (12.12-7b) we can find the force due to the electric field (the attraction between the positive and negative charges on the plates). This is

$$f_f = -\frac{1}{2}e_c^2 \frac{dC}{dx} \qquad\qquad (12.12\text{-}8)$$

But for a variable capacitor, from Equation (12.12-1)

$$\frac{dC}{dx} = -\frac{\epsilon_o A}{x^2}$$

It follows therefore that

$$f_f = \frac{1}{2}\frac{e_c^2 \epsilon_o A}{x^2} = \frac{1}{2}\frac{e_c^2 C^2 \epsilon_o A}{x^2 C^2} = \frac{1}{2}\frac{q^2 \epsilon_o A}{x^2 C^2} = \frac{1}{2}\frac{q^2 \epsilon_o A}{\epsilon_o^2 A} = \frac{1}{2}\frac{q^2}{\epsilon_o A} \qquad (12.12\text{-}9)$$

Also from Figure 12.12-1c we deduce the equation

$$L\frac{di}{dt} + e_c + Ri = E \qquad\qquad (12.12\text{-}10)$$

which, in terms of the charge q, since $i = dq/dt$, becomes

$$L\frac{d^2q}{dt^2} + R\frac{dq}{dt} + \frac{x}{\epsilon_o A}q = E \qquad (12.12\text{-}11)$$

The equilibrium of forces shown in Figure 12.12-1d yields the equation

$$M\frac{d^2x}{dt^2} + D\frac{dx}{dt} + Kx + \frac{1}{2\epsilon_o A}q^2 = f_a(t) \qquad (12.12\text{-}12)$$

Equations (12.12-11) and (12.12-12) show them to be coupled and nonlinear.

A linearized model of this device is possible by writing the variables in terms of the quiescent value plus the variation about this quiescent level (this is a general method for obtaining linearized equations). Thus we write

$$x = X + \bar{x} \qquad \text{(a)} \quad (12.12\text{-}13)$$

$$q = Q + \bar{q} \qquad \text{(b)}$$

$$f_a(t) = F_a + \bar{f}_a(t) \qquad \text{(c)}$$

where X, Q and F_a are the average values independent of time, and $\bar{x}$, $\bar{q}$ and $\bar{f}_a(t)$ are small variations about these values. Introduce these values into Equations (12.12-11) and (12.12-12), and noting that $d^2X/dt^2 = dX/dt = dQ/dt = 0$, the results become

$$L\frac{d^2\bar{q}}{dt^2} + R\frac{d\bar{q}}{dt} + \frac{1}{\epsilon_o A}(\bar{x}Q + \bar{q}X + XQ) = E \qquad \text{(a)} \quad (12.12\text{-}14)$$

$$M\frac{d^2\bar{x}}{dt^2} + D\frac{d\bar{x}}{dt} + K(X + \bar{x}) + \frac{1}{2\epsilon_o A}(Q^2 + 2Q\bar{q}) = F_a + \bar{f}_a(t) \qquad \text{(b)}$$

where the quantities $\bar{x}\bar{q}$ and $\bar{q}^2$ have been considered as negligible because they are of second order in the increments.

At equilibrium $\bar{q} = \bar{x} = 0$ and Equation (12.12-14) become

$$\frac{1}{\epsilon_o A}XQ = E \qquad \text{(a)} \quad (12.12\text{-}15)$$

$$KX + \frac{1}{2\epsilon_o A}Q^2 = F_a \qquad \text{(b)}$$

Now by combining Equations (12.12-15) with (12.12-14) the result is a set of linear equations that are independent of the applied equilibrium values. These equations are

$$L\frac{d^2\bar{q}}{dt^2} + R\frac{d\bar{q}}{dt} + \frac{1}{\epsilon_o A}(X\bar{q} + Q\bar{x}) = 0 \qquad \text{(a)} \quad (12.12\text{-}16)$$

$$M\frac{d^2\bar{x}}{dt^2} + D\frac{d\bar{x}}{dt} + K\bar{x} + \frac{Q}{\epsilon_o A}\bar{q} = \bar{f}_a(t) \tag{b}$$

A circuit representation of these two equations is shown in Figure 12.12-2.

EXAMPLE 12.12-1. Find the linearized output voltage e_o for the circuit of Figure 12.12-2 when $L = 0$.

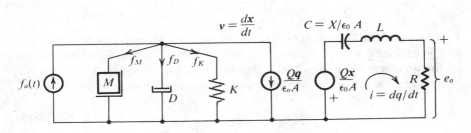

Figure 12.12-2. The circuit representation of the linearized capacitor microphone of Figure 12.12-1

SOLUTION. From Equation (12.12-16a) we find

$$R\frac{d\bar{q}}{dt} = -\frac{1}{\epsilon_o A}(X\bar{q} + Q\bar{x})$$

But $e_o(t) = -Ri = -R\,dq/dt$, and so

$$e_o(t) = \frac{1}{\epsilon_o A}(X\bar{q} + Q\bar{x}) \tag{12.12-17}$$

where $\bar{x}$ and $\bar{q}$ are the solutions of Equations (12.12-16).

□ □ □

EXAMPLE 12.12-2. Find the transfer function of the capacitor microphone.

SOLUTION. The Laplace transforms of Equations (12.12-16) are written

$$\left(Ls^2 + Rs + \frac{1}{\epsilon_o A}X\right)\bar{Q}(s) = -\frac{Q}{\epsilon_o A}\bar{X}(s) \tag{a} \quad (12.12\text{-}18)$$

$$(Ms^2 + Ds + K)\bar{X}(s) + \frac{Q}{\epsilon_o A}\bar{Q}(s) = \bar{F}_a(s) \tag{b}$$

Now eliminate $\bar{X}(s)$ from these equations to find

$$\frac{\bar{Q}(s)}{\bar{F}_a(s)} = -\frac{\dfrac{Q}{\epsilon_o A}}{\left(Ls^2 + Rs + \dfrac{X}{\epsilon_o A}\right)(Ms^2 + Ds + K) - \left(\dfrac{Q}{\epsilon_o A}\right)^2}$$

But $\bar{E}_o(s) = -Rs\bar{Q}(s)$ so that

$$H(s) = \frac{\bar{E}_o(s)}{\bar{F}_a(s)} = \frac{\dfrac{QR}{\epsilon_o A}s}{\left(Ls^2 + Rs + \dfrac{X}{\epsilon_o A}\right)(Ms^2 + Ds + K) - \left(\dfrac{Q}{\epsilon_o A}\right)^2} \qquad (12.12\text{-}19)$$

□ □ □

ROTATING MACHINERY

The analysis of the performance of rotating machines, because these are gross motion devices, proceeds in a manner that is different from that adopted to discuss incremental motion transducers. In fact, gross motion electromechanics requires considerations that are unique to such devices. Important considerations in the study include features of the design, whether the machine is to operate on dc or ac power lines, and whether the machine is operating as a motor or as a generator.

12.13 THE MAGNETIC STRUCTURE OF ROTATING MACHINES

We first direct our attention to the magnetic structure and geometry of the typical rotating machine. The usual machine consists of two major structural elements of iron—usually high quality magnetic steel: an outer stationary member and an inner rotating member which is mounted in bearings which are fixed to the stationary member. Windings are usually attached to each of these members.

In the case of dc machines, owing to the need for a *commutator* (the purpose of which will be discussed below), the rotating member is the armature winding. The stationary members are so constructed with coils to provide the magnetic field, and hence make up the field assembly. Usually field poles are attached to an outer frame, or *yoke*, the winding direction of the field coils and the excitation being such as to produce alternate north and south magnetic fields. Figure 12.13-1 illustrates the general features of the dc machine. A machine with isolated poles of the type illustrated is known as a *salient pole machine*.

Alternating current machines may be of the salient pole type or they may be of the nonsalient pole type, depending on the machine and its application. The sketches in Figures 12.13-2 show the general features of synchronous machines of the salient pole and the nonsalient pole types. In the nonsalient pole

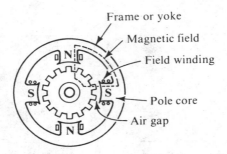

Figure 12.13-1. Diagrammatic sketch of a salient pole machine

machine the windings on the rotating or field members are such as to produce an effective north and south pole even though the field structure is cylindrical without any projecting poles.

As indicated in Figures 12.13-1 and 12.13-2, stator windings are almost always distributed uniformly over the entire surface for better utilization of space and material in the machine. For such machines the radial distribution in the airgap of the flux produced by the field structure may be pictured by a developed sketch of the machine. A typical sketch of the dc machine structure showing the airgap flux distribution is given in Figure 12.13-3. Observe that the flux density distribution shown approximates a square wave, a desirable flux distribution for the dc machine. In the case of most salient pole ac machines, the pole faces are usually shaped to provide a sinusoidal flux distribution. In a nonsalient pole machine with a uniform airgap the field, windings are ordinarily so distributed on the rotor surface as to yield an effective sinusoidal flux density distribution.

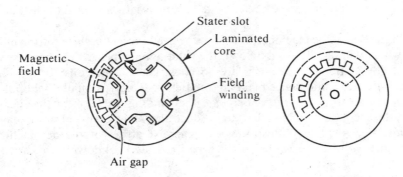

Figure 12.13-2.   Diagrammatic sketch of salient pole and nonsalient pole synchronous machines

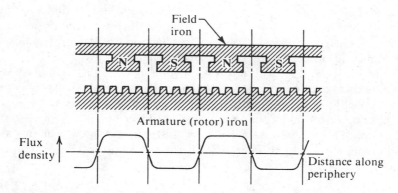

Figure 12.13-3. Developed sketch of a dc machine structure showing the airgap flux distribution for the excitation of the field alone

12.14 DISTRIBUTED WINDINGS AS CURRENT SHEETS

Suppose that the armature iron of Figure 12.13-3 has windings placed in the slots. Figure 12.14-1a illustrates a *full pitch* two layer *lap winding*. A full pitch winding is one in which the coil side in one slot, such as under a north pole, has its return side in the same relative position under the south pole. Such windings progress from slot to slot until all slots are filled. Figure 12.14-1b shows a two

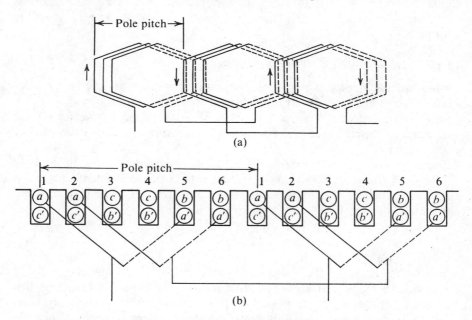

Figure 12.14-1. (a) A developed sketch of a full pitch two layer lap winding with three slots per pole per phase
(b) A two-thirds pitch lap winding with six slots per pole

layer winding for a three-phase machine, with six slots per pole and a coil pitch equal to two-thirds of the pole pitch. In this case each slot contains coil sides belonging to different phases. This has an effect on the leakage reactance of the winding and on the resultant mmf of the winding.

Refer to Figure 12.13-3 with a full pitch winding within the armature slots. The symmetrical configuration of slots and conductors ensures that only small changes of energy occur as the armature rotates; that is, as one tooth leaves the pole-tip, another tooth is coming under the influence of the same pole at its opposite tip. The torque associated with this coil, averaged over this short time-interval, is given by the simplified form of Equation (12.4-5), namely

$$\mathcal{T}_c = i \frac{d\psi}{d\varphi} \qquad (12.14\text{-}1)$$

where i is the current in the conductors and $d\psi/d\varphi$ is the mean rate at which the flux linkage with the coil changes with respect to angular movement of the rotor. Note that this result makes no distinction between a coil in the actual generator with that in a corresponding coil of an ideal generator having a smooth rotor with conductors carried on its outside surface. The flux density at a point in the airgap of this ideal machine is the same as that at the corresponding point in the real machine, except that the variations due to the teeth in the real machine are smoothed out. Because of these considerations, and similar conclusions exist for the emf induced in coils in actual and ideal machines, all subsequent calculations will implicitly assume an ideal machine configuration.

12.15   THE COMMUTATED WINDING

Since dc machines and a class of commutator ac machines are very important, we shall examine carefully a winding structure that is provided with a commutator. Consider first the case when the rotating structure is provided with a single concentrated coil plus a split ring commutator, as illustrated in Figure 12.15-1.

Suppose that the flux density distribution in the airgap is sinusoidal, as shown in Figure 12.15-1b. As the armature rotates, the coil cuts the magnetic field perpendicularly, thereby inducing a voltage therein. The coil sides are connected in series, hence the total emf is

$$e_c = 2lBv = 2lBr\omega \qquad \text{V} \qquad (12.15\text{-}1)$$

where l is the length of the armature (meters), r is its radius (meters), and ω is the angular velocity (rad/sec). The instantaneous voltage is a maximum when the conductor is along the magnetic axis (it cuts the maximum flux in this position) and is zero when the conductor is midway between the poles (when the conductor is moving along the magnetic flux lines (in terms of Figure 12.13-3 at the point where the flux density is zero).

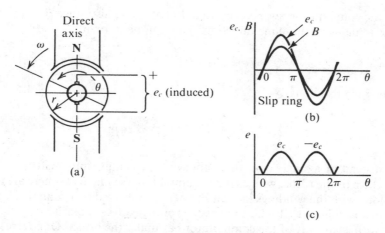

Figure 12.15-1. (a) A concentrated winding assembly, with the coil ends connected to the commutator (b) The variation of the flux density B and the emf of the coil as a function of angle θ (c) The output voltage

Now, because there is a moving contact between the commutator segments or commutator bars (these are usually of copper) and the fixed brushes (and ordinarily these are of carbon), as the moving segment passes from one brush to the next, a reversal of polarity occurs, i.e., rectification takes place. The brushes are positioned at the point where the motional emf between the commutator segments is zero. As noted the emf is zero at the point midway between the N and S pole; therefore the brush axis is in space quadrature with the field axis. Because of the rectification, the terminal voltage is given by

$$e = 2\omega lr |B(\theta)| \tag{12.15-2}$$

as shown in Figure 12.15-1c. The average value is given by

$$e_{av} = \frac{1}{\pi}\int_0^\pi e\, d\theta = \frac{1}{\pi}\int_0^\pi 2\omega B(\theta) lr\, d\theta = \frac{2}{\pi}\omega \int B(\theta)\, dA = \frac{2}{\pi}\Phi\omega \quad \text{V} \tag{12.15-3}$$

where $lr\, d\theta = dA =$ element of armature surface, and Φ is the magnetic flux of one pole.

If there is a current i_a in the coil, there is a force on each conductor

$$f = Bli_a \quad \text{N} \tag{12.15-4}$$

The torque on the armature is, therefore

$$\mathcal{T} = 2fr = 2Bli_a r \quad \text{N-m} \tag{12.15-5}$$

Since the commutator reverses the direction of i_a and also since B reverses, the torque remains in the same direction. This can be written

$$\mathcal{T} = 2i_a lr |B(\theta)| \tag{12.15-6}$$

The average torque is

$$\mathcal{T}_{av} = \frac{1}{\pi} \int_0^\pi 2i_a lr B(\theta)\, d\theta = \frac{2}{\pi}\Phi i_a \qquad \text{N-m} \tag{12.15-7}$$

If, instead of a single coil, the rotor winding is uniformly distributed over the surface of the rotor, with as many commutator segments as there are armature slots, with the windings in each slot being connected to a commutator bar, as shown in Figure 12.15-2a, then as the rotor revolves, polarity reversals will occur with each shift of the commutator bar under the brush. Of course, since the rotor winding is continuous, the entire winding will contribute to the output voltage. Now the situation is more nearly that shown in Figure 12.15-2b. In this case, not only has a smoother voltage been achieved, a desirable end in itself if a dc output is desired, but what has also been achieved is a configuration which has lost any preferred orientation properties. The general features of construction of a dc machine are shown in Figure 12.15-3. We shall examine the operation of such machines.

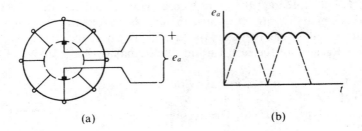

(a)   (b)

Figure 12.15-2.   A distributed winding equipped with a commutator, and the form of the output voltage

12.16   THE SEPARATELY EXCITED DC MACHINE

We shall first consider the separately excited dc machine when it is operated as a generator and then when it is operated as a motor. A simplified schematic diagram of the machine is given in Figure 12.16-1. This figure is drawn according to conventional practice. However, it must be kept in mind that the brush axis is in quadrature (90 electrical degrees) displaced from the field axis.

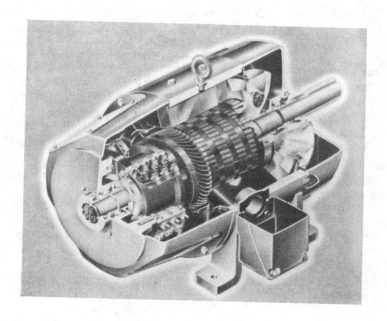

Figure 12.15-3. Cutaway of a dc machine showing the commutator

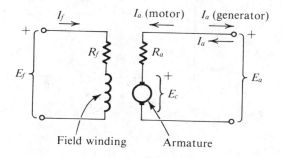

Figure 12.16-1. The schematic diagram of the separately excited dc generator under steady state operation

Generator Operation

When a dc dynamo is used as a generator, the output quantities of interest are the armature voltage, current, and power. We consider initially the voltage relations. The general equations for the machine shown are

$$E_f = R_f I_f \qquad \text{(a)} \quad (12.16\text{-}1)$$

$$E_a = -R_a I_a + E_c = -R_a I_a + G\omega_m I_f \qquad \text{(b)}$$

where the subscripts f relate to the field, the subscripts a relate to the armature circuit, and G is the motional emf factor which relates the voltage E_c and the field current and ω_m is the motor speed. The G factor has the units of henry, and it is usually termed *rotational inductance*. Since the magnetic flux Φ is proportional to the field current I_f, the induced or generated voltage is often written $E_c = k\Phi\omega_m$, where $G\bar{I}_f = k\Phi$. The interaction between the field windings and the armature windings occurs in the airgap of the machine and through the magnetic flux that couples both windings. By combining Equations (12.16-1a) and (12.16-1b) by eliminating the field current I_f, there results

$$E_a = \frac{G\omega_m}{R_f}E_f - R_a I_a \qquad (12.16\text{-}2)$$

A plot of this equation with field voltage E_f as a parameter, is given in Figure 12.16-2. This plot gives the so-called *external* characteristics of the separately excited dc generator.

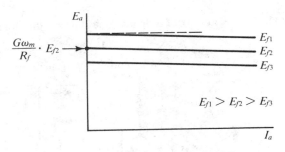

Figure 12.16-2. The external characteristics of the separately excited dc generator

Motor Operation

When the machine is used as a motor, the output quantities of interest are speed, torque, or power, depending upon the application to which the machine is to be put. The input quantities are E_f and E_a, although for speed control, a resistor is often placed in series with the armature circuit to control the armature current I_a. Speed can also be controlled by varying the applied voltage E_f.

Torque Considerations

To establish the torque conventions, refer to Figure 12.16-3. This figure shows that the application of a mechanical torque $\mathcal{T}_m$ to the shaft of the machine in the reference direction for ω_m results in mechanical power passing into the machine. Likewise, the application of a mechanical torque of elec-

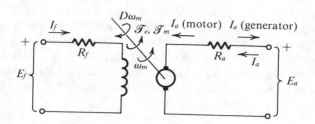

Figure 12.16-3. The dc machine drawn to establish torque convention

trical origin to the shaft in the reference direction for ω_m also results in mechanical power passing into the machine. These torques are opposed or resisted by inertial and dissipative elements. The torque balance equation is then

$$\mathcal{T}_e + \mathcal{T}_m = D\omega_m \qquad (12.16\text{-}3)$$

For the convention adopted, apart from losses, positive voltage and current mean motoring action, and positive torque and speed mean generating action. From conservation of energy, we write

power into electrical ports + power into mechanical port

$$= \text{power stored} + \text{power dissipated} \qquad (12.16\text{-}4)$$

The controlling equations for the two electrical ports and the one mechanical port are

$$E_f = R_f I_f \qquad\qquad \text{(a)} \quad (12.16\text{-}5)$$

$$E_a = G\omega_m I_f + R_a I_a \qquad \text{(b)}$$

$$\mathcal{T}_m = D\omega_m - \mathcal{T}_e \qquad\quad \text{(c)}$$

Multiply the first equation by I_f, the second by I_a, and the third by ω_m, and add the resulting equations. Rearrange the terms as follows:

$$(E_f I_f + E_a I_a) + \mathcal{T}_m \omega_m = (R_f I_f^2 + R_a I_a^2 + D\omega_m^2) + (G\omega_m I_f I_a - \mathcal{T}_e \omega_m)$$

Compare this equation with Equation (12.16-4) and identify corresponding terms. From this it follows that

$$- \mathcal{T}_e \omega_m + G\omega_m I_f I_a = 0$$

since $E_f I_f + E_a I_a + \mathcal{T}_m \omega_m = R_f I_f^2 + R_a I_a^2 + D\omega_m^2$. Hence it follows that

$$_e = G I_f I_a \qquad\qquad (12.16\text{-}6)$$

This specifies the electrical torque developed by the motor. It specifies that if I_f and I_a are both positive (the motor configuration) then the mechanical torque of electric origin is in the direction to cause rotation in the positive ω_m direction. It shows also that $\mathcal{T}_e$ is independent of $\mathcal{T}_m$, and good starting characteristics are inherent in dc motors. Since the magnetic flux produced by the field winding is proportional to I_f and to the reluctance of the magnetic path, Equation (12.16-6) is often written in the form

$$\mathcal{T}_e = k\,\Phi\,I_a \qquad (12.16\text{-}7)$$

where this k has the same value as that introduced in connection with the induced emf in Equation (12.16-1).

For a motor I_f and I_a are in the reference directions so that $\mathcal{T}_e$, the mechanical torque that is converted from electrical form in the machine, produces rotation in the positive direction for ω_m. Since in the motor the applied torque causes mechanical power to flow out of the machine at positive speed, it is convenient to write

$$\mathcal{T}_L = -\mathcal{T}_m \qquad (12.16\text{-}8)$$

When operating as a motor, speed is controlled in two different ways: field voltage control with constant armature current, and armature voltage control with constant field current.

FIELD VOLTAGE CONTROL WITH CONSTANT ARMATURE CURRENT. This method of control is used extensively in position control devices requiring small amounts of power. The analysis proceeds from Equation (12.16-5c) which yields

$$\omega_m = \frac{1}{D}(\mathcal{T}_e - \mathcal{T}_L) \qquad (12.16\text{-}9)$$

This variation is shown in Figure 12.16-4. This curve shows that the speed is sensitive to torque variations.

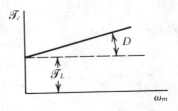

Figure 12.16-4. **Steady state speed-torque variation**

ARMATURE VOLTAGE CONTROL WITH CONSTANT FIELD CURRENT. This method of control finds extensive application for large machines. The combination of the steady state form of Equations (12.16-5) leads to the equation

$$\omega_m = AE_a - B\mathcal{T}_L \qquad (12.16\text{-}10)$$

where A and B involve the machine constants. This equation predicts a slight fall in speed as the load torque increases, as shown in Figure 12.16-5a. A physical explanation of this drooping characteristic is contained in Equations (12.16-5) under steady state conditions. From the second of these it is seen that the armature current actually depends on the difference between the applied voltage and the rotational emf. Under conditions of no load, this difference is very small, with a corresponding small armature current I_a. The value of I_a must be such that the electromagnetic torque produced by the machine is just sufficient to overcome the frictional and other losses. When a load is applied, the difference between the applied voltage and the rotational emf must increase. The resulting armature current will increase and the machine will thereby produce sufficient torque for the load as well as for the losses. As a result the speed must decrease. Ordinarily the change in speed for a considerable change in electrical torque is not large, and so the motor will operate at a reasonably constant speed over its full operating range.

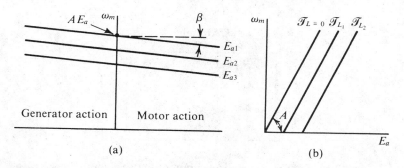

Figure 12.16-5. (a) Speed torque curves of the dc machine with E_a as a parameter (b) Speed-excitation curves, with torque as a parameter

EXAMPLE 12.16-1. A dc generator is rated at 5 kilowatt, 200 volt and 25 ampere at 500 rpm. The armature resistance is $R_a = 0.5$ ohm; the field resistance is $R_f = 60$ ohm. Find the no-load voltage at 500 rpm; the full load voltage at 400 rpm. The field current is kept constant.

SOLUTION. From Equation (12.16-1b)

$$E_a = E_c - R_a I_a$$

For no load, $I_a = 0$, and this relation gives $E_a = E_c = \text{emf} = E_{anl}$. From this equation, therefore

$$E_{anl} = E_{afl} + R_a I_a = 200 + 25 \times 0.5 = 212.5 \quad V$$

Since the field current is constant, then for linear operation the emf E_c is directly proportional to the speed. Then at 400 rpm

$$E_{anl} = E_c = 212.5 \times \frac{400}{500} = 170 \quad V$$

The output voltage at full load is

$$E_{afl} = E_c - R_a I_a = 170 - 0.5 \times 25 = 157.5 \quad V$$

□ □ □

12.17 THE SHUNT MACHINE

In the shunt machine the armature and field voltages are equal, that is, these windings are connected in parallel, as shown in Figure 12.17-1. The controlling equations for this machine under steady state conditions are the following:

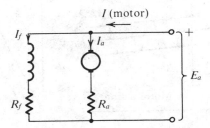

Figure 12.17-1. The schematic diagram of the dc shunt machine

$$E_f = R_f I_f \qquad \qquad \text{(a)} \quad (12.17\text{-}1)$$

$$E_a = G\omega_m I_f + R_a I_a \qquad \text{(b)}$$

$$\mathcal{T}_e = G I_f I_a \qquad \qquad \text{(c)}$$

$$\mathcal{T}_e = D\omega_m + \mathcal{T}_L \qquad \text{(d)}$$

Actually, this linear model and the linear set of equations leads to difficulties. Specifically in the steady state, we will find that

$$I_f = \frac{E_f}{R_f} = \frac{E_a}{R_f} \qquad \text{(a)} \qquad (12.17\text{-}2)$$

$$I_a = -\frac{G\omega_m E_a}{R_f R_a} + \frac{E_a}{R_a} \qquad \text{(b)}$$

and the expression for the electrical torque becomes

$$\mathcal{T}_e = GI_f I_a = \frac{E_a^2 G}{R_a R_f}\left(1 - \frac{G\omega_m}{R_f}\right) \qquad (12.17\text{-}3)$$

This equation shows a linear relationship between $\mathcal{T}_e$ and ω_m, with the no-load speed being that for which $\mathcal{T}_e = 0$, or when

$$G\omega_m = R_f \qquad (12.17\text{-}4)$$

However, the actual machine does not show this critical condition.

Another view of the difficulty appears when the shunt connected machine is operated as a generator. Suppose that the speed is maintained constant at ω_m. The terminal voltage falls with load, as specified by Equation (12.17-1a) and (12.17-1b) since

$$E_f = E_a = R_f I_f \qquad \text{(a)} \qquad (12.17\text{-}5)$$

so that

$$E_a = G\omega_m I_f - R_a I_a \qquad \text{(b)}$$

where due account has been taken of the fact that for a generator I_a is opposite to the chosen reference direction. Write this

$$E_a = \frac{G\omega_m E_a}{R_f} - R_a I_a \qquad (12.17\text{-}6)$$

which leads to

$$E_a = \frac{R_a}{\dfrac{G\omega_m}{R} - 1} I_a \qquad (12.17\text{-}7)$$

Observe that, according to this equation, E_a becomes infinite when

$$G\omega_m = R_f$$

An explanation of the difficulty requires that the effects of saturation, as reflected through the magnetization curve (the open circuit E_a, I_f curve, with ω_m as a parameter) must be known. Figure 12.17-2 shows three magnetization curves for the dc machine, with rotor speed as a parameter. In general, upon the application of voltage E_a to the armature, the machine will accelerate until it reaches such a speed that the generated emf E_c is equal to the applied voltage. This occurs when the saturation curve crosses the R_f line for $E_a = E_c$, as illustrated. But owing to the nonlinear magnetization curve, the machine will not generate a voltage equal to E_c at the particular speed at which $G\omega_m$ is equal to R_f. This requires that we revise our analysis to account for the nonlinearity, which may be taken to show that G is a function of I_f.

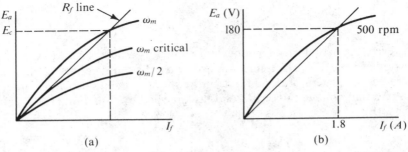

(a)   (b)

Figure 12.17-2. **(a) Magnetization curves of the dc machine for three values of speed (b) Magnetization curve for Example 12.17-1. Also shown are the field resistance lines**

A more precise relation for the voltage is possible if we represent the saturation curve in the neighborhood of the crossover point by a piecewise linear approximation, as shown in Figure 12.17-3. This curve is written explicitly as

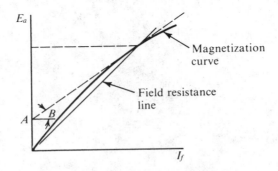

Figure 12.17-3. **Piecewise approximation to the saturation curve**

$$E_a = A + BI_f \qquad (12.17\text{-}8)$$

Under this approximation, we would write in place of Equation (12.17-5)

$$E_a = \left(A + \frac{BE_a}{R_f} \right) - R_a I_a$$

From this it follows that

$$E_a = \frac{A}{1 - B/R_f} - \frac{R_a I_a}{1 - B/R_f} = E_{nl} - \frac{R_a I_a}{1 - B/R_f} \qquad (12.17\text{-}9)$$

where

$$E_{nl} = \frac{A}{1 - B/R_f}$$

This equation shows that the terminal voltage will fall linearly with load current I_a. This agrees well with the performance of the actual machine over the entire operating range from zero to full load.

When operated as a motor, the speed at which the machine operates under steady state conditions of load can be calculated from Equation (12.17-2b). Thus, we write

$$\omega_m = \frac{R_f R_a}{G E_a} \left(\frac{E_a}{R_a} - I_a \right) = \frac{R_f}{G} \left(1 - \frac{I_a}{E_a/R_a} \right) \qquad (12.17\text{-}10)$$

Here E_f is a constant, I_f is a constant, and G assumes a single value for this I_f, with $G\omega_m$ representing the slope of the saturation curve for the specified I_f. Writing for the crossover point of the R_f line and the saturation curve

$$G\omega_{mo} = R_f$$

then Equation (12.17-8) becomes

$$\omega_m = \omega_{mo} \left(1 - \frac{I_a}{E_a/R_a} \right) \qquad (12.17\text{-}11)$$

But since in general $E_a/R_a \gg I_a$, the second term in the speed relation is small, even for rated armature current. Hence the speed decrease of the shunt machine with load is small, and the machine is considered to be a substantially constant speed machine.

EXAMPLE 12.17-1. The magnetization curve of the dc generator of Example 12.16-1 is shown in Figure 12.17-2b. Find the required resistance R to be added to R_f so that the no-load voltage is 180 V.

SOLUTION. The essential requirements are $I_f = 1.8$ A, $E_a = 180$ V, and $\omega_m = 500$ rpm. From Equation (12.17-1a) we have

$$E_a = (R_f + R)I_f$$

so that

$$R = \frac{E_a}{I_f} - R_f = \frac{180}{1.8} - 60 = 40 \quad \Omega$$

□ □ □

EXAMPLE 12.17-2. A dc shunt motor draws 30 A armature current from 220 V lines. Other important data are $R_a = 0.5\ \Omega$, $\omega_m = 1600$ rpm, $I_f =$ constant. Determine the following: (a) An increase in load causes the armature current to increase to 50 A. What is the new speed? (b) The load is completely removed, and the armature current drops to 5 A. What is the no-load speed of the motor?

SOLUTION. (a) Use Equation (12.17-11) to write

$$\omega_m = \omega_{mo}\left(1 - \frac{50}{220/0.5}\right) \qquad 1600 = \omega_{mo}\left(1 - \frac{30}{220/0.5}\right)$$

The ratio of these two numbers yields

$$\omega_m = 1522 \text{ rpm}$$

(b) Use this same equation to write

$$1600 = \omega_{mo}\left(1 - \frac{30}{220/0.5}\right) \qquad \omega_m = \omega_{mo}\left(1 - \frac{5}{220/0.5}\right)$$

From these it is found that

$$\omega_m = 1713 \quad \text{rpm}$$

This differs very little from the value of $\omega_{mo} = 1717$ rpm which exists theoretically for $I_a = 0$.

□ □ □

12.18 THE SERIES MOTOR

In the series machine, the armature and the field windings are connected in series, as shown in Figure 12.18-1. As a practical matter, since the field carries the full armature current, its resistance will be rather low. Under steady state conditions, the controlling equations are

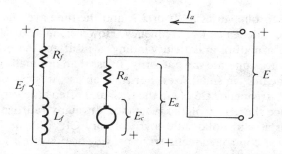

Figure 12.18-1. Schematic diagram of the series motor

$$E = E_f + E_a = (R_f + R_a + G\omega_m)I_a \qquad \text{(a)} \quad (12.18\text{-}1)$$

$$\mathcal{T}_e = GI_a^2 = \frac{G}{(R_f + R_a + G\omega_m)^2}E^2 \qquad \text{(b)}$$

An important feature of this motor follows from the second of these equations. This indicates a maximum when $\omega_m = 0$, or under starting conditions

$$\mathcal{T}_e\big|_{start} = \frac{G}{R_f + R_a}E^2 \qquad (12.18\text{-}2)$$

The torque-speed and the torque-voltage variations are shown in Figure 12.18-2. Another feature of the series motor that follows from Equation (12.18-1b) is that under full excitation E, the speed can become very high if the external load, and hence $\mathcal{T}_e$ is small. Under no load conditions, the speed is limited only by internal friction and other losses. Such motors should be used in services where the load is permanently connected or where properly designed controllers are included.

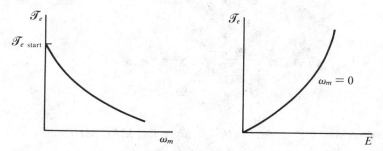

Figure 12.18-2. (a) Torque-speed (b) Torque-voltage variations of the series motor

An important feature of the series motor, and these are used in small sizes in electrical appliances and tools and in large sizes in electric railroad engines, is that they will operate on either ac or dc excitation. That this is so follows from the fact that the torque varies as I_a^2 or E^2, and the time average value is different from zero, independent of frequency. However, in ac use the inductive reactance of the armature and field windings will affect the output performance. Series motors operate satisfactorily, if less than optimally, in appliance applications on ac lines in small sizes. For traction use, it is customary to provide power at low frequency (25 Hz in the U.S. and often at lower frequency in Europe) to reduce the effect of the reactance. In many railroad systems the primary power is ac with solid state thyristors or SCRs (Silicon Control Rectifier) being used as controlled rectifiers to provide dc power for variable speed operation.

EXAMPLE 12.18-1. A dc series motor operates at 750 rpm from 230 volt lines with a line current of 80 ampere. Given: $R_a = 0.14$ ohm, $R_f = 0.11$ ohm. Suppose that the flux corresponding to a current of 20 ampere is 40 percent of that corresponding to the current of 80 ampere. Find the motor speed when $I_a = 20$ ampere.

SOLUTION. From Figure 12.18-1 we can write

$$E_c = E - I_a(R_a + R_f) = 230 - 80(0.25) = 210 \quad V$$

Since $E_c = k\Phi\omega_m$, then corresponding to 210 V

$$k\Phi = \frac{210}{750} = 0.280$$

When $I_a = 20$ A

$$E_c = 230 - 20(0.25) = 225 \quad V$$

Then

$$\omega_m = \frac{225}{0.4 \times 0.28} = 2009 \quad rpm$$

□   □   □

12.19   DYNAMIC CHARACTERISTICS OF DC MACHINES

When a dc machine does not operate under steady state conditions, which is the case in starting such machines or in certain control applications, the effects inclusion of winding inductance is necessary. The circuit representation is shown in Figure 12.19-1. The modified form of Equations (12.16-5) and (12.16-6) that correspond to the modified conditions illustrated are

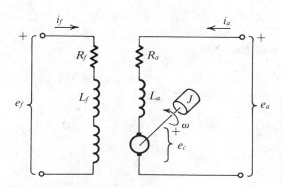

Figure 12.19-1. **Schematic diagram of the separately excited dc machine under general operating conditions**

$$e_f = R_f i_f + L_f \frac{di_f}{dt} \qquad \text{(a)} \qquad \text{(12.19-1)}$$

$$e_a = e_c + R_a i_a + L_a \frac{di_a}{dt} \qquad \text{(b)}$$

$$\mathcal{T}_e = G i_f i_a \qquad \text{(c)}$$

$$\mathcal{T}_m = D \omega_m + J \frac{d\omega_m}{dt} - \mathcal{T}_e \qquad \text{(d)}$$

$$e_c = G \omega_m i_f \qquad \text{(e)}$$

Observe that product terms of the independent variables exist. This leads to nonlinear differential equations whose solutions would normally be accomplished with numerical methods. However, in many practical problems one of these variables is a constant. This usually leads to linear differential equations, handled readily using standard techniques.

EXAMPLE 12.19-1. Find i_f and e_c for the separately excited dc generator under steady rotation and without electrical load when a constant voltage E_f is applied to the field winding at $t = 0$.

SOLUTION. This problem requires solving Equation (12.19-1a). This first order differential equation was solved in Chapter 3 with the result

$$i_f = \frac{E_f}{R_f}(1 - e^{-t/(L_f/R_f)})$$

The generated emf e_c is given by Equation (12.19-1e), and is

$$e_c = G \omega_m i_f = \frac{G \omega_m E_f}{R_f}(1 - e^{-t/(L_f/R_f)}) \qquad \text{(12.19-2)}$$

□ □ □

EXAMPLE 12.19-2. Develop the block diagram and determine the transfer function $E_a(s)/E_f(s)$ of a separately excited dc generator at constant rotational speed with an inductive load L_t.

SOLUTION. Equation (12.19-1a) and Equation (12.19-1b) modified for a generator, in Laplace transformed form, are

$$E_f(s) = R_f I_f(s) + L_f s I_f(s) = (R_f + L_f s) I_f(s) \qquad \text{(a)} \quad (12.19\text{-}3)$$

$$G \omega_m I_f(s) = R_a I_a(s) + L_a s I_a(s) + L_t s I_a(s) \qquad \text{(b)}$$

$$E_a(s) = L_t s I_a(s) \qquad \text{(c)}$$

Write these equations in the form

$$\frac{1}{L_f s}[E_f(s) - R_f I_f(s)] = I_f(s)$$

$$\frac{1}{L_a s}[G \omega_m I_f(s) - (R_a + L_t s) I_a(s)] = I_a(s)$$

These can be transferred to block diagram form, as shown in Figure 12.19-2. From this block diagram the transfer function is found, using Table 6.5-1,

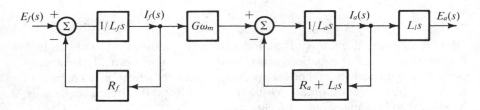

Figure 12.19-2.   Block diagram representation of a separately excited dc generator

$$H(s) = \frac{E_a(s)}{E_f(s)} = \frac{G \omega_m L_t s}{(R_f + L_f s)[R_a + (L_a + L_t)s]}$$

□   □   □

EXAMPLE 12.19-3. Find the $[E_m(s), \Omega_m(s)]$ block diagram representation of a separately excited armature voltage controlled dc motor, assuming constant field current.

SOLUTION. Write Equation (12.19-1) in the following form [see Equation (12.16-8) also]

$$E_a(s) = K\Omega_m(s) + (R_a + L_a s)I_a(s)$$

$$-\mathcal{T}_L = (D + Js)\Omega_m(s) - KI_a(s)$$

$$\mathcal{T}_L = G_m\Omega_m(s)$$

where $K = GI_f =$ constant, and G_m is a constant that relates the speed and torque of the load. The block diagram representation of these equations is shown in Figure 12.19-3.

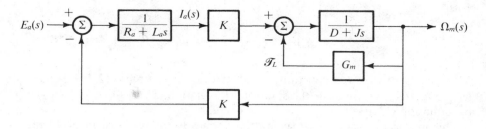

Figure 12.19-3.   Block diagram representation of a separately excited dc motor

□   □   □

Consider the case of a dc motor for which the field current I_f is constant and with no mechanical load, $\mathcal{T}_L = 0$. At $t = 0$ a supply voltage $E_a =$ constant is switched across the armature. Initially, neglecting the armature inductance for simplicity, then

$$E_a = E_c + R_a I_a = G\omega_m I_f + R_a I_a = K\omega_m + R_a I_a \qquad (12.19\text{-}4)$$

and

$$J\frac{d\omega_m}{dt} = \mathcal{T}_e = GI_f I_a = KI_a \qquad (12.19\text{-}5)$$

Hence we can write

$$E_a = K\omega_m + \frac{R_a J}{K}\frac{d\omega_m}{dt} \qquad (12.19\text{-}6)$$

The solution of this differential equation is (see Chapter 3)

$$\omega_m = \frac{E_a}{K}(1 - e^{-t/(R_a J/K^2)}) \qquad (12.19\text{-}7)$$

This equation shows that ω_m attains its final value E_a/K in a time depending on how fast the exponential term decays. This time constant depends on the electromechanical factor $\tau_m = R_a J/K^2$.

If the armature inductance is taken into consideration, a second order differential equation will result, with a somewhat complicated solution. However, if the armature time constant $\tau_a = L_a/R_a$ is smaller than τ_m, which is often the case, the electrical and the mechanical transients can be treated independently.

(a) For $t \ll \tau_m$, $\omega_m \doteq 0$ and $E_a = L_a(di_a/dt) + R_a i_a$. This has a solution of the form

$$i_a = \frac{E_a}{R_a}(1 - e^{-t/(L_a/R_a)})$$

(b) For $t \gg \tau_m$, $I_a \doteq \text{constant}$, and from Equation (12.19-4) $I_a = (E_a - K\omega_m)/R_a$, where ω_m is the solution of Equation (12.19-6) which is given by Equation (12.19-7).

This important principle of separation applies to many transient problems of electrical machines.

12.20 MACHINE EFFICIENCY

Under steady-state operating conditions, the basic machine equations are

$$\mathscr{T}_e = KI_a \qquad\qquad\qquad\qquad \text{(a)} \quad (12.20\text{-}1)$$

$$E_c = K\omega_m \qquad\qquad\qquad\qquad \text{(b)}$$

$$E_a = E_c + R_a I_a \qquad\qquad\qquad \text{(c)}$$

Multiply Equation (12.20-1a) by ω_m and Equation (12.20-1c) by I_a to obtain

$$\omega_m \mathscr{T}_e = KI_a \omega_m \qquad\qquad\qquad\qquad \text{(a)} \quad (12.20\text{-}2)$$

$$E_a I_a = K\omega_m I_a + R_a I_a^2 = \mathscr{T}_e \omega_m + R_a I_a^2 \qquad \text{(b)}$$

The second of these equations shows that the electrical input power is used to provide mechanical power and the copper losses that are converted into heat.

The overall efficiency of the machine is given by

$$\eta = \frac{\text{output power}}{\text{input power}} = \frac{\text{input power} - \text{losses}}{\text{input power}}$$

$$\eta = 1 - \frac{\text{losses}}{\text{input power}} \qquad\qquad (12.20\text{-}3)$$

It is ordinarily difficult to measure accurately the output power of a machine. Therefore, it is customary to measure the losses by whatever methods are most appropriate. The losses can be classified into four main categories: copper losses, mechanical losses, no load core losses, and stray losses. The following diagram presents pictorially the loss distribution (Figure 12.20-1) in the dc motor, and gives some estimate of the magnitude of the losses in percentage of the total power applied to the machine terminals.

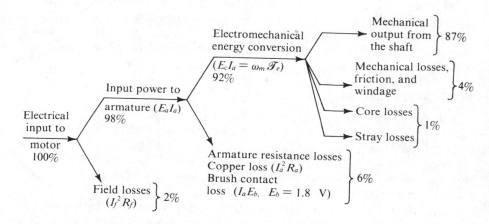

Figure 12.20-1. Power flow diagram of a dc motor

EXAMPLE 12.20-1. The losses for a typical 3 horsepower motor are given as

Electrical losses:

Copper losses in the armature	210 W
Copper losses in the field winding	140 W
Iron losses — eddy current and hysteresis principally in the armature	100 W
Brush contact loss	50 W

Mechanical losses:

Bearing friction; windage	80 W
Brush friction	20 W
	600 W

Calculate the efficiency of the motor.

SOLUTION.

$$\text{Output} = 3 \text{ hp} \times 746 \text{ W/hp} = 2238 \text{ W}$$

$$\text{Input} = 2238 + 600 + 2838 \text{ W}$$

$$\text{Efficiency} = \frac{2238}{2838} = 0.789 \quad \text{or} \quad 78.9\%$$

□ □ □

AC ROTATING MACHINERY

Most larger general purpose industrial machines operate from ac lines and are of the polyphase variety, usually three-phase. This means that the input, in the case of motors, or the output, in the case of alternators, comprises three equal voltages which differ by 120 degrees in time phase. It is a feature of such three-phase machines that they are not provided with commutators, but we shall discuss the need for slip rings in synchronous machines. We shall later show the relation between the polyphase machine and the single phase ac machine.

12.21 ROTATING MAGNETIC FIELDS

Although most larger polyphase machines are of the three-phase variety, many of the smaller appliance and control motors are essentially two-phase machines. We shall find it desirable to give some attention to the two-phase machine because there is a convenient relation between the two-phase and the single phase machine. No special difficulty arises in any calculations since these are usually done on a per-phase basis.

A consideration of special importance in polyphase machines is that when the phases are appropriately excited, the result is a magnetic field of constant amplitude which rotates in time at a frequency that is dependent on the excitation frequency. Specifically for the three-phase machine which is provided with three independent windings which are 120 degrees apart in space, when excited with currents which are 120 degrees apart in time phase, the component fields are

$$\phi_a = \Phi_m \sin(\omega t + \varphi_o) \qquad \text{(a)} \quad \text{(12.21-1)}$$

$$\phi_b = \Phi_m \sin(\omega t + 120 + \varphi_o) \qquad \text{(b)}$$

$$\phi_c = \Phi_m \sin(\omega t + 240 + \varphi_o) \qquad \text{(c)}$$

where φ_o is the reference phase angle with respect to some specified time reference. Correspondingly for the two-phase machine, the windings are 90 degrees apart in space and when excited with currents which are 90 degrees apart in time phase, the component fields are

$$\phi_a = \Phi_m \cos(\omega t + \varphi_o) \qquad \text{(a)} \quad \text{(12.21-2)}$$

$$\phi_b = \Phi_m \sin(\omega t + \varphi_o) \qquad \text{(b)}$$

It proves to be slightly less complex to consider the two-phase case, and we consider time and space portraits of the situation specified by Equation (12.21-2). These portraits are given in Figures 12.21-1. Note that to reverse the direction of rotation of the magnetic field requires only that the leads to a-a' or b-b' be reversed. This changes the *phase sequence* from a-b shown in Figure 12.21-1a to b-a.

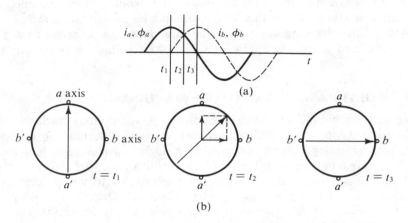

Figure 12.21-1.   (a) Excitation   (b) Resultant flux distribution in a two-phase machine

Figures 12.21-1b show the flux components of the individual phases and the resultant flux at the three times t_1, t_2 and t_3 of Figure 12.21-1a. Observe that the net effect of the time variation of phase fluxes is a progressive shift of the resultant flux, a 90 degree change in time phase being accompanied by a 90 degree change in space phase. Thus as time passes, the flux wave moves uniformly in space. The amplitude of the resultant flux remains constant, and a one cycle time change in excitation is accompanied by a 360 electrical degree space change. There is a 180 electrical degree spread between effective north and south pole positions; that is, if the machine is wound for 4 poles, 360 electrical degrees would correspond to 180 mechanical degrees.

The results shown in Figure 12.21-1b can be developed analytically since the resultant flux at any instantaneous space angle φ can be written

$$\phi = \phi_a e^{j\varphi} + \phi_b e^{j(\varphi+\pi/2)} = e^{j\varphi}(\phi_a + \phi_b e^{j\pi/2})$$

which is

$$\phi = e^{j\varphi}(\phi_a + j\phi_b) \qquad (12.21\text{-}3)$$

It follows from this, for equal flux amplitudes of Equation (12.21-1), that the magnitude of the resultant flux is

$$|\phi| = \sqrt{\phi_a^2 + \phi_b^2} = \Phi_m$$

This shows, as discussed above, that the magnitude of the resultant flux is a constant and equal to the unit of flux for the phase fluxes, as it rotates within the field structure of the machine at a uniform rate.

The procedure for the three-phase machine would exactly parallel this development with similar results. Phase sequence reversal in this case is accomplished by interchanging any two of the three input leads, assuming a Y or delta connected source that provides single phase voltages between any two leads.

12.22 POLYPHASE SYNCHRONOUS MACHINE

We shall discuss the operation of a polyphase synchronous machine under balanced load conditions. Such a machine in its most elementary form is provided with a rotating member that provides a single North and South magnetic pole structure (compare with Figure 12.13-2) which is excited with dc current and has a two-phase winding (two separate windings displaced 90 degrees in space) on the other magnetic member (see Figure 12.22-1) for the two-phase machine, and has three separate windings displaced 120 degrees in space for the three-phase machine. For slow speed sources, as in hydroelectric systems, there may be as many as 36 magnetic poles on the rotating spider, with the stator winding appropriate to the number of dc poles.

When a synchronous machine is operated as an alternator, the dc field is rotated by an external source of power. This generates motional emfs in the stationary armature conductors. For the two-phase machine, the output power is two phase in the two sets of windings. For the three phase machine the output is three phase in the three sets of windings. The frequency is specified by the rotational mechanical speed of the dc field, the number of pairs of poles on the rotor, and the effective number of poles for which the stator windings have been wound. In such a machine, an increasing electrical output power reflects itself immediately through the airgap fields to the rotor, and so to the external mechanical driving source.

When the machine is operated as a synchronous motor, two phase ac power is applied to the stator windings and the rotor is dc excited. As discussed above, the ac excitation of the stator produces a rotating magnetic field of constant amplitude. If the dc field is rotating in the direction and at the synchronous speed of the ac excited stator windings with the North-South of the ac field being along the S-N of the rotating field, magnetic locking occurs between these two magnetic fields, and the rotor continues to turn. As the rotor is loaded externally, the machine continues to rotate at synchronous speed although a phase displacement occurs between the center line or axis of the ac produced rotating field and the axis of the dc field. Should the magnetic lock be broken, whether because of the loss of excitation or because of overload, the net average torque becomes zero and the motor will stop. Evidently, therefore, a synchronous motor is not self-starting, and auxiliary methods must be employed to bring the rotor up to synchronous speed and magnetic lock before loading is possible.

A number of methods have been devised for starting synchronous motors. One of the simplest is to provide "damper windings" which are attached to the rotor pole faces (see Figure 12.22-2). These damper windings serve, when start-

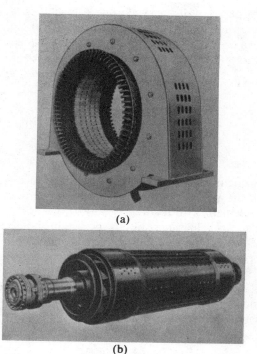

(a)

(b)

**Figure 12.22-1.   (a) Stator of a synchronous machine
(b) Two-pole non-salient pole (cylindrical) synchronous rotor**

ing, as a squirrel-cage winding, and the machine starts as an induction motor
(the induction motor is discussed in Section 12.23). When the machine gets up
to speed, magnetic locking takes place and the machine can then operate as a
synchronous machine. The damper windings serve, during normal operation
of the motor, to reduce hunting (oscillations of the rotor about the average
speed).

Figure 12.22-2.   Salient pole synchronous rotor and damper windings

To analyze the operation of the synchronous machine, we shall assume that the machine is operating under balanced conditions. On a per phase basis, the basic relations for generated voltage and developed torque are appropriate extensions of Equations (12.15-3) and (12.15-7) and are (see also Section 12.16-1)

$$e_c = G\omega_m i_f = k\phi\omega_m \qquad \text{(a)} \qquad (12.22\text{-}1)$$

and

$$\mathscr{T}_e = G i_f i_a = k\phi\,\Phi_m \sin\delta \qquad \text{(b)}$$

where δ is the torque angle and takes account of the fact that the axis of the rotating field and the axis of the induced rotating field due to the ac windings will show a displacement with loading.

To study the electrical characteristics of the synchronous alternator, refer to Figure 12.22-3 which shows a circuit diagram of the alternator under steady state operating conditions. The reactance jX_q that appears in the phasor diagram of Figure 12.22-3b is known as the quadrature axis synchronous reactance, and gets its name from the quadrature relation between the axis of the magnetic field and the axis of the induced voltage (see Section 12.15). The external characteristic per phase is defined by

$$E = E_c - I(R_a + jX_q) \doteq E_c - jIX_q \qquad \text{(a)} \qquad (12.22\text{-}2)$$

or

$$E_c = E + jIX_q \qquad \text{(b)}$$

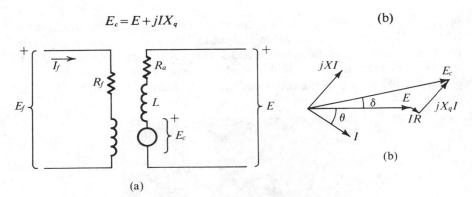

(a)

Figure 12.22-3.   Electrical characteristics of an alternator
(a) Circuit diagram   (b) Phasor diagram

When operating as a motor, the torque developed by the machine is given by Equation (12.22-1b), when the input power is $EI \cos\theta$. But the current is

$$I = \frac{E_c - E}{jX_q} = -j\left[\frac{E_c\underline{/\delta} - E\underline{/0}}{X_q}\right] = -j\left[\frac{E_c(\cos\delta + J\sin\delta) - E}{X_q}\right]$$

The real part of I is $(E_c/X_q) \sin \delta$, and this is equal to $I \cos \theta$. Then the electrical power developed per phase is $EI \cos \theta$ or

$$P = \frac{EE_c}{X_q} \sin \delta \qquad (12.22\text{-}3)$$

The developed torque is

$$\mathcal{T}_e = \frac{P}{\omega_m} = \frac{EE_c}{\omega_m X_q} \sin \delta \qquad (12.22\text{-}4)$$

A plot of Equation (12.22-3) gives the so-called "power angle characteristic" of the nonsalient pole or cylindrical rotor machine. This is given in Figure 12.22-4. Also shown in Figure 12.22-4 is the power angle characteristic of a salient pole machine. This shows a slight advantage for the salient-pole construction, with a higher maximum or pull-out torque and a smaller torque angle for a given load.

Observe from this figure that the torque (P/ω_m) is zero for $\delta = 0$, or when the applied and the induced voltages are aligned. Positive power corresponds to motor operation. Also, for the cylindrical rotor machine, beyond $\delta = \pi/2$ the power decreases with increasing angle, thereby leading to unstable operation. Negative δ leads to negative torque and so to generator operation. For increasing load δ will increase, and for δ greater than $\pi/2$, the rotor will break out of synchronism and the machine will come to a halt.

A practical feature of importance in the operation of a synchronous motor is that the power factor angle θ of the line current is a function of the excitation

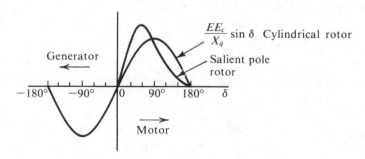

Figure 12.22-4. Power angle characteristic for synchronous motors

level of the dc field. That is, as the field current I_f is increased E_c will increase, and for a fixed load, the power factor angle will change. The general behavior of the line current I as the field current I_f is varied for fixed load is exhibited in the so-called V-curves, which have the form illustrated in Figure 12.22-5. Under normal operation the field excitation would be adjusted to provide nearly unity power factor.

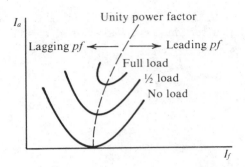

Figure 12.22-5.   Synchronous motor V-curves

The ability of the synchronous motor to draw leading current when over-excited is often used to improve the power factor to an industrial establishment that makes heavy use of induction motors and other equipment that draws power at lagging power factors. In special cases the machine may be a sealed unit that is helium or hydrogen filled to reduce rotational friction without a shaft, and so is run without load. Such over-excited machines are often called synchronous capacitors.

EXAMPLE 12.22-1. A two-phase, 4-pole alternator is rated at 10 kVA, 220 V, 60 Hz. The synchronous reactance is 2.8 Ω. Determine: (a) rated speed, (b) generated voltage E_c when the machine operates at 0.8 power factor lagging.

SOLUTION. (a) 60 Hz = 120π rad/s = $120\pi \times 57.3$ elec. deg/s. For a 4-pole machine, there are 720 elec. deg/rev. Hence

$$n = \frac{120\pi \times 57.3}{720} \times 60 = 1800 \quad \text{rpm}$$

(b) For a phase voltage $E = 220$ V rms, the rated phase current is

$$I = \frac{VA/2}{220} = \frac{10,000/2}{220} = 22.73 \quad \text{A}$$

$$IX_q = 22.73 \times 2.8 = 63.64 \quad \text{V}$$

The phasor diagram is shown.

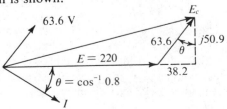

Therefore

$$E_c = 220 + 38.2 + j50.9 = 258.2 + j50.9 = 263.2\underline{/11.2°} \quad \text{V}$$

□ □ □

EXAMPLE 12.22-2. The machine of Example 12.22-1 is constructed with a cylindrical rotor. Determine the maximum total power and the pull-out torque.

SOLUTION. Maximum power occurs when $\delta = 90$ degrees.

$$P_{max} = \frac{2 \times 220 \times 263.2}{2.8} = 41,360 \text{ W} = \text{N-m/s}$$

At 1800 rpm the pull-out torque is

$$\mathcal{T}_{max} = \frac{P_{max}}{\omega_m} = \frac{41,360 \times 60}{2\pi \times 1800} = 689.33 \quad \text{N-m}$$

Observe that the maximum power is more than four times the rated value.

□ □ □

12.23 THE INDUCTION MACHINE

The polyphase induction machine is provided with two or three stator windings which are space-phased by 90 or 120 electrical degrees, as for the two- or three-phase synchronous machine. The rotor of the *squirrel-cage* machine comprises a series of closely spaced bars on the rotor surface with short-circuiting end rings (see Figure 12.23-1a). The rotor of the *wound rotor* machine is provided with two windings which are space-phased by 90 electrical degrees. In the wound rotor machine slip rings are often provided in order to permit the addition of external resistance into the rotor circuit for improved starting torque, as shall be discussed below (see Figure 12.23-1b).

It is helpful when considering the operation of the induction machine to view the machine as a transformer, the short-circuited winding being mounted in bearings to allow rotation. Physically the operation depends on the fact that, upon the application of a two phase excitation to the two phase stator windings, a rotating magnetic field is produced, as discussed in Section 12.21. As a result currents are induced in the short circuited rotor. These currents interact with the rotating magnetic field to cause the rotor to turn. When the machine has reached operating speed, which will be only slightly less than the synchronous field established by the stator windings, the currents will be just adequate to provide for the load. The frequency of the rotor currents will be the difference between the applied excitation frequency and the rotational frequency of the rotor. This difference is known as the *slip* frequency. When the machine operates as a motor, the speed is just below that of the synchronous

(a)

(b)

**Figure 12.23-1.   (a) Squirrel cage rotor
(b) Rotor of a medium size three-phase CW wound rotor induction motor**

speed, and the slip is positive. When the machine is driven to operate as an induction generator, the slip is negative; that is, the rotor must be driven slightly faster than the synchronous speed. However, when the machine operates as an induction generator, external excitation is required in order to establish the output frequency. In addition, this external source must also provide the reactive power demands of the external load, since the induction generator will not provide this component. Observe that if the rotor turns at synchronous speed, there is no relative motion of the rotor conductors with respect to the synchronous field, no motional emf is induced, and no rotor currents result.

When the induction machine is operating as a motor, power is supplied from the power lines. At standstill, the passing stator field will induce an emf of magnitude E_c in one phase of the rotor winding with angular frequency ω_s. The current is

$$I_2 = \frac{E_c}{R_2 + j\omega_s L_2} = \frac{E_c}{R_2 + jX_2} \tag{12.23-1}$$

where R_2 and L_2 are the effective resistance and inductance of the rotor winding on a per phase basis.

When the machine is operating as a motor at angular speed ω_m, which is just below that of ω_s, the slip s

$$s = \frac{\omega_s - n\omega_m}{\omega_s} \tag{12.23-2}$$

where n is the number of poles in the machine. From this $s\omega_s$ represents the slip frequency. Since E_c depends directly on the speed of cutting conductors then the induced emf is now sE_c, the rotor frequency is $s\omega_s$, and the rotor reactance is sX_2. The rotor current is

$$I_2 = \frac{sE_c}{R_2 + jsX_2} = \frac{E_c}{\dfrac{R_2}{s} + jX_2} \tag{12.23-3}$$

This is written in the form

$$I_2 = \frac{E_c}{R_2 + jX_2 + R_2\dfrac{(1-s)}{s}} \tag{12.23-4}$$

This equation can be depicted in two network forms, as shown in Figures 12.23-2. From these figures $R_2[(1-s)/s]$ is the effective load of the machine. From the second circuit E_g is the effective voltage involved in the energy conversion in the machine. The important relations are

$$E_g = I_2 R_2 \left(\frac{1-s}{s} \right) \qquad\qquad \mathcal{T}_e = \frac{E_g I_2}{\omega_m} \tag{12.23-5}$$

EXAMPLE 12.23-1. A 5 horsepower 4-pole 60 Hz 2-phase wound-rotor induction motor draws 4,400 W from the power lines. The losses in the machine are core loss 250 W, stator copper loss 200 W, rotor copper loss 90 W, friction and windage loss 70 W. Determine: (a) power transferred across the air gap; (b) mechanical power in W developed by the rotor; (c) mechanical output power in W; (d) efficiency; (e) slip; (f) torque in N-m.

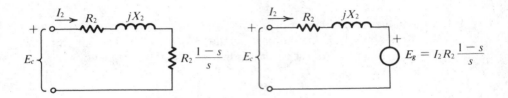

Figure 12.23-2.   Two circuit models of the rotor of an induction motor

SOLUTION. (a) Power across the air gap

$$4400 - 250 - 200 - 90 = 3900 \quad W$$

(b) Power developed by rotor

$$3900 - 90 = 3810 \quad W$$

(c) Power output:

$$3810 - 70 = 3740 \quad W$$

(d) Efficiency:

$$\frac{3740}{4400} \times 100 = 84.2\%$$

(e) Slip. Solve for s from the expression for power

$$P = I_2^2 R_2 \left(\frac{1-s}{s}\right) \qquad\qquad s = \frac{I_2^2 R_2}{P + I_2^2 R_2}$$

$$s = \frac{90}{3810 + 90} = 0.023$$

(f) Torque

$$\mathcal{T}_e = \frac{P}{\omega_m} = \frac{3740}{2\pi \times \dfrac{60}{2}(1 - 0.023)} = 20.3 \quad N\text{-}m$$

□   □   □

An important characteristic of the induction motor is the speed-torque curve. This is given by Equation (12.23-5) and is written

$$\mathcal{T}_e = \frac{I_2^2}{\omega_m}\left(\frac{1-s}{s}\right)R_2 = \frac{I_2^2 R_2}{s\omega_s} \tag{12.23-6}$$

Detailed calculations for the torque-speed variations over the full range of motor speeds is beyond the scope of this text. The results are shown graphically in Figure 12.23-3. Figure 12.23-3a shows a certain starting torque ($\omega_m = 0$) that depends on the rotor resistance. The curve also shows that at the normal operating range the torque varies almost linearly with speed, the speed variation being small over the operating range. For this reason the induction motor is a substantially constant speed machine.

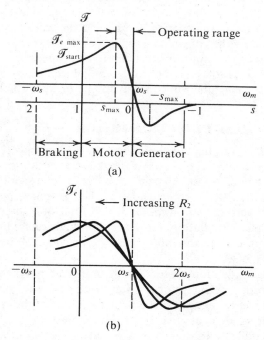

Figure 12.23-3. Torque speed curves of balanced induction motor
(a) No added R in rotor   (b) Effect of increasing R_2

The curves of Figure 12.23-3b show the effect of adding resistance to the rotor circuit. Observe that the maximum torque remains constant but the slope of the operating range has been shifted, thereby allowing the starting torque to be varied. Clearly, the rotor resistance should be kept as small as possible so that the speed variation is very small with torque changes. It is a feature of the wound-rotor machine which allows external resistors to be included to improve the starting torque, and these would then be removed from the circuit after the machine is up to speed. Observe also that a maximum torque capability exists, and loading beyond this point would cause the machine to come to a halt.

To reverse the direction of rotation of an induction motor requires that the direction of the rotating magnetic field be reversed. This is readily accomplished, as previously noted, by reversing the phase sequence of the exciting currents. For the 3-phase machine this involves interchanging any two leads. For the 2-phase machine, the leads on one phase must be reversed.

A large number of two-phase induction motors in small sizes for use in home appliances are manufactured for use on single phase lines. Here one phase is fed directly from the power lines and the second is fed through a capacitor having a large capacitance. Because of the capacitance, the current in this phase is leading the voltage, and while not 90 degrees leading in time, it is sufficient to permit the motor to start and to continue to run as a two-phase machine. If the capacitor is removed from the circuit by a centrifugally operated switch, the machine will continue to operate as a single-phase induction motor.

12.24 SINGLE PHASE INDUCTION MOTOR

As noted above, a two phase induction motor, if running with a moderate or light load, will continue to run if one of the phase excitations is opened. That is, the machine will continue to run as a single phase motor, and with operating characteristics not unlike those of the two-phase machine. This is also true for a 3-phase induction motor which loses one wire and thereby is reduced to single phase excitation. However, the single phase induction motor has no starting torque, and the motor must be provided with some auxiliary starting device.

The single phase induction motor is not unlike the polyphase machine in general design except that the stator is wound with only a single winding. Such a machine has a lower capacity than a polyphase motor of the same weight and dimensions. In the single phase machine the airgap mmf is stationary in space but oscillates periodically in time. But a pulsating field can be resolved into two rotating fields, one of which rotates at ω_s and the second of which rotates at $-\omega_s$, as illustrated in Figure 12.24-1. If we now associate the torque characteristics appropriate to each rotating magnetic field, the results have the form shown in Figure 12.24-2. Observe that the resultant torque, while zero at start, does show an operational characteristic like that of a polyphase induction motor in the region of small slip. Also clearly shown is the fact that the machine will operate equally satisfactorily in either direction of rotation.

Since, as noted, the single phase induction motor is not self-starting, such machines are provided with some auxiliary starting device. The auxiliary starting device will dictate the direction of rotation. Among the starting methods are those illustrated in Figure 12.24-3.

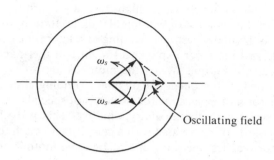

Figure 12.24-1.   The decomposition of an oscillating field into two oppositely rotating fields

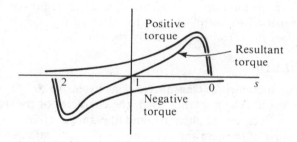

Figure 12.24-2.   Resultant torque due to oppositely rotating component fields

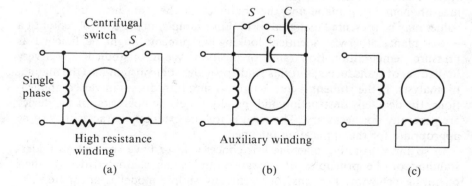

Figure 12.24-3.   Single phase induction motors — starting methods
(a) Split phase   (b) Capacitor   (c) Shaded pole

In the split phase machine, a high resistance winding is provided in quadrature with the main stator winding. Upon excitation, the current reaches its maximum in the high resistance winding at a later time owing to the larger time constant, and the rotor experiences a shift in the magnetic field which provides the starting torque. When the motor is almost up to speed, a centrifugally operated switch opens the auxiliary winding circuit.

In the capacitor motor, a capacitor, which is of special electrolytic design, is connected in series with the auxiliary winding. This provides the necessary phase shift for start. It is provided with a centrifugal switch to open the circuit when the motor reaches operating speed. In some motors two capacitors are provided. The larger gives good starting torque and is switched out of the circuit; the smaller remains in the circuit to improve the operating efficiency and power factor.

In the shaded pole motor a heavy copper short circuited coil is wound around half of each salient stator pole. Induced currents in the shorted turn causes a delay in the buildup of magnetic flux in that region of the pole. As a result, the magnetic flux vector appears to shift as a function of time, and the rotor experiences the effect of a partially rotating field.

12.25   POSTLUDE

The range of incremental transducers is as extensive as the measurements that are to be made. The materials used, the character of the design, and the physical size, reflect the application and the range of imagination of the designers. Because of the ease and convenience of electrical interconnections in measurements, many of such devices have electrical outputs. Thus, depending on the application, for example as part instrumentation or control, indicating or recording devices appear at the output terminals. These usually indicate either a current or a voltage, but the scale markings will be appropriate to the measurement being made and the character of the transducer itself. These values may be presented in digital form. For example, in the control center of a power plant, otherwise identical looking instruments might be labelled as pressure, temperature, flow rates, or position. We have studied only a very limited set of transducers, but this study provides some insight into the manner of analysis. If the student is interested in using transducers in varied applications, the detailed construction and the physics of the operation of the device are generally not necessary. The need is for the external characteristics to be appropriate for the application intended.

In so far as rotating machinery is concerned, we have stressed an understanding of the principles of operation and some characteristics of their operating behavior. For this, our generally simple model is adequate. The design details, involving the properties of the materials; the winding details; mechanical aspects of slots, bearings, frames, etc.; the inherent nonlinearities; and even armature reaction (the effect of the rotor currents on the flux distribution produced by the main field currents), have received little consideration. Special machines have not been discussed and very little has been said about the dynamic behavior of rotating machines, of considerable importance in feedback control systems. Much remains to be said, and subsequent studies will provide the detailed extension to the many significant problems.

SUMMARY

- Incremental motion transducers of the electromechanical types are two-port devices with mechanical input or output and electrical output or input.

- Coupling between the electrical and the mechanical variables occurs in the airgap in which the electromagnetic coupling field energy is stored.

- There are four important types of magnetic field transducers: singly excited, multiply excited, permanent magnetic, magnetostriction devices.

- A number of important electric field transducers exist. These include two basic types: capacitor types and piezoelectric devices.

- Detailed analyses yield equations which allow equivalent network configurations to be drawn that show the equivalent input and output port connections.

- The dc dynamo consists of a stationary field structure which establishes the dc magnetic field through the rotating armature structure so that the conductors on the surface of the armature cut magnetic flux lines as they rotate. A commutator is provided for current into or out of the armature windings, depending on whether the dynamo is being used as a motor or as a generator.

- The armature windings span the distance from a point under the north pole to a corresponding point under a south pole for a full pitch winding. Often a fractional pitch winding is used.

- It is the function of the commutator to rectify the inherent ac wave that would otherwise be generated by the basic configuration of a coil moving in the dc field.

- Dc dynamos can be of a number of types, depending on the windings and the excitation methods. The machines studied include separately excited; shunt excited; series excited; compound wound, including both a shunt and a series field.

- The general equations for dc machines are

$$e_f = \left(R_f + L_f \frac{d}{dt}\right) i_f$$

$$e_a = G\omega_m i_f + \left(R_a + L_a \frac{d}{dt}\right) i_a$$

$$\mathscr{T}_m = J \frac{d\omega_m}{dt} + D\omega_m - \mathscr{T}_e$$

$$\mathscr{T}_e = G i_f i_a$$

- The separately excited machine shows good speed characteristics when used as a motor, and good voltage characteristics when used as a generator.

- The shunt machine has characteristics like those of the separately excited machine. As a generator the terminal voltage will fall almost linearly with load current.

- The series motor can be used on ac and dc supply lines. The torque produced is a square law function of applied voltage, and so can produce a high starting torque.

- Polyphase ac machines (synchronous) combine a rotating dc field structure which is excited through slip rings, and two or three essentially separate windings each displaced by 90 degrees for the two-phase machine and by 120 degrees for the three-phase machine. This produces in the three-phase machine a set of 3 independent voltages which differ by 120 and 240 degrees in time phase.

- Conversely, three-phase currents that differ by 120 degrees in time when applied to three windings which are spaced 120 degrees electrical, will produce a rotating magnetic field of constant amplitude. The rotational speed of the field depends on the angular frequency of the exciting current. At 60 Hz a 2-pole machine has a synchronous speed of 3600 rpm, a 4-pole machine has a synchronous speed of 1800 rpm, etc.

- A synchronous motor for operation must establish a magnetic lock between the dc field produced by the rotating element and the rotating field produced by the ac excitation. Such a machine is not self-starting and must operate at synchronous speed. If the magnetic lock is broken, the machine will come to a halt.

- Auxiliary starting of synchronous motors is required. Often this is provided by a damper winding in the face of the poles, and this serves both to prevent hunting during normal operation and as the squirrel cage winding for starting purposes.

- Two types of induction motors exist: the squirrel cage and the wound rotor. The wound rotor type includes provision for adding resistance to the rotor circuit to improve the starting properties. The resistance is reduced to zero during operation.

- Many small appliance motors are two-phase induction machines, one phase being excited directly from the power lines, the other phase being fed through a capacitor having a large capacitance to give a leading current, in effect providing a two-phase excitation source, for ready start. In many cases centrifugal switches are included to open the capacitor circuit since the capacitor (often of special electrolytic design) cannot be used to sustain an ac current. When the capacitor is switched out of the circuit, the machine is operating as a single-phase motor.

- Single phase induction motors have operating characteristics like those of the polyphase machine, but they are not self-starting. A number of different auxiliary methods exist, depending on the size of the machine.

- Induction motors will run equally well in either direction. To reverse the direction of rotation of a three-phase motor any two of the three input wires must be interchanged. This reverses the phase sequence of the exciting currents. For a single phase motor, the starting device dictates the direction of rotation. Often provision is made for ready reversal, when necessary.

REVIEW QUESTIONS

1. In an incremental transducer the controlling electromechanical equation might be of the form

$$Bli = M\frac{dv}{dt} + Dv + K\int v\, dt$$

   Draw and label the equivalent circuit configuration, and discuss the meaning of this expression.
2. Name the four important types of magnetic field transducers. Discuss the significant features of each.
3. Magnetic transducers are non-reciprocal devices. What does this mean?
4. Prepare an energy balance for a transducer.
5. Show the connections of the following dc machines: separately excited, shunt, series, compound.
6. What happens if the field connection of a fully loaded shunt motor is accidentally broken? Repeat for a lightly loaded motor.
7. How does a series motor react electrically to an increase in load?
8. Distinguish between a salient-pole and a cylindrical rotor machine.
9. Explain the production of a rotating magnetic field by stationary coils.
10. How does a synchronous motor react to an increase in shaft load?
11. Discuss the starting of a synchronous motor. What conditions must be met for continued rotation?
12. How would you reverse the direction of rotation of a synchronous motor? An induction motor? A dc motor?
13. Discuss the operation of a polyphase induction motor.
14. Discuss why a polyphase induction motor will operate on single phase. Is it self-starting?

REFERENCES

1. Edwards, J. D., *Electrical Machine—An Introduction to Principles and Characteristics*, Interext Books, Bucks, England, 1973.
   This text provides a lucid presentation of electrical machines. The level is appropriate to the non-specialist, but the rigor provides a basis for more advanced studies.

2. Fitzgerald, A. E., C. Kingsley, Jr. and A. Kusko, *Electrical Machinery*, 3rd ed., McGraw Hill Book Co., New York, NY, 1971.

  One of the classics over the years. Develops the field of electromechanical energy conversion in some detail. It is written at an intermediate level.

3. Daniels, A. R., *Introduction to Electrical Machines*, Matrix Publishers, Inc., Portland, OR, 1976.

  Analyzes the well-established different machine types through the use of the "general machine."

PROBLEMS

12.2-1. Find the flux linkages $d\psi$ for the virtual displacement shown in Figure P12.2-1.

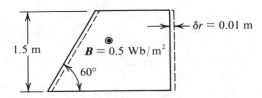

Figure P12.2-1

12.4-1. Refer to Example 12.4-1.

  (a) If the device is to measure current (a dynamometer ammeter), the two coils are connected in series. What is the deflection law of the device?

  (b) If one coil is voltage excited from the line and the second coil is carrying the circuit current, to what is the reading of the device proportional?

12.5-1. Consider the closed magnetic circuit shown in Figure P12.5-1. The value of the line integral of H taken once around the core is the mmf V_H. Also, the average total magnetic flux around the core is given by the surface integral

$$\Phi = \int_s \bar{B} \cdot \bar{n} \, dS$$

assuming that there is no leakage of flux. Combine these two results to show that

$$V_H = \Phi \frac{l}{\mu S} \qquad l = 2\pi a \qquad \mu = \text{permeability}$$

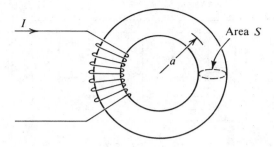

Figure P12.5-1

By analogy with the resistance of an electric circuit, a quantity $\mathscr{R}$, the reluctance, is defined by the relation

$$\mathscr{R} = \frac{V_H}{\Phi} \qquad \text{ampere turns/weber}$$

Show that for the core shape in the figure the reluctance assumes the form

$$\mathscr{R} = \frac{l}{\mu S}$$

This development shows that a magnetic circuit can be discussed by an equivalent ohm's law formulation. Discuss this.

12.5-2. A steel ring of mean diameter 50 cm and cross-sectional area 20 cm² is uniformly wound with a coil of 500 turns. The flux density is 1 Wb/m² when the exciting current is 4 A.

   (a) Calculate the coil inductance under these operating conditions.
   (b) Calculate the exciting current necessary to maintain this flux density when an air gap of 0.5 cm is cut across the ring. Find the new coil inductance. Neglect fringing and leakage.

12.5-3. Consider the magnetic core of square cross section that is illustrated in Figure P12.5-3. It is required to find the air-gap flux density when the total number of ampere-turns is 200. The magnetic material is silicon steel, and this is assumed to have a constant permeability $\mu_r = 4000$. The dimensions are the following:

$A_A = A_B = A_C = 3.5 \times 3.5$ in² $\qquad\qquad l_A = l_B = 38.5$ in

$A_g = 1.035 A_C$ to account for fringing $\quad l_C = 13.5$ in $\quad l_g = 0.03$ in.

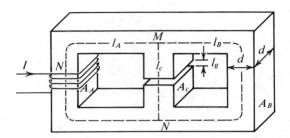

Figure P12.5-3

12.6-1. For the magnetic structure shown in Figure P12.6-1 find the torque as a function of angle, for small displacements. The area of each pole face is $A = r\varphi d$, where d is the width of the poles.

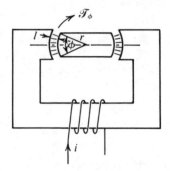

Figure P12.6-1

12.6-2. Refer to Example 12.6-1. Show that $\mathcal{T}_\varphi = 0$ for the case $\omega_m \neq \omega$; also that $\mathcal{T}_\varphi = I_m^2 L_1/2$ when $\omega_m = \omega$.

12.6-3. The circuit shown in Figure P12.6-3 is that of a simple two coil transformer. The material of the magnetic circuit is laminated steel with a constant permeability μ. Determine the emf induced in coil N_2. What is the voltage per turn? For a step-up ratio of 5, what must be the turns ratio N_2/N_1?

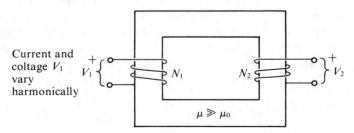

Current and coltage V_1 vary harmonically

Figure P12.6-3

12.9-1. Determine and plot the velocity response of the transducer shown in Figure 12.9-2 when the voltage source is a unit step function.

    (a) Assume zero mass and applied force.
    (b) Assume zero inductance and applied force.

    In both cases, assume zero initial conditions.

12.9-2. (a) Determine the equivalent circuit for the transducer shown in Figure P12.9-2.
    (b) Find the transfer function $H(s) = V(s)/E(s)$.
    (c) Find and plot the velocity function, if $e(t) = u_o(t) = $ delta function.

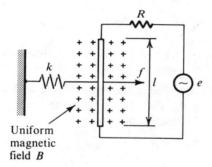

Figure P12.9-2

12.10-1. Determine the angular velocity response to a unit step function input voltage to the galvanometer shown in Figure 12.10-1, if $L = J = 0$.

12.10-2. Determine the sensitivity of the rotary electromechanical transducer shown in Figure 12.10-1 (the d'Arsonval meter) in radians/volt.

12.11-1. A potentiometer has the form shown in Figure P12.11-1. Find the output voltage as a function of distance along the potentiometer. Assume that the resistance per unit length follows a sinusoidal distribution covering a total of 90 degrees.

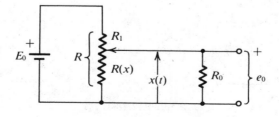

Figure P12.11-1

12.12-1. Find the force between two parallel plates of dimensions 10×10 cm² charged to 100 V. The distance between the plates is 3 cm. Neglect fringing and assume that a vacuum exists between the plates.

12.12-2. For the capacitor microphone represented in Figure 12.12-2, find its impulse response for $f_a(t) = u_o(t) =$ delta function, if $L = M = D = 0$.

12.12-3. The equations governing an electromechanical system are the following:

$$M\frac{d^2z}{dt^2} + kz - \frac{Q_o}{\epsilon A}q = f$$

$$-\frac{Q_o z}{\epsilon A} + \frac{q}{C_o} = e$$

(a) Draw a two-port structure for the system characterized by these equations.

(b) By changes in variables, deduce a two-port without dependent sources.

12.15-1. A two-coil dc machine is shown in Figure P12.15-1. If the magnetic field is sinusoidally distributed over the rotor surface, plot the emf for each coil and the output emf e_c.

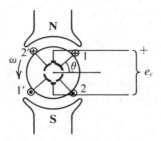

Figure P12.15-1

12.16-1. (a) Determine the block diagram representation of the two dc generators connected in cascade, as shown in Figure P12.16-1. The input and output variables are e_1 and e_3, respectively.

(b) Specify the system function of this assembly.

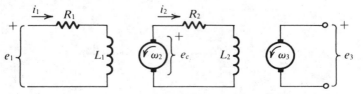

Figure P12.16-1

12.16-2. The dc generator in Example 12.16-1 is running without load. If the speed is increased by 15% and the field is decreased by 10%, predict the new terminal voltage.

12.16-3. A dc machine that is being operated as a separately excited generator has the following parameters:

$$R_f = 30 \ \Omega \qquad R_a = 0.015 \ \Omega \qquad R_L = 0.315 \ \Omega$$
$$G = 0.168 \ H \qquad \omega_m = 1800 \ \text{rpm}$$

The armature is being driven at constant rated speed. Find I_f and E_L when a 230 V excitation is applied to the field terminals.

12.17-1. A 20 hp, 230 V, 75 A, dc shunt motor is operating under full load at 1200 rpm. $R_a = 0.14 \ \Omega$.

(a) If the resultant airgap flux is increased by 8 percent, what is the speed?
(b) If a 1.5 Ω resistor is connected in series with the armature but with the airgap flux at its initial value, what is the speed?
(c) With the series resistor of (b) in the armature circuit, the resultant airgap flux is again increased by 8 percent, what is the speed?

12.17-2. A shunt motor is started using a *starting box*, the connections being those shown in Figure P12.17-2. The switch S is first closed and the moving contact lever L is moved to the first button R_1. As the motor speeds up, the lever is advanced. At the last button, it is held in position by magnet M against the pull of a spring. Explain the functions of R_1, R_2 and M in terms of desired starting conditions for the motor.

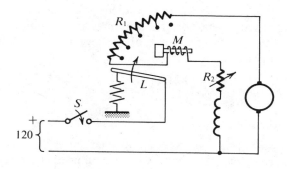

Figure P12.17-2

12.18-1. A dc series motor that is driving a particular load at 1200 rpm is excited from a 230 V source and draws an armature current of 16.3 A. The torque to drive the load varies as $\omega^{1.8}$. What must be the input voltage and current if the speed is to be 1750 rpm? The resistance of the armature plus field $R_a + R_f = 1.0 \, \Omega$.

12.18-2. A compound wound dc machine includes both a shunt and a series field winding, in the manner illustrated in Figure P12.18-2. If the effect of the series field flux is to oppose the effect of the shunt field flux, the machine is *differentially* wound. If the fluxes produced by the two fields add, the machine is *cumulatively* compounded.

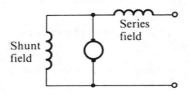

Figure P12.18-2

(a) Discuss the external characteristics (terminal voltage versus load current) of the machine under the two connections. Show the results on a sketch.

(b) Is *flat compounding*, i.e., full load terminal voltage equal to the no load terminal voltage, possible with either connection? Explain.

12.21-1. (a) Develop the rotating space portrait produced by a three-phase structure that is excited by a three-phase supply.

(b) Show analytically that the resulting field at any instant is a constant.

12.22-1. A two-phase two-pole 60 Hz nonsalient pole synchronous machine is operating as an alternator. The windings are distributed sinusoidally in space around the periphery of the airgap. The machine has the following parameters:

$$L_a = L_b = 0.21 \text{ H} \qquad\qquad G = 0.20 \text{ H}$$
$$R_a = R_b = 1 \, \Omega \qquad\qquad I_f = 3.6 \text{ A}$$

Deduce the following:

(a) The rotor phase voltages on open circuit.

(b) The rotor phase currents when each phase is connected to a 50 Ω resistive load.

(c) The average power converted from mechanical to electrical form.

12.22-2. The field current of a synchronous motor which is running without load is adjusted for minimum stator input current. The motor is then loaded, with a resulting torque angle $\delta = 22$ degrees.

   (a) Draw a phasor diagram for the machine, with input voltage as a horizontal reference.

   (b) Suppose now that the field current is decreased by 25%. Draw the new phasor diagram and predict the new power angle and power factor.

12.22-3. A synchronous motor operates under rated load conditions at unity power factor. The line current is 50 A, the torque angle is 20 degrees and the field current is 2.8 A. For constant power output, calculate I and I_f for 0.8 power factor leading and lagging. This will yield three points on the V-curve (see Figure 12.22-5).

12.22-4. A 25 hp, 1800 rpm synchronous motor operates at full load at a leading power factor of 0.8. It draws 100 A from 230 V three-phase lines, and is operating at 90.2% efficiency ($P = \sqrt{3}\ VI \cos\theta$ for a balanced three-phase load, with V being the line-line voltage). The synchronous reactance is 1.2 Ω and the field current is 3.9 A.

   (a) Determine the reactive VARs required by the motor.

   (b) Suppose that the motor is operated without shaft load as a synchronous capacitor. Estimate the capacitive VARs of the machine and estimate the field required.

12.23-1. A 15 hp induction motor at rated load runs at 1740 rpm from three-phase 60 Hz lines. Determine:

   (a) The speed of the rotor field with respect to the stator field.

   (b) The slip frequency, the frequency of the rotor currents.

12.23-2. Consider two squirrel cage induction motors which are identical except that the rotor of one machine has conductors of aluminum of conductivity σ, while the rotor of the second machine has copper conductors of conductivity 1.5σ. If the starting torque of motor 1 is $\mathcal{T}_e$, estimate the starting torque of motor 2 in relation to $\mathcal{T}_e$.

12.24-1. Specify your selection for a type of electric motor that would best meet the following requirements:

   (a) Provide constant speed under all loads.

   (b) Provide an easily adjusted speed which remains nearly constant over a wide range of loads.

   (c) Operate from dc lines and provide relatively high starting torque.

   (d) Operate from single-phase lines and provide relatively high starting torque.

   (e) Operate from ac lines, provide a high starting torque, and permit some variation of speed under load.

Chapter Thirteen

Automatic Control

In our complex world, feedback control is employed in almost all branches of technology. We can find many examples of feedback also within our biological world, for example, the ability of the human body to maintain a constant temperature over a wide range of external ambients, and the ability of the eye to focus almost instantly on objects of different sizes at varying distances.

In some of our previous work, particularly when we drew signal flow graphs and block diagrams to represent system interconnections, we referred to feedback and feedforward paths. This chapter will study the details of feedback since the design of appropriate controllers makes possible machines which can perform specific tasks in very precise ways.

13.1 PRINCIPLES OF CONTROL SYSTEMS

A control system may be considered to be a combination of elements with the purpose of controlling a quantity of interest in a machine, mechanism or a plant. Control systems can be broadly distinguished as closed loop and open loop systems.

Open Loop Systems

Any physical system which does not automatically correct its output is called an *open loop* control system. Figure 13.1-1 depicts two open loop control systems. Figure 13.1-1b is a simple open loop arrangement for controlling a room heater. Another example of an open-loop control system is the switching system for controlling the traffic lights at an intersection. Such a system will go through its cycle without any concern for the actual traffic pattern.

Closed Loop Systems (Feedback Control Systems)

A feature of a feedback system is that the input is determined in whole or in part by the output. A feedback system is conveniently discussed in terms of

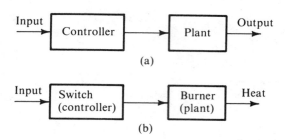

**Figure 13.1-1.   Examples of open loop control systems   (a) General system
(b) Typical home electric heater with ON-OFF switch**

signal properties. Refer to Figure 13.1-2 which shows a block diagram of such
a system. This diagram shows clearly that a part of the output is being combined with the input signal. The arrows call attention to the forward transmission path from input to output, and a reverse transmission (the feedback) path
from output to input.

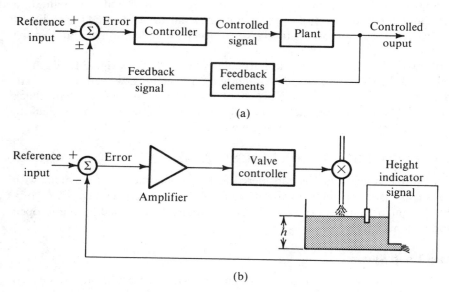

**Figure 13.1-2.   The elements of a simple feedback system
(a) Schematic representation   (b) Physical system**

As discussed in Section 7.13, feedback is defined as being either positive or
negative. If the net effect of the feedback is to increase the effective input
signal and thereby increase the magnitude of the change at the output, the
feedback is called *positive, direct,* or *regenerative.* If the resultant input signal
is reduced by the feedback which in turn results in a decrease in the magnitude

of the output, the feedback is called *negative, inverse,* or *degenerative.* We shall find that many of the system performance properties are markedly altered by the presence of feedback.

A feature of feedback control design that makes it different from general system design is that it often requires altering the performance of a given system or plant without having access to the plant at other than prescribed input terminals or ports. Consequently, control system design is often an add-on problem to make the system performance meet a given set of specifications. It is the responsibility of the controller to accept the error information and to convert it to an appropriate signal for the particular plant.

Modern minicomputers and microcomputers are used extensively in control applications. An interesting application of the digital computer is its use as the controller in the control loop. An important aspect of this operation is the presence of memory and the machine's ability to be programmed to make control decisions. Owing to the computational speed of such computers, a single machine can often act as the controller for a number of independent control loops.

Feedback control systems possess certain special attributes compared to open loop controllers: improved accuracy; a reduction of the sensitivity of the ratio of output to input due to variations in the system characteristics; an increase in the bandwidth of the system, thereby yielding improved performance; and a reduction in the effect of distortion and nonlinearities.

13.2   CHARACTERISTICS OF FEEDBACK SYSTEMS

In contrast to the open loop system, the feedback system, as depicted by the simple feedback system shown in Figure 13.2-1 is driven by two (or more) signals, the input signal and a second signal derived from the output. Because of this feedback connection, such feedback systems are capable of being designed to be self-correcting and to adjust their outputs to reduce the amount of an error signal.

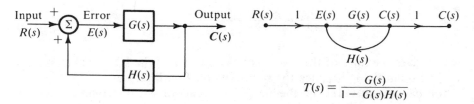

$$T(s) = \frac{G(s)}{1 - G(s)H(s)}$$

Figure 13.2-1.   The basic feedback system in block diagram and signal flow graph representations

One of the advantages in using feedback is an ability to reduce the sensitivity of the system to parameter variations. Parameters may vary with time, with changes in environment (e.g., temperature variations). Hence *sensitivity* is a measure of the effectiveness of the feedback system in reducing the effect of these variations on the system performance. To explore this matter in some detail, refer to the transfer function of the feedback system illustrated in Figure 13.2-1. The expression for $T(s)$ is (see Sections 6.4 and 6.5)

$$T(s) = \frac{C(s)}{R(s)} = \frac{G(s)}{1 - G(s)H(s)} \qquad (13.2\text{-}1)$$

For the case when $G(s)H(s)$, the *return ratio*, is greater than unity, the system becomes approximately

$$T(s) \doteq \frac{G(s)}{-G(s)H(s)} = -\frac{1}{H(s)} \qquad (13.2\text{-}2)$$

This shows that when $GH \gg 1$, the system performance is dependent on the feedback system alone. Therefore, if H is independent of frequency, the transfer function $T(s)$ of the system will be independent of frequency, at least over substantial ranges. With the proper selection of the feedback network $H(s)$ almost any desired frequency characteristic is possible, in principle.

When $GH \gg 1$, then $T = -1/H \ll -G$. This means the overall gain of the system with feedback is less than the nominal gain of the system without feedback. This is essentially the cost for the advantages of negative feedback, a price that is often modest. In many cases this is an advantage and not a price or cost.

Note from Equation (13.2-2) that only the feedback network is involved. Hence effects of temperature on any of the elements or components of the system will not influence T. In fact, even if GH is not markedly greater than unity, a substantial improvement will result in system sensitivity. Suppose that the plant system function changes by an amount ΔG; this change is conveniently measured in terms of the *fractional* change in the function $\Delta G/G$. The desired relation is written

$$\frac{\Delta T}{T} = S_G^T \frac{\Delta G}{G} \qquad (13.2\text{-}3)$$

which gives the ratio of the fractional change in T to the fractional change in G. The quantity S_G^T is called the *sensitivity* of T with respect to G.

It is convenient to replace the incremental fractions by differential fractions which allow the use of ordinary differential calculus in the calculations, although this approach does restrict the values to small changes. To find S_G^T in terms of the system parameters, Equation (13.2-3), is rearranged to

$$S_G^T = \frac{\partial T/T}{\partial G/G} = \frac{G}{T} \frac{\partial T}{\partial G} \qquad (13.2\text{-}4)$$

By taking the derivative $\partial T/\partial G$ of Equation (13.2-1) and substituting this in Equation (13.2-4) the result is

$$S_G^T = \frac{(1-GH)+GH}{(1-GH)^2} \frac{G}{G/(1-GH)} = \frac{1}{1-GH} \qquad (13.2\text{-}5)$$

This relation shows that if $GH \gg 1$, then a 10 percent change in the fraction $\Delta G/G$ due to any cause will appear as an approximate $0.10/GH$ change in the overall system T. That is,

$$\frac{\Delta T}{T} \doteq -\frac{1}{GH}\frac{\Delta G}{G} = -\frac{0.10}{GH}$$

Another advantage of negative feedback in a system is that internal or external disturbances are often reduced considerably in their effect. Often such disturbances may be of significant concern. An example can be found in controlling the direction of the large parabolic antenna used for satellite communication. Wind gusts can introduce forces and motions that cannot be tolerated. We can represent the disturbance by R_d, which is assumed to be introduced internal to the total system, with G_1 denoting the system function from input to the point of the disturbance, and G_2 denoting the balance of the system function, so that $G = G_1 G_2$. The resulting system is now that shown in Figure 13.2-2. It follows from the figure that

$$[G_1(CH+R)+R_d]G_2 = C$$

or

$$C = \frac{G_1 G_2 R}{1 - G_1 G_2 H} + \frac{G_2 R_d}{1 - G_1 G_2 H} \qquad (13.2\text{-}6)$$

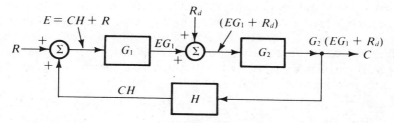

Figure 13.2-2. Feedback system with a disturbing signal

which gives the system output $C(s)$ in terms of the desired input $R(s)$ and the disturbance $R_d(s)$. This equation can be rearranged to the form

$$C = \frac{G}{1 - GH}\left(R + \frac{R_d}{G_1}\right) \tag{13.2-7}$$

This equation indicates that the disturbance source can be replaced by an equivalent source R_d/G_1 at the input, as shown in Figure 13.2-3. From Equation (13.2-6) the effect at the output of the disturbance is given by

$$C|_{R=0} = \frac{G_2}{1 - GH} R_d \tag{13.2-7}$$

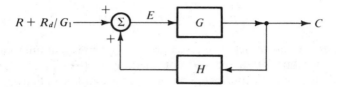

Figure 13.2-3.   Equivalent representation of the disturbance as an input source

Since the systems that we are considering are linear, we can find the transfer function of a system with multiple inputs by adding the transfer functions for each input when all the others are set to zero. Therefore from Equation (13.2-6) we have

$$T_1 = \left.\frac{C}{R}\right|_{R_d=0} = \frac{G_1 G_2}{1 - G_1 G_2 H} \quad \text{and} \quad T_2 = \left.\frac{C}{R_d}\right|_{R=0} = \frac{G_2}{1 - G_1 G_2 H}$$

and thus the transfer function is given by

$$T = T_1 + T_2 = \frac{G_1 G_2}{1 - G_1 G_2 H} + \frac{G_2}{1 - G_1 G_2 H}$$

An additional feature of feedback on the system response is to be found in the transient response of the system as, for example, in a step-function input. Here consideration is given to the time constant of the system response, and the feedback differential equation will reflect this factor. To display this aspect of feedback dynamics, consider the simple system shown in Figure 13.2-4a. The open loop transfer function (gain) of the system is

$$T(s) = \frac{C(s)}{R(s)} = \frac{a}{s + p} \tag{13.2-8}$$

where a and p are taken to be real numbers. For an impulse input $u_o(t)$ $[\pounds\{u_o(t)\} = 1]$ the output of the system is (see Table 6.5-1)

$$C(s) = \frac{a}{s + p} R(s) = \frac{a}{s + p} 1$$

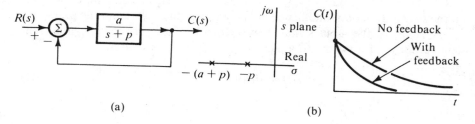

Figure 13.2-4. (a) Feedback system with $H=1$
(b) Time response of open and closed loop system

and its inverse Laplace transform yields (see Table 5.2-1)

$$c(t) = ae^{-pt} \quad \text{(open loop system)} \tag{13.2-9}$$

For the feedback system excited by a unit impulse signal, the output function is (see Table 6.5-1.6)

$$C(s) = \frac{\dfrac{a}{s+p}}{1 + \dfrac{a}{s+p}1} R(s) = \frac{a}{s+p+a}1$$

The corresponding inverse transform (see Table 5.2-1) is

$$c(t) = ae^{-(p+a)t} \quad \text{(feedback system)} \tag{13.2-10}$$

It thus appears that feedback affects the dynamics of the system in a significant way. This can be discussed in terms of the location of the poles of the system function, which means that any adjustments to the pole locations must be accomplished with care, otherwise the stability of the system might be seriously affected. The question of stability of control systems will be treated in a later section.

13.3   TIME RESPONSE OF FEEDBACK SYSTEMS

First Order Systems

Control systems must perform under both transient and steady state conditions. It is important that performance studies be made under both. Often the situation is complicated by the fact that the input signals may not be precisely known, and at other times the signals may be random. It is usual, however, to analyze system behavior and to test performance under standard test signals such as impulse, step, ramp (constant velocity), and parabolic (constant acceleration). In addition, the use of the sinusoidal signal is quite common, since the steady state response to a sinusoidal signal yields important information about the system.

Recall that the stability of any system under a transient signal input depends on the system function, and hence on the number and location of its poles, not on the shape of the input signal. It is adequate, therefore, to study the transient response of a system to a step function, which is written

$$r(t) = Au_{-1}(t) \qquad (13.3\text{-}1)$$

where

$$u_{-1}(t) = \begin{cases} 1 & t>0 \\ 0 & t<0 \end{cases}$$

$$A = \text{constant}$$

EXAMPLE 13.3-1. Find the time response of the system shown in Figure 13.3-1a.

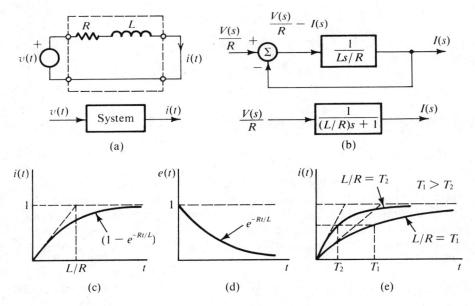

Figure 13.3-1. **(a) System** **(b) Block diagram representation**
(c) Output time response **(d) Error response** **(e) Effect of time constant**

SOLUTION. Proceed by writing the system function (see also Section 6.5)

$$T(s) = \frac{I(s)}{V(s)} = \frac{1}{L} \cdot \frac{1}{\left(s + \dfrac{R}{L}\right)} = \frac{1}{R} \cdot \frac{1}{\dfrac{L}{R}s + 1} \qquad (13.3\text{-}2)$$

This is given in block diagram representation in Figure 13.3-1b. If it is now assumed that $v(t)$ is a unit step function of unit amplitude, then

$$\mathcal{L}[v(t)] = \mathcal{L}[u_{-1}(t)] = \frac{1}{s}$$
(13.3-3)

and the output is

$$I(s) = \frac{1}{Rs} \frac{1}{\frac{L}{R}s + 1} = \frac{1}{L} \frac{1}{s} \frac{1}{s + \frac{R}{L}}$$
(13.3-4)

This expression is now written in the form

$$\frac{1}{s\left(s + \frac{R}{L}\right)} = \frac{A}{s} + \frac{B}{s + \frac{R}{L}} = \frac{(A + B)s + \frac{R}{L}A}{s\left(s + \frac{R}{L}\right)}$$

By equating the corresponding powers of s in the numerator, this yields $A + B = 0$ and $RA/L = 1$. By solving these, there results $A = L/R$ and $B = -L/R$, and Equation (13.3-4) becomes

$$I(s) = \frac{1}{R}\left[\frac{1}{s} - \frac{1}{s + \frac{R}{L}}\right]$$
(13.3-5)

The inverse Laplace transform of this expression is (see Table 5.2-1)

$$i(t) = \frac{1}{R}(1 - e^{-Rt/L})$$
(13.3-6)

as previously found. L/R denotes the time constant of the response.

If we define the speed of response as the time that it takes a system to reach a particular percentage of its final value, this provides a means for ascertaining how rapidly a system responds. Clearly, a short time constant corresponds to a rapid response, and a large time constant characterizes a sluggish system. Figure 13.3-1e graphically shows the effect of the time constant on the system response.

The error response is obtained from

$$E(s) = \frac{V(s)}{R} - I(s)$$
(13.3-7)

and so

$$e(t) = \pounds^{-1}\left\{\frac{V(s)}{R} - I(s)\right\} = \frac{1}{R}\pounds^{-1}\{V(s)\} - \pounds^{-1}\{I(s)\} = \frac{1}{R}v(t) - i(t)$$

or

$$e(t) = 1 - (1 - e^{-t/(L/R)}) = e^{-t/(L/R)} \tag{13.3-8}$$

which is plotted in Figure 13.3-1d. The steady state error is given by

$$e_{ss} = \lim_{t \to \infty} e(t) = 0 \tag{13.3-9}$$

which indicates that the system tracks the unit step input with zero steady state error.

□   □   □

EXAMPLE 13.3-2. Find the response of the system described in Example 13.3-1 when the input signal is a ramp function, $u_{-2}(t) = t$.

SOLUTION. The Laplace transform of the ramp function $1/s^2$ (see Table 5.2-1). Equation (13.3-2) becomes

$$I(s) = \frac{1}{L}\frac{1}{s^2}\frac{1}{s + \dfrac{R}{L}} \tag{13.3-10}$$

A partial fraction expansion of the function is undertaken

$$\frac{1}{L}\frac{1}{s^2}\frac{1}{s + \dfrac{R}{L}} = \frac{1}{L}\left[\frac{A}{s^2} + \frac{B}{s} + \frac{C}{s + \dfrac{R}{L}}\right] \tag{13.3-11}$$

Multiply both sides of this equation by $s + R/L$ and set $s = -R/L$. This gives $C = 1/(R/L)^2$. Next, multiply the expression by s^2 and set $s = 0$. This yields $A = 1/(R/L)$. With these two values of the unknown constants, Equation (13.3-11) becomes

$$\frac{1}{Ls^2}\frac{1}{s + \dfrac{R}{L}} = \frac{1}{L}\left[\frac{1}{R}\frac{1}{L}\frac{1}{s^2} + \frac{B}{s} + \frac{1}{\left(\dfrac{R}{L}\right)^2}\frac{1}{s + \dfrac{R}{L}}\right] \tag{13.3-12}$$

To find B, introduce an arbitrary but appropriate value of s and then solve for B. Specifically by setting $s = R/L$ and expanding Equation (13.3-12) it will be found that $B = -1/(R/L)^2$. Thus the final partial fraction expansion is

$$I(s) = \frac{1}{Rs^2} - \frac{L}{R^2}\frac{1}{s} + \frac{L}{R^2}\frac{1}{s + \dfrac{R}{L}} \tag{13.3-13}$$

The inverse Laplace transform of this equation (see Table 5.2-1) is

$$i(t) = \frac{1}{R}t - \frac{L}{R^2}(1 - e^{-Rt/L}) \tag{13.3-14}$$

The error signal is

$$e(t) = v(t) - Ri(t) = \frac{L}{R}(1 - e^{-t/(L/R)}) \tag{13.3-15}$$

The steady state error is given by

$$e_{ss} = \lim_{t \to \infty} e(t) = \frac{L}{R} = \text{system time constant} \tag{13.3-16}$$

which indicates that this system will track the unit ramp input with a steady state error L/R, which is equal to the time constant of the system, as shown in Figure 13.3-2.

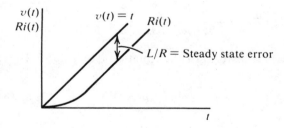

Figure 13.3-2.   The ramp response of a first order system

□   □   □

*Second Order System

Consider the second order system shown in Figure 6.6-2 with its transfer function given by Equation (6.6-4)

$$\frac{Q(s)}{V(s)} = \frac{\dfrac{1}{L}}{s^2 + \dfrac{R}{L}s + \dfrac{1}{LC}} = C\frac{\dfrac{1}{LC}}{s^2 + \dfrac{R}{L}s + \dfrac{1}{LC}} \tag{13.3-17}$$

Incorporate C in $V(s)$ and set $\omega_n^2 = 1/LC$, $\zeta = \frac{1}{2}\sqrt{R^2C/L}$. Equation (13.3-17) now becomes

$$\frac{Q(s)}{CV(s)} = \frac{\omega_n^2}{s^2 + 2\zeta\omega_n s + \omega_n^2} = \frac{p(s)}{q(s)} \qquad (13.3\text{-}18)$$

where

$$\omega_n = \text{undamped natural frequency}$$

$$\zeta = \text{damping factor}$$

The roots of the denominator polynomial $q(s) = 0$ are the poles of the system. These are important since $q(s)$ actually denotes the homogeneous function of the controlling differential equation, and so measures the transient behavior of the system. For $\zeta < 1$ the two roots are

$$s_1 = -\zeta\omega_n + j\omega_n\sqrt{1 - \zeta^2} = -\zeta\omega_n + j\omega_n\beta$$
$$s_2 = -\zeta\omega_n - j\omega_n\sqrt{1 - \zeta^2} = -\zeta\omega_n - j\omega_n\beta \qquad (13.3\text{-}19)$$

For an assumed step input function $v(t) = u_{-1}(t)/C$, and so $£[v(t)] = 1/sC$ the output is then specified by

$$Q(s) = \frac{1}{s}\frac{\omega_n^2}{(s + \zeta\omega_n + j\omega_n\beta)(s_n + \zeta\omega_n - j\omega_n\beta)} \qquad (13.3\text{-}20)$$

The inverse Laplace transform of the equation (see Table 5.2-1) is given by

$$q(t) = 1 - \frac{1}{\beta}e^{-\zeta\omega_n t}\sin(\omega_n\beta t + \theta) \qquad \text{(a)} \quad (13.3\text{-}21)$$

where

$$\beta = \sqrt{1 - \zeta^2} \qquad \text{(b)}$$

$$\theta = \tan^{-1}\left(\frac{\beta}{\zeta}\right) \qquad \text{(c)}$$

The general features of this second order response for different values of ζ are shown in Figure 13.3-3.

If $\zeta > 1$, the two roots Equation (13.3-19) become real, and Equation (13.3-18) can be separated easily into partial fraction form. The inverse Laplace transform can then be found using the procedure in Example 13.3-2.

It will be observed in Figure 13.3-3 that the response for $\zeta < 1$ is underdamped (hence damped oscillatory), for $\zeta = 1$ is critically damped (just non-oscillatory), for $\zeta > 1$ is overdamped, and for $\zeta = 0$ the response is pure oscilla-

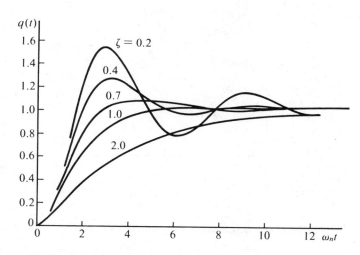

Figure 13.3-3. Transient response of a second order system for step input

tory. Figure 13.3-4 shows the location of the poles for these different values of ζ.

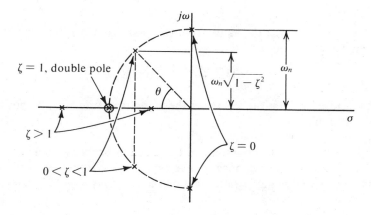

Figure 13.3-4. Pole locations of a second order system for different values of the damping factor ζ

Refer to Figure 13.3-5 which shows the details of a second order system under underdamped conditions. Several performance indexes can be distinguished which characterize how fast the system follows the input, how oscillatory it is, and how long it takes for the system to reach its steady state value. The important indexes are:

(a) Delay time, t_d: the time it takes the signal to reach 50% of its final value.

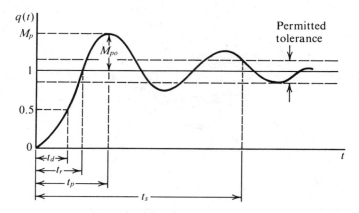

Figure 13.3-5. Response of a second order system

(b) Rise time, t_r: for the underdamped case t_r is the time it takes the system to go from 0 to 100% of its final value; for the overdamped case, it is the time to go from 10% to 90% of its final value.

(c) Peak time, t_p: the time it takes for the system to reach the first peak overshoot.

(d) Peak overshoot, M_{po}: the value from the peak from the final value; the percentage overshoot is:

$$\text{P.O.} = \frac{M_p - 1}{1} \times 100\%$$

(e) Settling time, t_s: the time it takes the signal to settle with a specified tolerance limit.

Before proceeding we will show some of the inherent problems in a compensation design. Consider the response of a second order system [see Equations (13.3-18) and (13.3-21)] which is described by the relations

$$\frac{Q(s)}{CV(s)} \overset{\Delta}{=} \frac{C(s)}{R(s)} = \frac{\omega_n^2}{s^2 + 2\zeta\omega_n s + \omega_n^2} \qquad \text{(a)} \quad (13.3\text{-}22)$$

and

$$q(t) \overset{\Delta}{=} c(t) = 1 - \frac{1}{\beta}e^{-\zeta\omega_n t} \sin(\omega_n \beta t + \theta) \qquad \text{(b)}$$

where

$$\beta = \sqrt{1 - \zeta^2} \qquad \text{(c)}$$

$$\theta = \tan^{-1}\left(\frac{\beta}{\zeta}\right) \qquad \text{(d)}$$

The derivative of Equation (13.3-22b) when set equal to zero yields a maximum of the curve. For an optimum

$$\tan (\omega_n \beta t + \theta) = \tan \theta$$

requires that

$$\omega_n \beta t = \pi \tag{13.3-23}$$

The peak time t_p is then

$$t_p = \frac{\pi}{\omega_n \beta} = \frac{\pi}{\omega_n \sqrt{1 - \zeta^2}} \tag{13.3-24}$$

and the peak value $M_p = c(t_p)$ is

$$M_p = 1 - \frac{1}{\beta} e^{-\zeta \omega_n (\pi / \omega_n) \beta} \sin \left(\omega_n \beta \frac{\pi}{\omega_n \beta} + \theta \right) = 1 + e^{-\zeta \pi / \sqrt{1 - \zeta^2}} \tag{13.3-25}$$

where use was made of the formula $\sin \theta = \tan \theta / \sqrt{1 + \tan^2 \theta}$. For a second order system with a closed loop damping constant $\zeta \omega_n$ the response remains within 2 percent of the final response after four time constants, or

$$t_s = 4\tau = \frac{4}{\zeta \omega_n} \tag{13.3-26}$$

The peak time and the peak overshoot vs. damping factor ζ are plotted in Figure 13.3-6. This figure shows that t_p and M_p are not independent quantities and the need for compromise decisions is inherent in such designs. In the compromise between the rapidity of response and the allowable peak above the steady state value, how might one alter one or the other of these factors? This matter will be addressed when we discuss compensation.

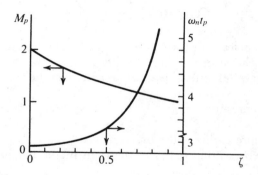

Figure 13.3-6. Peak value and peak time versus damping factor for a second order system

13.4 FEEDBACK AND STABILITY

Stability is a time domain concept and implies that a system, when initially at rest, will remain at rest in the absence of a signal or disturbance. Further, when subject to a transient disturbance, the system response will tend toward zero, or at most, to some bounded or limited response. One or the other of these ideas is involved in the study of the stability of a system.

Different methods of ascertaining stability have been developed. The Routh-Hurwitz and the Nyquist techniques are very important ones. The Routh-Hurwitz method studies the roots of the characteristic equation of the system. The Nyquist method involves mapping of a selected contour in the s-plane for the system function. The root locus method is a graphical method for drawing the locus of roots in the s-plane as a parameter is varied. We shall examine the basic features of these methods.

The Routh-Hurwitz and the Nyquist methods begin with the fact that the transient behavior of a system is intimately related to the system function $T(s)$ which will be expressed as the ratio of two polynomials in s in the forms

$$T(s) = \frac{p(s)}{q(s)} = \frac{b_m s^m + b_{m-1} s^{m-1} + \ldots + b_o}{a_n s^n + a_{n-1} s^{n-1} + \ldots + a_o} \tag{13.4-1}$$

$$= K \frac{(s - s_a)(s - s_b) \ldots (s - s_m)}{(s - s_1)(s - s_2) \ldots (s - s_n)}$$

$$= \frac{A_1}{s - s_1} + \frac{A_2}{s - s_2} + \ldots + \frac{A_k}{s - s_k} + \ldots + \frac{A_n}{s - s_n}$$

When expressed in the second form in terms of the roots, since the basic controlling differential equation has real coefficients, the roots of both $p(s)$ and $q(s)$ either are real, or if complex, will occur in complex conjugate pairs. Specifically, a system with simple poles s_k that is subjected to a sudden excitation function of any sort will contain the sum of exponential terms of the form $A_k e^{s_k t}$, with A_k and s_k being finite real or complex numbers. Remember that if

$$C(s) = R(s) \frac{A_k}{s - s_k} = 1 \frac{A_k}{s - s_k}$$

then its inverse Laplace transform is $c(t) = A_k e^{s_k t}$. The nature of the response depends on the location of s_k in the s-plane.

Three general cases exist that depend intimately on the location of s_k in the s-plane:

1. The point represnting s_k lies to the left of the imaginary axis in the s-plane.

2. The point representing s_k lies on the $j\omega$-axis.

3. The point representing s_k lies to the right of the imaginary axis in the s-plane.

CASE 1. s_k lies in the left half of the s-plane. In this case s_k will be of the form $s_k = \sigma_k + j\omega_k$, with $\sigma_k < 0$. The response will then be of the form

$$\text{response} = A_k e^{(\sigma_k + j\omega_k)t} = A_k e^{\sigma_k t} e^{j\omega_k t} \tag{13.4-2}$$

Since $\sigma_k < 0$, then as t increases, the value of $e^{\sigma_k t}$ decreases. After a lapse of time, the response will become vanishingly small. This is also the situation when the roots are real and simple, where now $\omega_k = 0$.

Suppose that there are one or more pairs of complex conjugate roots. Now, corresponding to each root s_k there will also be a root s_k^*. For each such pair of roots the response will contain terms of the form

$$\text{response} = A_k e^{s_k t} + A_k^* e^{s_k^* t} \tag{13.4-3}$$

where A_k and A_k^* specify the appropriate amplitude factors. The response terms may be combined, noting that in general $A_k = a + jb$, so that

$$\text{response} = (a + jb)e^{(\sigma_k + j\omega_k)t} + (a - jb)e^{(\sigma_k - j\omega_k)t}$$

This expression reduces to the form

$$\text{response} = 2\sqrt{a^2 + b^2}\ e^{\sigma_k t} \cos(\omega_k t + \beta_k) \qquad \text{(a)} \quad (13.4\text{-}4)$$

where

$$\beta_k = \tan^{-1}\left(\frac{b}{a}\right) \qquad\qquad \text{(b)}$$

This response term is a damped sinusoid, which has the form shown in Figure 13.3-4. As a general conclusion, therefore, systems with simple poles in the left half plane are *stable*.

CASE 2. s_k lies on the imaginary axis. This is a special case under Case 1, but now $\sigma_k = 0$. The response for complex conjugate poles is, from Equation (13.4-4)

$$\text{response} = 2\sqrt{a^2 + b^2}\ \cos(\omega_k t + \beta_k) \tag{13.4-5}$$

Observe that there is no damping and the response is thus a sustained oscillatory function. Such a system has a bounded response to a bounded input, and the system is defined to be *stable* even though it is oscillatory.

CASE 3. s_k lies in the right half plane. The response function will be of the form

$$\text{response} = A_k e^{s_k t} \tag{13.4-6}$$

for real roots, and will be of the form

$$\text{response} = 2\sqrt{a^2 + b^2}\, e^{\sigma_k t} \cos(\omega_k t + \beta_k) \tag{13.4-7}$$

where

$$\beta = \tan^{-1}\left(\frac{b}{a}\right)$$

for conjugate complex roots. Because both functions increase with time without limit even for bounded inputs, the system for which these are roots is said to be *unstable*.

The conclusions that result from these three cases are as follows: a system with simple poles is unstable if one or more of its poles appear in the right half plane; and, conversely, a system with simple poles is stable when all of the poles are in the left half plane or on its boundary. In fact, the distance of the points representing the poles from the imaginary axis gives a measure of the decay rate of the response with time.

The impulse response of a system and the location of its simple poles are shown in Figure 13.4-1.

We now wish to reexamine the situation when multiple order poles exist. We must again consider the three cases.

CASE 1. Multiple real poles in the left half plane. As previously discussed (see Table 5.2-1), a second order real pole (two repeated roots) gives rise to the response function

$$\text{response} = (A_{k1} + A_{k2}t)e^{\sigma_k t} \tag{13-4.8}$$

For negative values of σ_k, the exponential time function decreases faster than the linearly increasing time factor. The response ultimately dies out, the rapidity of decay depending on the value of σ_k. The system with such poles is stable.

CASE 2. Multiple poles on the imaginary axis. The response function is made up of the responses due to each pair of poles, and is

$$\text{response} = (A_{k1} + A_{k2}t)e^{j\omega_k t} + (A_{k1}^* + A_{k2}^*t)e^{-j\omega_k t} \tag{13.4-9}$$

This result can be written, following the procedure discussed above for the simple complex poles

$$\text{response} = 2\sqrt{a^2 + b^2}\, \cos(\omega_k t + \beta_k) + 2\sqrt{c^2 + d^2}\, t \cos(\omega_k t + \gamma_k) \tag{13.4-10}$$

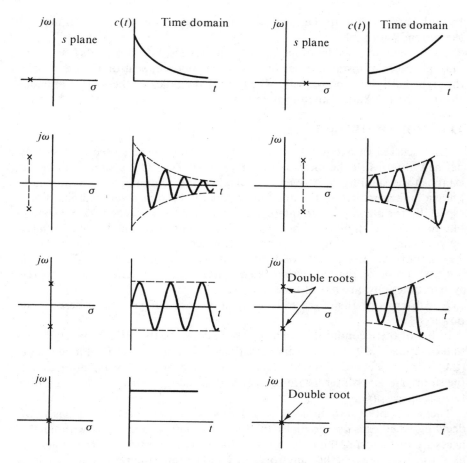

Figure 13.4-1. **Location of poles and corresponding impulse response of the system**

The first term on the right is a sustained oscillatory function. The second term is a time modulated oscillatory function which increases with time. Clearly, the system in this case is unstable.

CASE 3. Multiple roots in the right half plane. The solutions in this case will be, for real roots

$$\text{response} = (A_{k1} + A_{k2}t)e^{\sigma_k t} \qquad (13.4\text{-}11)$$

and for complex roots,

$$\text{response} = e^{\sigma_k t}[2\sqrt{a^2 + b^2}\,\cos(\omega_k t + \beta_k) + 2\sqrt{c^2 + d^2}\,\cos(\omega_k t + \gamma_k)] \qquad (13.4\text{-}12)$$

In both cases, owing to the factor $e^{\sigma_k t}$, the response increases with time, and the system is unstable.

The foregoing considerations can be summarized as follows: a system with multiple poles is unstable if one or more of its poles appear on the j-axis or in the right half plane; conversely, when all of the poles of the system are confined to the left half plane, the system is stable.

13.5   ROUTH-HURWITZ TEST

As discussed in Section 13.4, the stability of a linear system is precisely defined in terms of the location of the poles of $T(s)$. It is a simple matter to establish the stability of a given system when the denominator polynomial is known in factored form. Finding these roots can become a very tedious chore, especially for a complicated interconnected system with feedback. We should like to ascertain stability without being compelled to factor the denominator polynomial. Several simple tests do exist, especially for certain special cases. Two important tests are the following: a system is unstable if

1. All terms of the characteristic equations, i.e., the denominators of the system functions, are not of the same sign.

2. All terms of the characteristic equations are not present in descending powers.

Either of these conditions can be applied directly to the differential equation that describes the system. Observe specifically that these tests are not adequate (the sufficiency condition) when all terms of the characteristic equation are of the same sign and all terms are present in descending powers. More elaborate tests are necessary.

The work of Routh in 1877 and Hurwitz in 1895 provides a basis for deciding whether a polynomial has roots with positive real parts without the necessity of factoring the polynomial. That is, the Routh-Hurwitz test can be used to determine whether any roots of an algebraic equation lie in the right half of the s-plane. If the coefficients of the equation are known only in literal form, the test yields a set of inequality conditions for stability. If numerical coefficients are available, the test permits a check on stability.

The Routh-Hurwitz test requires developing a table from the coefficients of the algebraic equation. Consider the general algebraic equation

$$a_n s^n + a_{n-1} s^{n-1} + \ldots + a_1 s + a_o = 0 \tag{13.5-1}$$

We now develop a schedule of the form shown in Figure 13.5-1. The entries in this schedule are deduced as follows:

Row 1. Alternate coefficients of the given equation

$$a_n, \, a_{n-2}, \, a_{n-4}, \, \ldots$$

$$
\begin{array}{|lllll}
a_n & a_{n-2} & a_{n-4} & a_{n-6} & a_{n-8} \\
a_{n-1} & a_{n-3} & a_{n-5} & a_{n-7} \\
b_{n-1} & b_{n-3} & b_{n-5} & b_{n-7} \\
c_{n-1} & c_{n-3} & c_{n-5} \\
d_{n-1} & d_{n-3} & d_{n-5} \\
e_{n-1} & e_{n-3} \\
f_{n-1} & f_{n-3} \\
g_{n-1}
\end{array}
$$

Figure 13.5-1.   Schedule for the Routh-Hurwitz test

Row 2. The remaining coefficients of the original equation

$$a_{n-1},\ a_{n-3},\ a_{n-5},\ \ldots$$

Row 3. The b-factors are deduced from Rows 1 and 2

$$b_{n-1} = -\frac{1}{a_{n-1}} \begin{vmatrix} a_n & a_{n-2} \\ a_{n-1} & a_{n-3} \end{vmatrix} = \frac{a_{n-1}a_{n-2} - a_n a_{n-3}}{a_{n-1}}$$

$$b_{n-3} = -\frac{1}{a_{n-1}} \begin{vmatrix} a_n & a_{n-4} \\ a_{n-1} & a_{n-5} \end{vmatrix} = \frac{a_{n-1}a_{n-4} - a_n a_{n-5}}{a_{n-1}}$$

$$b_{n-5} = -\frac{1}{a_{n-1}} \begin{vmatrix} a_n & a_{n-6} \\ a_{n-1} & a_{n-7} \end{vmatrix} = \frac{a_{n-1}a_{n-5} - a_n a_{n-7}}{a_{n-1}} \quad \text{etc.}$$

Row 4. These are deduced from Rows 2 and 3 as follows

$$c_{n-1} = -\frac{1}{b_{n-1}} \begin{vmatrix} a_{n-1} & a_{n-3} \\ b_{n-1} & b_{n-3} \end{vmatrix} = \frac{b_{n-1}a_{n-3} - a_{n-1}b_{n-3}}{b_{n-1}}$$

$$c_{n-3} = -\frac{1}{b_{n-1}} \begin{vmatrix} a_{n-1} & a_{n-5} \\ b_{n-1} & b_{n-5} \end{vmatrix} = \frac{b_{n-1}a_{n-5} - a_{n-1}b_{n-5}}{b_{n-1}}$$

$$c_{n-5} = -\frac{1}{b_{n-1}} \begin{vmatrix} a_{n-1} & a_{n-7} \\ b_{n-1} & b_{n-7} \end{vmatrix} = \frac{b_{n-1}a_{n-7} - a_{n-1}b_{n-7}}{b_{n-1}} \quad \text{etc.}$$

Row 5, etc. Repeat the procedure shown using Rows 3 and 4 until all the elements of a row are zero.

The Routh-Hurwitz test states: the number of roots of Equation (13.5-1) that lie in the right half s-plane equals the number of sign changes of the elements of the first column of the schedule of Figure 13.5-1.

EXAMPLE 13.5-1. The characteristic polynomial of a system is given as

$$s^5 + 2s^4 + 3s^3 + 7s^2 + 14s + 22 = 0$$

Use the Routh-Hurwitz test to ascertain whether the system is stable.

SOLUTION. Prepare the Routh-Hurwitz schedule. The result is that shown

1	3	14
2	7	22
$-\frac{1}{2}$	3	
19	22	
$^{68}/_{19}$		
22		

This schedule shows one sign change in going from the second to the third row and another sign change in going from the third row to the fourth row. Consequently, two roots of the given equation lie in the right half s-plane.

□   □   □

While the Routh-Hurwitz test does provide useful information when the algebraic equation is known, there are several important features of the test that are not fully satisfactory. While it is certainly helpful to know whether a system is stable or not, it would be most desirable, and often necessary, to be able to answer the following:

(a) What is the degree of instability?
(b) What might be done to stabilize the system?

The relative stability of a system can be found by shifting the imaginary axis to the left and then checking for the stability of the system. This is accomplished by substituting $s - \sigma$ for s in the characteristic equation and then applying the Routh-Hurwitz test. If the results indicate a stable system, then all of the real roots are to the left of $-\sigma$.

While it is not a failure of the test, nevertheless the test is not useful in those real experimental situations when the coefficients of the characteristic polynomial cannot be found. This situation can be particularly true for closed loop systems because of the impact of the feedback on the system function.

13.6 THE NYQUIST CRITERION

The Nyquist test provides a rather different approach for testing the stability of a linear system. Before proceeding with the details of the test, we must look at the class of systems for which this test will be of particular importance. Let us consider the simple feedback loop shown in Figure 13.6-1. As we know, the total transmittance of this system is

$$\frac{G(s)}{R(s)} = T(s) = \frac{G(s)}{1 + G(s)H(s)}$$

In order to investigate the stability of this system, we consider the characteristic equation, which is

$$F(s) = 1 + G(s)H(s) = 1 + L(s) = 0 \qquad (13.6\text{-}1)$$

For a system to be stable, all of the zeros of $F(s)$ must lie in the left-hand s-plane. This means that the roots of a stable system [the zeros of $F(s)$] must lie to the left of the $j\omega$-axis in the s-plane.

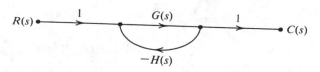

Figure 13.6-1. A simple feedback system

As we shall discuss below, the Nyquist criterion is concerned with the mapping of the characteristic equation and the number of encirclements of the origin of the $F(s)$ plane. Alternatively, we find it desirable to define the function $F_1(s)$ by

$$F_1(s) = F(s) - 1 = L(s) \qquad (13.6\text{-}2)$$

This change of functions is very convenient because $L(s)$ is typically available in factored form while $1 + L(s)$ is not. What this means, therefore, is that we may infer the stability of a closed loop system from a study of the open loop characteristics of the system. Initially, however, we shall address the function $F(s)$, since it is the function of ultimate interest. Then we shall show the value of the change suggested by Equation (13.6-2).

As noted, the Nyquist criterion is based on mapping contours in the s-plane into the $1 + G(s)H(s)$ or $F(s)$ plane. To see what this means, consider the special case when

$$F(s) = 1 + G(s)H(s) = s + 2 \qquad (13.6\text{-}3)$$

This may also be written in the form

$$F(s) = u(\sigma, \omega) + jv(\sigma, \omega) = (\sigma + 2) + j\omega \qquad (13.6\text{-}4)$$

By equating real and imaginary parts, then

$$u = \sigma + 2 \qquad\qquad v = \omega \qquad (13.6\text{-}5)$$

Now refer to Figure 13.6-2 which shows a designated path in the s-plane. For each point on the path there corresponds a point in the $F(s)$ plane which is obtained using Equation (13.6-4), which is the "mapping" function. For example, the point $s = (0, j1)$ becomes, through Equation (13.6-5), $(u, v) = (2, j1)$. By traversing the contour in the s-plane, we obtain the corresponding mapped contour in the $F(s)$ plane. The results are contained in Figure 13.6-2. Observe that both contours in this special example are traversed in the same direction, and the mapping preserves the angles. Transformations that preserve the angles are called *conformal mappings*. Note specifically that the contour in the s-plane did not enclose the point $s = -2$, the root of $F(s) = 0$, which in this particular case is a zero of the function $F(s)$.

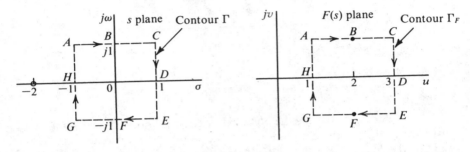

Figure 13.6-2. **Mapping of a contour in the s-plane to a contour in the $F(s)$ plane through the transformation $F(s) = s + 2$**

We generalize the foregoing considerations by noting that if the contour in the s-plane, say in the clockwise direction shown in Figure 13.6-3a, encircles a zero of the $F(s)$ function, then the corresponding contour in the $F(s)$ plane encircles the origin also in the clockwise direction, as shown in Figure 13.6-3b. If the closed contour in the s-plane encloses two zeros of the $F(s)$ function in the clockwise direction, the corresponding mapping in the $F(s)$ plane would encircle the origin twice in the clockwise direction. This situation is illustrated in

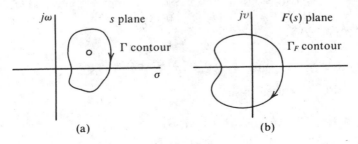

Figure 13.6-3. **(a) A closed contour enclosing a zero of the $F(s)$-function in the s-plane (b) The corresponding mapping in the $F(s)$ plane**

Figure 13.6-4. Of course the actual shape of the Γ_F contours in both Figures 13.6-3 and 13.6-4 will depend on the choice of the Γ-contours and the form of the mapping function.

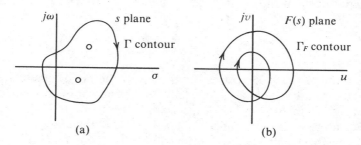

Figure 13.6-4. (a) A closed contour enclosing two zeros in the s-plane (b) The corresponding mapping in the $F(s)$ plane

Now consider the case when the closed contour in the clockwise direction encloses a pole in the s-plane. The mapping in the $F(s)$ plane encloses the origin in the counterclockwise direction, as shown in Figure 13.6-5. Consistent with this discussion is the fact that if a closed contour in the counterclockwise direction in the s-plane encloses neither poles nor zeros, then the mapping in the $F(s)$ plane will be a closed contour also in the counterclockwise direction, but which does not enclose the origin. Likewise, a closed contour in the counterclockwise direction in the s-plane that encloses an equal number of poles and zeros will map into a closed contour in the counterclockwise direction in the $F(s)$ plane, but does not enclose the origin.

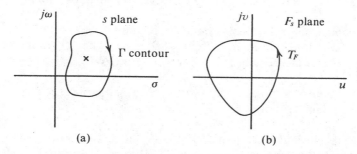

Figure 13.6-5. (a) A closed contour enclosing a pole of the $F(s)$-function in the s-plane (b) The corresponding mapping in the $F(s)$ plane

We shall now use these ideas of mapping for the function $F(s) = 1 + G(s)H(s)$ of Equation (13.6-1) which, in the general case, is the ratio of two polynomials of the form given in Equation (13.4-1). Moreover, we are concerned with roots in the right half plane that might produce instability. These are the poles of

$1 + G(s)H(s)$. To include right half-plane poles, if any, the contour in the s-plane is chosen to extend from $-j\infty$ to $+j\infty$ which is closed by a semicircle at infinity in the clockwise direction. In general the total number N of clockwise encirclements of the origin in the $F(s) = 1 + G(s)H(s) = 1 + L(s)$ plane will be

$$N = Z - P \qquad (13.6\text{-}6)$$

where $Z =$ number of clockwise encirclements of the origin due to the zeros with real parts in the right half plane, and $P =$ the number of counterclockwise encirclements of the origin due to the poles with real parts in the right half plane. For no zeros in the right half plane $Z = 0$, and the number of counterclockwise encirclements about the origin will equal the number of poles with positive real parts, and

$$N = -P \qquad (13.6\text{-}7)$$

From this we conclude that for no zeros and no poles in the right half plane (RHP), a system is stable if it does not encircle the origin.

To adapt the foregoing to the closed loop system we oberve from the transmittance function that the system is unstable if the denominator is zero, that is

$$L(s) = G(s)H(s) = -1 \qquad (13.6\text{-}8)$$

But since $L(s) = F(s) - 1$, our discussion about encirclements of the origin in the $F(s)$ plane becomes equivalent to encirclements of the -1 point in the $L(s)$ plane. This permits the following statements of the Nyquist stability criterion:

A feedback control system is stable if and only if the contour Γ_L in the $L(s)$-plane does not encircle the $(-1,0)$ point when the number of poles of $L(s)$ in the right half s-plane is zero $(P=0)$.

When the number of poles of $L(s)$ in the right half s-plane is different from zero, the Nyquist criterion is

A feedback control system is stable if and only if the number of counterclockwise encirclements of the $(-1,0)$ point within the contour Γ_L in the $L(s)$ plane is equal to the number of poles of $L(s)$ with positive real parts.

According to the discussion above, the procedure is to find the locus (also referred to as the image) of the imaginary axis for the function $G(s)H(s)$, as shown in Figure 13.6-6, which is now written $G(j\omega)H(j\omega)$. For the Γ contour shown in the s-plane the Γ_L contour in the $G(j\omega)H(j\omega)$ plane is assumed clockwise (no right half plane poles), and since the contour does not encircle the

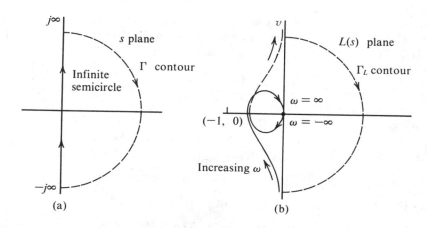

Figure 13.6-6. (a) Contour in the *s*-plane for the Nyquist test
(b) An assumed form for $G(j\omega)H(j\omega)$ for the system under survey

point $(-1,0)$ the system is stable. Figure 13.6-6 is typical of systems that have no right half plane poles, an important case. In this case the Nyquist stability criterion can be simplified to

A feedback system with no right half plane poles is stable if and only if $G(j\omega)H(j\omega)<1$ when the arg $G(j\omega)H(j\omega)=180$ degrees.

Special attention must be given to poles of $G(s)H(s)$ that lie on the imaginary axis or at the origin in the *s*-plane. These points are avoided by detouring around them with very small semicircular contours to the right. By this procedure all of the above discussion remains pertinent.

In summary, the following data are required in the Nyquist procedure:

1. Magnitude and phase angle of $G(j\omega)H(j\omega)$ for ω from $-\infty$ to $+\infty$.

2. The behavior of $G(s)H(s)$ at the poles that lie on the imaginary axis or at the origin of the *s*-plane.

3. The number of $G(s)H(s)$ right half plane poles.

The Nyquist diagram provides a qualitative indication of the sensitivity of the system stability to changes in system parameters. That is, since instability is evidenced by the $G(j\omega)H(j\omega)$ locus covering or encircling the point $(-1,0)$, then it is reasonable to expect that the greater the distance of the locus from the point $(-1,0)$ the smaller the likelihood that the system will become unstable with small changes in the system parameters.

EXAMPLE 13.6-1. Discuss the stability, using the Nyquist criterion, of a system that is defined by

$$L(s) = G(s)H(s) = \frac{2}{s-1} \qquad (13.6-9)$$

SOLUTION. The function $L(s)$ has one pole in the right half plane. It is enclosed by the Γ-contour as shown in Figure 13.6-7a. To find the Γ_L-contour on the $L(s)$ plane, write Equation (13.6-9) in the form

$$L(s) = u(\sigma,\omega) + jv(\sigma,\omega) = \frac{2}{(\sigma-1)+j\omega} = \frac{2(\sigma-1)}{(\sigma-1)^2 + \omega^2} - j\frac{2\omega}{(\sigma-1)^2 + \omega^2}$$

It follows that

(a) For $\sigma=0$ and $\omega=0$, $u=-2$ and $v=0$.

(b) For $\sigma=0$ and $\omega=1$, $u=-1$ and $v=-1$.

(c) For $\sigma=0$ and $\omega\to\infty$, $u\to 0-$ and $v\to 0-$.

(d) On the semicircle $L(s) = 2/(re^{j\theta}-1) \doteq 2/re^{j\theta}$, then $|L(s)| = 2/\infty = 0$. This implies that the entire hemisphere is mapped at the origin.

(e) Since the lower semicircle is described for ω over the range from 0 to ∞ the rest of the Γ_L-contour can be completed by drawing a symmetric curve with respect to the u-axis.

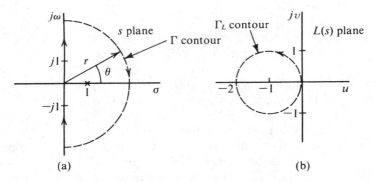

Figure 13.6-7.   (a) The Nyquist contour
(b) $L(s)$ plot corresponding to the Nyquist contour

Since the Γ_L-contour encloses the $(-1,0)$ point counterclockwise once and there is one pole with positive real part, then the system is stable.

□ □ □

EXAMPLE 13.6-2. Determine the stability of the system given by

$$L(s) = G(s)H(s) = \frac{1}{(s+1)(s+2)}$$

SOLUTION. Follow the same procedure as in Example 13.6-1. The Nyquist contour and the Γ_L-contour are shown in Figure 13.6-8.

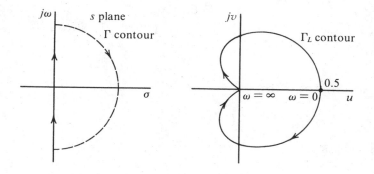

Figure 13.6-8. The Nyquist and Γ_L-plots of a system

For $\sigma = 0$

$$L(j\omega) = \frac{1}{(j\omega + 1)(j\omega + 2)} = \frac{1}{(\omega^2 + 4)^{1/2}(\omega^2 + 1)^{1/2}} \underline{\left/ -\tan^{-1}\left(\frac{\omega}{2}\right) - \tan^{-1}\omega\right.}$$

and for $\omega = 0$

$$L(j0) = 0.5 \underline{/0°}$$

For $\omega \to \infty$

$$L(j\omega) \to 0 \underline{/-180°}$$

For $r \to \infty$ and any angle, $|L(s)| \to 0$ which implies that the semicircle is mapped into the origin. Observe again the symmetry of the Γ_L-contour. Since the Γ_L-contour does not encircle the point $(-1, 0)$, the system is stable.

□ □ □

13.7 ROOT LOCUS

The root locus method is a graphical one for providing an indication of the *migration* of the poles of the closed loop system function $T(s)$

$$T(s) = \frac{G(s)}{1 + G(s)H(s)} \tag{13.7-1}$$

as a function of the gain K in the expression for $G(s)H(s)$ written in a form to display the zeros and the poles

$$G(s)H(s) = K\frac{(s-z_1)(s-z_2)\ldots(s-z_n)}{(s-p_1)(s-p_2)\ldots(s-p_m)} \qquad (13.7\text{-}2)$$

The method studies the migration of the roots of the characteristic equation of Equation (13.7-1) $[1 + G(s)H(s) = 0]$, which can be written

$$GH = -1 = e^{-jr\pi} \qquad\qquad r = \pm1, \pm3, \pm5,\ldots \qquad (13.7\text{-}3)$$

Hence the angle of $G(s)H(s)$ is

$$\underline{/GH} = r\pi \qquad\qquad\qquad \text{(a)} \quad (13.7\text{-}4)$$

and the magnitude is

$$|GH| = 1 \qquad\qquad\qquad \text{(b)}$$

Clearly, all points in the s-plane that satisfy Equation (13.7-3) are points on the root locus.

By combining Equation (13.7-2) with Equation (13.7-4), we obtain the equations

$$\sum_{i=1}^{m} \underline{/(s-z_i)} - \sum_{j=1}^{n} \underline{/s-p_j} = r\pi \qquad r = \pm1, \pm3, \pm5,\ldots \qquad \text{(a)} \quad (13.7\text{-}5)$$

and

$$\frac{\displaystyle\prod_{j=1}^{n}|(s-p_j)|}{\displaystyle\prod_{i=1}^{m}|(s-z_i)|} = K \qquad\qquad\qquad \text{(b)}$$

To check whether a specific point $s = s_o$ lies on the root locus requires that $s = s_o$ be used in Equations (13.7-5) and the results checked to see whether these equations are satisfied. This can be a very time consuming procedure. Fortunately, several rules developed by Evans make it possible to sketch root loci easily. These rules, for $K>0$, are stated without proof:

Rule 1. Root loci begin on open-loop poles [the poles of $G(s)H(s)$] and terminate on open-loop zeros [the zeros of $G(s)H(s)$].

Rule 2. The segment of the root locus on the real axis always lies in a section of the real axis for which the sum of the real-axis poles and zeros of $G(s)H(s)$ that lie to the right of the segment is odd.

Rule 3. The $(n-m)$ loci terminate at ∞ along asymptotes at angles $k\pi/(n-m)$ for $k = 1, 3, 5,\ldots$.

Rule 4. The centroid of the asymptotes on σ is given by

$$\sigma = \frac{\displaystyle\sum_{j=1}^{n} p_j - \sum_{i=1}^{m} z_i}{n - m}$$

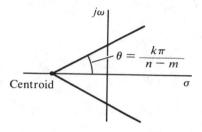

$$\theta = \frac{k\pi}{n - m}$$

Rule 5. Root locus intersections can occur at points which are roots of

$$\frac{d}{ds}[G(s)H(s)] = 0$$

Rule 6. If the root locus crosses the $j\omega$-axis, the points where this occurs can be found by applying the Routh-Hurwitz method to the characteristic equation.

Rule 7. When the poles of GH are complex, the root loci depart (arrive) from the poles (zeros) at angles specified by Equation (13.7-5a).

To illustrate these rules, two examples are considered.

EXAMPLE 13.7-1. Draw the root locus for the system for which

$$G(s)H(s) = \frac{K}{s(s+2)}$$

The block diagram of the system is shown in Figure 13.7-1a.

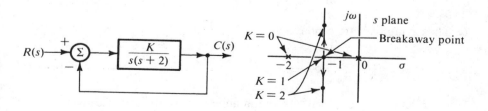

Figure 13.7-1.   (a) A feedback system   (b) The root locus diagram

SOLUTION. The given expression for GH leads to the characteristic equation

$$1 + G(s)H(s) = 0 \quad \text{or} \quad s^2 + 2s + K = 0$$

$G(s)H(s)$ has two poles and no zeros ($n=2$, $m=0$). The two branches of the root locus go to infinity at angles $k\pi/(n-m) = \pm\pi/2, \pm 3\pi/2$. The centroid of the asymptotes is given by $(0-2)/2 = -1$.

The breakaway point is

$$\frac{d}{ds}\frac{K}{s(s+2)} = -\frac{2K(s+1)}{s^2(s+2)^2} = 0$$

and therefore $s = -1$. The root locus does not cross the $j\omega$-axis. The results are shown in Figure 13.7-1b.

◻ ◻ ◻

EXAMPLE 13.7-2. Find the root locus for the system for which

$$G(s)H(s) = \frac{K}{s(s+1)^2} = \frac{K}{s^3 + 2s^2 + s}$$

SOLUTION. The corresponding characteristic equation is

$$s^3 + 2s^2 + s + K = 0$$

By an application of the rules for drawing root loci, we have:

1. Loci start from poles at $s=0$, -1, -1.
2. Loci all terminate at infinity since no open-loop zeros exist.
3. There are 3 loci.
4. For all values of K, there must be at least 1 real root; the others being real or occurring as a complex conjugate pair.
5. The asymptotes are, for $n=3$, $m=0$

$$\theta_A = \frac{k\pi}{n-m} = \frac{\pi}{3}, \frac{3\pi}{3}, \frac{5\pi}{3} = 60°, 180°, 300°$$

6. The asymptotes are centered at

$$\sigma = \frac{(0-1-1)-0}{3} = -\frac{2}{3}$$

7. Intersections of the loci with the imaginary axis are deduced using the Routh-Hurwitz table

$$\begin{array}{c|cc} & 1 & 1 \\ & 2 & K \\ \hline & \dfrac{2-K}{2} & 0 \\ & K & \end{array} \qquad \text{Roots } K = 2$$

For $K = 2$

$$s^3 + 2s^2 + s + 2 = 0 = (s + \alpha)^2(s + \beta) = s^3 + s^2 + \alpha^2 s + \alpha^2 \beta$$

$$\beta = 2 \qquad\qquad \alpha^2 = 1$$

and so

$$s = \pm j1$$

8. Breakaway points are found from

$$\frac{d}{ds} \frac{K}{s^3 + 2s^2 + s} = -K \frac{3s^2 + 4s + 1}{s^3 + 2s^2 + s} = 0$$

from which

$$3s^2 + 4s + 1 = 0$$

or

$$s = \frac{-4 \pm \sqrt{16 - 12}}{6} = -1, \ -\frac{1}{3}$$

A sketch of the root locus is given in Figure 13.7-2.

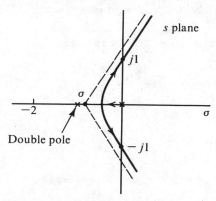

Figure 13.7-2. The root locus diagram for the specified system

Attention is called to the existence of rather sophisticated computer routines for drawing root loci.

□ □ □

13.8 THE CLOSED LOOP FREQUENCY RESPONSE

We have discussed the open- and closed-loop frequency response for a single loop system through the Nyquist criterion with reference to the closeness of the frequency locus to the point $(-1,0)$. Further, we found in Section 13.3 that the magnitude of the closed-loop frequency response is related to the damping ratio ζ yielding the peak overshoot M_p. The relationship between the closed-loop frequency response and the transient response is a useful one in discussing compensation. Hence we wish to determine M_p from the plots completed for the investigation of the Nyquist criterion. That is, it is desirable to obtain the closed-loop frequency response given by

$$T(j\omega) = \frac{C(j\omega)}{R(j\omega)} = \frac{G(j\omega)}{1 + G(j\omega)H(j\omega)} = \frac{1}{H(j\omega)}\left[\frac{G(j\omega)H(j\omega)}{1 + G(j\omega)H(j\omega)}\right] \qquad (13.8\text{-}1)$$

from the open loop $G(j\omega)H(j\omega)$ frequency response.

The relation between the closed-loop and open-loop frequency response is readily obtained by considering this equation when $H(j\omega) = 1$. This creates no problem because Figure 13.2-1 can be replaced by the equivalent Figure 13.8-1

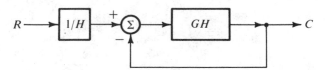

Figure 13.8-1.   System equivalent to the system of Figure 13.2-1

(see Table 6.5-1). Thus we consider the function

$$T(j\omega) = M(\omega)e^{j\varphi(\omega)} = \frac{G(j\omega)}{1 + G(j\omega)} \qquad (13.8\text{-}2)$$

Write for convenience

$$L(j\omega) = G(j\omega) = u + jv$$

The magnitude of the closed-loop response $M(\omega)$ is

$$M = \left|\frac{G(j\omega)}{1 + G(j\omega)}\right| = \left|\frac{u + jv}{1 + u + jv}\right| = \frac{(u^2 + v^2)^{1/2}}{[(1 + u)^2 + v^2]^{1/2}}$$

Square this equation and rearrange it to find

$$(1 - M^2)u^2 + (1 - M^2)v^2 - 2M^2u = M^2$$

Divide this expression by $(1 - M^2)$ and add the term $[M^2/(1 - M^2)]^2$ to both sides. The result is

$$u^2 + v^2 - \frac{2M^2u}{1 - M^2} + \left(\frac{M^2}{1 - M^2}\right)^2 = \left(\frac{M^2}{1 - M^2}\right) + \left(\frac{M^2}{1 - M^2}\right)^2$$

Upon rearranging this equation, there results

$$\left(u - \frac{M^2}{1 - M^2}\right)^2 + v^2 = \left(\frac{M}{1 - M^2}\right)^2$$

This is the equation of a circle on the u, v plane with center at

$$u = \frac{M^2}{1 - M^2} \qquad v = 0$$

and with radius $|M/(1 - M^2)|$. The curves of Figure 13.8-2 are contours of constant M in the L (or G) plane ($H = 1$).

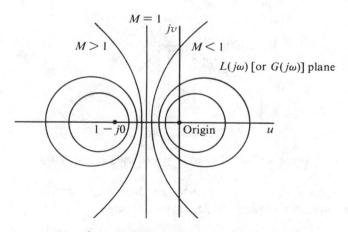

Figure 13.8-2. Contours of constant M in the G-plane

The open-loop frequency response for a system is shown in Figure 13.8-3 for two values of gain K, with $K_2 > K_1$ [see Equation (13.7-2)]. The frequency response curve for the system with gain K_1 is tangent to the circle M_1 at the frequency ω_{r1}. The corresponding frequency response curve for the system with gain K_2 is tangent to the magnitude circle M_2 at ω_{r2}. Refer specfically to the

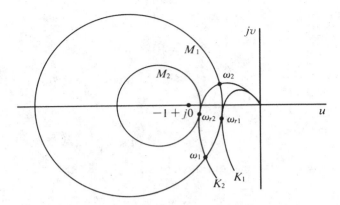

Figure 13.8-3. Nyquist plot of $L(j\omega) = G(j\omega)$ for two values of gain K with superimposed M-circles tangent to the plots

system with gain K_2 and observe that the closed loop system response has equal values at ω_2 and ω_1 $(M = M_1)$ with the peak at ω_{r2} equal to M_2. The resulting shape of the curve would be obtained by moving appropriate M circles along the u axis and noting the frequencies of intersection with the open-loop Nyquist plot. The results would be somewhat as shown in Figure 13.8-4.

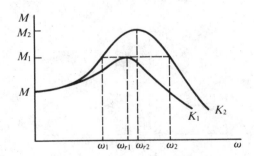

Figure 13.8-4. Closed-loop frequency response $T(j\omega)$

In a similar way, circles of closed-loop phase angles can be deduced. Begin with the angle relation implied in Equation (13.8-2)

$$\varphi = \underline{/T(j\omega)} = \underline{/(u+jv)/(1+u+jv)} = \tan^{-1}\frac{v}{u} - \tan^{-1}\frac{v}{1+u}$$

Write $N = \tan \varphi$, take the tangent of both sides and rearrange the results. This yields

$$u^2 + v^2 + u - \frac{v}{N} = 0$$

Add the term $\frac{1}{4}[1 + (1/N^2)]$ to each side of the equation and simplify to get

$$\left(u + \frac{1}{2}\right)^2 + \left(v - \frac{1}{2N}\right)^2 = \frac{1}{4}\left(1 + \frac{1}{N^2}\right)$$

This is the equation of a circle with its center at $u = -\frac{1}{2}$ and $v = (1/2N)$ and with radius $\frac{1}{2}[1 + (1/N^2)]^{1/2}$. The constant phase angle curves can be obtained for various values of N in a manner similar to the M-circles.

The M and φ contours aid greatly in performing the transformation from open- to closed-loop frequency response. Further, they are used to facilitate the design of a system when the shape of the G-function is to be altered in order to improve the system performance.

As already noted in connection with Equation (13.8-1), when the system feedback is nonunity, a slight change in procedure is necessary. Now the closed-loop response is written

$$T(j\omega) = \frac{1}{H(j\omega)} \frac{G(j\omega)H(j\omega)}{1 + G(j\omega)H(j\omega)} = \frac{1}{H(j\omega)} \frac{G'(j\omega)}{1 + G'(j\omega)} = \frac{1}{H(j\omega)} T'(j\omega)$$

This shows that a feedback system with nonunity $H(j\omega)$ is equivalent to a unity feedback system $T'(j\omega)$ in cascade with another system having a transfer function $1/H(j\omega)$. Therefore, it is a matter of manipulating $T'(j\omega)$ so that the resultant plot due to $T'(j\omega)$ times $1/H(j\omega)$ yields the desired characteristics.

13.9 COMPENSATION

In general, feedback is applied to a system to insure that it performs within specified limits which have been set by design requirements. The required behavior may be specified in terms of its transient response or its steady-state error (see Section 13.3). For a second order system (see Figure 13.3-5) the peak overshoot M_p may be limited to a specified bound, or the response may be required to have a prescribed rise time.

Often the criteria set by the requirements or by the designer are such that the direct feedback system cannot meet these requirements. It is usually possible to achieve the desired results by introducing an additional corrective system known as a *compensator*. The job of the compensator is clear, but selecting an appropriate compensator and establishing its proper injection point into the system are critical matters. In a single loop feedback system, the compensator can be included in the forward path; this is called *cascade* compensation. If the compensator is in the feedback path, it is called *feedback* compensation. The compensator can be included in the input or the output portions of the system. The block diagrams of Figure 3.9-1 show cascade and feedback compensation. The selection of a particular compensation scheme depends upon the power levels of the signals, the specifications at hand, the availability of networks, etc.

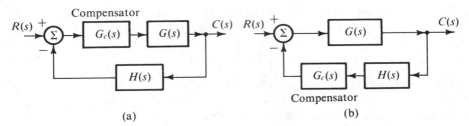

Figure 13.9-1.   Block diagram showing plans of compensation

The approaches to compensation can be studied through the methods of system analysis already discussed; namely, frequency response, root locus, and time domain methods. Another useful approach to system design is known as *optimum design* in which a set of parameter values is sought such that the system gives optimum performance in some defined sense for the particular application.

In this section we shall present only very simple cases so that the general direction for compensation is understood. We do not intend to discuss the many possibilities of compensation. We shall restrict our attention to designs involving frequency response considerations.

Setting the Gain for a Specified M_p

An important problem that is encountered in control system design is how to determine the open-loop gain K required to produce a specified degree of stability. As discussed in connection with the Nyquist criterion, the stability of the system is determined by the location of the $G(j\omega) = KG'(j\omega)$ locus relative to the point $-1 + j0$, the degree of stability being specified by the closeness of approach to the point $-1 + j0$. Also, as discussed, if the degree of stability as measured by M_p is specified, K is uniquely determined. The determination of K for a specified M_p is usually accomplished by a graphical construction in the polar or gain-phase plane. Refer to Figure 13.9-2a. The angle ψ, which is determined by the tangent to the M_p-circle and the negative real axis, is given by

$$\sin \psi = \frac{cb}{oc} = \frac{\dfrac{M_p}{M_p^2 - 1}}{\dfrac{M_p^2}{M_p^2 - 1}} = \frac{1}{M_p} \qquad\qquad M_p > 1$$

In addition

$$oa = ob \cos \psi = \sqrt{\overline{oc}^2 - \overline{cb}^2} \ \sqrt{1 - \sin^2 \psi}$$

$$= \left[\left(\frac{M_p^2}{M_p^2 - 1} \right)^2 - \left(\frac{M_p}{M_p^2 - 1} \right)^2 \right]^{1/2} \left[1 - \frac{1}{M_p^2} \right]^{1/2} = 1$$

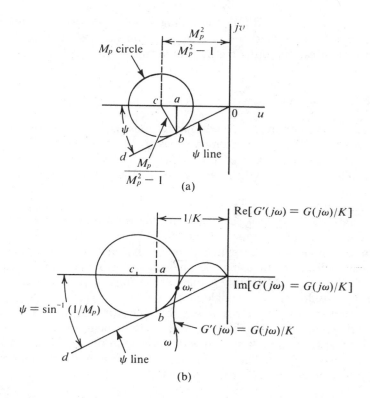

Figure 13.9-2.   Construction for gain determination on the $G'(j\omega)$ plane

This shows that point a coincides with the point $-1 + j0$.

The procedure to determine K is the following (see Figure 13.9-2b):

1. Plot $G(j\omega)/K = G'(j\omega)$ in the complex plane, for varying ω.

2. Draw a line obd at an angle $\psi = \sin^{-1}(1/M_p)$.

3. Draw a circle with its center on the negative real axis which is tangent to both obd and $G'(j\omega)$.

4. Draw a perpendicular line to the real axis from the point of tangency of the ψ-line (point b in the figure).

5. If all of the phasors in the complex plane are now enlarged by a factor K, then a will be on the $-1 + j0$ point. The enlarged complex plane plot will become $G(j\omega) = KG'(j\omega)$, and so

$$K\overline{oa} = 1 \quad \text{or} \quad K = \frac{1}{oa}$$

6. The point of tangency of the M_p-circle with the $G(j\omega)/K$ locus is the resonant frequency of the closed loop system for the specified M_p (see Figure 13.9-2b).

The construction required for determining K for a specified M_p is simplified somewhat when special diagrams, known as Nichols charts, are used. The student will study these and other methods in his more advanced courses on control theory.

Approximate Procedures

The peak magnitude of the closed-loop response is not the only measure of the degree of stability that is commonly used. More direct but less reliable descriptions of the approach of the $G(j\omega)$ locus to the point $-1+j0$ are available. These measures of the degree of stability are called *phase margin* and *gain margin*.

The phase margin of the open loop function $G(j\omega)$ of a unity feedback system equals $180° + \underline{/G(j\omega)}$ at the frequency for which the magnitude of $G(\omega)$ is unity. The gain margin of the open loop function is the reciprocal of the magnitude of $G(\omega)$ at the frequency for which the angle of $G(j\omega)$ is $-180°$. The primary advantage of using the phase margin or the gain margin as a measure of the degree of stability is that calculations can be made directly on separate magnitude and phase angle plots.

The phase margin is used more widely than the gain margin as a degree-of-stability criterion, with the resulting gain margin being a measure of the goodness of performance. A system with a low gain margin is considered to have a poor performance. The usual ranges of phase margin and gain margin that provide generally satisfactory performance are the following:

$$30° < \text{phase margin} < 60° \qquad \text{(a)} \quad \text{(13.9-1)}$$

$$2.5 < \text{gain margin} < 10 \qquad \text{(b)}$$

When the phase margin is used as a degree-of-stability criterion for setting the gain K of the feedback system, the procedure is essentially the following:

1. The amplitude and phase versus ω plots (or the gain-phase plot) of $G(j\omega)/K$ are constructed. With appropriate scaling, these are the Bode plots.
2. The frequency at which

$$\text{angle } \frac{G(j\omega)}{K} = -180° + \text{phase margin}$$

is determined.

3. The magnitude $G(j\omega)/K$ is determined at this frequency
4. Choose K such that $G(j\omega) = 1$.

For rough approximate purposes, the asymptotic magnitude curves are used rather than the true magnitude and phase curves. We show this by means of an example.

EXAMPLE 13.9-1. A specific transfer function is specified. Sketch the Bode plots for this, and from these determine the phase margin and gain margin.

$$G(j\omega) = \frac{4(1+j0.5\omega)}{j\omega(1+j0.1\omega)\left[1+j0.4\left(\dfrac{\omega}{30}\right)+\left(\dfrac{j\omega}{30}\right)^2\right]} \quad (13.9\text{-}2)$$

SOLUTION. Write this equation to separate the log amplitude and the phase factors. That is, the amplitude factor is

$$20 \log G(\omega) = 20 \log 4 + 20 \log \left|\left(1+j\frac{\omega}{2}\right)\right| - 20 \log |j\omega| \quad (13.9\text{-}3)$$

$$- 20 \log \left|\left(1+j\frac{\omega}{10}\right)\right| - 20 \log \left|\left[1+j\omega\left(\frac{0.4}{30}\right)+\left(\frac{j\omega}{30}\right)^2\right]\right|$$

and the phase angle factor is

$$\varphi(\omega) = 0 + \tan^{-1}(0.5\omega) - 90° - \tan^{-1}(0.1\omega) - \tan^{-1}\left(\frac{0.4\times30\omega}{30^2-\omega^2}\right) \quad (13.9\text{-}4)$$

The factors that are of importance in these expressions as the frequency increases are
1. The constant gain $= 4$.
2. A pole at the origin.
3. A zero at $\omega = -2$.
4. A pole at $\omega = -10$.
5. A pair of complex roots at $\omega = \omega_n = 30$ (see Section 13.4).
The asymptote of each factor in Equation (13.9-3) is shown in Figure 13.9-3. The component curves include the following:
1. The constant gain is $20 \log 4 = 12.04$ dB.
2. Since $\log 1 = 0$, the pole at the origin produces a magnitude variation which extends from $\omega = 0$ to $\omega = \infty$ with a negative slope of -20 dB/decade. This curve crosses the 0 dB line at $\omega = 1$.
3. The component curve resulting from the zero at $\omega = 2$ has a slope of 20 dB/decade for $\omega \gg 1$. Note that $20 \log 0.5\omega = 20 \log 0.5 + 20 \log \omega = -6.02059 + 20 \log \omega$. This indicates that $20 \log 0.5\omega = 0$ at $\omega = 1/0.5 = 2$, and as an approximation, the asymptote will start from zero at the break frequency $\omega = 2$.
4. The asymptotic approximation of the magnitude component curve appropriate to the pole at $\omega = -10$ has a slope of -20 dB/decade beyond the break frequency at $\omega = 10$.
5. The asymptotic behavior of the curve corresponding to the pair of complex poles at $\omega = \omega_n = 30$ has a slope of -40 dB/decade due to the term $(\omega/30)^2$.
The total magnitude curve is the sum of the component curves, and has the form shown by the broken line curve in Figure 13.9-3. The exact curve is also shown.

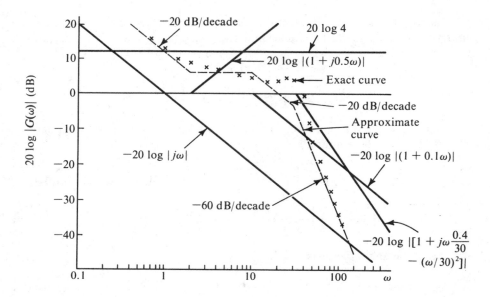

Figure 13.9-3.   Bode plots for the transfer function of Equation (13.9-2)

The phase can be found in the same general manner, and is shown in Figure 13.9-4. It is observed that

1. No phase is contributed by the gain factor.
2. The phase due to the pole at the origin is constant $= -90°$.

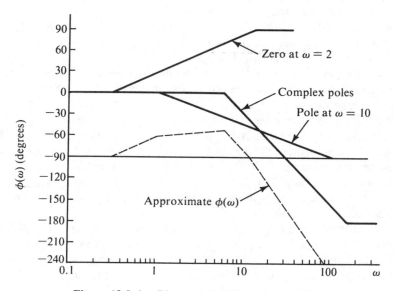

Figure 13.9-4.   Phase $\varphi(\omega)$ of Equation (13.9-4)

3. A linear phase approximation due to the zero at $\omega = 2$ is shown in Figure 13.9-4. There is a phase of $+45°$ at $\omega = 2$.

4. A linear phase approximation resulting from the pole at $\omega = 10$ is shown, with a phase of $-45°$ at $\omega = 10$.

5. The phase approximation for the complex roots is shown with a phase $-90°$ at $= 30$ and with such an inclination that at $\omega = 5 \times 30$ the phase is $-180°$, and with a phase $\varphi = 0$ at $\omega = 30/5$. The two limits of 5 and 1/5 times $\omega = \omega_n$ provide reasonable approximations.

The broken line of Figure 13.9-4 which is the sum of the phases contributed by each component, is the approximate phase function $\varphi(\omega)$ of the transfer function. Figure 13.9-5 shows how the gain margin and phase margins are

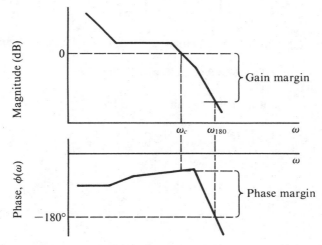

Figure 13.9-5.   The procedure for finding the two margin factors

found on the Bode diagrams. An application of this method yields, from Figures 13.9-3 and 13.9-4 $\omega_c = 20 =$ cross-over frequency, $\omega_{180} = 32$, with phase margin $= 55°$ and gain margin $= 6$ db. This shows a generally stable system.

□   □   □

Reshaping the Open Loop Locus

The introduction of a compensation function in the loop of the feedback system can be viewed as a method for reshaping the open-loop frequency response to permit a higher gain to be used for the specified degree of stability. If M_p is the degree-of-stability criterion that is used, the gain can be increased by causing the phase and gain margins of the function $G_c(j\omega)[G(j\omega)H(j\omega)]/K$ to increase by a proper choice of $G_c(j\omega)$.

The two most commonly used compensation networks for reshaping the open-loop frequency locus are the lag network and the lead network.

PHASE LEAD COMPENSATOR. In using a lead function compensator to reshape an open-loop frequency response, advantage is taken of the fact that the lead function possesses positive phase shift. We examine these features of the lead network shown in Figure 13.9-6a. As shown in Figure 13.9-6b for this network, the zero lies closer to the origin than does the pole.

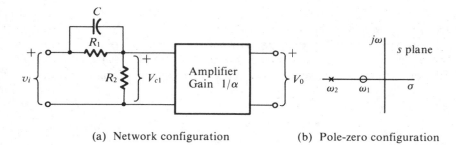

(a) Network configuration   (b) Pole-zero configuration

Figure 13.9-6.   Electrical lead network

The transfer function of the circuit is given by

$$G_c(\omega) = \frac{V_o(s)}{V_i(s)} = \frac{V_{o1}(s)}{V_i(s)} \frac{1}{\alpha} = \alpha \frac{1+s/\omega_1}{1+s/\omega_2} \frac{1}{\alpha} = \frac{1+s/\omega_1}{1+s/\omega_2} \qquad \text{(a)} \quad (13.9\text{-}5)$$

where

$$\alpha = \frac{R_2}{R_1+R_2} < 1; \quad \tau = R_1 C = \frac{1}{\omega_1}; \quad \omega_2 = \frac{1}{\alpha\tau} = \frac{\omega_1}{\alpha} \qquad \text{(b)}$$

Here α is an attenuation factor and τ is the time constant. Observe that by adjusting the time constant τ, it is possible to add positive phase angle to the fixed element response $G(j\omega)$ in a region where the negative phase shift of the fixed elements is too great to secure an M_p-contour tangency. Hence the lead function can decrease the effective negative phase shift of the composite function $G_c(j\omega)[G(j\omega)H(j\omega)]/K$, thereby allowing an M_p tangency to occur for a larger value of gain K. In many cases an increase in the resonant frequency of the system also obtains with the lead compensation.

There is a tendency of lead compensation to increase the bandwidth of the system with a resulting greater sensitivity of the system to noise. In addition, the linear range of operation is restricted. In practical situations the attenuation factor α usually does not exceed 20. The adjustment of the time constant τ is a matter of trial and error. The details of the design of the lead network are given below.

Note that the magnitude function is given by

$$20 \log |G_c(\omega)| = 10 \log \left[1 + \left(\frac{\omega}{\omega_1}\right)^2 \right] - 10 \log \left[1 + \left(\frac{\omega}{\omega_2}\right)^2 \right] \qquad \text{(a)} \quad (13.9\text{-}6)$$

The phase function is

$$\varphi(\omega) = \tan^{-1}\left(\frac{\omega}{\omega_1}\right) - \tan^{-1}\left(\frac{\omega}{\omega_2}\right) \qquad \text{(b)}$$

or

$$\tan \varphi = \frac{\dfrac{\omega}{\omega_1}\left(1 - \dfrac{\omega_1}{\omega_2}\right)}{1 + \dfrac{\omega^2}{\omega_1 \omega_2}}$$

The Bode plots of these equations are given in Figure 13.9-7.

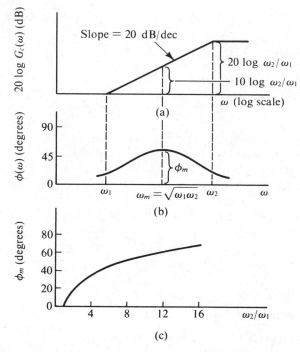

Figure 13.9-7. Bode plots of the phase-lead network of Figure 13.9-6

To find the maximum phase lead, examine $d\varphi/d\omega = 0$, which leads to

$$\omega_m = \frac{\omega_1}{\sqrt{\omega_1/\omega_2}} = \sqrt{\omega_1 \omega_2} \qquad (13.9\text{-}7)$$

This shows that ω_m is the geometric mean of the two corner frequencies of the compensator. The maximum value of the phase shift is found by substituting

ω_m into Equation (13.9-6b). This gives

$$\tan \varphi_m = \frac{1}{2}\sqrt{\frac{\omega_2}{\omega_1}}\left(1 - \frac{\omega_1}{\omega_2}\right) \qquad\qquad \text{(a)} \quad (13.9\text{-}8)$$

or

$$\sin \varphi_m = \frac{\left(1 - \dfrac{\omega_1}{\omega_2}\right)}{1 + \dfrac{\omega_1}{\omega_2}} = \frac{\omega_2 - \omega_1}{\omega_2 + \omega_1} \qquad\qquad \text{(b)}$$

$$\frac{\omega_1}{\omega_2} = \frac{1 - \sin \varphi_m}{1 + \sin \varphi_m} \qquad\qquad \text{(c)}$$

The magnitude of $G_c(\omega)$ at $\omega = \omega_m$ is given by [see Equation (13.9-7)]

$$|G_c(\omega_m)| = \left|\frac{1 + j(\omega_m/\omega_1)}{1 + j(\omega_m/\omega_2)}\right| = \frac{\sqrt{1 + \omega_m^2/\omega_1^2}}{\sqrt{1 + \omega_m^2/\omega_2^2}} = \frac{1}{\sqrt{\omega_1/\omega_2}} \qquad (13.9\text{-}9)$$

Equation (13.9-8c) can be used to compute the ω_1/ω_2 parameter of the phase lead network for a specified maximum phase. A plot of φ_m versus ω_2/ω_1 is given in Figure 13.9-7c.

The steps required to design a lead compensator are the following:

1. Determine the gain K of the forward transfer function to satisfy a specified error constant.

2. Use this value of K to determine the phase margin of the uncompensated system.

3. The required phase lead is found from the relation

$$\varphi_l = \varphi_r - \varphi_u + \varphi_s$$

where

φ_l = phase lead

φ_r = required phase margin

φ_u = phase margin of the uncompensated system

φ_s = safety margin since the crossover frequency will increase after compensation. Values of 5°-10° are common for a slope of -40 dB/dec.

4. Let $\varphi_m = \varphi_l$ and find ω_1/ω_2 for the network using Equation (13.9-8c).
5. Calculate 10 log (ω_2/ω_1) at ω_m (see Figure 13.9-7a). Locate the frequency at which the uncompensated system has a gain of -10 log (ω_2/ω_1). This is the cross-over frequency $\omega_{c2} = \omega_m$ of the compensated system.

6. Compute the corner frequencies

$$\omega_{1c} = \omega_m \sqrt{\frac{\omega_1}{\omega_2}} \qquad\qquad \omega_{2c} = \frac{\omega_m}{\sqrt{\omega_1/\omega_2}}$$

7. Draw the Bode diagrams for the compensated system and check the phase margin. If the margin is low, increase the value of φ_s and repeat from step 3.

EXAMPLE 13.9-2. The forward transfer function of an uncompensated system is

$$G(s) = \frac{10}{s^2}$$

It is required that the phase margin be limited to $\varphi_r = 35°$. Determine the compensating network in cascade to achieve the desired behavior.

SOLUTION. The Bode diagrams of the uncompensated system are given in Figure 13.9-8. From these curves we deduce the following:

1. $K = 10$.

2. Phase margin $\varphi_u = 0°$ $[180° - \arg G(\omega)]$.

3. $\varphi_l = 35° - 0° + 5° = 40°$.

4. $\dfrac{\omega_1}{\omega_2} = \dfrac{1 - \sin \varphi_m}{1 + \sin \varphi_m} = \dfrac{1 - \sin 40°}{1 + \sin 40°} = 0.217$.

5. The magnitude contribution of the compensating network at ω_m (see Figure 13.9-7a) is

$$10 \log \left(\frac{\omega_2}{\omega_1}\right) = 10 \log \left(\frac{1}{0.217}\right) = 6.63 \quad \text{dB}$$

The new cross-over frequency $\omega_{c2} = \omega_m$ can be determined as the frequency at which the uncompensated system has a dB gain of $-10 \log (1/0.217) = -6.63$ dB. From the Bode diagram we find that

$$\omega_{c2} = \omega_m = 4.63$$

This is also given by the relation $20 - 40 \log \omega = -6.63$.

6. The lower corner frequency $\omega_{1c} = \omega_m \sqrt{\omega_1/\omega_2} = 4.63\sqrt{0.217} = 2.15$. The upper corner frequency $\omega_{2c} = \omega_m \sqrt{\omega_2/\omega_1} = 4.63\sqrt{1/0.217} = 9.94$.

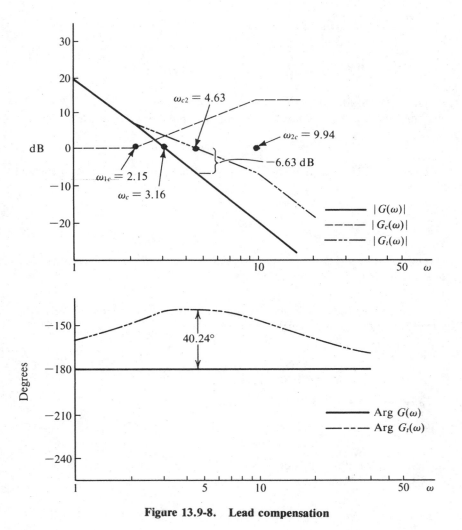

Figure 13.9-8. Lead compensation

7. The transfer function of the lead network including the amplifier with gain ω_2/ω_1 is

$$G_c(s) = \frac{1+s/2.15}{1+s/9.94} = \frac{1+0.465s}{1+0.100s}$$

The open loop transfer function is given by

$$G_t(s) = G_c(s)G(s) = \frac{10}{s^2}\frac{1+0.465s}{1+0.100s}$$

This function is plotted on Figure 13.9-8. From this figure, it is observed that the phase margin has increased from $0°$ to $40.24°$, and this indicates an increase in the relative stability of the system. The resonant frequency (crossover), which is an indication of rise and settling times, has increased from 3.16 rad/sec to 4.63 rad/sec.

□   □   □

PHASE-LAG COMPENSATOR. The circuit of the phase-lag compensating network is shown in Figure 13.9-9a. The location of its pole and zero are shown in

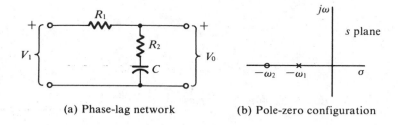

(a) Phase-lag network   (b) Pole-zero configuration

Figure 13.9-9.   The phase lag network

Figure 13.9-9b. The transfer function of the circuit is given by

$$G_c(s) = \frac{V_o(s)}{V_i(s)} = \frac{1 + s/\omega_2}{1 + s/\omega_1} \qquad \text{(a)} \qquad (13.9\text{-}10)$$

where

$$\omega_2 = \frac{1}{R_2 C}; \; \omega_1 = \frac{\omega_2}{\beta}; \; \beta = \frac{R_1 + R_2}{R_2}; \; \omega_1 < \omega_2 \qquad \text{(b)}$$

The complex transfer function of the lag network is, therefore,

$$G_c(\omega) = \frac{1 + j\omega/\omega_2}{1 + j\beta\omega/\omega_2} \qquad (13.9\text{-}11)$$

Since $\beta > 1$, the steady state output has a lagging phase angle with respect to the phase of a sinusoidal input. The Bode diagram of the lag network is shown in Figure 13.9-10.

By following the same procedures as those for the phase-lead network, it will be found that for the phase-lag network

$$\omega_m = \sqrt{\omega_1 \omega_2} \qquad \text{(a)} \qquad (13.9\text{-}12)$$

and

$$|G_c(\omega_m)| = \sqrt{\frac{\omega_1}{\omega_2}} = \frac{1}{\sqrt{\beta}} \qquad \text{(b)}$$

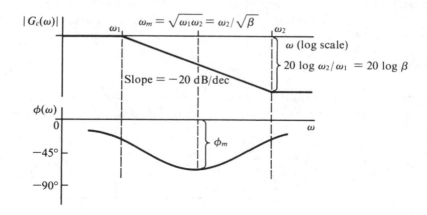

Figure 13.9-10.   Bode plots of the phase-lag network of Figure 13.9-9a.

The procedure from here in carrying out the details of the design parallels that given above for the phase-lead network.

In using the lag function to reshape the open-loop response, the choice of the attenuation factor is usually governed by the gain increase that is sought. In practice βs greater than 20 are rarely used. A good rule of thumb is that the gain increase lies in the range from 0.7β to 0.9β. Two considerations limit the choice of $\tau = 1/\omega_2 = R_2C$. Since the lag function introduces a negative phase shift, the time constant should be such that this phase shift does not occur in the region where the open-loop response passes near the $-1 + j0$ point. Consequently, the lag function is usually adjusted so that its major phase contribution occurs at low frequencies. This means that τ cannot be made too small without affecting the stability of the system. On the other hand, if τ is made too large, the transient response of the system tends to deteriorate as a result of excessive peaking and a long settling time. A rule of thumb for adjusting the lag function is to choose τ so that a phase shift of $-5°$ to $-10°$ is introduced at the uncompensated resonant frequency of the system.

13.10   POSTLUDE

As has been noted, feedback and feedback control exists in all branches of technology, in the biological world, in the business world, in the computer world. Consequently, the character of the application and its point of injection is dependent on the particular objective to be achieved. This chapter has introduced the concepts and some of the analytical tools available for studying feedback systems. The broad study of feedback control goes far beyond our simple considerations, since multiple loop systems are important, and system optimization is most significant in many cases.

More advanced studies, which include nonlinear as well as linear systems, often employ advanced mathematical techniques and require, therefore, a good background in linear algebra, in calculus of variations, and for numerical results a good working knowledge of computer programming. Work in what has become known as *modern control theory* and *optimum control theory* requires mathematical sophistication. The techniques go far in achieving an ability to develop very sophisticated control systems, especially those dealing with noise and other disturbances.

SUMMARY

- Basically there are two types of control systems, open- and closed-loop.

- The essential elements of a closed loop feedback system are controller, plant, and feedback element.

- A feedback system is stable if all the roots of its characteristic equation (the denominator of its transfer function) have negative real parts.

- For the basic feedback system shown, we define the factors

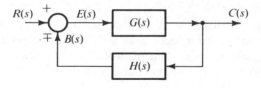

$$R(s) = \text{input signal}$$
$$E(s) = \text{error signal}$$
$$B(s) = \text{feedback signal}$$
$$G(s) = C(s)/E(s) = \text{forward transfer function}$$
$$H(s) = B(s)/C(s) = \text{feedback transfer function}$$
$$C(s) = \text{output signal}$$
$$G(s)H(s) = B(s)/E(s) = \text{loop transfer function}$$
$$T(s) = C(s)/R(s) = \text{control ratio} = \text{closed loop transfer function}$$
$$1 \pm G(s)H(s) = 0 = \text{characteristic equation}$$

$$T(s) = \frac{G(s)}{1 \pm G(s)H(s)}$$

- Sensitivity is an important concept for ascertaining the influence of a given factor on the system performance. The overall sensitivity S_G^T is the ratio of the fractional change in $T(s)$ to a fractional change in $G(s)$.

- Negative feedback usually effects a reduction in internal or external disturbances.

- In the time domain response of a simple system, negative feedback causes more rapid response to input changes. This effectively reduces the system time constant.

- System stability can be expressed in terms of the roots of the denominator polynomial of the system function. The results are summarized as follows: with simple poles, a system is unstable if one or more of its poles appears in the right half plane; the system is stable when all of its poles are in the left half plane or on the boundary. A system with multiple poles is unstable if one or more of its poles appears on the j-axis or in the right plane. Conversely, when all poles of the system are confined to the left half plane, the system is stable.

- The Routh-Hurwitz test provides a means for ascertaining whether a polynomial has zeros with positive real roots. The method does not locate the roots.

- The Nyquist test uses the polar diagram of the open loop gain $G(s)H(s)$ to ascertain the stability of a closed loop system. This test requires a knowledge of the number of zeros and the number of poles enclosed by a contour in the s-plane along the ω-axis extending from $-j\infty$ to $+j\infty$ and which is closed by a semicircle at infinity in a clockwise direction.

- The Nyquist criterion states: a closed loop feedback system is stable if and only if its open loop transfer locus does not enclose the point $(-1,0)$ and if the number of clockwise encirclements about $(-1,0)$ equals the number of poles of $G(s)H(s)$ with positive real parts.

- The root locus method provides a test of stability by examining graphically the location of the poles of $T(s)$ as a function of the gain factor K of the system.

- Compensators are used to modify feedback control system performance.

- Two common networks used as compensators are the lead and the lag networks.

REVIEW QUESTIONS

1. Name the different elements of a feedback control system.
2. Describe an open- and closed-loop system with which you have had contact.
3. What are the most important features of a feedback system?
4. What is meant by a mathematical model?
5. What is the transfer function of a system?
6. What is the characteristic equation of a feedback system?
7. What is the gain constant of a feedback system.
8. Define the summing and the pickoff points.

9. For a feedback system, clearly explain the following: (a) forward transfer function, (b) loop transfer function, (c) closed loop transfer function, (d) feedback signal, and (e) error signal.
10. What is the return ratio of a feedback system?
11. What is the time constatnt of a system?
12. Draw the step response of a second-order underdamped system, and define the following: (a) delay time, (b) rise time, (c) peak time, (d) peak overshoot, and (e) settling time.
13. What does the Routh-Hurwitz test accomplish?
14. What are the differences and similarities between the Nyquist criterion and the Routh-Hurwitz test?
15. What does the root-locus test accomplish?
16. What are the effects of a lead compensator on feedback system performance?
17. What are the effects of a lag compensator on feedback system performance?

REFERENCES

1. Sage, A. P., *Linear Systems Control*, Matrix Publishers, Inc., Portland, OR, 1978.

    This text presents in a clear and lucid manner the basic details of linear automatic control theory and practice. It provides an introductory presentation to the field which will permit further study of advanced topics in automatic control.

2. Sage, A. P., and C. C. White, *Optimum Systems Control*, 2nd ed., Prentice-Hall, Inc., Englewood Cliffs, NJ, 1977.

    This text addresses in detail the subject of optimum control and related topics. It is written at a higher level for seniors and first year graduate students.

3. DiStefano, J. J., A. R. Stubberud and I. J. Williams, *Theory and Problems of Feedback and Control Systems*, Schaum's Outline Series, McGraw Hill Book Co., New York, NY, 1967.

    A good reference book with a large number of solved problems.

4. Truxal, J. G., *Control System Synthesis*, McGraw Hill Book Co., New York, NY, 1955.

    One of the classics in the control field. Contains a wealth of material.

PROBLEMS

13.1-1. Represent the man-machine control system of an automobile in its block form and give a physical interpretation of the operation.

13.2-1. An amplifier with a gain of 200 has a superposed power line hum of 60 Hz. The hum level is 0.4 volts when the output is 12 volts. Design a feedback network that will reduce the hum to 0.01 volts for a 12 volt output signal.

13.2-2. A furnace provides heat for a home. It maintains the house temperature at a value of $T_{ref} \pm 2°$ centered about T_{ref}. The furnace is on when the house temperature $T_{ref} - 2 < T_h < T_{ref} + 2$ and is off when $T_h > T_{ref} + 2$. A block diagram of the system is shown in Figure P13.2-2a. The heating cycle is shown in Figure P13.2-2b. An equivalent network representation is shown in Figure P13.2-2c.

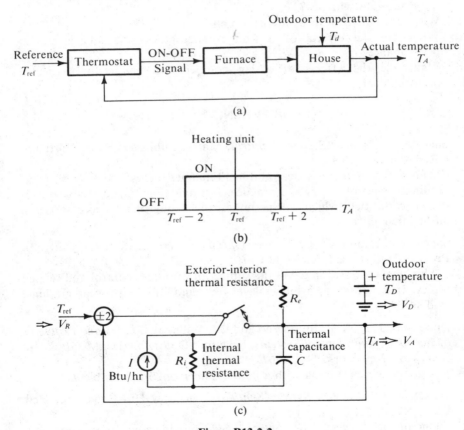

(a)

(b)

(c)

Figure P13.2-2

(a) Find an expression for the thermal time constant.

(b) For an assumed $\tau = 2$ hr, $R_i = 2R_e$ and with $T_d = 36°$ F, how long will it take for the house temperature to rise from 55° to 68° F? To establish the heat output from the furnace, assume that it can maintain the house at a constant 66° when the outdoor temperature is a constant 0° F.

(c) When the furnace is off, how long does it take for the house temperature to fall from 70° to 66°?

13.2-3. An automatic speed control system for an automobile is shown in Figure P13.2-3. The throttle controller system function is $T_1(s) = K_1 + K_2/s$.

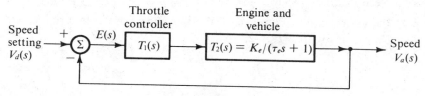

Figure P13.2-3

(a) Deduce an expression for the overall response $V_a(s)/V_d(s)$.
(b) Deduce an expression for $E(s)$.

13.2-4. An electronic pacemaker for regulating the frequency of the heart pump is shown in Figure P13.2-4. Deduce an expression for the overall response R_A/R_d; also the equivalent source due to the disturbance.

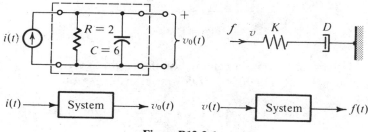

Figure P13.2-4

13.3-1. Find the time response of the systems shown in Figure P13.3-1 to a unit step function; to a ramp function. Determine the steady state error in both cases.

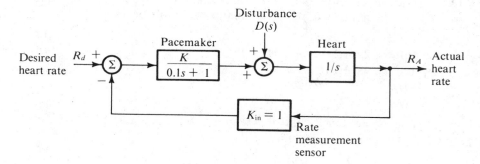

Figure P13.3-1

13.3-2. Find the impulse response of the second order system given by Equation (13.3-18) for $\zeta < 1$. Choose $v(t) = \delta(t)/C$ ($\pounds[v(t)] = 1/C$.)

13.3-3. Find the impulse response of the second order system given by Equation (13.3-18) for $\zeta > 1$. Set $v(t) = \delta(t)/C$.

13.4-1. Verify Equations (13.4-4) and (13.4-10).

13.4-2. Draw the impulse response of the systems whose poles are located as shown in Figure P13.4-2.

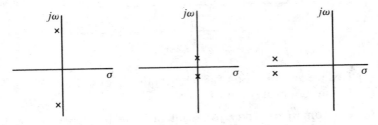

Figure P13.4-2

13.5-1. Use the Routh-Hurwitz test to ascertain if the systems with the following polynomials in the denominator are stable or not:

(a) $s^3 + s^2 + 2s + 21$
(b) $s^5 + 2s^4 + 2s^3 + 4s^2 + 11s + 9$
(c) $s^4 + 8s^3 + 18s^2 + 16s + 2$
(d) $5z^5 + 3z^4 + 2z^3 + 2z^2 + z + 2$
(e) $s^5 + s^4 + 2s^3 + s^2 + s + K$

13.5-2. A unity feedback control system is shown in Figure P13.5-2. Determine the relative stability of the system for

(a) $G(s) = \dfrac{20}{s(s^3 + 10s^2 + 25s + 40)}$
(b) $G(s) = \dfrac{4(s+3)(s+6)}{s(s+5)^2}$

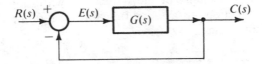

Figure P13.5-2

13.6-1. Map a square contour centered on the origin of the s-plane with sides of magnitude 2 under the following transformations:

(a) $L(s) = 3s + 1$
(b) $L(s) = \dfrac{s}{2s+1}$
(c) $L(s) = \dfrac{s}{s+0.5}$

13.6-2. Sketch the polar plot of the frequency response for the functions

(a) $G(s)H(s) = L(s) = \dfrac{1}{(1+s)(1+3s)}$ (d) $L(s) = \dfrac{2}{s(s+1)}$

(b) $L(s) = \dfrac{s+2}{s^2+2s+8}$ (e) $L(s) = \dfrac{1}{s(s-1)}$

(c) $L(s) = \dfrac{20(s+10)}{s(s+3)(s+6)}$

13.6-3. A system has unity negative feedback with a plant transfer function

$$T(s) = \frac{2(s+2)}{s^2-1}$$

(a) Construct the Bode diagram for this transfer function.
(b) From this plot the polar diagram.
(c) Is the system stable?

13.6-4. For the polar plots of Problem 13.6-2 use the Nyquist criterion to ascertain the stability of the several systems. In each case specify N, P, Z.

13.6-5. Sketch the polar diagram and determine whether the following system is stable, using the Nyquist criterion.

$$G(s)H(s) = \frac{K}{s(s^2+s+4)}$$

If the system is stable, find the maximum value of K by determining the point where the polar plot crosses the real axis.

13.7-1. Single loop feedback systems possess the characteristic equations shown. Draw the root locus for each when $0 < K < \infty$.

(a) $G(s)H(s) = \dfrac{K}{s(s+4)}$ (d) $G(s)H(s) = \dfrac{K}{s(s+1)(s+2)}$

(b) $G(s)H(s) = \dfrac{K}{s(s+4)^2}$ (e) $G(s)H(s) = \dfrac{K}{(s^2+s+1)(s+1)}$

(c) $G(s)H(s) = \dfrac{K}{(s+2)^2}$

13.8-1. A unity feedback system has the open-loop frequency response

$$G(j\omega) = \frac{K(0.2j\omega+1)}{j\omega\left[\left(j\dfrac{\omega}{10}\right)^2 + 0.6j\dfrac{\omega}{10} + 1\right]}$$

Find K and ω_r for $M_p = 1.5$

13.9-1. Design a lead compensator for a system with forward transfer gain

$$G(s) = \frac{8}{s^2(0.2s+1)}$$ The required phase margin is 30°.

13.9-2. The transfer function of the fixed elements of a unity feedback system
is given by

$$G(s) = \frac{1}{s(0.3s + 1)(0.1s + 1)}$$

A 45° phase margin is to be used as the criterion for the stability of the
system. Design a lag compensator with $\alpha = 10$. The allowable negative
phase shift that the lag function contributes at the magnitude (or
asymptote) crossover frequency of the uncompensated system shall be
5°.

13.9-3. Repeat Problem 13.9-2 for a lead compensator with $\alpha = 10$.

Chapter Fourteen

Discrete Time Signals
and Systems

As previously noted, if the essential features of a signal are of interest only at specific instants of time, the signal is said to be a *discrete time* signal. To identify a discrete time signal, we will write t_k for the time variable, where k takes on integral values. An example of a discrete time signal is illustrated in Figure 14.0. Another interpretation of a discrete time signal is that it represents the ordered sequence of numbers of the parameter t_k: $u(t_{-1})$, $u(t_0)$, $u(t_1), \ldots$. For notational convenience, the discrete time signal is often denoted $u(k)$ instead of $u(t_k)$.

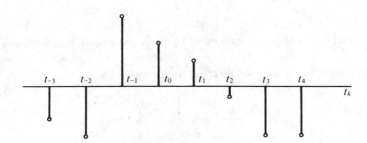

Figure 14.0. A discrete time signal

A *discrete time system* is one whose essential signals are discrete time. We shall find that an ordinary difference equation relates the input and output signals of a discrete time system instead of an ordinary differential equation that applies for the continuous case.

In this chapter we shall learn how to write discrete time signals, the usefulness of difference equations and how to solve them, the use of Z-transforms to express discrete time signals and difference equations, and finally, how to operate on a given discrete time signal (*digital filtering*) to produce another discrete time signal having some desired characteristics. It will become evident from this chapter that there is a discrete time counterpart for the work of Chapter 13.

14.1 DISCRETE SIGNALS

As noted, a discrete time system is one which operates on a discrete time input to generate a discrete time output. The rules by which this operation occurs and the character and properties of the devices for accomplishing this are now to be examined in some detail. The discrete time input is taken as a set of numbers $u(k)$ which is ordered by the variable k. For example, the sequence

$$u(-2)=2; \; u(-1)=3; \; u(0)=0; \; u(1)=-4; \; u(2)=1;\ldots$$

will have the features illustrated in Figure 14.1-1a. A discrete time system is depicted in Figure 14.1-1b.

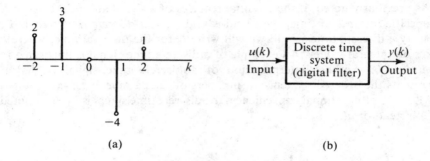

(a)   (b)

Figure 14.1-1. A specific sequence of numbers and a discrete time system

Of particular interest are the discrete time sequences

(a) Unit impulse $\quad u_o(k) = \begin{cases} 1 & \text{for } k=0 \\ 0 & \text{for } k=\pm 1,\,\pm 2,\,\pm 3,\ldots \end{cases}$ (a) (14.1-1)

(b) Unit step $\quad u_{-1}(k) = \begin{cases} 1 & \text{for } k=0,\,1,\,2,\ldots \\ 0 & \text{for } k=\text{negative} \end{cases}$ (b)

(c) Unit alternating sequence $\quad u_{\pm 1}(k) = \begin{cases} 0 & \text{for } k=\text{negative} \\ (-1)^k & \text{for } k=0,\,1,\,2,\ldots \end{cases}$ (c)

(d) Unit ramp $\quad u_{-2}(k) = \begin{cases} k & \text{for } k=0,\,1,\,2,\ldots \\ 0 & \text{for } k=\text{negative} \end{cases}$ (d)

These functions are illustrated in Figure 14.1-2.

A sequence $u(k)$ is said to be periodic if

$$u(k)=u(k\pm k_p) \qquad\qquad k=0,\,\pm 1,\,\pm 2,\ldots \qquad (14.1-2)$$

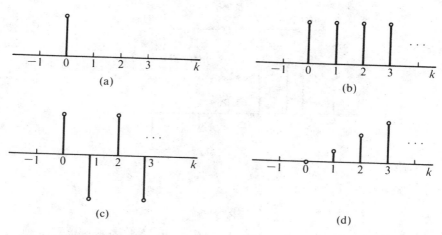

Figure 14.1-2. Useful elementary discrete functions (a) **Unit pulse** $u_o(k)$
(b) **Unit step** $u_{-1}(k)$ (c) **Unit alternating sequence** $u_{\pm}(k)$ (d) **Unit ramp** $u_{-2}(k)$

for any k and some specific k_p. The smallest value of k_p for which Equation (14.1-2) is true is called the period of the sequence.

We can postulate the essentials of an algebra of discrete sequences:

1. The sum of two sequences of numbers is the sum of the corresponding elements of each sequence; i.e., $u(k) = u_1(k) + u_2(k)$, for $k = 0, \pm 1, \pm 2, \ldots$.

2. The difference of two sequences of numbers is the difference of the corresponding elements of each sequence; i.e., $u(k) = u_1(k) - u_2(k)$, for $k = 0, \pm 1, \pm 2, \ldots$.

3. A constant times a sequence is defined as a sequence, each term of which is the constant times the original value of the sequence.

14.2 SAMPLING A CONTINUOUS TIME FUNCTION

Many processes are inherently continuous in nature, although often readings of particular features of the system are made at discrete times. This gives the sampled value at the times t_k. A model for the process of sampling a continuous time function is shown in Figure 14.2-1. Here the sampler is a switch that closes and then opens instantaneously at times $t = t_k$. The sampled values may then be the sequence illustrated in Figure 14.2-1. Clearly, sampling can be considered as a modulation of a pulse train by the continuous function $u(t)$.

While the sampling times can be random, the sampling process that is most frequency used is one in which the sampling switch closes at regular intervals every T seconds. This is *uniform* sampling, and in this case the sampling process has the features discussed above. We shall consider only uniformly sampled systems, and we shall write $u(k)$ instead of $u(kT)$. A representative illustration for different sampling periods is given in Figure 14.2-2. Note

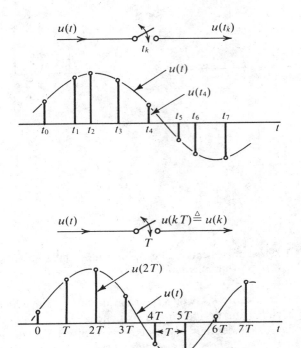

Figure 14.2-1.   The sampling process and the output samples
(a) Nonuniform sampling   (b) Uniform sampling

specifically that even though the function is written $u(k)$, the sampling period must be known. We also observe that when the sampling interval increases, the resulting discrete time sampled function loses its original shape. That is, if we join the tops with straight line segments, the resulting function does not resemble the original one. Therefore the choice of a proper sampling interval is critical. This observation is the essence of the *sampling theorem* which was discussed in Chapter 11 and which relates the highest frequency contained in the signal and the sampling interval T or *sampling frequency* $f_s = 1/T$. An instrument for sampling and providing the output in digital form is called an A/D converter (see Chapter 8).

14.3   FIRST-ORDER LINEAR DISCRETE SYSTEMS

As already noted, a discrete time system is one which operates on an input sequence of numbers (the input signal) $u(k)$ and which produces an output sequence of numbers (the output signal) $y(k)$. We may refer to the system as a discrete signal processor or a digital filter. An important aspect of our study is to define the properties of the signal processor on the basis of the operations to be performed.

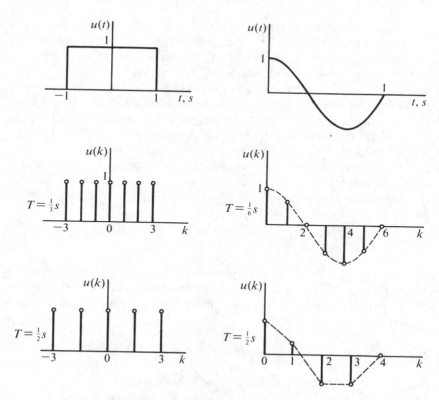

Figure 14.2-2. **Uniform sampling of two different functions with different-length intervals**

A discrete process that is familiar to most persons is that associated with a savings account in a bank. Consider a savings plan which pays interest at a rate r compounded n times per year ($n = 4$ corresponds to quarterly compounding). In such a plan, interest is computed at the rate of r/n for each conversion period. It will be assumed that the deposit earns no interest until the next conversion period. Now let us denote

$y(k)$ = the total bank account balance at the end of the kth conversion period

$u(k)$ = the totality of deposits during the kth conversion period

At the conclusion of any given conversion period, the total bank account balance is equal to the sum of the bank account balance at the beginning of the conversion period, the interest accrued on that amount, and the deposits made during that period. This result can be expressed mathematically as

$$y(k) = y(k-1) + \frac{r}{n}y(k-1) + u(k) = \left(1 + \frac{r}{n}\right)y(k-1) + u(k)$$

This is a linear *first-order* difference equation since k and $k-1$ differ by one unit. The solution can be carried out numerically if $u(k)$ is known. An analytic solution to this difference equation is generally possible. To solve this equation by hand or by machine, an initial value $y(0)$ and the sequence of inputs $u(k)$, $k=1, 2, \ldots$ must be entered and stored in storage registers. The quantity $(1+r/n)$ must be evaluated, and then the multiplication with $y(k-1)$ effected. This result is stored in the accumulator, and with the addition of $u(k)$ the updated $y(k)$ results. During the next period the present $y(k)$ will become the $y(k-1)$ and the process can be repeated. For known interest rate, initial deposit $y(0)$, and a specified sequence $u(k)$, the difference equation is readily solved to establish the subsequent values.

We study a general first-order linear discrete system that is characterized by the difference equation

$$y(k) - \alpha_1 y(k-1) = \beta u(k) + \beta_1 u(k-1) \tag{14.3-1}$$

where α_1, β, and β_1 are constants whose values are determined by the dynamical system under survey. If we assume that the input signal is first applied at time $k=0$, then $u(k)=0$ for k negative. Specifically, suppose that the input is the sequence

$$0, 0, 0, u(0), u(1), u(2), \ldots$$

Now combine these date with Equation (14.3-1) and we have the first equation of the set

$$y(0) = \beta u(0) + \beta_1 u(-1) + \alpha_1 y(-1)$$

but since $u(-1)=0$, this becomes

$$y(0) = \beta u(0) + \alpha_1 y(-1)$$

This requires that we know the value of the output signal just prior to the application of the input signal, i.e, $y(-1)$, in order to calculate $y(0)$. The next element in the output sequence $y(1)$ becomes, by writing $k=1$ in Equation (14.3-1)

$$y(1) = \beta u(1) + \beta_1 u(0) + \alpha_1 y(0)$$

where $y(0)$ had been determined one iteration previously and was stored (on paper, if a hand calculation, or in the memory of a computer, if a computer calculation). This same procedure can be continued to ascertain the complete system response $y(k)$.

Attention is called to the need for the system response $y(-1)$ in order to carry out the calculation above. This term is called the system's *initial condi-*

tion, and it specifies the state of the system just prior to the application of the input signal. Of course, input signals can be first applied at times other than $k = 0$.

EXAMPLE 14.3-1. Determine the voltage output when a current source $i(t) = 2u_{-1}(t)$ is applied across an initially uncharged capacitor as shown in Figure 14.3-1.

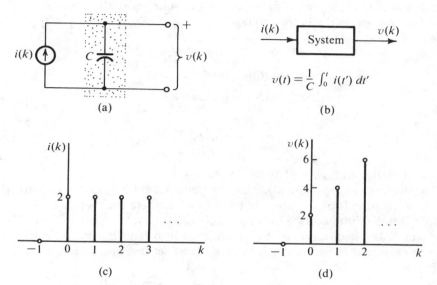

Figure 14.3-1. A capacitor system

SOLUTION. Before we proceed to solve the problem as a discrete time system we must represent the input-output relationship of the system in discrete form. For a sampling time interval T the relation shown in Figure 14.3-1b takes the form

$$v(kT) = \frac{1}{C} \int_0^{kT} i(t') \, dt' \qquad\qquad k = 0, 1, 2, \ldots \qquad (14.3\text{-}2)$$

or equivalently

$$v(kT) = \frac{1}{C} \int_0^{kT-T} i(t') \, dt' + \frac{1}{C} \int_{kT-T}^{kT} i(t') \, dt' \qquad (14.3\text{-}3)$$

By comparison of this expression with Equation (14.3-2), Equation (14.3-3) takes the form

$$v(kT) = v(kT - T) + \frac{1}{C} \int_{kT-T}^{kT} i(t') \, dt' \qquad (14.3\text{-}4)$$

The integral represents the area under the curve $i(t)$ in the interval $kT - T \leqslant t \leqslant kT$ and it is approximately equal to $Ti(kT)$. Therefore, Equation (14.3-4) becomes

$$v(kT) = v(kT - T) + \frac{1}{C} Ti(kT) \qquad k = 0, 1, 2, 3, \ldots \qquad (14.3\text{-}5)$$

which will give an approximate value for the voltage. Setting, for instance, $C = T = 1$ we obtain the output voltage

$$v(0) = v(-1) + i(0) = 0 + 2 = 2$$
$$v(1) = v(0) + i(1) = 2 + 2 = 4$$
$$v(2) = v(1) + i(2) = 4 + 2 = 6$$

$$
\begin{array}{cccc}
\cdot & \cdot & \cdot & \cdot \\
\cdot & \cdot & \cdot & \cdot \\
\cdot & \cdot & \cdot & \cdot
\end{array}
$$

which is plotted in Figure 14.3-1d.

The numerical integration algorithm of Equation (14.3-5) can be presented in block diagram form as shown in Figure 14.3-2 where the triangle indicates amplification (multiplication by a constant) and the square indicates delay by one unit T. The significance of the symbol z^{-1}, which denotes a unit time delay, will be explained in Section 14.5. Here we consider it simply as a time delay operator.

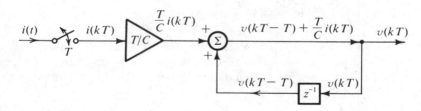

Figure 14.3-2.   Numerical integration algorithm for Equation (14.3-5)

□   □   □

EXAMPLE 14.3-2. Determine the velocity v if a force $f(t) = 2t$, $t \geqslant 0$ is applied to a spring which is initially at rest, as shown in Figure 14.3-3.

SOLUTION. The relation of Figure 14.3-3b at $t = kT$ is

$$v(kT) = \frac{1}{K} \frac{df(kT)}{dt} \doteq \frac{1}{K} \underbrace{\frac{f(kT) - f(kT - T)}{T}}_{\text{slope}}$$

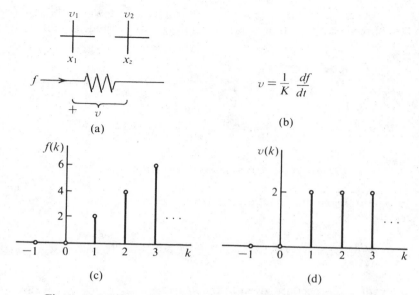

(a)

$$v = \frac{1}{K} \frac{df}{dt}$$

(b)

(c)

(d)

Figure 14.3-3. **Spring system excited by a discrete-type force**

or

$$v(kT) = \frac{1}{KT}[f(kT) - f(kT - T)] \qquad k = 0, 1, 2, 3, \dots \qquad (a) \quad (14.3\text{-}6)$$

For the special case $K = T = 1$

$$v(k) = f(k) - f(k-1) \qquad f(k) = 2k, \, k \geqslant 0, \, v(-1) = 0 \qquad (b)$$

The solution for $v(k)$ is plotted in Figure 14.3-3d. The numerical process
described by Equation (14.3-6) is shown in Figure 14.3-4.

□ □ □

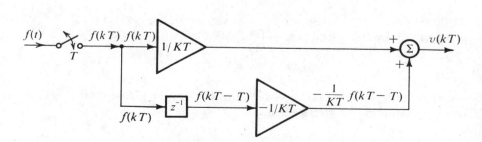

Figure 14.3-4. **Numerical algorithm for Equation (14.3-6)**

Let us now consider the system shown in Figure 14.3-5 where the input is a voltage source and the output is the current $i(t)$. Apply the Kirchhoff voltage

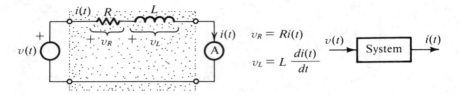

Figure 14.3-5. A voltage-current system concept

law to obtain the circuit equation (no voltage drop exists across an ideal ammeter), we have

$$L\frac{di(t)}{dt} + Ri(t) = v(t) \qquad \text{or} \qquad \frac{di(t)}{dt} + \frac{R}{L}i(t) = \frac{1}{L}v(t) \qquad (14.3\text{-}7)$$

By following the procedure given in the last example, we let

$$\frac{di(t)}{dt} \doteq \frac{i(kT) - i(kT-T)}{T}$$

Equation (14.3-7) takes the form

$$i(kT) = \frac{\frac{1}{L}T}{1 + \frac{R}{L}T}v(kT) + \frac{1}{1 + \frac{R}{L}T}i(kT-T) \qquad (14.3\text{-}8)$$

This can be written, for notational convenience, in the form

$$i(k) = \frac{(T/L)}{(1 + RT/L)}v(k) + \frac{1}{1 + (RT/L)}i(k-1) \qquad (14.3\text{-}9)$$

Equation (14.3-9) represents a particular version of the general form of first-order system given by Equation (14.3-1). We write this

$$y(k) = \beta u(k) + \alpha_1 y(k-1) \qquad (14.3\text{-}10)$$

where α_1 and β are constants. We wish to explore the response of this first-order system to a unit step sequence

$$v(k) = u_{-1}(k) = \begin{cases} 0 & \text{for } k \text{ negative} \\ 1 & \text{for } k = 0, 1, 2, \ldots \end{cases} \qquad (14.3\text{-}11)$$

Further, we consider the system to be "initially relaxed"; i.e., it is in a zero state prior to the application of the excitation, $y(-1) = 0$. We can now proceed systematically as follows:

$$k = 0 \quad y(0) = \beta u(0) + \alpha_1 y(-1) = \beta + 0 = \beta$$

$$k = 1 \quad y(1) = \beta u(1) + \alpha_1 y(0) = \beta 1 + \alpha_1 \beta = (1 + \alpha_1)\beta$$

$$k = 2 \quad y(2) = \beta u(2) + \alpha_1 y(1) = \beta 1 + \alpha_1(1 + \alpha_1)\beta = (1 + \alpha_1 + \alpha_1^2)\beta$$

$$k = 3 \quad y(3) = \beta u(3) + \alpha_1 y(2) = \beta 1 + \alpha_1(1 + \alpha_1 + \alpha_1^2)\beta = (1 + \alpha_1 + \alpha_1^2 + \alpha_1^3)\beta$$

.
.
.

or, by induction,

$$y(k) = (1 + \alpha_1 + \alpha_1^2 + \ldots + \alpha_1^k)\beta \qquad\qquad k = 0, 1, 2, \ldots$$

But the finite series (geometric series of $k+1$ terms) is

$$1 + \alpha_1 + \alpha_1^2 + \ldots + \alpha_1^k = \frac{1 - \alpha_1^{k+1}}{1 - \alpha_1} \qquad \text{for} \qquad \alpha_1 \neq 1$$

and so finally we have

$$y(k) = \beta \frac{(1 - \alpha_1^{k+1})}{1 - \alpha_1} \tag{14.3-12}$$

For values of $\alpha_1 > 1$, the factor $(1 - \alpha_1^{k+1})$ becomes arbitrarily large as k increases, which indicates a condition of *instability*. For α_1 less than 1, $(1 - \alpha_1^{k+1})$ approaches 1 as k grows, and the unit step response approaches the value

$$y(k) \doteq \frac{\beta}{1 - \alpha_1} \qquad\qquad k \text{ large} \tag{14.3-13}$$

For the particular circuit with the discrete time representation of Equation (14.3-9) we obtain

$$y(k) = i(k) = \frac{1}{R} \qquad\qquad k \text{ large}$$

which is indeed the steady state current for this physical example.

EXAMPLE 14.3-3. Deduce the solution of the difference equation

$$y(k) + 4y(k-1) = 2.5$$

with $y(-1) = 0$.

SOLUTION. This equation is precisely the form in Equation (14.3-10) with

$$\beta = 2.5 \qquad\qquad u(k) = 1 \qquad\qquad \alpha_1 = -4$$

The solution is given by Equation (14.3-12) and is, for the parameters used here,

$$y(k) = \frac{2.5[1 - (-4)^{k+1}]}{1 - (-4)} = 0.5[1 - (-4)^{k+1}]$$

We write this as

$$y(k) = 0.5[1 - (-4)^k(-4)^1] = 0.5[1 + 4(-4)^k]$$

or finally

$$y(k) = 0.5 + 2(-4)^k$$

which shows that this is an unstable system.

□ □ □

EXAMPLE 14.3-4. Find the solution of the difference equation

$$y(k) - 4y(k - 1) = k + 1$$

with $y(-1) = 0$.

SOLUTION. We consider this as the superposition of two equations

$$y_1(k) - 4y_1(k - 1) = k$$
$$y_2(k) - 4y_2(k - 1) = 1$$

with

$$y(k) = y_1(k) + y_2(k)$$

Consider the equation in $y_1(k)$ with a ramp function input. We proceed to build up the solution, as was done for the step function in the previous example. Therefore we have

$$k = 0 \quad y_1(0) = 0 + 4y_1(-1) = 0$$
$$k = 1 \quad y_1(1) = 1 + 4y_1(0) = 1 + 4 \times 0$$
$$k = 2 \quad y_1(2) = 2 + 4y_1(1) = 2 \times 1 + 4 \times 1 = (2 + 4) \times 1$$

$$k=3 \quad y_1(3) = 3 + 4y_1(2) = 3 \times 1 + 4 \times (2+4) \times 1 = (3 + 2 \times 4 + 4^2) \times 1$$

$$k=4 \quad y_1(4) = 4 + 4y_1(3) = 4 \times 1 + 4 \times (3 + 2 \times 4 + 4^2) \times 1$$

$$= (4 + 3 \times 4 + 2 \times 4^2 + 4^3) \times 1$$

$$\cdot \quad \cdot \quad \cdot \quad \cdot$$

Thus for

$$k=k \quad y_1(k) = [k + (k-1)4 + (k-2)4^2 + (k-3)4^3 + \dots] \times 1 = 1 \times \sum_{n=0}^{k} (k-n)4^n$$

For the unit step function, by Equation (14.3-12)

$$y_2(k) = 2.5 \frac{(1 - 4^{k+1})}{1-4} = -\frac{2.5}{3}[1 - 4^1 4^k] = -\frac{2.5}{3} + \frac{10}{3} 4^k$$

The total solution is then

$$y(k) = \sum_{n=0}^{k} (k-n)4^n - \frac{2.5}{3} + \frac{10}{3} 4^k$$

$$\square \quad \square \quad \square$$

14.4 PROPERTIES OF FIRST-ORDER DIFFERENCE EQUATIONS WITH CONSTANT COEFFICIENTS

We continue with our previously established first-order linear *nonhomogeneous* difference equation

$$y(k) = \alpha_1 y(k-1) + \beta u(k) \tag{14.4-1}$$

When we set the input to the system, $u(k) = 0$, the equation

$$y(k) - \alpha_1 y(k-1) = 0 \tag{14.4-2}$$

is called the *homogeneous* difference equation corresponding to the nonhomogeneous difference equation, Equation (14.4-1). Without proof we shall state a fundamental theorem associated with difference equations:

THEOREM 14.4-1: If $y_{(h)}$ is a solution of the homogeneous equation and $y_{(p)}$ is the solution of the nonhomogeneous equation, known as *particular solution*, then $y_{(h)} + y_{(p)}$ is a solution of the nonhomogeneous equation. It is called the *general solution* of the complete equation.

We shall limit ourselves in our studies to a special class of signals or excitation functions $u(k)$. These bear much the same place in the solution of discrete equations as the particular solution $x(t) = \exp[s_p t]$ does in finding the particular solution of differential equations. This class of signals is defined by

$$\{u(k)\} = \psi_p^k \qquad (14.4\text{-}3)$$

Important forms for ψ_p are 1, $e^{\pm aT}$, $e^{\pm j\omega T}$.

We begin this study by reference to the simple first-order difference equation

$$y(k) - \alpha_1 y(k-1) = u(k) \qquad (14.4\text{-}4)$$

This equation is displayed in block diagram and signal flow graph form in Figure 14.4-1.

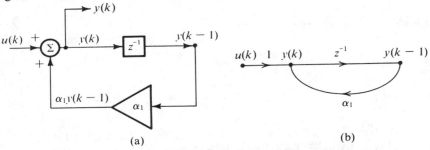

(a)   (b)

Figure 14.4-1.   Graphical representation of Equation (14.4-4)
(a) Block diagram   (b) Signal flow graph

Assume that the input signal is specified by

$$u(k) = U\psi_p^k u_{-1}(k) = \begin{cases} 0 & k < 0 \\ U\psi_p^k & k \geq 0 \end{cases} \qquad (14.4\text{-}5)$$

We shall assume that the output for this input will be of the form

$$y_p(k) = Y\psi_p^k \qquad (14.4\text{-}6)$$

To check this assumption, substitute this trial solution into the original equation. This yields

$$Y\psi_p^k - \alpha_1 Y\psi_p^{k-1} = U\psi_p^k$$

This relation is true for any k, and we shift the time axis to point k, which equivalently sets $k = 1$. Thus

$$Y(\psi_p - \alpha_1) = U\psi_p$$

from which

$$Y = \frac{\psi_p}{\psi_p - \alpha_1} U \tag{14.4-7}$$

This yields the particular solution, and accounts for the subscript p in Equation (14.4-6). The explicit form is

$$y_{(p)}(k) = \frac{\psi_p}{\psi_p - \alpha_1} U \psi_p^k \tag{14.4-8}$$

As required by Theorem 14.4-1, the complete solution to Equation (14.4-4) must include a solution to the homogeneous equation

$$y_{(h)}(k) - \alpha_1 y_{(h)}(k-1) = 0 \tag{14.4-9}$$

We assume as a solution to this homogeneous equation the form

$$y_{(h)}(k) = A \psi^k \tag{14.4-10}$$

where A is a constant. Substitute this in Equation (14.4-9), which then yields

$$A \psi^k - \alpha_1 A \psi^{k-1} = 0$$

from which

$$\psi = \alpha_1 \tag{14.4-11}$$

Thus, Equation (14.4-10) becomes

$$y_{(h)}(k) = A \alpha_1^k \tag{14.4-12}$$

The complete solution of Equation (14.4-4) is

$$y(k) = y_{(p)}(k) + y_{(h)}(k) = \frac{\psi_p}{\psi_p + \alpha_1} U \psi_p^k + A \alpha_1^k \qquad k \geqslant 0 \tag{14.4-13}$$

To evaluate the constant A, use is made of the original difference equation with $k = 0$ (initial conditions) so that

$$y(0) = U + \alpha_1 y(-1)$$

But if the system is at rest prior to the excitation, then

$$y(-1) = 0 \qquad \text{and} \qquad y(0) = U$$

Combine this result with Equation (14.4-13) for $k=0$ to find ($\psi_p^0 = 1$)

$$U = \frac{\psi_p}{\psi_p - \alpha_1} U + A$$

From this

$$A = U - \frac{U\psi_p}{\psi_p - \alpha_1} = U \left(\frac{-\alpha_1}{\psi_p - \alpha_1} \right) \qquad (14.4\text{-}14)$$

Therefore the complete solution becomes

$$y(k) = \frac{\psi_p}{\psi_p - \alpha_1} U\psi_p^k - \frac{\alpha_1}{\psi_p - \alpha_1} U\alpha_1^k \qquad k \geqslant 0$$

or

$$y(k) = \frac{U}{\psi_p - \alpha_1}[\psi_p^{k+1} - \alpha_1^{k+1}]u_{-1}(k) \qquad (14.4\text{-}15)$$

For the special case when $\psi_p = 1$ and $U = 1$, the excitation is

$$u(k) = u_{-1}(k)$$

The solution is given by

$$y(k) = \frac{1}{1 - \alpha_1}[1 - \alpha_1^{k+1}]u_{-1}(k) = \frac{1 - \alpha_1^{k+1}}{1 - \alpha_1} u_{-1}(k)$$

This is the same result as that in Equation (14.3-12).

Observe from the general solution, Equation (14.4-15), that for both ψ_p and α_1 real, that as k becomes large, the particular term ψ_p^{k+1} will be the dominant one, if

$$|\psi_p| > |\alpha_1|$$

Moreover, to avoid having the solution "blow up" (become unbounded) we must have that $|\psi_p| < 1$.

14.5   DELAY OPERATIONS AND SIGNALS

We have already mentioned in Chapter 6 special operations on signals. In this section we shall expand on this notion by adding *delay* operations. First, however, we recall that two scalors in cascade as shown in Figure 14.5-1 are equivalent to one scalor whose transmittance is the *product* of the transmittances of the individual scalor. The delayors are so defined that delayors in

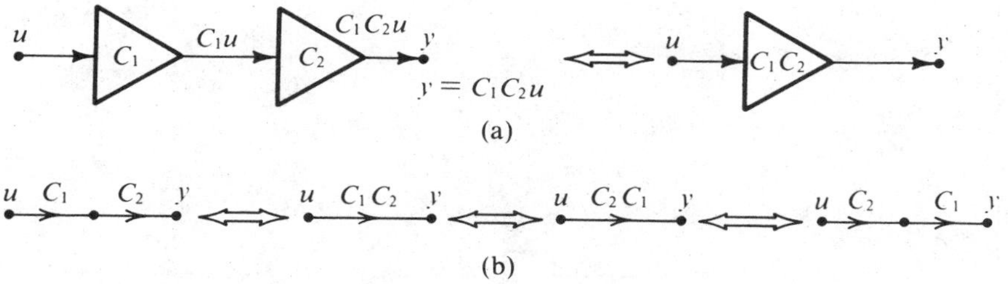

Figure 14.5-1. Diagrammatic representation of scalors
(a) Block-diagram representation   (b) Flow-graph representation

cascade are additive. This suggests that delayors be written in an exponential representation, where z^{-T} denotes a delay of T, and z^{-1} denotes a unit time delay. These are shown graphically in Figure 14.5-2.

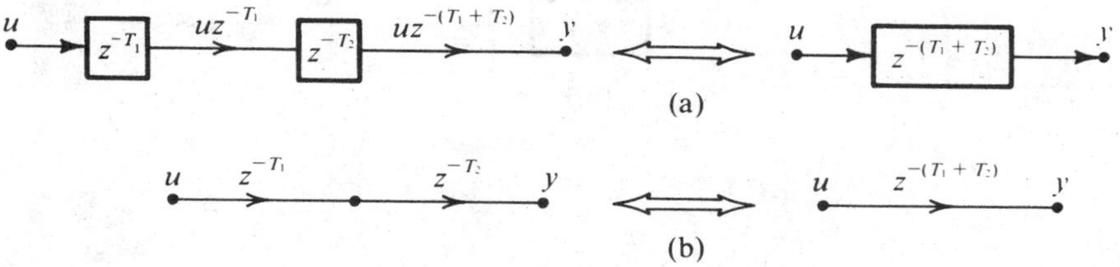

Figure 14.5-2.   Representation of delayors
(a) Block-diagram representaion   (b) Flow-graph representation

EXAMPLE 14.5-1. A signal generator produces a signal of the form

$$u(k) = \begin{cases} 0 & k<0 \\ k & 0 \leqslant k \leqslant 2 \\ 0 & k>2 \end{cases} \qquad (14.5\text{-}1)$$

Using this signal source as a basic construct, draw block diagrams and flow graphs of systems for which the output signal has the forms shown in Figures 14.5-3a, b, and c.

SOLUTION. We observe that the first signal is just the original signal that has been delayed by one unit. The block and flow graph representations are shown in Figures 14.5-3a_1 and a_2. Since the second signal is delayed by two time units its representation is easily found by cascading two delayors, as shown in Figures 14.5-3b_1 and b_2. The third signal can be thought of as the sum of the signal itself and another replica of the signal that has been delayed by three

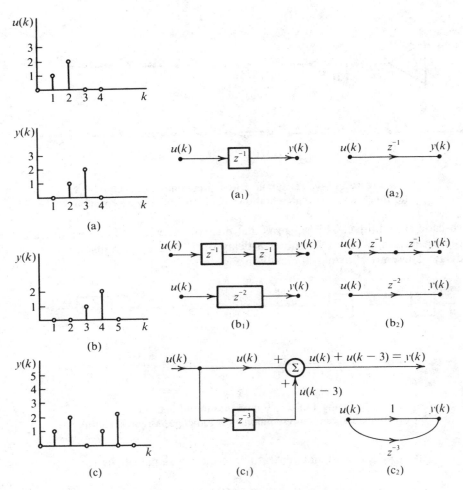

Figure 14.5-3. Diagrammatic representation of delayed signals

time units. The graphical representation of such an operation is shown in
Figures 14.5-3c_1 and c_2. The reader should realize that we would find the same
general results if continuous signals were used.

□   □   □

EXAMPLE 14.5-2. A signal generator produces the signal

$$u_o(k) = \begin{cases} 0 & k<0 \\ 1 & k=0 \\ 0 & k>0 \end{cases} \qquad (14.5\text{-}2)$$

With this signal source draw the block and flow graph diagrams of systems for which the output signal has the form shown in Figures 14.5-4a and b.

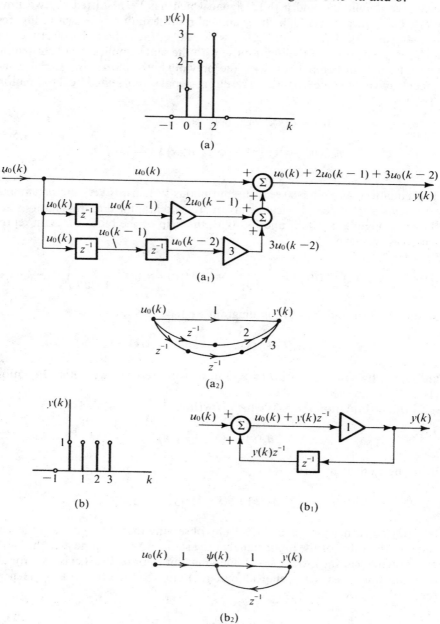

Figure 14.5-4. Diagrammatic representation of delayed signals

SOLUTION. In the manner of the previous example, the signal of Figure 14.5-4a is the sum of an unshifted signal, a second signal by one unit and of twice the amplitude, and a third signal which has been shifted by two time units, being three units high. Its graphical representation is shown in Figures 14.5-4a$_1$ and a$_2$. The second signal, which is, in fact, the unit step function $u_{-1}(k)$ is a repetition of the input pulse with the same amplitude but shifted by one time unit in comparison with the previous pulse. Since the signal components have the same heights the resulting signal is reprsented by the equation

$$y(k) = u_o(k) + u_o(k)z^{-1} + u_o(k)z^{-2} + \ldots$$

$$= u_o(k)(1 + z^{-1} + z^{-1} + \ldots) = u_o(k)\left(\frac{1}{1-z^{-1}}\right) \tag{14.5-3}$$

This equation, as we have seen for continuous systems, is very important and represents a feedback physical behavior. Its two graphical representations are shown in Figures 14.5-4b$_1$ and b$_2$. With the help of the block diagram representation we have

$$u_o(k) + y(k)z^{-1} = y(k) \qquad \text{or} \qquad y(k) = u_o(k)\left(\frac{1}{1-z^{-1}}\right)$$

Similarly, from the flow graph diagram we have

$$\psi(k) = 1u_o(k) + y(k)z^{-1} \qquad \text{and} \qquad y(k) = 1\psi(k)$$

and, thus, by substituting $\psi(k) = y(k)$ in the first relation we obtain Equation (14.5-3) as expected.

Consider Equation (14.5-3) which is written

$$u_o(k) + y(k)z^{-1} = y(k)$$

or in the equivalent form

$$u_o(k) + y(k-1) = y(k)$$

We may construct the signal 14.5-4b by observing that the signal at time k is equal to the value of the input signal at the same instant of time plus the value of the signal y at the instant $k-1$, one time unit prior to k. $u_o(k)$ is zero for all $k<0$ and since u causes y, the value of $y(k)$ must be zero for all $k<0$. Hence, for $k=0$ we have

$$u_o(0) = y(0) = 1$$

which tells us that y is identical to u_o at $k=0$.

Next we consider y at the instant $k = 1$. At this time $u_o(1) = 0$ and the above relation becomes

$$y(0) = y(1)$$

The value of $y(1)$ is just the value of $y(0)$ one time unit earlier, and this has already been found to be equal to $u_o(0)$. Following the same reasoning, we easily create the signal shown in Figure 14.5-4b.

□ □ □

The output of a system having a form

$$y(k) = u(k) \left(\frac{1}{1 - az^{-1}} \right) = u(k) + u(k)az^{-1} + u(k)a^2z^{-2} + \ldots \qquad \text{(a)} \quad (14.5\text{-}5)$$

or

$$y(k) = u(k) + au(k-1) + a^2u(k-2) + \ldots \qquad \text{(b)}$$

is *unstable* $[y(k) \to \infty$ as $k \to \infty]$ if $a > 1$, and *stable* $[y(k) \to 0$ as $k \to \infty]$ if $a < 1$. If a unit pulse shown in Figure 14.5-5a is applied to a system described by the block and flow graphs in Figures 14.5-5a₁ and a₂, the output is that shown in Figure 14.5-5b which indicates an unstable system. However, if the constant $a = 0.5$ then the output signal is shown in Figure 14.5-5c which indicates a stable system since $y(k) \to 0$ as $k \to \infty$.

14.6 THE Z-TRANSFORM

The techniques already discussed for the solution of difference equations do not lend themselves well to a systematic study of linear systems of order higher than one. The Z-transform is a much more powerful method for solving difference equations. This transform converts a sequence of numbers into a function of the complex variable z. Because of the Z-transform structure and properties, the solution of difference equations is reduced to simple algebraic manipulations in much the same way that the Laplace transform permits the solution of differential equations.

Consider the *one-sided sequence* of numbers $y(k)$, which may be impulse sampled values of $y(t)$ at uniform time intervals

$$\{y(k)\} = y(0), \, y(1), \, y(2), \ldots, \, y(k) \ldots \qquad (14.6\text{-}1)$$

If we now introduce the time *delay operator* $1/z$, this number sequence can be written

$$Y(z) = y(0) + \frac{y(1)}{z} + \frac{y(2)}{z^2} + \frac{y(3)}{z^3} + \ldots \qquad (14.6\text{-}2)$$

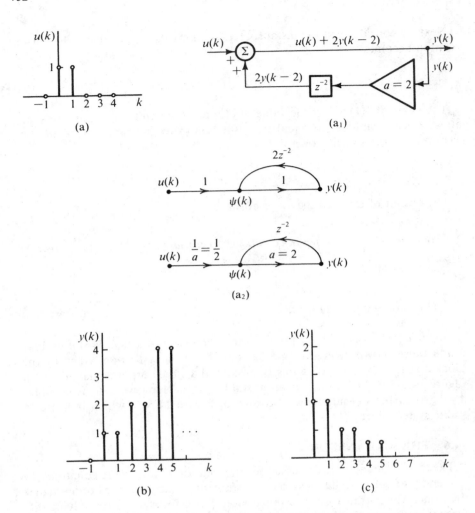

Figure 14.5-5.   Description of a stable and an unstable system

This procedure changes a function $y(k)$ of k to a function $Y(z)$, which is called the *Z-transform* of $y(k)$. We can express this infinite summation in the compact form,

$$Y(z) = \mathcal{Z}\{y(k)\} = \sum_{k=0}^{\infty} y(k) z^{-k} \qquad (14.6\text{-}3)$$

In these forms, while z^{-1} denotes a time delay as noted, in a formal mathematical context z is taken as a complex variable.

In its broader concept, the Z-transform at a specific value of the complex variable z given by the infinite summation (14.6-3) may be either finite or infinite. The set of z in the complex z-plane for which the magnitude of $Y(z)$ is finite is called the *region of convergence* for $Y(z)$, whereas the set of z for which the magnitude of $Y(z)$ is infinite is the *region of divergence* of $Y(z)$. We shall not explore the mathematical properties of the Z-transform, but will introduce only those aspects needed for our purposes. We generally speak of the Z-transformation as a mapping (transformation) from the *time domain* to the z-domain (*frequency domain*).

We develop some important properties of the Z-transform for sequences with zero elements for $k<0$.

1. Linearity:

$$\mathcal{F}\{ay_1(k) + by_2(k)\} = a\mathcal{F}\{y_1(k)\} + b\mathcal{F}\{y_2(k)\} \qquad (14.6\text{-}4)$$

where a and b are any constants.

2a. Right-Shift Property:

$$\mathcal{F}\{y(k - n)\} = z^{-n}\mathcal{F}\{y(k)\} \qquad (a) \quad (14.6\text{-}5)$$

Proof: From the definition of the Z-transform we have

$$Y(z) = \sum_{k=0}^{\infty} y(k)z^{-k}$$

Multiply first by z^{-n} and then substitute $-n-k = -m$; we obtain

$$z^{-n}Y(z) = \sum_{m=n}^{\infty} y(m-n)z^{-m} = \sum_{m=0}^{\infty} y(m-n)z^{-m} = \sum_{k=0}^{\infty} y(k-n)z^{-k} = \mathcal{F}\{y(k-n)\}$$

Since m is a dummy index we changed it to letter k. The third term was obtained by accepting that the functions $y(k)$ which we consider in this work are zero for $k = -1, -2, \ldots$. Therefore

$$\mathcal{F}\{y(k - n)\} = z^{-n}Y(z) = z^{-n}\mathcal{F}\{y(k)\}$$

2b. Left-Shift Property:

$$\mathcal{F}\{y(k + n)\} = z^{n}Y(z) - \sum_{k=0}^{n-1} y(k)z^{n-k} \qquad (b) \quad (14.6\text{-}5)$$

Proof: From

$$\mathcal{F}\{y(k + 1)\} = \sum_{k=0}^{\infty} y(k + 1)z^{-k}$$

by setting $k + 1 = m$ we obtain

$$\mathcal{F}\{y(k+1=m)\} = \sum_{m=1}^{\infty} y(m)z^{-m+1} = z\sum_{m=1}^{\infty} y(m)z^{-m}$$

$$= z\sum_{m=0}^{\infty} y(m)z^{-m} - zy(0) = zY(z) - zy(0)$$

In a like manner, we can show that the general left-shifting property is

$$\mathcal{F}\{y(k+n)\} = z^{n}Y(z) - z^{n}y(0) - z^{n-1}y(1) - \ldots - zy(n-1)$$

$$= z^{n}Y(z) - \sum_{k=0}^{n-1} y(k)z^{n-k}$$

3. Unit Shift:

$$\mathcal{F}\{y(k-1)\} = z^{-1}Y(z) = z^{-1}\mathcal{F}\{y(k)\} \qquad (14.6\text{-}6)$$

4. Time Scaling:

$$\mathcal{F}\{a^{k}y(k)\} = Y(a^{-1}z) = \sum_{k=0}^{\infty}(a^{-1}z)^{-k}y(k) \qquad (14.6\text{-}7)$$

Proof: Again using the definition of the Z-transform, we have

$$\mathcal{F}\{a^{k}y(k)\} = \sum_{k=0}^{\infty} a^{k}y(k)z^{-k} = \sum_{k=0}^{\infty} y(k)(a^{-1}z)^{-k} = Y(a^{-1}z)$$

5. Periodic Sequences:

$$\mathcal{F}\{y(k)\} = \frac{z^{N}}{z^{N}-1}\mathcal{F}\{y_{(1)}(k)\} \qquad (14.6\text{-}8)$$

where N indicates the number of time units in a period, $y_{(1)}(k)$ is the first period of the periodic sequence, and $y(k) = y(k+N)$.

Proof: The Z-transform of the first period is

$$\mathcal{F}\{y_{(1)}(k)\} = \sum_{k=0}^{N-1} y_{(1)}(k)z^{-k} = Y_{(1)}(z)$$

Because the period is repeated every N discrete time units, we can use property 2a to write

$$\mathscr{F}\{y(k)\} = \mathscr{F}\{y_{(1)}(k)\} + \mathscr{F}\{y_{(1)}(k-N)\} + \mathscr{F}\{y_{(1)}(k-2N)\} + \dots$$

$$= Y_1(z) + z^{-N} Y_1(z) + z^{-2N} Y_1(z) + \dots$$

$$= Y_1(z)(1 + z^{-N} + z^{-2N} + \dots) = \frac{z^N}{z^N - 1} Y_1(z)$$

EXAMPLE 14.6-1. Find the Z-transform of the discrete function

$$y(k) = \begin{cases} 0 & k \leqslant 0 \\ 0.5 & k = 1 \\ 1 & k = 2 \\ 0 & k \geqslant 3 \end{cases} \qquad (14.6\text{-}9)$$

SOLUTION. By definition [see Equation (14.6-3)]

$$Y(z) = \mathscr{F}\{y(k)\} = \sum_{k=0}^{\infty} z^{-k} y(k) = 0.5 z^{-1} + 1 z^{-2} = \frac{0.5 z + 1}{z^2} \qquad (14.6\text{-}10)$$

If we select the value $z = 0$ the function $Y(0)$ becomes infinity. As for other analytic functions, points where a function becomes unbounded are the poles. Equation (14.6-10) becomes zero if $z = -1/0.5 = -2$. Points at which a function becomes zero are the zeros, and both poles and zeros are shown in the pole-zero diagram of Figure 14.6-1b. Figure 14.6-1c is a plot of the magnitude

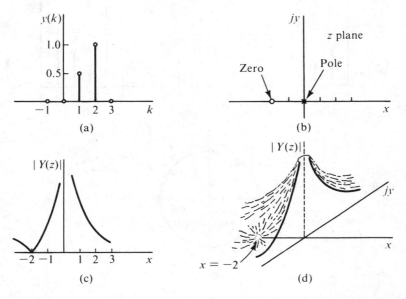

Figure 14.6-1. A discrete function showing zeros and poles location

of the transformed signal $|Y(z)|$ versus the real variable x. A three-dimensional plot of the amplitude of the same function over the complex plane is shown in Figure 14.6-1d. The surface looks like a stretched rubber sheet whose height approaches infinity at the poles and becomes zero at the zeros. It is of great value to know the location of poles and zeros since they uniquely define the Z-transform, except for a constant scale factor.

□   □   □

EXAMPLE 14.6-2. Find and discuss the properties of the Z-transform of the signal

$$f(k) = \begin{cases} 0 & k = -1, -2, \ldots \\ c^k & k = 0, 1, 2, \ldots \end{cases} \qquad (14.6\text{-}11)$$

The constant c takes values: (a) $0 < c < 1$, (b) $c > 1$.

SOLUTION. The time functions $f(k)$ for the two cases are shown in Figures 14.6-2a and b. We observe that in the time domain the signal is converging (bounded) for $0 < c < 1$ and diverging (unbounded) for $c > 1$.

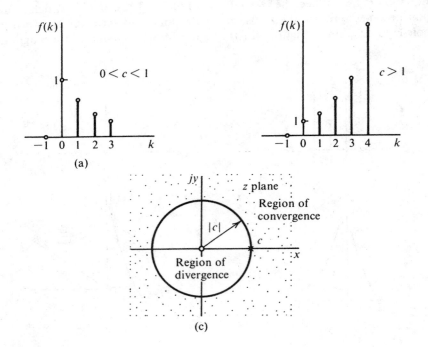

Figure 14.6-2.   The discrete signal c^k

Apply property 4 with $f(k) = a^k y(k) = a^k [y(k) = 1]$. The Z-transform of $f(k)$ is

$$F(z) = \sum_{k=0}^{\infty} (c^{-1}z)^{-k} = 1 + cz^{-1} + c^2 z^{-2} + \ldots + c^n z^{-n} + \ldots \qquad (14.6\text{-}12)$$

The sum of the first n terms of this geometric series is given by

$$F_n(z) = \frac{1 - (cz^{-1})^n}{1 - cz^{-1}} \qquad (14.6\text{-}13)$$

If we set $cz^{-1} = |cz^{-1}| e^{j\theta}$, where θ is the argument of the complex number z^{-1}, then we see that

$$(cz^{-1})^n = |cz^{-1}|^n e^{jn\theta}$$

Therefore for values of z (points in the complex plane) for which $|cz^{-1}| < 1$ the magnitude of the complex number $(cz^{-1})^n$ approaches zero as $n \to \infty$. As a consequence

$$F(z) = \lim_{n \to \infty} F_n(z) = \frac{1}{1 - cz^{-1}} = \frac{z}{z - c} \qquad |cz^{-1}| < 1 \qquad (14.6\text{-}14)$$

For the general case where c is a complex number, the inequality $|cz^{-1}| < 1$ leads to $|c| < |z|$ which implies that the series converges when the magnitude of $|z| > |c|$ and diverges for $|z| < |c|$. We have thus established the *regions of convergence and divergence* in the complex plane for the transformed signal. These two regions are shown in Figure 14.6-2c.

We must establish a separate test to determine whether the boundary of the circle belongs to the convergence or divergence region. In our case, by applying L'Hopital's rule,

$$\lim_{z \to c} F_n(z) = \lim_{z \to c} \frac{\dfrac{d}{d(cz^{-1})}[1 - (cz^{-1})^n]}{\dfrac{d}{d(cz^{-1})}[1 - (cz^{-1})]} = \lim_{z \to c} \frac{-n(cz^{-1})^{n-1}}{-1} = n$$

and

$$\lim_{n \to \infty} F_n(z) \to \infty$$

Thus the boundary belongs to the region of divergence.

□ □ □

EXAMPLE 14.6-3. Find and discuss the properties of the impulse functions

$$y(k) = u_o(k) = \begin{cases} 1 & k=0 \\ 0 & k \neq 0 \end{cases} \quad \text{and} \quad y(k) = u_o(k) = \begin{cases} 1 & k=N \\ 0 & k \neq N \end{cases}$$

SOLUTION. (a) Apply the definition Equation (14.6-3) to obtain

$$Y(z) = y(0)z^{-0} = 1 \times 1 = 1 \tag{14.6-15}$$

$Y(z)$ is independent of z and thus the region of convergence is the whole z-plane; (b) Apply the same definition to obtain the Z-transform of the shifted delta function, $u_o(k-N)$,

$$Y(z) = z^{-N} \mathcal{Z}\{u_o(k)\} = z^{-N} \tag{14.6-16}$$

Since for $z=0$, $Y(z) \rightarrow \infty$, the region of convergence is the whole z-plane except an infinitesimal region around the origin.

□   □   □

EXAMPLE 14.6-4. Find the Z-transform of the function $(T=1)$

$$y(k) = \begin{cases} a^k \sin(k\omega) & k \geq 0 \\ 0 & k < 0 \end{cases} \qquad a > 0 \tag{14.6-17}$$

which is shown in Figure 14.6-3a, b for two different values of a. Indicate the divergence region, the convergence region, and the poles and zeros.

SOLUTION. We first write $\sin k\omega$ in the form $(e^{jk\omega} - e^{-jk\omega})/2j$, and Equation (14.6-3) becomes

$$Y(z) = \sum_{k=0}^{\infty} a^k \sin(k\omega)z^{-k} = \sum_{k=0}^{\infty} \frac{a^k e^{jk\omega}z^{-k} - a^k e^{-jk\omega}z^{-k}}{2j}$$

$$= \frac{1}{2j} \sum_{k=0}^{\infty} (ae^{j\omega}z^{-1})^k - \frac{1}{2j} \sum_{k=0}^{\infty} (ae^{-j\omega}z^{-1})^k \tag{14.6-18}$$

Each of the series converges if $|ae^{j\omega}z^{-1}| = |a||e^{j\omega}||z^{-1}| = a|z^{-1}| < 1$ or $|z| > a$. By summing the geometric series of Equation (14.6-18) we have

$$Y(z) = \frac{1}{2j} \left[\frac{1}{1-ae^{j\omega}z^{-1}} - \frac{1}{1-ae^{-j\omega}z^{-1}} \right] = \frac{z^{-1}a \sin b}{1 - 2az^{-1} \cos \omega + a^2 z^{-2}}$$

$$|z| > a \tag{14.6-19}$$

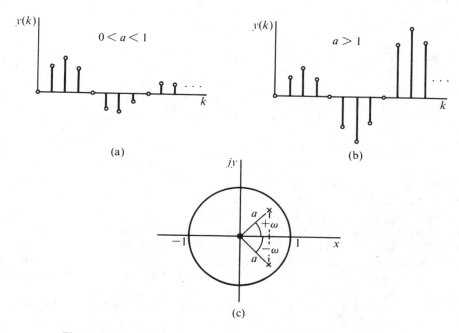

Figure 14.6-3. **The sinusoidal discrete signal and its poles and zeros**

Multiplying numerator and denominator of Equation (14.6-19) by z^2, we obtain

$$Y(z) = \frac{za \sin \omega}{z^2 - 2a \cos \omega z + a^2} \tag{14.6-20}$$

$$= \frac{za \sin \omega}{[z - a(\cos \omega + j \sin \omega)][z - a(\cos \omega - j \sin \omega)]}$$

$$= \frac{za \sin \omega}{(z - ae^{j\omega})(z - ae^{-j\omega})}$$

The zeros and poles are shown in Figure 14.6-3c for the case $a<1$.

□   □   □

EXAMPLE 14.6-5. Find the Z-transform of the *convolution* summation

$$w(k) = \sum_{m=0}^{\infty} u(m)v(k-m) = \sum_{m=0}^{\infty} u(k-m)v(m) = u(k)*v(k) \tag{14.6-21}$$

where the symbol $*$ denotes convolution.

SOLUTION.

$$W(z) = \sum_{k=0}^{\infty} w(k)z^{-k} = \sum_{k=0}^{\infty} \left[\sum_{m=0}^{\infty} u(m)v(k-m) \right] z^{-k} \qquad (14.6\text{-}22)$$

$$= \sum_{m=0}^{\infty} u(m) \left[\sum_{k=0}^{\infty} v(k-m)z^{-(k-m)} \right] z^{-m} = \sum_{m=0}^{\infty} u(m)z^{-m} V(z)$$

$$= V(z) \sum_{m=0}^{\infty} u(m)z^{-m} = V(z)U(z)$$

The convolution summation (convolution integral for continuous signals) is a very important relation, since for linear and time-invariant systems the output $w(k)$ of a system is the convolution summation of the input signal $u(k)$ and the *impulse response* characterizing the particular system. The impulse response is the output signal of the system if the input is an impulse function $u_o(k)$. To understand how Equation (14.6-21) works consider the input signal $u(m)$ and the impulse response $v(m)$ of a system to be those shown in Figure 14.6-4a and b. In Figure 14.6-4c the convolved signal $u(-m)$ is also shown (folded over signal). Figures 14.6-4d through h are self-explanatory. It is noted that when the shift $v(4-m)$ is introduced the two functions do not coincide at all and thus their product is zero. The output signal $w(k)$ of this system is shown in Figure 14.6-4h.

□   □   □

EXAMPLE 14.6-6. Write the Z-transform of the function

$$f(t) = Ae^{-at} \qquad\qquad t \geq 0 \qquad\qquad (14.6\text{-}23)$$

which is sampled every T seconds, i.e., $t = kT$.

SOLUTION. The sampled values are written

$$\{f(kT)\} = [A,\ Ae^{-aT},\ Ae^{-2aT}, \ldots]$$

The Z-transform of this sequence can be written as

$$F(z) = A \left[1 + \left(\frac{e^{-aT}}{z} \right) + \left(\frac{e^{-aT}}{z} \right)^2 + \ldots \right]$$

This expression can be written in closed form by recalling that the expansion

$$\frac{1}{1-x} = 1 + x + x^2 + \ldots \qquad\qquad x < 1$$

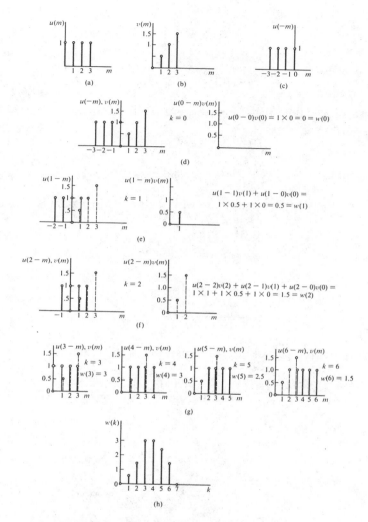

Figure 14.6-4. **The convolution of two discrete functions**

Thus we have that

$$F(z) = \frac{A}{1 - \left(\dfrac{e^{-aT}}{z}\right)} = \frac{Az}{z - e^{-aT}} \qquad (14.6\text{-}24)$$

This infinite series converges for

$$\left| \frac{e^{-aT}}{z} \right| < 1$$

or

$$|z| > e^{-aT}$$

□   □   □

EXAMPLE 14.6-7. Find the Z-transform of the function

$$f(t) = 2e^{-t} + e^{-2t} \qquad (14.6\text{-}25)$$

which is sampled at intervals $T = 0.1$ seconds.

SOLUTION. We write, in accordance with the results of Example 14.6-6

$$F(z) = \frac{2z}{z - e^{-0.1}} + \frac{z}{z - e^{-0.2}}$$

which is

$$F(z) = \frac{2z}{z - 0.905} + \frac{z}{z - 0.819}$$

In this form $F(z)$ is a partial fraction expansion of the function

$$F(z) = \frac{2z(z - 0.819) + z(z - 0.905)}{(z - 0.905)(z - 0.819)} = \frac{3z^2 - 2.543z}{z^2 - 1.724z + 0.741}$$

By long division we find that

$$\begin{array}{r} 3 + \dfrac{2.629}{z} + \ldots \\[4pt] z^2 - 1.724z + 0.741 \overline{)\, 3z^2 - 2.543z } \\ 3z^2 - 5.172z + 2.223 \\ \hline 2.629z - 2.223 \\ \text{etc.} \end{array}$$

This process leads to

$$F(z) = 3 + \frac{2.629}{z} + \frac{2.309}{z^2} + \ldots \qquad (14.6\text{-}26)$$

From this expansion we have the sequence $\{f(kT)\} = [3, 2.629, 2.309, \ldots]$. Note that in many cases when problems are being solved, a partial fraction expansion is sought in order that the subsequent time function can be deduced therefrom.

□   □   □

14.7 Z-TRANSFORM PAIRS

It is implicit in the foregoing that one can proceed in two directions: given an $f(k)$, the Z-transform $F(z)$ can be deduced according to Section 14.6; and, given an $F(z)$, the reverse process will lead to $f(k)$. These processes are shown functionally as

$$\mathscr{Z}\{f(k)\} = F(z) \qquad \text{(a)} \quad (14.7\text{-}1)$$

$$\mathscr{Z}^{-1}\{F(z)\} = f(k) \qquad \text{(b)}$$

where $\mathscr{Z}^{-1}$ denotes the inverse Z-transform. In a formal way, determining the inverse transform involves a knowledge of complex function theory plus a knowledge of contour integration in the complex plane. This mathematical procedure can usually be circumvented by recognizing that by its very nature the transform pair, obtained according to Equation (14.7-1) is valid with either a specified $Z\{f(k)\}$ resulting in $F(z)$, or with the inverse transform of $F(z)$, $Z^{-1}[F(z)]$, resulting in the original $f(k)$. Consequently, what is needed is a table of Z-transform pairs. It is convenient to generate a table of Z-transform pairs with as many entries as might be needed for normal purposes. A table of common Z-transform pairs is found in Table 14.7-1. A number of the entries in this table follow directly from the results of Examples 14.6-6 and 14.6-7. By the proper selection of the exponent a, e.g., $a = 0$, we have entry 1, for entries 8 and 9, $a = \pm j\omega T$.

Table 14.7-1. Common Z-Transform Pairs

Entry No.	$f(k)$ for $k \geqslant 0$	$F(z) = \displaystyle\sum_{k=0}^{\infty} f(k)z^{-k}$	Radius of Convergence $\lvert z \rvert > R$
1	1	$\dfrac{z}{z-1}$	1
2	$u_o(k)$	1	0
3	$u_o(k-m)$	z^{-m}	0
4	a^k	$\dfrac{z}{z-a}$	$\lvert a \rvert$
5	k	$\dfrac{z}{(z-1)^2}$	1
6	k^2	$\dfrac{z(z+1)}{(z-1)^3}$	1
7	$\dfrac{a^k}{k!}$	$e^{a/z}$	0

Entry No.	$f(k)$ for $k \geqslant 0$	$F(z) = \sum\limits_{k=0}^{\infty} f(k)z^{-k}$	Radius of Convergence $\lvert z \rvert > R$
8	$\sin k\omega T$	$\dfrac{z \sin \omega T}{z^2 - 2z \cos \omega T + 1}$	1
9	$\cos k\omega T$	$\dfrac{z(z - \cos \omega T)}{z^2 - 2z \cos \omega T + 1}$	1
10	$a^k \sin k\omega T$	$\dfrac{az \sin \omega T}{z^2 - 2az \cos \omega T + a^2}$	
11	$a^k \cos k\omega T$	$\dfrac{z(z - a \cos \omega T)}{z^2 - 2az \cos \omega T + a^2}$	
12	ka^k	$\dfrac{az}{(z-a)^2}$	$\lvert a \rvert$
13	$k^2 a^k$	$\dfrac{az(z+a)}{(z-a)^3}$	$\lvert a \rvert$
14	$\dfrac{k(k-1)}{2!}$	$\dfrac{z}{(z-1)^3}$	1
15	$\dfrac{k(k-1)(k-2)}{3!}$	$\dfrac{z}{(z-1)^4}$	1
16	$\dfrac{k(k-1)(k-2)\ldots(k-m+1)}{m!}$	$\dfrac{z}{(z-1)^m}$	1
17	$(k+1)a^k$	$\dfrac{z^2}{(z-a)^2}$	$\lvert a \rvert$
18	$\dfrac{(k+1)(k+2)a^k}{2!}$	$\dfrac{z^3}{(z-a)^3}$	$\lvert a \rvert$
19	$\dfrac{(k+1)(k+2)\ldots(k+m)a^k}{m!}$	$\dfrac{z^{m+1}}{(z-a)^{m+1}}$	$\lvert a \rvert$

14.8 THE INVERSE Z-TRANSFORM

In our studies we shall assume that $F(z)$ corresponds to a sequence $f(k)$ that is bounded as $k \to +\infty$. To find the inverse Z-transform we shall, as already noted, cast the transformed functions into forms that are amenable to simple tabular look-up. This is quite possible since the functions with which we shall be concerned are rational functions of z; that is, they are the ratio of two polynomials. Ordinarily these are *proper fractions* since the degree of the numerator polynomial is less than the degree of the denominator polynomial. If these are not rational functions, we divide the numerator polynomial by the denominator polynomial, carrying out the long division until the numerator polynomial is of degree one less than the denominator polynomial. This results in power terms plus a proper fraction. The following examples will clarify the most commonly used approaches.

EXAMPLE 14.8-1. Find the inverse Z-transform of the function

$$F(z) = \frac{1}{1 - 0.1z^{-1}} \tag{14.8-1}$$

SOLUTION. The function converges outside the unit circle in the complex plane since its pole is located at 0.1. A long division results in an infinite series in power of z^{-1}

$$
1 - 0.1z^{-1} \overline{)\,1} \quad \frac{1 + 0.1z^{-1} + (0.1)^2 + z^{-2} + \ldots}{}
$$

$$
\begin{array}{r}
\underline{1 - 0.1z^{-1}} \\
0.1z^{-1} \\
\underline{0.1z^{-1} - (0.1z^{-1})^2} \\
(0.1z^{-1})^2
\end{array}
$$

etc.

or

$$F(z) = 1 + 0.1z^{-1} + (0.1)^2 z^{-2} + (0.1)^3 z^{-3} + \ldots \tag{14.8-2}$$

Comparing Equation (14.8-2) with the definition of the Z-transform Equation (14.6-2) we see that the time function is

$$f(k) = \begin{cases} 1, 0.1, (0.1)^2, (0.1)^3, \ldots & k \geq 0 \\ 0 & k < 0 \end{cases} \qquad \text{(a)} \quad (14.8-3)$$

$$f(k) = (0.1)^k \qquad k \geq 0 \qquad \qquad \text{(b)}$$

□ □ □

EXAMPLE 14.8-2. Find the inverse Z-transform of the function

$$F(z) = \frac{1}{(1 - 0.2z^{-1})(1 + 0.2z^{-1})} = \frac{1}{1 - 0.04z^{-2}} \tag{14.8-4}$$

SOLUTION. (a) A long division will result in the following polynomial

$$F(z) = 1 + 0.04z^{-2} + (0.04)^2 z^{-4} + \ldots = (0.2)^{2k} (z^{-1})^{2k}$$

which corresponds to the time function

$$f(k') = \begin{cases} (0.2)^{k'} & k' = 2k & k \geqslant 0 \\ 0 & k' = 2k & k < 0 \end{cases} \tag{14.8-5}$$

(b) Let us try to separate the function $F(z)$ into two fractions (partial fraction representation) as follows

$$\frac{1}{1 - 0.04z^{-2}} = \frac{A}{1 - 0.2z^{-1}} + \frac{B}{1 + 0.2z^{-1}} = \frac{(A + B) + 0.2z^{-1}(A - B)}{1 - (0.2z^{-1})^2} \tag{14.8-6}$$

Since the first and the last fractions must be the same, it is required that $A + B = 1$ and $A - B = 0$. Hence $A = B = 1/2$ and Equation (14.8-6) becomes

$$F(z) = \frac{1}{2} \frac{1}{1 - 0.2z^{-1}} + \frac{1}{2} \frac{1}{1 + 0.2z^{-1}} = \frac{1}{2} \left[\frac{1}{1 - 0.2z^{-1}} + \frac{1}{1 - (-0.2)z^{-1}} \right]$$

This has the inverse transform (see Table 14.7-1)

$$f(k) = \begin{cases} \frac{1}{2}(0.2)^k + \frac{1}{2}(-0.2)^k & k \geqslant 0 \\ 0 & k < 0 \end{cases} \tag{14.8-7}$$

The reader can easily verify that Equations (14.8-7) and (14.8-5) are identical.

□   □   □

EXAMPLE 14.8-3. Find the inverse Z-transform of the function

$$F(z) = \frac{z^2}{(1 - 0.2z^{-1})} \tag{14.8-8}$$

SOLUTION. First write Equation (14.8-8) in the form

$$F(z) = \frac{z^3}{z - 0.2} = az^2 + bz + \frac{cz}{z - 0.2} = \frac{az^3 - 0.2az^2 + bz^2 - 0.2bz + cz}{z - 0.2}$$

Equate factors having the same powers of z. This yields: $a = 1$, $b = 0.2$, $c = (0.2)^2$. Thus Equation (14.8-8) becomes

$$F(z) = z^2 + 0.2z + (0.2)^2 \frac{z}{z - 0.2}$$

The inverse Z-tranform of this function is, using the table,

$$f(k) = u_o(k + 2) + 0.2u_o(k + 1) + (0.2)^2(0.2)^k$$

or

$$f(k) = \begin{cases} (0.2)^{k+2} & k \geq -2 \\ 0 & k < -2 \end{cases} \qquad (14.8\text{-}9)$$

Keep in mind that we could also expand Equation (14.8-8) in the form

$$F(z) = z^2 + 0.2z + (0.2)^2 z^0 + (0.2)^3 z^{-1} + (0.2)^4 z^{-2} + \dots$$

$$= z^2 \left[1 + \frac{0.2}{z} + \frac{(0.2)^2}{z^2} + \dots \right]$$

The inverse Z-transform of the bracketed term is $(0.2)^k$. The factor z^2 indicates a shift to the left of two sample periods; thus Equation (14.8-9) is realized.

Observation: To find the inverse Z-transform, we must ignore any factor of the form z^k, for k an integer; expand the remaining part into a partial fraction; use Z-transform table (or Z-transform properties) to obtain the inverse Z-transform of each term in the expansion; and combine the results and do the necessary shifting due to z^k left out in step a.

□ □ □

14.9 DIGITAL FILTERS

The input-output relation of the circuit shown in Figure 14.3-5 is a first-order difference equation of the form [see Equation (14.3-10)]

$$y(k) = \beta u(k) + \alpha_1 y(k-1) \qquad (14.9\text{-}1)$$

Suppose that $y_1(k)$ and $y_2(k)$ are the two outputs corresponding to two different inputs $u_1(k)$ and $u_2(k)$, respectively. Therefore the following equations hold:

$$y_1(k) = \beta u_1(k) + \alpha_1 y_1(k-1)$$

$$y_2(k) = \beta u_2(k) + \alpha_1 y_2(k-1)$$

If we multiply the first by a constant a and the second by another constant b and then add the two results, we obtain

$$a y_1(k) + b y_2(k) = \beta[a u_1(k) + b u_2(k)] + \alpha_1[a y_1(k-1) + b y_2(k-1)]$$

or

$$\underset{\sim}{y}(k) = \beta \underset{\sim}{u}(k) + \alpha \underset{\sim}{y}(k-1)$$

where the tilda under the variable denotes the sum functions. This indicates that the system is *linear*.

If in Equation (14.9-1) we substitute for k the quantity $k - q$, q being any integer, we find the relation

$$y(k - q) = \beta u(k - q) + \alpha_1 y(k - q - 1)$$

which shows that when the input is time-shifted by an amount q the output is also shifted by the same amount. Because of this, the system is called *time-invariant*. We have used properties of linearity and time invariance earlier in this chapter; we have here demonstrated some of the formal consequences of these properties.

The Z-transform of Equation (14.9-1) is

$$Y(z) = \beta U(z) + \alpha_1 z^{-1} Y(z)$$

or

$$Y(z) = \frac{\beta}{1 - \alpha_1 z^{-1}} U(z) = H(z) U(z) \tag{14.9-2}$$

This equation relates the input-output relation explicitly in the transformed domain of a discrete system. The proportionality function $H(z) = Y(z)/U(z)$ is the system function or transfer function for the discrete system.

When a unit impulse function $u_o(k)$ is the input, then $Z\{u_o(k)\} = U(z) = 1$ (see Example 14.6-3) and the output of the system is equal to its transfer function $H(z)$. The inverse transform of the transfer function $H(z)$ is the *impulse response* $h(k)$ of the system.

We have already noted that a linear time-invariant discrete time system that is initially at rest and subject to an input for $k \geq 0$ can be described by the convolution summation [see Equation (14.6-21]

$$y(k) = \sum_{m=0}^{\infty} u(m)h(k - m) \qquad \text{(a)} \quad \text{(14.9-3)}$$

or

$$y(k) = \sum_{n=0}^{\infty} u(k - n)h(n) \qquad \text{(b)}$$

where $\{u(k)\}$ and $\{y(k)\}$ are the input and output signals and $\{h(k)\}$ is the impulse response of the system. Equation (14.9-3b) shows that the output of the system at time k is the sum of the present input $u(k)$ $(n=0)$ and all the past inputs, each one being *weighted* by an amount $h(n)$.

Consider the first order system of Equation (14.9-1) with zero initial conditions. We obtain the following sequence

$$y(0) = \beta u(0)$$

$$y(1) = \beta u(1) + \alpha_1 y(0) = \beta u(1) + \alpha_1 \beta u(0)$$

$$y(2) = \beta u(2) + \alpha_1 y(1) = \beta u(2) + \alpha_1 [\beta u(1) + \alpha_1 \beta u(0)]$$
$$= \alpha_1^2 \beta u(0) + \alpha_1 \beta u(1) + \beta u(2)$$

$$y(3) = \beta u(3) + \alpha_1 y(2) = \beta u(3) + \alpha_1 [\alpha_1^2 \beta u(0) + \alpha_1 \beta u(1) + \beta u(2)$$
$$= \alpha_1^3 \beta u(0) + \alpha_1^2 \beta u(1) + \alpha_1 \beta u(2) + \beta u(3)$$

$$\vdots$$

$$y(k) = \beta u(k) + \beta \alpha_1 u(k-1) + \beta \alpha_1^2 u(k-2) + \ldots + \beta \alpha_1^k u(0)$$
$$= \sum_{n=0}^{k} u(k-n)[\beta \alpha_1^n] = \sum_{n=0}^{k} u(k-n)h(n)$$

This is equivalent to Equation (14.9-3) since $h(n) = \beta \alpha_1^n$ is the unit impulse response of Equation (14.9-1).

By comparing Equations (14.9-1) and (14.9-3) we observe that to solve the first equation we need to store only the initial value of $y(k-1)$ since we can obtain $u(k)$ in real time. For the form given in Equation (14.9-3) we need to store all of the past inputs to the system from the present time back to $k = 0$. We note, therefore, that the convolution summation is used only for analytical considerations whereas the difference equation representation is used as the basis for building devices to perform the necessary calculations. A time-invariant discrete-time system is commonly called a *digital filter*.

It is possible to represent a linear digital filter in the form

$$y(k) = \sum_{m=0}^{M} a_m u(k-m) - \sum_{l=1}^{L} b_l y(k-l) \tag{14.9-4}$$

where $\{u(k)\}$ is the input signal, $\{y(k)\}$ is the output signal, and the a_m-s and b_l-s are constants. This representation is useful since in practice it is possible to specify the constants for the filtering process in order to yield certain desired characteristics. Analog signals converted to digital signals by analog-to-digital electronic converters (A/D) can be processed by a digital filter stored in the computer in the form of Equation (14.9-4). The digital output from the computer can be reconverted to an analog signal by a D/A converter.

As a comparison of continuous versus digital filters, we note that the processing of analog signals is accomplished by means of passive *analog filters* (combinations of R, L, and C components). They have two main disadvantages: they are bulky, and they have no flexibility, in the sense that once a filter has been designed, it is difficult to change the filter coefficients. More recently active filters [R, C, plus active elements (tubes or transistors)] have become very important. These are flexible, but because of temperature sensitive and noise producing elements, they too possess certain limitations. On the other hand, the digital filter is not temperature sensitive, and is very flexible since we need only change a few entries in the program to change the characteristic behavior of the filter.

Taking the Z-transform of Equation (14.9-4), we find that

$$Y(z) = \sum_{m=0}^{M} a_m \mathcal{F}\{u(k-m)\} - \sum_{l=1}^{L} b_l \mathcal{F}\{y(k-l)\}$$

or

$$Y(z) = \left(\sum_{m=0}^{M} a_m z^{-m} \right) U(z) - \left(\sum_{l=1}^{L} b_l z^{-l} \right) Y(z) \qquad \text{(a) \quad (14.9-5)}$$

or

$$Y(z) = \frac{\displaystyle\sum_{m=0}^{M} a_m z^{-m}}{1 + \displaystyle\sum_{m=0}^{L} b_l z^{-l}} U(z) = H(z)U(z) \qquad \text{(b)}$$

and

$$H(z) = \frac{\displaystyle\sum_{m=0}^{M} a_m z^{-m}}{1 + \displaystyle\sum_{l=1}^{L} b_l z^{-l}} \qquad \text{(c)}$$

where $H(z)$ is the transfer function of the filter (system). Consider Equation (14.9-5b) and observe that its inverse Z-transform is the *convolution* representation of the digital filter given by Equation (14.9-3). Hence the two forms are equivalent. However, the second representation builds up the output by using the present and the previous M inputs and the previous L outputs. Since no future input or output is used to construct the present output, the filter is *physically realizable* or *causal*. In causal filters the impulse response $\{h(k)\}$ has the property $h(k) = 0$ for $k < 0$.

A digital filter is called *recursive* if some past outputs are needed for the present output, that is, when not all b_l-s are zero. If, however, the filter has all its b_l-s equal to zero, it is called a *nonrecursive* filter. For nonrecursive filters $H(z)$ becomes a polynomial in z^{-1}. Hence, the impulse response of a nonrecursive filter is the coefficient sequence $\{a_m\}$

$$h(k) = \begin{cases} a_k & 0 \leqslant k \leqslant M \\ 0 & \text{otherwise} \end{cases} \tag{14.9-6}$$

A nonrecursive filter is called a *finite impulse response* filter (FIR) and a recursive filter is called an *infinite impulse response filter* (IIR).

Suppose that we have a digital signal (or sampled values of a continuous signal) as shown in Figure 14.9-1a and we wish to smooth the output. To ac-

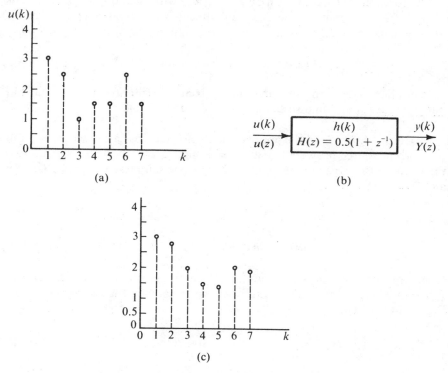

(a)

(b)

(c)

Figure 14.9-1.   A digital signal with fluctuations

complish the smoothing, we devise a simple averaging digital filter which is represented by the following difference equation

$$y(k) = \frac{u(k) + u(k-1)}{2} \qquad \text{a nonrecursive filter} \tag{14.9-7}$$

where $u(k)$ is the input and $y(k)$ is the output. The transfer function of this filter is readily found by taking the Z-transform of Equation (14.9-7). This yields

$$Y(z) = 0.5(1 + z^{-1})U(z) \qquad \text{(a)} \quad (14.9-8)$$

so that

$$H(z) = 0.5(1 + z^{-1}) \tag{b}$$

The result of this operation is shown schematically in Figure 14.9-1b, the resulting output signal being shown in Figure 14.9-1c. Observe that some degree of smoothing has been accomplished.

The foregoing procedure can be generalized with each output sample being the average of n input samples, each of which is weighted differently. The difference equation representing a generalized nonrecursive filter is given by

$$y(k) = a_1 u(k) + a_2 u(k-1) + \ldots + a_n u(k-n+1) \tag{14.9-9}$$

The following example examines how a recursive filter behaves when the input signal is (a) an impulse signal, and (b) a step signal.

EXAMPLE 14.9-1. Find the approximate voltage across a capacitor, if an input current source provides (a) an impulse signal, and (b) a step signal. Take the value of the capacitor to be $C = 1.25$ and the sampling time $T = 1$ (see Example 14.3-1).

SOLUTION. Using the given values, Equation (14.3-5) becomes

$$v(k) = 0.8i(k) + v(k-1) \tag{14.9-10}$$

Compare this equation with Equation (14.9-2) and observe that the transfer function of the digital filter is equivalent to the analog filter system shown in Figure 14.9-2. This is

$$H(z) = \frac{0.8}{1 - z^{-1}} \qquad \text{recursive filter} \tag{14.9-11}$$

where $M = m = 0$, $= 1$, $a_o = 0.8$ and $b_1 = -1$ in Equation (14.9-5c). Therefore the output for an impulse function $i(k) = u_o(k)$ is, since $\mathscr{F}\{u_o(k)\} = 1$

$$V(z) = H(z)I(z) = \frac{0.8}{1 - z^{-1}} 1 = 0.8(1 + z^{-1} + z^{-2} + \ldots) \tag{14.9-12}$$

and so, from the definition of the inverse transform

$$v(k) = \begin{cases} 0.8 & k \geqslant 0 \\ 0 & k < 0 \end{cases} \tag{14.9-13}$$

The output of the filter is shown in Figure 14.9-2a. Obviously, an impulse current source charges the capacitor to a specific voltage depending on the value of C and T.

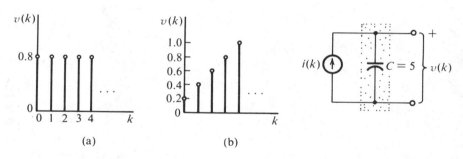

Figure 14.9-2. **The impulse and step responses of a capacitor to an input current**

Since the Z-transform of a step function is $1/(1 - z^{-1})$ (see Table 14.7-1), the desired output for a $C = 5$

$$V(z) = H(z)I(z) = \frac{0.2}{1 - z^{-1}} \frac{1}{1 - z^{-1}} = 0.2 \frac{1}{(1 - 2z^{-1} + z^{-2})}$$

whose inverse transform is (see Table 14.7-1 or use long division)

$$v(k) = \begin{cases} 0.2(k + 1) & k \geq 0 \\ 0 & k < 0 \end{cases}$$

This last function is plotted in Figure 14.9-2b. The figure shows that the capacitor is charged by an equal amount at each unit time, as is expected from physical considerations.

□ □ □

14.10 RESPONSE OF DIGITAL FILTERS TO SINUSOIDAL INPUTS

As in analog filters, it is important to know how effectively a filter transmits a desired band of frequencies. This requires that we investigate how a linear time invariant discrete filter responds to a sampled sinusoidal signal

$$u(k) = \begin{cases} A \sin k\omega T & k = 0, 1, 2, \ldots \\ 0 & k = -1, -2, \ldots \end{cases} \tag{14.10-1}$$

The Z-transform of this time function is found in Table 14.7-1, entry 8 [see also Equation (14.6-20)]

$$U(z) = A \frac{z^{-1} \sin \omega T}{(1 - e^{j\omega T}z^{-1})(1 - e^{-j\omega T}z^{-1})} \tag{14.10-2}$$

Also the Z-transform of a recursive filter having the form

$$y(k) = au(k) + by(k-1) \qquad (14.10\text{-}3)$$

is given by the relation

$$Y(z) = \frac{a}{1 - bz^{-1}} U(z) = H(z)U(z) \qquad (14.10\text{-}4)$$

The output signal in the Z-domain of this filter to the sampled sinusoid is

$$Y(z) = A \frac{z^{-1} \sin \omega T}{(1 - e^{j\omega T}z^{-1})(1 - e^{-j\omega T}z^{-1})} \frac{za}{z - b} \qquad (14.10\text{-}5)$$

To proceed, we must express this equation in partial fraction form. To do this, we write this as

$$A \frac{z \sin \omega T}{(z - e^{j\omega T})(z - e^{-j\omega T})} H(z) = \frac{C_1 z}{z - e^{j\omega T}} + \frac{C_2 z}{z - e^{-j\omega T}} + \frac{C_3 z}{z - b} \qquad (14.10\text{-}6)$$

where C_1, C_2, C_3 are constants. We proceed in the standard manner to find these. These are:

$$C_1 = A \left. \frac{H(z) \sin \omega T}{z - e^{-j\omega T}} \right|_{z = e^{j\omega T}} = \frac{A}{2j} H(e^{j\omega T}) \qquad \text{(a)} \quad (14.10\text{-}7)$$

$$C_2 = A \left. \frac{H(z) \sin \omega T}{z - e^{j\omega T}} \right|_{z = e^{-j\omega T}} = -\frac{A}{2j} H(e^{-j\omega T}) \qquad \text{(b)}$$

$$C_3 = Aa \left. \frac{\sin \omega T}{(z - e^{j\omega T})(z - e^{-j\omega T})} \right|_{z = b} = \frac{Aa \sin \omega T}{(b - \cos \omega T)^2 + \sin^2 \omega T} \qquad \text{(c)}$$

where

$$H(e^{j\omega T}) = \frac{e^{j\omega T}a}{e^{j\omega T} - b} \qquad\qquad H(e^{-j\omega T}) = \frac{e^{-j\omega T}a}{e^{-j\omega T} - b} \qquad \text{(d)}$$

But since

$$H(e^{j\omega T}) = H(e^{-j\omega T})* \qquad (14.10\text{-}8)$$

we see that

$$H(e^{j\omega T}) = H_o e^{j\theta} \qquad \text{(a)} \quad (14.10\text{-}9)$$

$$H(e^{-j\omega T}) = H_o e^{-j\theta} \qquad \text{(b)}$$

where $H_o = |H(e^{j\omega T})| = |H(e^{-j\omega T})|$ and where $\theta = \arg H(e^{j\omega T})$. Upon introducing these constants into Equation (14.10-6) we obtain

$$Y(z) = \frac{H_o}{2j} A \left(\frac{ze^{j\theta}}{z - e^{j\omega T}} - \frac{ze^{-j\theta}}{z - e^{-j\omega T}} \right) + C_3 \frac{z}{z - b}$$

The inverse Z-transform is

$$y(k) = \frac{H_o}{2j} A(e^{j(k\omega T + \theta)} - e^{-j(k\omega T + \theta)}) + C_3 b^k$$

$$= H_o A \sin (k\omega T + \theta) + C_3 b^k \qquad (14.10\text{-}10)$$

where C_3 has the value determined above [Equation (14.10-7c)].

For stable filters $b < 1$, and at steady state $k \to \infty$, $C_3 b^k \to 0$, and Equation (14.10-10) becomes

$$y(k) = H_o A \sin (k\omega T + \theta) \qquad (14.10\text{-}11)$$

From Equations (14.10-1) and (14.10-11) we observe the following:

1. The steady state response, $k \to \infty$, of a stable filter, $b < 1$, to a sinusoidal input of frequency ω is a sinusoid of the same frequency.

2. The output amplitude is that of the input modified by the absolute value of the transfer function at the same frequency, $|H(e^{j\omega T})| = H_o$.

3. The phase of the output is that of the input modified by the argument of the transfer function, $\arg H(e^{j\omega T}) = \theta$.

4. The amplitude of $|H(e^{j\omega T})|$ versus frequency ω is called the *amplitude response* of the digital filter.

5. The argument of $H(e^{j\omega T})$ versus frequency ω is called the *phase characteristic* of the digital filter.

From Equation (14.10-7d) the absolute value of $H(e^{j\omega T})$ is

$$|H(e^{j\omega T})| = \frac{|e^{j\omega T}|a}{|e^{j\omega T} - b|} = \frac{a}{|(\cos \omega T - b) + j \sin \omega T|}$$

$$= \frac{a}{\sqrt{(\cos \omega T + b)^2 + \sin^2 \omega T}} \qquad (14.10\text{-}12)$$

But

$$\cos \omega T = \cos \left[\left(\omega + \frac{2\pi}{T} \right) T \right] \qquad \text{and} \qquad \sin \omega T = \sin \left[\left(\omega + \frac{2\pi}{T} \right) T \right]$$

and therefore Equation (14.10-12) is a periodic function of ω, with $\omega = 2\pi/T$ rad/s. However, the sampling theorem tells us that for a signal with the highest angular frequency $\omega_o = 2\pi f_o = 2\pi/T_o$ we must sample it at least twice as often as $1/T_o$, or

$$T \leqslant \frac{\pi}{\omega_o} \qquad \text{or} \qquad \omega_o \leqslant \frac{\pi}{T}$$

in order that the signal be recovered from its samples. Therefore it is only necessary to plot $|H(e^{j\omega T})|$ in the interval $0 \leqslant \omega \leqslant \pi/T$, which corresponds to one-half of its period to provide the data for signal recovery.

14.11 DESIGNING DIGITAL FILTERS

To provide an understanding of the details for designing digital filters. Consider the RC digital filter shown in Figure 14.11-1 which is subject to sinusoidal signals having different frequencies.

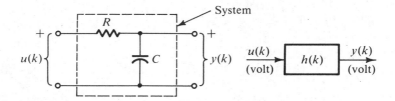

Figure 14.11-1.   An RC digital filter

We use the voltage-current relation for each element as explained in Chapter 1 and the Kirchhoff voltage law. We obtain

$$u(t) - Ri(t) - \frac{1}{C}\int i\, dt = 0$$

or

$$u(t) - R\frac{dq(t)}{dt} - \frac{1}{C}\int \frac{dq}{dt}\, dt = u(t) - RC\frac{d\left(\dfrac{q(t)}{C}\right)}{dt} - \int d\left(\frac{q(t)}{C}\right) = 0$$

or

$$u(t) - RC\frac{dy(t)}{dt} - y(t) = 0 \qquad\qquad (14.11\text{-}1)$$

where the instantaneous output voltage $y(t) = q(t)/C$. Equation (14.11-1) is converted into discrete time form by employing Equation (14.3-6). The discretized equation is

$$u(kT) - \frac{CR}{T}[y(kT) - y(kT - T)] - y(kT) = 0 \qquad (a) \quad (14.11\text{-}2)$$

or

$$y(k) = \frac{T}{T+CR}u(k) + \frac{RC}{1+RC}y(k-1) \qquad \text{(b)}$$

By taking the Z-transform of Equation (14.11-2b), we have

$$Y(z) = \frac{1}{1+RC}U(z) + \frac{RC}{1+RC}z^{-1}Y(z) \qquad \text{(a)} \quad \text{(14.11-3)}$$

or

$$Y(z) = \frac{1}{1+RC}\frac{1}{\left(1 - \frac{RC}{1+RC}z^{-1}\right)}U(z) = H(z)U(z) \qquad \text{(b)}$$

where we have assumed unit sampling time $T=1$ inside the function, for simplicity.

If the input is the sinusoidal digital signal $A \sin \omega k$ (T was taken equal to 1, for simplicity) then the output of the filter is [see Equation (14.10-11)]

$$y(k) = |H(e^{j\omega})| A \sin(k\omega + \theta) \qquad \text{(a)} \quad \text{(14.11-4)}$$

where

$$|H(e^{j\omega})| = \frac{1}{1+RC}\left| \frac{e^{j\omega}}{e^{j\omega} - \frac{RC}{1+RC}} \right| = C_1 \frac{1}{|e^{j\omega} - C_2|} \qquad \text{(b)}$$

$$= C_1 \frac{1}{\sqrt{(\cos \omega - C_2)^2 + \sin^2 \omega}}$$

$$C_1 = \frac{1}{1+RC} \qquad\qquad C_2 = \frac{RC}{1+RC} \qquad \text{(c)}$$

$$\text{Arg } H(e^{j\omega}) = \text{Arg } e^{j\omega} - \text{Arg } [e^{j\omega} - C_2] = \omega - \tan^{-1}\frac{\sin \omega}{\cos \omega - C_2} \qquad \text{(d)}$$

Curves of the normalized amplitude and phase spectra of the filter are shown in Figure 14.11-2 and Figure 14.11-3, respectively. These characterize a low pass filter.

A quantity of importance in filter design is the *bandwidth* of the filter. The most commonly used definition of the bandwidth (see Section 4.5) is the range of frequencies within which the magnitude of $|H|$ drops to $1/\sqrt{2} = 0.707$ of its normalized value. Figure 14.11-2 shows the bandwidth for the filter discussed with $RC=1$. Since the bandwidth varies with the constants R and C of the filter, it is a matter of finding an approach not only to establish these constants for a desired bandwidth, but at the same time to restrict the amplitude to a

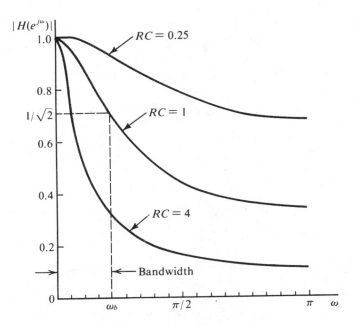

Figure 14.11-2.   Normalized plots of Equation (14.11-4b)

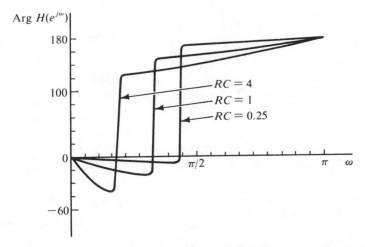

Figure 14.11-3.   Normalized plots of Equation (14.11-4c)

predetermined value for the frequencies outside of the bandwidth range. We shall not pursue this matter here since it is outside the scope of this book. However, it is important that the student should appreciate the fact that digital filters can be designed to provide bandpass, highpass and lowpass filtering characteristics.

EXAMPLE 14.11-1. Find the amplitude spectra of a digital filter that is characterized by the difference equation

$$y(k) = 2u(k) - 0.5y(k-1) \qquad (14.11\text{-}5)$$

Also determine the bandwidth.

SOLUTION. The Z-transform of this equation is

$$Y(z) = 2U(z) - 0.5z^{-1}Y(z)$$

or

$$Y(z) = H(z)U(z) = \frac{2}{1 + 0.5z^{-1}} U(z) \qquad \text{(a)} \quad (14.11\text{-}6)$$

where

$$H(z) = \frac{2z}{z + 0.5} \qquad \text{(b)}$$

The steady state response to the input $u(k) = \sin k\omega T$ is [see Equations (14.10-11) and (14.10-9)]

$$y(kT) = |H(e^{j\omega T})| \sin(k\omega T + \theta) \qquad \text{(a)} \quad (14.11\text{-}7)$$

where

$$|H(e^{j\omega T})| = 2\frac{|e^{j\omega T}|}{|e^{j\omega T} + 0.5|} = \frac{2}{\sqrt{(\cos \omega T + 0.5)^2 + \sin^2 \omega T}} \qquad \text{(b)}$$

and

$$\text{Arg } H(e^{j\omega T}) = \theta = \omega T - \tan^{-1}\left[\frac{\sin \omega T}{\cos \omega T + 0.5}\right] \qquad \text{(c)}$$

The amplitude and phase spectra are plotted in Figure 14.11-4. The amplitude spectrum plot indicates that this is a high-pass filter, and its bandwidth is equal to $4\pi/18T$ rad/s. Hence, if the sampling were at 1 MHz, or $T = 10^{-6}$ s, the bandwidth of this filter is $(2\pi/9) \times 10^6$ Hz.

□   □   □

We call attention to the fact that the transfer functions of the two filters that we have considered above are of the form

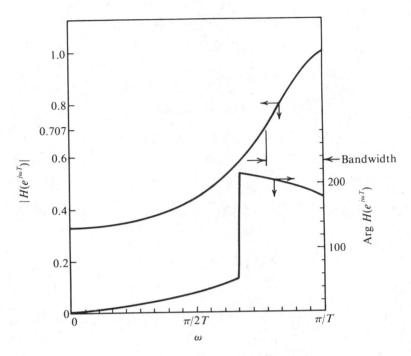

Figure 14.11-4.   Normalized plots of Equation (14.11-7)

$$H(z) = a_o \frac{z - \alpha}{z - \beta} \qquad (14.11\text{-}8)$$

where a_o, α and β were real numbers. However, in a general situation for more extensive filters, these numbers can be complex. When we introduce $z = e^{j\omega T}$ into Equation (14.11-8) and ask for the quantity $|H(e^{j\omega T})|$ we actually ask for the number

$$|H(e^{j\omega T})| = a_o \frac{|e^{j\omega T} - \alpha|}{|e^{j\omega T} - \beta|} = a_o \frac{|a|}{|b|} \qquad (14.11\text{-}9)$$

at each value of ω for a particular sampling period T. The values $|a|$ and $|b|$ are shown graphically in Figures 14.11-5a and 14.11-5b for two values of ω. Thus to plot the amplitude of any digital filter one procedure is to graphically measure the distance $|a|$ and $|b|$ at each ω and then perform the appropriate operations dictated by Equation (14.11-9).

The angles, Arg $H(e^{j\omega T})$ are easily found from Equation (14.11-8) to be

$$\text{Arg } H(e^{j\omega T}) = \Phi = \theta - \varphi \qquad (14.11\text{-}10)$$

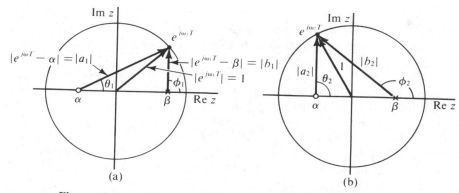

Figure 14.11-5. Graphical representation of the complex numbers associated with amplitude spectra

The two values of Arg $H(e^{j\omega T})$ corresponding to Figures 14.11-5a and 14.11-5b are

$$\Phi_1 = \theta_1 - \varphi_1 \qquad\qquad \Phi_2 = \theta_2 - \varphi_2 \qquad\qquad (14.11\text{-}11)$$

A transfer function with two zeros and three poles is shown in Figure 14.11-5. The amplitude and the phase values for a given are given by

$$|H(e^{j\omega T})| = \frac{|a_1|\,|a_2|}{|b_1|\,|b_2|\,|b_3|} \qquad\qquad \text{(a)} \quad (14.11\text{-}12)$$

$$\text{Arg } H(e^{j\omega T}) = \Phi = \theta_1 + \theta_2 - \varphi_1 - \varphi_2 - \varphi_3 \qquad\qquad \text{(b)}$$

From Figure 14.11-6 it is observed that when ω takes on such values that $|b_2|$ is its minimum, the value of the function $H(e^{j\omega T})$ will be greatly affected if the pole is very close to the unit circle. This is also true for the zeros. A somewhat

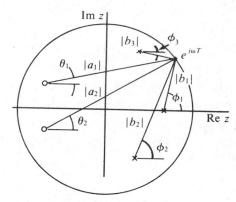

Figure 14.11-6. Typical diagram of a transfer function with 2 zeros and 3 poles

similar discussion was included in Section 4.5 in connection with $H(j\omega)$. Our observations may be summarized as follows:

1. The amplitude spectra are mostly influenced by the poles and zeros which are closest to the unit circle.

2. When a pole is located at an angle $\omega_o T$ inside the unit circle, it has an enlarging effect on the amplitude spectra for frequencies ω close to ω_o.

3. When a zero is located at an angle $\omega_o T$ inside the unit circle, it has a diminishing effect on the amplitude spectra for frequencies ω close to ω_o.

The conclusion from this discussion is that ways exist from which we can determine the location and the number of poles and zeros so that a desired filtering is accomplished. These matters will be developed in the student's further studies involving digital filtering.

14.12   POSTLUDE

Among the areas involving discrete time systems that will probably arise in the student's later programs are signal processing and automatic control of machines and machinery. Both of these fields are extensive and will intimately involve the use of digital computers of general purpose or dedicated types. Digital filters and their relation to signal processing is of considerable importance in communications, in radar applications, and in almost any signal processing requirement. In the control engineering field, discrete time control systems, and the analysis and design of sampled data control systems researchers have developed extensive and sophisticated methodology. The future in these areas continues to brighten as knowledge rapidly increases.

Of special importance in this chapter has been the introduction of transformation methods for solving mathematical problems. The Z-transform, developed from a simple mathematical procedure for solving difference equations, is essential to more advanced studies. Additionally, the system function and its relationship to system behavior is extremely important. In most studies involving discrete time design, whether it be digital filters or control systems, the system function and its description in terms of its pole-zero constellation play a fundamental role.

SUMMARY

- The discrete time input to a system is taken as a set of numbers denoted by $\{u(k)\}$ ordered by the discrete variable $k = 0, \pm 1, \pm 2, \ldots$.

- A discrete time system is one which operates on an input sequence of numbers (the input signal) $u(k)$ and which produces an output sequence of numbers (the output signal $y(k)$.

- The integral

$$v(t) = \int_0^t i(t) \, dt$$

which is sampled at time intervals $T = 1$ is given in discrete form by

$$v(k) = v(k-1) + i(k)$$

- The derivative $v(t) = df/dt$ sampled at time intervals $T = 1$ is given in discrete form by

$$v(k) = f(k) - f(k-1)$$

- The general solution $y(k)$ of a difference equation is equal to the sum of the solution of the homogeneous equation (input = zero) $y_h(k)$ and the particular solution $y_p(k)$, which is the solution of the nonhomogeneous equation. The arbitrary constants which appear with the homogeneous solution are found by applying the boundary or initial conditions of the problem at hand.

- A system with block diagram and signal flow graph representations as shown includes the fundamental property of feedback, with $y(k) = u(k)[1/(1-z^{-1})]$.

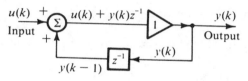

Figure S14.3-1

- The one-sided Z-transform of a sequence $\{y(k)\}$ is given by

$$Y(z) = \mathcal{Z}\{y(k)\} = \sum_{k=0}^{\infty} y(k)z^{-k}$$

- The Z-transform possesses the following properties:

Linearity $\qquad \mathcal{Z}\{ay_1(k) + by_2(k)\} = a\mathcal{Z}\{y_1(k)\} + b\mathcal{Z}\{y_2(k)\}$

Right shift $\qquad \mathcal{Z}\{y(k-n)\} = z^{-n}\mathcal{Z}\{y(k)\} = z^{-n}Y(z)$

Left shift $\qquad \mathcal{Z}\{y(k+n)\} = z^{n}Y(z) - \sum_{k=0}^{n-1} y(k)z^{n-k}$

Time scaling $\qquad \mathcal{Z}\{a^{k}y(k)\} = Y(a^{-1}z) = \sum_{k=0}^{\infty}(a^{-1}z)^{-k}y(k)$

Periodic sequence $\quad \mathcal{Z}\{y(k)\} = \dfrac{z^{N}}{z^{N}-1}\mathcal{Z}\{y_{(1)}(k)\} \qquad \left\{ \begin{array}{l} N = \text{period} \\ y_{(1)}(k) = \text{first period} \end{array}\right.$

- The Z-transform of the convolution of two sequences is given by

$$W(z) = \mathcal{Z}\{w(k)\} = \mathcal{Z}\left\{ \sum_{m=0}^{\infty} u(m)v(k-m) \right\} = U(z)V(z)$$

- Time invariant discrete time systems, commonly called digital filters, can be described by the following input-output relationship

$$y(k) = \sum_{m=0}^{\infty} u(m)h(k-m) = \sum_{n=0}^{\infty} u(k-n)h(n)$$

where $h(k)$ is the impulse response of the system. A second representation is that given by the relationship

$$y(k) = \sum_{m=0}^{M} a_m u(k-m) - \sum_{l=1}^{L} b_l y(k-l)$$

- A digital filter is called recursive, infinite impulse response (IIR), if some past outputs are needed for the present output. If none of the past outputs are required for the present output, the digital filter is called nonrecursive, or finite impulse response (FIR) filter.

REVIEW QUESTIONS

1. What is the difference between a discrete time and a continuous time signal? Plot two such signals.
2. Can we construct a discrete time signal from a continuous time signal and vice versa? Explain.
3. Define sampling and sampling frequency.
4. What type of equations describe the behavior of discrete time systems and signals?
5. When is a difference equation called homogeneous, and when is it called nonhomogeneous?
6. Define the particular and the general solution of a difference equation.
7. Which of the solutions of a difference equation describes the transient phenomenon of a system?
8. Define the input impedance of a circuit.
9. What is the ratio I/V called?
10. Can you give an example of a feedback system in humans (or animals)?
11. What are the poles and zeros of a function?
12. Describe in words the mathematical relations known as convolution.
13. What is a transfer function (or system function) of a system?
14. What is the impulse response of a system? Why is it significant for linear time-invariant systems?
15. What is the difference between a recursive and a nonrecursive filter?

REFERENCES

1. Antoniou, A., *Digital Filters, Analysis and Design*, McGraw Hill Book Co., New York, NY, 1979.

   An intermediate level text that combines theories, techniques and procedures for analyzing, designing, and implementing digital filters.

2. Cadzow, J. A., *Discrete Time Systems*, Prentice-Hall, Inc., Englewood Cliffs, NJ, 1973.

This text develops the basic concepts of linear discrete time systems. The text is self-contained, requires only standard college preparatory mathematics, and covers a wealth of material.

3. Goldberg, S., *Introduction to Difference Equations*, John Wiley & Sons, Inc., New York, NY, 1958.

Presents the basic ideas and techniques involved in setting up and solving difference equations. Assumes a minimum of mathematical preparation.

PROBLEMS

14.1-1. Find and sketch the sum and the difference of the unit step and unit alternating discrete functions.

14.1-2. Plot the discrete functions given by

    (a) $u(k) = u_o(k) + 2u_o(k-1)$
    (b) $u(k) = -0.5u_o(k) + 2u_o(k-3)$
    (c) $u(k) = u_{-1}(k) - u_{-1}(k-4)$
    (d) $u(k) = u_{-1}(k+2)$
    (e) $u(k) = a^k$ for $k \geqslant 0$, and for (1) $a < 1$ and (2) $a > 1$.

14.3-1. Determine the response of the savings account system for which the input and output signals are related by the relation

$$y(k) = u(k) + 1.015y(k-1)$$

where $u(k) = 0$; $k = -1, -2, -3, -4, \ldots$; $y(-1) = 300$; $u(0) = 100$, $u(1) = -200$.

14.3-2. Approximate the value of the integrals

    (a) $\displaystyle\int_0^1 (1 + t^2)^{3/2} \, dt$
    (b) $\displaystyle\int_0^{60°} \cos^2 \theta \, d\theta$
    (c) $\displaystyle\int_0^1 \frac{t^3 \, dt}{\sqrt{t+1}}$

14.3-3. Show graphically the difference between the slope $[dy(kT)]/dt$ and the slope $[y(kT) - y(kT - T)]/T$.

14.3-4. Find the velocity of a mass element if the applied force is $u_{-1}(k)$ and $T = K = 1$. Sketch the block representation of the numerical algorithm.

14.3-5. Find the current for the system shown in Figure 14.3-5 if the input voltage is $v(t) = u_{-2}(k)$ (unit ramp). Assume zero initial conditions.

14.3-6. Find the output voltage of the system shown in Figure P14.3-6 with $RC = 1$ and $T = 1$. Initial conditions are taken to be zero and $v_i(t) = u_{-1}(t)$ (unit step function).

    Hint: Remember $i = dq/dt$ and $q(t)/C = v_o(t)$; the system equation is

$$\frac{dv_o(t)}{dt} + \frac{1}{RC} v_o(t) = \frac{1}{RC} v_i(t)$$

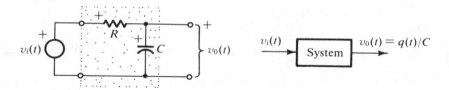

Figure P14.3-6

14.3-7. A unit step sequence source of heat is added at discrete times to an insulated container containing ten kilograms of distilled water at an initial temperature 15°C. Find the temperature.

14.3-8. A mechanical rotating system is shown in Figure P14.3-8. Find the angular velocity of the system and draw its numerical algorithm for the input torque function shown.

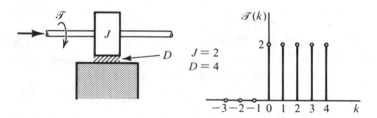

Figure P14.3-8

14.4-1. Show that the general solution of equation

$$y(k) = \alpha y(k-1) + \beta$$

is given by

$$y(k) = \begin{cases} \alpha^{k+1} y(-1) + \beta \dfrac{1 - \alpha^{k+1}}{1 - \alpha} & \text{if } \alpha \neq 1 \\ y(-1) + \beta(k+1) & \text{if } \alpha \neq 1 \end{cases} \quad \text{for } k = 0, 1, 2, \ldots$$

14.4-2. Find the complete solutions of the following difference equations:

(a) $y(k) + 3y(k-1) = 4$

(b) $y(k) - y(k-1) = 2$

(c) $2y(k) - 4y(k-1) = 6k + 2$

14.5-1. A signal generator produces the following signal

$$u(k) = \begin{cases} 0 & k<0 \\ 1 & 0 \leqslant k \leqslant 2 \\ 0 & k>0 \end{cases}$$

Find the flow-graph representation of the system that will produce the output signal shown in Figure P14.5-1.

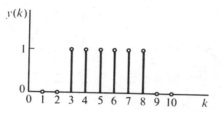

Figure P14.5-1

14.5-2. Plot the output signal and the flow graph representation of the system if

(a) $y(k) = u(k) \left(\dfrac{a}{1 - az^{-1}} \right)$

(b) $y(k) = u(k) \left(\dfrac{b}{1 - abz^{-1}} \right)$

The input signal is the one given in Problem 14.5-1.

14.5-3. A signal generator produces a pulse as shown in Figure P14.5-3a. When the signal is introduced into a system its output is that shown in Figure P14.5-3b. Find the flow-graph representation of the system.

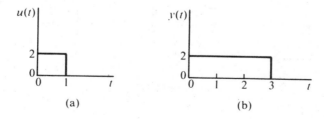

(a)   (b)

Figure P14.5-3

14.5-4. Plot the output of a system in the time interval $0 \leqslant t \leqslant 10$ whose flow-graph representation is shown in Figure P14.5-4a for the input signals shown in Figures P14.5-4b, c, d, and e.

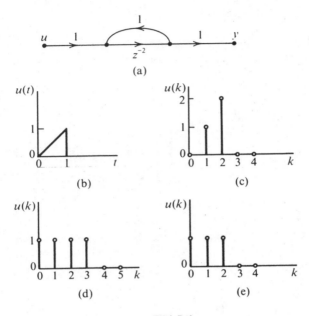

Figure P14.5-4

14.5-5. Plot the output of a system in the time interval $0 \leqslant t \leqslant 10$ whose flow-graph representation is shown in Figure P14.5-5a with an input function that is shown in Figure P14.5-5b.

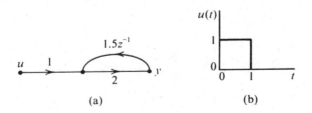

Figure P14.5-5

14.5-6. Find the input-output relations for the systems represented by the SFGs of Figure P14.5-6.

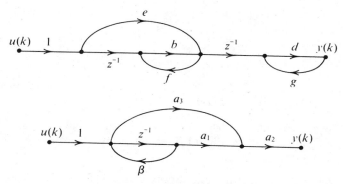

Figure P14.5-6

14.6-1. Determine the Z-transform of the unit step function, find the regions of convergence and divergence, and indicate its poles and zeros on the Z-plane.

14.6-2. Determine the Z-transform of the function

$$y(k) = \begin{cases} a^k \cos(kb) & k \geqslant 0 \\ 0 & k < 0 \end{cases}$$

Find the regions of convergence and divergence, and indicate the poles and zeros on the Z-plane. [Hint: see Example 14.6-4.]

14.6-3. Find the Z-transform of the function

$$y(k) = c^k = a^k e^{jbk} \qquad k \geqslant 0$$

Show that its real and imaginary parts are the Z-transforms of the functions given in Problem 14.6-2 and Example 14.6-4, respectively.

14.6-4. Find the Z-transforms, their regions of convergence and divergence, and plot the pole-zero patterns of the following signals (sequences) for $k \geqslant 0$:

(a) $\{y(k)\} = 1 + k$
(b) $\{y(k)\} = k^2$

(c) $\{y(k)\} = a^k + a^{-k}$
(d) $\{y(k)\} = e^{j\theta k}$

14.6-5. Make a plot of the magnitude of the Z-transform $Y(z) = 1/(1 - 0.2z^{-1})$ for real values of the complex variable z.

14.8-1. Find the following inverse Z-transforms without the help of a table:

(a) $F(z) = \dfrac{z}{z-1} + \dfrac{z}{z^2 - 0.3}$

(b) $F(z) = \dfrac{4z}{(z-0.1)(z-0.4)}$

(c) $F(z) = \dfrac{z}{(z-0.2)} + 1$

(d) $F(z) = 1 + 3z^{-1} + 2z^{-2}$

14.8-2. Calculate the first seven nonzero sample values of the signals with the following Z-transforms:

(a) $F(z) = \dfrac{1}{(1-0.2z^{-1})^2}$

(c) $F(z) = \dfrac{1+0.4z^{-1}}{1-3.6z^{-1}+1.4z^{-2}}$

(b) $F(z) = \dfrac{1}{1-0.3z^{-1}+0.5z^{-2}}$

14.9-1. If the system function is given by $y(k) = u(k) + 0.8y(k-1)$, find and plot the output of the digital filter if the inputs are a delta function and a step function.

14.9-2. Find the impulse and step response of the filter shown in Figure P14.9-2. [Hint: $y(t) = Ri$.]

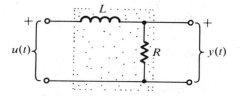

Figure P14.9-2

14.9-3. Find and plot the amplitude and phase characteristics of the transfer function belonging to the filter given in Problem 14.9-2.

14.11-1. Expand the following functions into partial fractions

$$F(z) = \frac{(z^3+1)}{(z-0.5)(z+0.5)(z+0.4)^2}$$

$$F(z) = \frac{z^2+3z+1}{z^2(z-1)^2}$$

14.11-2. Derive the transfer functions for the filters specified by:

(a) $y(k) = u(k) - 0.2y(k-1)$
(b) $y(k) = u(k) - 0.2y(k-2)$
(c) $y(k) = u(k) + 0.5u(k-1) - 0.5y(k-1)$

14.11-3. Find the amplitude spectra and the bandwidth of the transfer functions $(T=1)$

(a) $H(z) = \dfrac{0.2}{(1-0.5z^{-1})^2}$

(b) $H(z) = \dfrac{z^2}{(z-0.5e^{j30°})(z-0.5e^{-j30°})}$

Appendix 1

Complex Numbers

A complex number z is made up of two parts, a real component and an imaginary component. It is written

$$z = x + jy \qquad \text{(A1.1)}$$

where x and y are real numbers, and where $j = \sqrt{-1}$ denotes a phase shift of 90 degrees with respect to the axis of reals. The complex number z is represented by a point in the complex z-plane, as shown in Figure A1.1a. It can also be described by a directed line, as shown in Figure A1.1b. Figure A1.1c shows the

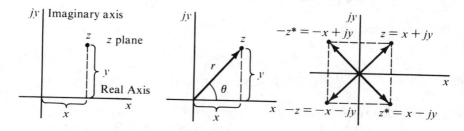

Figure A1.1.   Complex numbers

several complex numbers related to z. Here the conjugate z^* of the complex number is defined by

$$z^* = (x + jy)^* = x - jy \qquad \text{(A1.2)}$$

That is, z^* is obtained from z by reversing the sign of the imaginary term.

In the form given in Equation (A1.1), the representation of z is called the Cartesian or algebraic representation. Its polar representation given in Figure A1.1b is

$$z = re^{j\theta} = \sqrt{x^2 + y^2} \; e^{j \tan^{-1} (y/x)} \tag{A1.3}$$

By the DeMoivre law

$$e^{j\theta} = \cos \theta + j \sin \theta \tag{A1.4}$$

then

$$z = \sqrt{x^2 + y^2} \cos [\tan^{-1} (y/x)] + j\sqrt{x^2 + y^2} \sin [\tan^{-1} (y/x)]$$
$$= r \cos \theta + j \sin \theta \tag{A1.5}$$

The four basic mathematical operations: addition, subtraction, multiplication and division, of two complex numbers z_1 and z_2 are:

(a) Addition:

$$z = z_1 + z_2 = (x_1 + jy_1) + (x_2 + jy_2) = (x_1 + x_2) + j(y_1 + y_2) \tag{A1.6}$$
$$= r_1 e^{j\theta_1} + r_2 e^{j\theta_2}$$
$$= (r_1 \cos \theta_1 + jr_1 \sin \theta_1) + (r_2 \cos \theta_2 + jr_2 \sin \theta_2)$$
$$= (r_1 \cos \theta_1 + r_2 \cos \theta_2) + j(r_1 \sin \theta_1 + r_2 \sin \theta_2)$$

That is, the sum of two complex numbers is a complex number equal to the sum of the real parts and the sum of the imaginary parts.

(b) Subtraction

$$z = z_1 - z_2 = (x_1 + jy_1) - (x_2 - jy_2) = (x_1 - x_2) + j(y_1 - y_2) \tag{A1.7}$$
$$= (r_1 \cos \theta_1 - r_2 \cos \theta_2) - j(r_1 \sin \theta_1 - r_2 \sin \theta_2)$$

This shows that the difference of two complex numbers is a complex number equal to the difference between the real parts and the difference of the imaginary parts.

(c) Multiplication

$$z = z_1 z_2 = (x_1 + jy_1)(x_2 + jy_2) = x_1 x_2 + jx_1 y_2 + jx_2 y_1 + j^2 y_1 y_2 \tag{A1.8}$$
$$= (x_1 x_2 - y_1 y_2) + j(x_1 y_2 + x_2 y_1)$$
$$= r_1 e^{j\theta_1} r_2 e^{j\theta_2} = r_1 r_2 e^{j(\theta_1 + \theta_2)}$$

where

$$j^2 = -1; \quad j^3 = (j^2)j = -j; \quad j^4 = j^2 \times j^2 = (-1)(-1) = 1; \quad \text{etc.}$$

The product of two complex numbers is a complex number whose magnitude is the product of the magnitudes of the two complex numbers, and whose argument is the sum of the arguments of the two complex numbers.

(d) Division

$$z = \frac{z_1}{z_2} = \frac{x_1 + jy_1}{x_2 + jy_2} = \frac{(x_1 + jy_1)(x_2 - jy_2)}{(x_2 + jy_2)(x_2 - jy_2)} = \frac{(x_1 x_2 + y_1 y_2) + j(y_1 x_2 - x_1 y_2)}{x_2^2 + y_2^2} \quad \text{(A1.9)}$$

$$= \frac{x_1 x_2 + y_1 y_2}{x_2^2 + y_2^2} + j \frac{y_1 x_2 - x_1 y_2}{x_2^2 + y_2^2}$$

$$= \frac{r_1 e^{j\theta_1}}{r_2 e^{j\theta_2}} = \frac{r_1}{r_2} e^{j\theta_1} e^{-j\theta_2} = \frac{r_1}{r_2} e^{j(\theta_1 - \theta_2)}$$

The ratio of two complex numbers is a complex number whose magnitude is the ratio of the magnitudes of the two complex numbers and whose argument is the difference of the arguments of the two complex numbers.

EXAMPLE A1.1. Find the sum, difference, product and ratio of the complex numbers $z_1 = 3 + j5$ and $z_2 = 2 - j4$.

SOLUTION. (a) Addition

$$z = z_1 + z_2 = (3 + j5) + (2 - j4) = 5 + j1 = \sqrt{5^2 + 1^2} \; e^{j11.309°} = 5.099 e^{j11.309°}$$

(b) Subtraction

$$z = z_1 - z_2 = (3 - 2) + j(5 + 4) = 1 + j9 = \sqrt{1^2 + 9^2} \; e^{j83.659°} = 9.055 e^{j83.659°}$$

(c) Multiplication

$$z = z_1 z_2 = (3 + j5)(2 - j4) = 6 - j12 + j10 + 20 = 26 - j2 = \sqrt{26^2 + 2^2} \; e^{j(-4.398)°}$$
$$= 26.076 e^{-j4.398°}$$

(d) Division

$$z = \frac{z_1}{z_2} = \frac{(3 + j5)}{(2 - j4)} = \frac{\sqrt{9 + 25} \; e^{j59.036}}{\sqrt{4 + 16} e^{-j63.434}} = 1.3 e^{j122.47°}$$

□ □ □

Appendix 2

Resistor Color Code

Resistors are color coded to give the resistance and the tolerance limits of the indicated resistance.

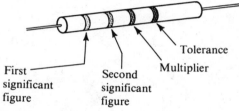

Significant figures	Color	Multiplier	Color	Tolerance
0	Black	1	Black or no color	±20%
1	Brown	10	Silver	±10%
2	Red	10^2	Gold	±5%
3	Orange	10^3		
4	Yellow	10^4		
5	Green	10^5		
6	Blue	10^6		
7	Violet			
8	Gray			
9	White			
	Gold	10^{-1}		
	Silver	10^{-2}		

Appendix 3

Cramer's Rule

Cramer's rule provides a systematic method for solving a set of simultaneous equations. The details are shown by finding the values of the three unknowns x_1, x_2, x_3 in the set of three algebraic equations:

$$a_{11}x_1 + a_{12}x_2 + a_{13}x_3 = b_1$$

$$a_{21}x_1 + a_{22}x_2 + a_{23}x_3 = b_2$$

$$a_{31}x_1 + a_{32}x_2 + a_{33}x_3 = b_3$$

The coefficients a_{ij} are known constants. The unknowns x_1, x_2, x_3 are given by the ratio of determinants

$$x_1 = \frac{\begin{vmatrix} b_1 & a_{12} & a_{13} \\ b_2 & a_{22} & a_{23} \\ b_3 & a_{32} & a_{33} \end{vmatrix}}{D} \qquad x_2 = \frac{\begin{vmatrix} a_{11} & b_1 & a_{13} \\ a_{21} & b_2 & a_{23} \\ a_{31} & b_3 & a_{33} \end{vmatrix}}{D} \qquad x_3 = \frac{\begin{vmatrix} a_{11} & a_{12} & b_1 \\ a_{21} & a_{22} & b_2 \\ a_{31} & a_{32} & b_3 \end{vmatrix}}{D}$$

where D is the determinant of the coefficients

$$D = \begin{vmatrix} a_{11} & a_{12} & a_{13} \\ a_{21} & a_{22} & a_{23} \\ a_{31} & a_{32} & a_{33} \end{vmatrix}$$

Observe that the procedure involves replacing the columns in D by the right hand column, in establishing the numerator determinants.

The value of a second order determinant is given by

$$\begin{vmatrix} a_{11} & a_{12} \\ a_{21} & a_{11} \end{vmatrix} = a_{11}a_{22} - a_{12}a_{21}$$

The value of a third order determinant is found using the Laplace expansion method. This requires expanding the determinant along a row or a column (here shown by expanding along the first row).

$$
\begin{vmatrix} a_{11} & a_{12} & a_{13} \\ a_{21} & a_{22} & a_{23} \\ a_{31} & a_{32} & a_{33} \end{vmatrix} = (-1)^{1+1} a_{11} \begin{vmatrix} a_{22} & a_{23} \\ a_{32} & a_{33} \end{vmatrix} + (-1)^{1+2} a_{12} \begin{vmatrix} a_{21} & a_{23} \\ a_{31} & a_{33} \end{vmatrix}
$$

$$
+ (-1)^{1+3} a_{13} \begin{vmatrix} a_{21} & a_{22} \\ a_{31} & a_{32} \end{vmatrix}
$$

The first number on the exponent (-1) designates the number of the row and the second number designates the number of the column.

The second order determinants in this expansion are one order lower than the order of the original determinant. These are called the minors, and they are obtained by deleting the row and column of the element in the expansion of the third order determinant. Essentially, therefore, each application of the Laplace expansion method reduces a determinant of a given order by a sum of determinants which are one order lower, each being multiplied by an appropriate coefficient.

Some important properties of determinants are

(a) Upon interchanging two adjacent rows or two adjacent columns, the value of the determinant changes sign.

(b) No change occurs in the value of the determinant if rows and columns are interchanged.

(c) If a row or a column contains a common factor, the value of the determinant is multiplied by the factor, which can be factored.

EXAMPLE A3.1. Find the unknown currents, given the following set of equations:

$$
i_1 - 2i_2 + i_3 = 0
$$

$$
3i_1 + 4i_2 - i_3 = 2
$$

$$
i_1 + i_2 + i_3 = 0
$$

SOLUTION. Apply Cramer's rule. Thus we evaluate the following determinants:

$$
D = \begin{vmatrix} 1 & -2 & 1 \\ 3 & 4 & -1 \\ 1 & 1 & 1 \end{vmatrix} = 1 \begin{vmatrix} 4 & -1 \\ 1 & 1 \end{vmatrix} + 2 \begin{vmatrix} 3 & -1 \\ 1 & 1 \end{vmatrix} + 1 \begin{vmatrix} 3 & 4 \\ 1 & 1 \end{vmatrix}
$$

$$
= 1(4+1) + 2(3+1) + 1(3-4) = 12
$$

$$i_1 = \frac{\begin{vmatrix} 0 & -2 & 1 \\ 2 & 4 & -1 \\ 0 & 1 & 1 \end{vmatrix}}{D} = \frac{0\begin{vmatrix} 4 & -1 \\ 1 & 1 \end{vmatrix} - 2\begin{vmatrix} -2 & 1 \\ 1 & 1 \end{vmatrix} + 0\begin{vmatrix} -2 & 1 \\ 4 & -1 \end{vmatrix}}{12} = \frac{6}{12} = \frac{1}{2}$$

$$i_2 = \frac{\begin{vmatrix} 1 & 0 & 1 \\ 3 & 2 & -1 \\ 1 & 0 & 1 \end{vmatrix}}{12} = \frac{(-1)^{1+1}0\begin{vmatrix} 3 & -1 \\ 1 & 1 \end{vmatrix} + (-1)^{2+2}2\begin{vmatrix} 1 & 1 \\ 1 & 1 \end{vmatrix} + (-1)^{3+2}0\begin{vmatrix} 1 & 1 \\ 3 & -1 \end{vmatrix}}{12}$$

$$= 0$$

$$i_3 = \frac{\begin{vmatrix} 1 & -2 & 0 \\ 3 & 4 & 2 \\ 1 & 1 & 0 \end{vmatrix}}{12} = \frac{(-1)^{1+3}0\begin{vmatrix} 3 & 4 \\ 1 & 1 \end{vmatrix} + (-1)^{2+3}2\begin{vmatrix} 1 & -2 \\ 1 & 1 \end{vmatrix} + (-1)^{3+3}0\begin{vmatrix} 1 & -2 \\ 3 & 4 \end{vmatrix}}{12}$$

$$= -\frac{6}{12} = -\frac{1}{2}$$

Observe that the third order determinant was expanded along the columns owing to the simplifications resulting from the presence of 0s as multipliers.

□   □   □

Appendix 4

Physical Constants and Units

Table A4.1.   Physical Constants

Quantity	Symbol	Value
Boltzmann constant	k	1.380612×10^{-23} J-$°$K^{-1}
Electronic charge	e	1.602189×10^{-19} C
Electron rest mass	m_e	9.109534×10^{-31} kg
Velocity of light	c	2.997924×10^{8} m-sec^{-1}
Permeability of vacuum	μ_o	$4\pi \times 10^{-7}$ H-m^{-1}
Permittivity of vacuum	ϵ_o	8.854187×10^{-12} F-m^{-1}
Planck's constant	h	6.626176×10^{-34} J-Hz^{-1}
Proton rest mass	m_H	1.672648×10^{-27} kg
Impedance of free space	Z_o	376.7304Ω

Appendix 5

Conversion Table

To Convert	Into	Multiply by
1. Mass		
kilogram	gram	1000
	pound	2.205
	slug $\left(\dfrac{\text{pound}}{\text{foot/sec}^2} \right)$	6.853×10^{-2}
2. Length		
meter	foot	3.281
3. Energy		
joule (or watt-second or newton-m)	erg	10^7
	foot-pound	0.7376
	kilowatt-hour	2.778×10^{-7}
	BTU	9.478×10^{-4}
	horsepower-hour	3.725×10^{-7}
	kilogram-meter	0.10197
4. Power		
watt (joule/second)	foot-pound/second	0.7376
	horsepower	1.341×10^{-3}
	BTU/second	9.478×10^{-4}
	kg-meter/second	0.10197
5. Force		
newton	dyne	10^5
	pound	0.2248

6. **Torque**
   newton-meter   pound-foot   0.7376

7. **Moment of Inertia**
   kg-meter^2 pound-foot^2 23.73

8. **Translational spring constant**
   newton/meter   pound/foot 68.59×10^{-3}

9. **Torsional spring constant**
   newton-meter/radian   pound-foot/radian   0.7376

10. **Translational damping constant**
    newton-second/meter   pound-second/foot 68.59×10^{-3}

11. **Torsional damping constant**
    newton-meter-second/radian   pound-foot-second/radian 0.7376

12. **Magnetic flux density**
    weber/meter^2 gauss 10^4
                                  lines/inch^2 6.452×10^4

13. **Magnetic intensity**
    ampere-turn/meter   ampere-turn/inch   0.0254

NOTE: For the reverse conversion, divide by the given conversion factor.

SELECTED BIBLIOGRAPHY

Bailie, R. C., *Energy Conversion Engineering*, Addison-Wesley Publishing Co., Reading, MA, 1978.

Bartree, T. C., *Digital Computer Fundamentals*, 4th ed., McGraw Hill Book Co., New York, NY, 1977.

Belove, C., H. Schachter and D. L. Schilling, *Digital and Analog Systems, Circuits, and Devices*, McGraw Hill Book Co., New York, NY, 1973.

Brophy, J. J., *Basic Electronics for Scientists*, 3rd ed., McGraw Hill Book Co., New York, NY, 1977.

Camp, R. C., T. A. Smay and C. J. Triska, *Microcomputer Systems Principles*, Matrix Publishers, Inc., Portland, OR, 1979.

Chirlian, P. M., *Analysis and Design of Digital Circuits and Computer Systems*, Matrix Publishers, Inc., Portland, OR, 1976.

Chirlian, P. M., *Introduction to Structured Fortran*, Matrix Publishers, Inc., Portland, OR, 1979.

Close, C. M., and D. K. Frederick, *Modeling and Analysis of Dynamic Systems*, Houghton Mifflin Co., Boston, MA, 1978.

Daniels, F., *Direct Use of the Sun's Energy*, Ballantine Books, New York, NY, 1964.

Del Toro, V., *Principles of Electrical Engineering*, 2nd ed., Prentice Hall, Inc., Englewood Cliffs, NJ, 1972.

Dorf, R. C., *Modern Control Systems*, Addison-Wesley Publishing Co., Reading, MA, 1967.

Doty, L. K., *Fundamental Principles of Microcomputer Architecture*, Matrix Publishers, Inc., Portland, OR, 1979.

Finizio, N., and G. Ladas, *Ordinary Differential Equations with Modern Applications*, Wadsworth Publishing Co., Belmont, CA, 1978.

Hayt, W., *Engineering Electromagnetics*, 3rd ed., McGraw Hill Book Co., New York, NY, 1974.

Kohonen, T., *Digital Circuits and Devices*, Prentice Hall, Inc., Englewood Cliffs, NJ, 1972.

Kraus, J. D., and K. R. Carver, *Electromagnetics*, 2nd ed., McGraw Hill Book Co., New York, NY, 1973.

Lewis, J. B., *Analysis of Linear Dynamic Systems*, Matrix Publishers, Inc., Portland, OR, 1977.

Lindsay, J. F., and S. Katz, *Dynamics of Physical Circuits and Systems*, Matrix Publishers, Inc., Portland, OR, 1978.

Lynch, W. A., and J. G. Truxal, *Signals and Systems in Electrical Engineering*, McGraw Hill Book Co., New York, NY, 1962.

Peatman, J. B., *The Design of Digital Systems*, McGraw Hill Book Co., New York, NY, 1972.

Peatman, J. B., *Microcomputer-Based Design*, McGraw Hill Book Co., New York, NY, 1977.

Sage, A. P., *Linear Systems Control*, Matrix Publishers, Inc., Portland, OR, 1978.

Seely, S., and A. D. Poularikas, *Electromagnetics — Classical and Modern Theory and Applications*, Marcel Dekker, Inc., New York, NY, 1979.

Seely, S., *Electromechanical Energy Conversion*, McGraw Hill Book Co., New York, NY, 1962.

Seely, S., *An Introduction to Engineering Systems*, Pergamon Press, Inc., Elmsford, NY, 1972.

Seely, S., *Electronic Circuits*, Holt, Rinehart and Winston, Inc., New York, NY, 1969.

Senturia, S. D., and B. D. Wedlock, *Electronic Circuits and Applications*, John Wiley and Sons, New York, NY, 1975.

Shearer, J. L., A. T. Murphy, and H. H. Richardson, *Introduction to System Dynamics*, Addison Wesley Publishing Co., Reading, MA, 1967.

Sifferlen, T. P., and V. Vartanian, *Digital Electronics with Engineering Applications*, Prentice Hall, Inc., Englewood Cliffs, NJ, 1970.

Smith, R. J., *Circuits, Devices and Systems*, 3rd ed., McGraw Hill Book Co., New York, NY, 1976.

Texas Instruments, Inc., *The TTL Data Book*, 1976.

Truxal, J. G., *Introductory Systems Engineering*, McGraw Hill Book Co., New York, NY, 1972.

Van Valkenburg, M. E., *Network Analysis*, ed ed., Prentice Hall, Inc., Englewood Cliffs, NJ, 196 .

Walsh, E. M., *Energy Conversion—Electromechanical, Direct, Nuclear*, Ronald Press Co., New York, NY, 1967.

Index